Research Techniques in Human Engineering

Jon Weimer, Ph. D.

Prentice Hall PTR
Englewood Cliffs, New Jersey 07632

Library of Congress Cataloging in Publication Data

Weimer, John.
Research techniques in human engineering / Jon Weimer.
p. cm. -- (Prentice Hall series in innovative technology)
Includes bibliographical references and index.
ISBN 0-13-097072-7
1. Human engineering. 2. Man-machine systems. I. Title.
TA166.W455 1994 94-36605
620.8'2'072--dc20 CIP

Editorial/production supervision: *Camille Trentacoste*
Cover design: *Aren Graphics, based on a concept by Jim Embach*
Cover art: *Proportions of the Human Figure, Leonardo da Vinci / Superstock*
Manufacturing manager: *Alexis R. Heydt*
Acquisitions editor: *Bernard Goodwin*
Editorial Assistant: *Diane Spina*

The publisher offers discounts on this book when ordered in bulk quantities.
For more information, contact:

Corporate Sales Department
PTR Prentice Hall
113 Sylvan Avenue
Englewood Cliffs, NJ 07632

Phone: 800-382-3419 or 201-592-2498 Fax: 201-592-2249
E-mail: dan_rush@prenhall.com

Printed in the United States of America
10 9 8 7 6 5 4 3 2 1

ISBN 0-13-097072-7

Prentice-Hall International (UK) Limited, *London*
Prentice-Hall of Australia Pty. Limited, *Sydney*
Prentice-Hall Canada Inc., *Toronto*
Prentice-Hall Hispanoamericana, S.A., *Mexico*
Prentice-Hall of India Private Limited, *New Delhi*
Prentice-Hall of Japan, Inc., *Tokyo*
Simon & Schuster Asia Pte. Ltd., *Singapore*
Editora Prentice-Hall do Brasil, Ltda., *Rio de Janeiro*

INTRODUCTION

As a graduate student, I'd been thoroughly schooled in human factors and ergonomic theories, but not in a broad range of research methods and issues. Thus, when I had to propose my dissertation, I didn't know which topic area to pursue. Most of the students who had graduated from my program had done their dissertations on vigilance, but I wanted to do something different. The question was what? Compounding my dilemma, the field of human factors had diversified to the extent of being daunting, with each subdiscipline (e.g., aerospace psychology) having its own set of research issues, techniques, and required equipment. My department had two DEC Rainbow 100's, a DEC PDP-11, and access to a VAX cluster. Clearly my options were limited. I thought: "I wish there was a primer on the research issues and techniques for each human factors subdiscipline, so I won't have to read a dozen journal articles in an area only to find it isn't right for me or that I need specialized equipment (e.g., flight simulator) to run an adequate experiment."

It's been almost nine years since I made that wish, and you're holding its fulfillment in your hands. I've tried to bring together some of the best human factors researchers: From ergonomics to human-computer interface design. Each chapter, written by a noted expert in the area, is a brief tutorial in conducting research in a particular subdiscipline. The range of contributors represents, as closely as possible, the diversity of human factors.

I chose to map the chapters of the book to the technical groups of the Human Factors and Ergonomics Society, though there are some departures (e.g., Bob Williges' chapter on experimental methods, my chapter on conducting an experiment, and the chapter on military applications). If there is a subdiscipline, which you think should have been included but wasn't, I apologize. Space limitations force me to be selective, thus I did not include subdisciplines of narrow interest or considerable overlap with other subdisciplines (e.g., environmental design). In other cases, such as Organizational Design and Management, I couldn't find an appropriate expert who was willing to contribute a chapter.

This book assumes you've had an undergraduate course in experimental methods (e.g., Experimental Psychology). While my chapter on experimental methods is meant to be a segue between a general, undergraduate methods course and the specialized research treatments given by the other contributors, it may be used as a brief primer on experimental methods; however, it is not intended to be a substitute for a semester-length course.

I hope you find this book useful, and I would welcome any comments.

Jon Weimer, Ph.D.

Address any comments to me:

c/o Mike Hays

PTR Editorial

Prentice-Hall

113 Sylvan Ave., Route 9W

Englewood Cliffs, NJ 07632

or Email them to: weimerj@aol.com

TABLE OF CONTENTS

INDEX OF FIGURES, TABLES, AND CASE STUDIES

FIGURES:

TABLES:

CASES:

Chapter 1
The Evolution of Human Engineering: A Selected Review

William F. Moroney
University of Dayton

1.0 Introduction

It was with considerable trepidation that I undertook the task of discussing the evolution of human engineering (HE). How does one discuss the undefinable? Licht, Polzella and Boff (1989) extracted 74 different definitions from the literature, definitions for terms such as: human factors, ergonomics, human engineering, human factors psychology, human factors engineering, applied ergonomics, and industrial engineering. The most inclusive terms are human factors and ergonomics. In the 1960s and 1970s, the former term was usually associated with psychology (mental workload and cognitive issues) while the latter term was usually associated with physical work. Human Engineering and its analogue Applied Ergonomics are concerned with the application of data derived from their respective traditions to the design, test and evaluation of equipment or systems. During the 1980s and 1990s, the boundaries between the terms Ergonomics and Human Factors have blurred as the use of the term ergonomics (which originated in Europe) increased in the United States. Christensen (1987) and Kroemer, Kroemer and Kroemer-Elbert (1994) consider the terms synonymous.

Kroemer, Kroemer and Kroemer-Elbert (1994) attribute the origin of the term ergonomics (ergos =work and nomos=laws) to K.F.H. Murrell in 1949. They also note that, Monod and Valentin (1979) reported the use of an analogous term 100 years earlier in Poland. In June 1949, Murrell hosted a meeting in the British Admiralty. This meeting led to the formation of the Ergonomics Research Society. Ten years later the International Ergonomics Association was formed and in 1961 it held its first formal meeting.[1] The origins of the Human Factors Society (HFS) follows a similar pattern. In 1955 a planning meeting was held in Southern California, and two years later the first national meeting was held in Tulsa, Oklahoma. In January 1993, recognizing the increased use of the term ergonomics and reflecting the varied interests of its members, the HFS added the term ergonomics to its title and became the Human Factors and Ergonomics Society (HFES).

---

[1] See Edholm and Murrell (1973) for a history of ergonomics.

The material that follows represents a limited examination of a very broad area which incorporates a wide variety of disciplines.[2] Human Factors/Ergonomics can be viewed from many perspectives. However, there is an interesting parallel in the evolution of Human Factors and Ergonomics: both have had considerable military support and experienced a major growth spurt during and immediately after World War II (WWII). Accordingly, the bulk of the following section reflects the interaction between the military (United States Department of Defense, DOD) and Human Engineering.

2.0 1900-1920

Hutchingson (1981) describes the first prehistoric man to use a tool for his protection or service as the founder of human factors thinking. Indeed, a study of people-powered farming tools (e.g. axe, sickle, scythe) reveals changes over time that informally reflect the system development cycle from requirements definition through limited production, test and evaluation and system retirement. However, the first organized effort in the profession is usually attributed to F.W. Taylor, who in 1898 restructured a ingot loading task at Bethlehem Steel (Adams, 1989). Prior to the restructuring, the average daily load moved per worker was 12.5 tons. However, Taylor demonstrated that by use of appropriate selection, training, and work-rest schedules, an individual could move 47.5 tons per day and do so repeatedly. Subsequently, he designed a series of shovels for handling different types of materials. Taylor delineated basic principles of work design and formalized time and motion studies which became the basis for today's task analysis. Frank Gilbreth, one of Taylor's students, is perhaps best known for his improvements to the bricklayer's task. Additionally, Sanders and McCormick (1993) report that during the early 1900s Frank and Lilian Gilbreth also studied skilled performance, workstation design and designs for the handicapped. Except for the type of work cited above, Hugo Munsterberg's investigations of industrial accidents and the efforts of Western Electric at the Hawthorne Plant[3], little progress was made in HE during this period except for interactions with the DOD.

The interaction between HFE and DOD has historically been synergistic. Indeed, as reported by Christensen (1987, p.5), "*to their credit, it was the authorities in the Department of Defense who first actively supported the human factors profession. Even today many industries are not yet at the stage of development with respect to human factors that DOD was a generation ago.*" Driskill and Olmstead (1989, p.43) trace psychology's initial involvement in the DOD to Robert Yerkes, who described the World War I (WWI) efforts in selection, training, motivation, and aviation as the first attempt to deal "scientifically and effectively with the principle human

[2] Individuals with different backgrounds have different perspectives. Thus, this chapter reflects in part the author's personal background, experience, interests, and biases.

[3] For a fascinating reexamination of the events describing the "Hawthorne Effect", the readers should consult Parsons (1974).

factors in military organization and activity". This effort involved some of the early leaders in psychometrics, including Thorndike and Thurstone. During WWI, psychology's major contribution was in the area of selection and classification of recruits. During this period, the Army Alpha and the Army Beta Tests were developed to evaluate the abilities of English-language literates and English-language illiterates (Taylor and Alluisi, 1993). Aviation Psychology was responsible for the development of what may have been psychology's first applied test battery, which was used to predict flying aptitude (Taylor and Alluisi, 1993). Finally, as ever higher altitudes were sought, the deleterious effects of hypoxia and hypothermia on aviators' performance were examined.

It is interesting to note that during WWI, Yerkes headed the Committee on Psychology of the National Research Council (NRC), an antecedent of today's Human Factors Committee of the NRC. This committee, in response to DOD concerns, has produced many excellent reviews in the area of HFE including: *Research Issues in Simulator Sickness* (McCauley, 1984), *Human Performance Models of Computer-Aided Engineering* (Elkind, Card, Hochberg, and Huey, 1989; *Human Factors Specialists' Education and Utilization: Results of a Survey* (Van Cott and Huey, 1992); and *Workload Transition: Implications for Individual and Team Performance* (Huey and Wickens, 1993).

3.0 1920-1940

The increased use of the automobile after WWI, provides an impetus for human factors studies of driving behavior. Forbes (1981) provides an interesting review (including the following citations) of early research beginning with work at Ohio State in 1927. A 1930 text by Weiss and Lauer describes epidemiological studies of automobile accidents, laboratory studies of estimated velocity, a moving belt "miniature highway" driving simulator and social characteristics of traffic regulation violators. Perceptual issues examined included head movement, foveal and peripheral vision reaction time and vision requirements. In 1938, Cobb concluded that correlational analysis of auto accidents, psychophysical testing and interview data could not be used to identify "accident-prone individuals". In 1939, Forbes concluded that the characteristics of normal drivers needed to be examined to determine what caused them to have accidents. Studies at Iowa State University (Lauer and Helwig, 1932) produced recommendations regarding the colors of signs. Mills (1933) examined sign visibility at night.

Within the DOD, a hiatus in HFE activity occurred between WWI and WWII, except in the area of aviation systems. Dempsey (1985) provides a fascinating overview of the work of aviation pioneers during an era in which both man and machine redefined the limits of aviation. In the U.S. Army Air Force (AAF, in 1947 it became the USAF), the emphasis was primarily medical/physiological, and fell under the leadership of Captain (later General) Harry Armstrong, namesake of the USAF Armstrong Laboratory.

Researchers, using both animals and man, examined the effects of altitude on performance. In 1935, Captains Armstrong and Stevens set a world altitude record of 72,000 feet during a flight in a National Geographic Balloon. During this same period, the effects of accelerative forces were also examined. Angular accelerations were produced by a 20-foot-diameter centrifuge, while a swing was used to produce linear accelerations. As early as 1937, a primitive "G-suit" had been developed and a recommendation was made to designers that in an aircraft exceeding nine Gs the pilot should be placed in the prone position. Today, more than 50 years later, research on the reclining seat continues, although with better simulators, higher G onset rates, and greater concern for both physiological and cognitive functions (Deaton and Hitchcock, 1991). The initial work on the effect of anthropometry on aircraft design and crew performance also began in 1935. This work continues today as the Armed Forces attempt to accommodate more fully both women and men into military cockpits and other systems.

During the early 1930s, Edwin Link marketed his aircraft flight simulator as a coin-operated amusement device (Fischetti and Truxal, 1983). However in 1934, the Army Air Corps purchased its first flight simulators and the foundation was laid for the development of flight simulation technology. Simulation and simulator technology have progressed considerably since then, but today's virtual reality environment is a descendant of Link's Trainer.

4.0 1940-1960

In 1939, as clouds of war gathered over Europe, the Army established a Personnel Testing Section, while the NRC created the Emergency Committee on Psychology to focus on personnel testing and selection. In 1941, The Army Air Force Aviation Psychology Program, directed by John Flanagan, was created to aid in selection and training of aircrew (Driskell and Olmstead, 1989). During the war, the Army General Classification Tests (AGCT) were developed and used in the selection, classification, and assignment of 13 million personnel by the end of the war. Based on the success of these testing programs, the DOD developed the Armed Forces Qualification Test (AFQT), a test of mental ability, that in 1950 was adopted by all the Armed Services. In 1974, the AFQT was incorporated into the Armed Services Vocational Aptitude Battery (ASVAB), which is administered annually to approximately 1.5 million potential recruits (Driskell and Olmstead, 1989). Computerized Adaptive Testing (CAT) versions of the ASVAB are currently being evaluated (Taylor and Alluisi, 1993).

Similar efforts in the area of aircrew personnel selection led to the Air-Crew Classification Test Battery, which provided predictions of success in training and combat (Taylor and Alluisi, 1993). Like other personnel tests, this battery used paper and pencil tests to evaluate aptitude and ability, however various apparati were used to measure coordination and decision time. Taylor and Alluisi note that because the predictive ability of paper-and-pencil tests appears to have been maximized, personnel selection is again focusing on apparatus-based testing. The return to apparatus-based performance testing has been greatly facilitated by the increased availability of personal computers. Readers interested in a recent comprehensive overview of selection, classification, and placement in the military services should consult Steege (1991).

In addition to test development efforts during WWII, HFE personnel actively assisted designers of military hardware. A good overview of the areas addressed during WWII is contained in an Office of Naval Research (ONR) sponsored text by Chapanis, Garner, Morgan, and Sanford (1947), which was assigned a "Restricted" classification during the war. The table of contents includes topics similar to those found in today's introductory HFE textbooks: psychophysics, design of experiments, working environment (temperature and humidity, acceleration, motion sickness, vibration, noise, etc), arrangement of equipment, speech, communication and hearing, auditory systems, optical illusions, legibility, display problems and psychophysical research. Chapanis et al. also describes the effect of perspective illusions on radar presentations and average ranges for spotting aircraft under winter skies in Britain. The work of Chapanis et al. was followed by the ONR sponsored *Handbook of Human Engineering Data for Design Engineers* (Naval Training Devices Center, 1949), prepared by the Tufts College Institute for Applied Experimental Psychology. This handbook was perhaps the first effort to consolidate knowledge in the field of HFE into one source. It was followed, in 1963, by the first edition of the *Human Engineering Guide to Equipment Design* by Morgan, Cook, Chapanis, and Lund and a later second edition by VanCott and Kinkade (1972). These works were precursors to the *Engineering Data Compendium* (Boff and Lincoln, 1988), and the *Handbook of Perception and Human Performance* (Boff, Kaufman and Thomas, 1986). Over the years, the DOD has supported the development of documents providing general knowledge in HFE, as well as documents in specialty areas such as submarine (NRC, 1949) and aircraft environments (ONR, 1978), underwater performance (Shilling, Werts, and Schandelmeier, 1976), and anthropometry of USAF women (Clauser, et al, 1972).

World War II also engaged HFE personnel at the AAF Aeromedical Research Unit, Wright Field, in a wide variety of activities including the development of: human tolerance limits for high altitude bailout, automatic parachute opening devices, cabin pressurization schedules, pressure breathing equipment and protective clothing for use at high altitudes, G-suits, and airborne medivac facilities. They also developed the first anthropomety data base for aircrew and initiated work on ejection seats (Dempsey, 1985).

In the late 1940s and early 1950s, commercial aviation was in its infancy. Ross A. McFarland effected a technology transfer as he integrated aviation related knowledge gained during WWII with other areas and wrote two texts dealing with human factors in air transport design (1946) and HF in air transportation (1953). Progress was also made in the automotive area when in 1949, the Institute of Transportation and Traffic Engineering was established at the University of California, Los Angeles. In 1954, McFarland and Moseley published a major text in this area entitled *Human Factors in Highway Transport Safety*.

While researchers in the area of audition had been at Bell Laboratories since 1925, it wasn't until 1946 that the first human factors group was established at Bell Laboratories (Bailey, 1989). This group advised designers on topics ranging from the weight of telephone handsets to the layout of keys for the push-button telephone pad. In 1967, a second human factors group was organized at the Bell Human Performance Technology Center. This group was established to ascertain that good human factors principles were applied not only to Bell System customers but to Bell System employees (particularly those working with computer systems). Despite its separation into smaller companies, many HFE personnel are today employed by relatives and descendants of the Bell System (e.g. AT&T, AT&T Bell Laboratories, Bell Communications Research and BELLCORE). Today, other communications corporations have similar groups.

Throughout the 1950s and 1960s, HFE personnel contributed to the accommodation of man in jet driven aircraft and explored the edges of space in rocket propelled aircraft. The DOD invested heavily in these areas. During that era, only DOD aviators were considered for Project Mercury and they received part of their training in DOD facilities. Today, descendants of DOD's technologies fly aboard the NASA shuttles.

Under the seas, the nuclear power industry was born as Navy personnel were deployed aboard nuclear powered submarines. The nuclear submarine, with its capability for remaining submerged for months, brought unique habitability problems (Barton and Webrew, 1957).

During these years, the development and testing of larger and more complex systems was undertaken by both military and civilian agencies. Many of these developments (including the following) are well described by Parsons (1972). The Laboratory of Aviation Psychology of Ohio State University, under the guidance of Paul M. Fitts, conducted a series of experiments on Air Traffic Control (ATC), with the sponsorship of the USAF Aerospace Medical Laboratory (now Armstrong Laboratory). These experiments had a military rather than a civilian focus and were performed in response to problems encountered during the Berlin airlift and the Korean War. Subsequently, related work was performed by the Systems Development Corporation, the MITRE corporation and the University of Illinois. Eventually the work transitioned to the National Aviation Facilities Experimental Center (NAEFEC) of the Federal Aviation Agency, now known as the Federal Aviation Administration (FAA). Thus the ground work for the existing ATC system had its origins in military aviation. Today, the FAA's National Airspace Program (1990) to upgrade the ATC system is underway and involves many human factors efforts.

5.0 1960-Present

During the 1960's, the application of human factors to computing systems was primarily limited to the traditional ergonomics role of designing interface hardware (e.g., the keyboards for computer terminals) (Boehm-Davis, 1994). Some human factors comparisons of programming languages and batch versus timesharing systems were reported by Sackman (1970), but serious empirical research in other areas did not appear until after 1970 (Boehm-Davis, 1994).

The early seventies saw the introduction of the Personal Computer (also known in those days as microcomputers). The earliest microcomputers required operators with programming skills. The personal computer brought with it the rapid emergence of applications software (word processing, graphics packages, etc.) rapidly emerged and the special purpose microprocessor evolved into the general purpose PC. In 1970, the Xerox Palo Alto Research Center (PARC) was established to perform research in "intelligent information systems" (Wasserman, 1989). PARC's innovations included the development of icons, windows, pull-down menus and mouse interactive systems. These interactive techniques have been adapted for use in Apple's Macintosh and Microsoft's Windows. PARC also developed the concept of " WYSIWYG" (What You See Is What You Get).

The 1970's also saw the emergence of the first, serious scientific inquiry into the human factors of the human-computer interface (Boehm-Davis, 1994). *Design of Man-Computer Dialogues* (Martin, 1972) was the first book to identify human-computer interface as an independent area of study (Boehm-Davis, 1994), while*The Psychology of Computer Programming* (Weinberg, 1971) was the first publication to emphasize the importance of controlled experimentation in evaluating performance in computer-related tasks, such as programming. In turn, the term "software psychology" first appeared in Ben Shneiderman's *Software Psychology* (1980) and refers to the study of psychological factors effecting the performance computer users.

Nickerson (1992) provides additional historical insight into the increasing role of human factors in the development of the human-computer interface (HCI). He reviewed the contents of the journal *Human Factors* for 1965, 1975 and 1985. In 1965, only one of the 58 articles published was related to computers or computer based systems, in 1975 only two of the 62 articles was related to HCI. However by 1985, approximately 1/3 of the 55 articles addressed HCI. 1979 also saw Ramsey and Atwood, with ONR sponsorship, publishing a comprehensive review of the HCI literature.

Smith and Mosier (1986), with USAF sponsorship, published the first comprehensive set of guidelines for designing user interfaces. In 1983, Card, Moran and Newell published the *Psychology of Human-Computer Interaction,* which examined the cognitive processes that humans use when using a computer interface. In 1985, Shneiderman published *Designing the User Interface: Strategies for Effective Human Computer Interaction.,* which offered practical guidance on the development of both hardware and software human computer interfaces.

Wasserman (1989) provides some fascinating insights into the role of human factors and industrial design in the marketplace during the 1970s and 1980s. The late 1970s and early/mid 1980s was a crisis era for the Xerox corporation, whose market share of the copying machine market had fallen from 82% in 1976 to 41% by 1982 (primarily due to Japanese competition). As part of its reorganization, Xerox combined the human factors and industrial design groups into one department called the Industrial Design/Operability. Thus Xerox, as a matter of corporate policy, placed considerable emphasis on system "operability". Focusing on the characteristics of the user and applying the principles/ techniques developed by PARC allowed Xerox to capture 55% of the copying machine market by 1985.

In the 1970s and 1980s, several factors converged within DOD to place additional emphasis on the role of humans. These included the evolution of the systems approach, more complex and costly systems, the cost of manpower, and the establishment of an all-volunteer force. In this regard, Meister (1976) clearly describes the human as a subsystem, whose behavior must be understood within the context of that system. HFE personnel were increasingly involved in the development and evaluation of training devices and simulators, particularly those used in aviation. Typical of that era was the work of: Orlansky and String (1980) on the cost effectiveness of flight simulators for military training and Jones, Hennessy and Deutsch (1985) on human factors aspects of simulation.

The March 28, 1979 operator induced accident at the Three Mile Island nuclear power plant increased the visibility of human factors. By the end of the event, the reactor core was destroyed, more than one million gallons of radioactive water filled the containment building, radioactive gas was released into the atmosphere, 90 percent of the fuel rods in the reactor core were damaged, and thousands of local residents were evacuated.

Let's briefly examine what happened (details are contained in Malone, et al. 1980). At approximately 4 AM, the feedwater pumps that supplied water to the steam generators failed, which automatically turned off the generators. Without this cooling water, the temperature of the reactor coolant increased, which led to a build up of pressure in the pressurizer. The pilot-operated relief valve (PORV) opened to relieve the overpressure and failed to reseat (a failure, which took 138 minutes and a new shift-supervisor to recognize). With the temperature still rising and the loss-of-coolant, the preprogrammed control rods dropped to halt nuclear fission and the emergency feedwater pump started pumping water into the steam generator. The operators misinterpreted what was happening and reduced the flow of coolant, which resulted in the devastating effects described previously.

What role did the human operator play in this accident? First, if the operators had not intervened, the situation might have been limited to a minor incident (but we will never be certain). Second, when they did intervene, they were dealing with confusing unintegrated information. The report of the President's Commission stated: " the information was presented in a manner to confuse operators"(Kameny, 1979, p.29). You will recall from the above summary that the PORV had failed in the open position. During the incident, the operator noted that the PORV indicator light was not illuminated which he interpreted as meaning that the PORV was closed, since according to the label below the light "Light ON" indicated OPEN. Unfortunately, the illuminated PORV light did not tell the operator about the position (OPEN/CLOSED) of the PORV, only that power had been sent to the PORV. However, in the operator's mental model of the system, by implication and with the lack of any information to the contrary, an unlit PORV light was assumed to mean that the PORV was closed. Inadequate, inappropriate feedback was the design deficiency in this particular case. Given sufficient time, the operators would eventually have determined the nature of the problem. However, problems in nuclear power plants can rapidly become disastrous accidents. It should also be noted that 100 unprioritized alarms sounded or were displayed to the operators within three minutes after the loss of the feedwater pumps. More of the 750 alarms were activated as the incident progressed. Thus the system which had been designed to advise the operators of all failures functioned as designed and the operators were faced with the dilemma of distinguishing between cause and effect as the system started to collapse.

This incident was of such proportions that the U.S. nuclear power industry has not yet recovered, as evidenced by the halt in the construction of nuclear power plants. Unfortunately, lessons were not learned and in the April 1986 the nuclear reactor at Chernobyl melted down and released 50 million tons of radioactive isotopes into the atmosphere. This early-morning catastrophe also involved human error (Medvedev, 1991).

In 1984, a manufacturing accident again brought human factors to the forefront. The leak of a pesticide in Bhopal, India resulted in more than 3500 dead, 200,000 permanently injured, and genetic changes continuing into the next and possibly future generations. Casey (1993), in a narrative, describes how the operators located leaks by sensing irritation to their eyes and respiratory systems and tried to extract system information from defective displays. Meshkati (1989a, p. 173) characterizes the operations at the facility as "a group of untrained and unprepared operators, working with an unsafe technology in an 'unkind [working] environment', using unfriendly hardware and unreliable instrumentation, being assembled in an unorganized facility, and supervised by unseasoned managers." Hopefully, lessons learned from this accident will transfer to the chemical industry and to industry in general.

Within the DOD, the critical role of human factors was brought to the attention of Congress in a 1981 report to Congress by the General Accounting Office (GAO). This report noted that while many DOD weapon systems "may have the capability to perform their missions, it is often of little value because not all the systems can be adequately operated, maintained or supported" (GAO,1981, p. i). Subsequently, the acquisition process was modified when the inclusion of human factors considerations early in the acquisition process was mandated by DOD Instruction 5000.2. The intent of that instruction is clearly stated in the current policy statement: "

> **Human considerations ... shall be effectively integrated into the design effort for defense systems to improve total system performance and reduce cost of ownership by focusing attention on the capabilities and limitations of the soldier, sailor, airman or marine." (1991, P.7-B-1).**

Figure 1-1 illustrates the DOD's evolving perception of the elements involved in Human Systems Integration (HSI) and clearly states DOD's objective. Note that elements of Human Factors exist under each of the column headings.

The 1980s have seen increased DOD emphasis on developing strategies and techniques to ascertain that the abilities/ limitations of the operator and maintainer were properly considered during system acquisition and development. Specifically:

- the Army developed MANPRINT (Manpower-Personnel Integration)
- the Navy developed HSI, formerly HARDMAN,(Hardware-Manpower Integration)
- the Air Force developed IMPACTS (Integrated Manpower, Personnel and Comprehensive Training and Safety).

The MANPRINT system integration philosophy incorporates the domains presented in Figure 1-1 and establishes procedures mandating their consideration during system development and deployment. This is a people oriented approach to systems development, with significant implications for both DOD and the civilian sectors. Booher (1990) provides a comprehensive overview of MANPRINT's philosophy and methodologies, which have been adopted by other government agencies, foreign governments, and private industry. Selected applications of MANPRINT techniques are discussed in the Systems Development section of the chapter on Military Systems.

6.0 Where Are We Going?

Howell's (1993) article "*Engineering Psychology in a Changing World*" contains some projections. He describes the major system design drivers as technology and society. Technological concerns include computerization, automation, task complexity/speed, and information display. These concerns translate to the following design issues: human computer interaction, skill maintenance, workload transition, cognitive demands, "technostress" and organizational consequences among others. The societal concerns include demographic considerations, skill/educational trends, geopolitical change and litigation/consumerism. These societal concerns translate to the following design issues: special populations (e.g. aging and diversified workforces), system requirements, talent shortfall (i.e. lack of appropriately educated personnel), military requirements/technology transfer and human error/safety.

Human Systems Integration

Human Factors Engineering	Manpower	Personnel	Training	Safety & Health Hazards
Physical & Mental Capabilities & Limitations Anthropometric & Biomechanical Critera Man-Machine Interface Mission, Function, & Human Requirements Analysis Skill, Knowledge, & Aptitudes Performance Assessment	Wartime Requirements Deployment Considerations Force Structure Operating Strength Manning Concepts	Personnel Classification & Selection Demographics Accession Rate Retention Rate Promotion Flow Training Flow	Training Concepts & Strategy Task Analysis Methods Media/ Equipment Simulation Op Tempo Training System Evaluation Training Development Plan	System Safety/ Health Hazards Plan Human Error Analysis System Reliability Analyses Lessons Learned Environmental Considerations Protective Equipment

Trade-Off Analyses

Enhance Total System Performance While Reducing Life-Cycle Cost

Figure 1-1. Areas of Human Systems Integration as Described in DODINST 5000.2 (1991, p. 7-B-2)

Perrow (1984) argues that as technology "shrinks" the world, what in previous years would have been a localized accident, will now have significant geopolitical/social impact in other areas. Three Mile Island,

Chernobyl, and Bhopal are the leading edge of that trend, which provide new challenges to HFE. While we are involved in accident prevention, we need to develop strategies to reduce the impact of accidents when they occur.

Sheridan's discussion (1991) of "New Realities of Human Factors" describes the following sociotechnical areas as posing challenges for human factors: environment, automation and productivity, health, criminal and civil justice, space, air and ground transportation and basic education. He comments that while we may have developed techniques for addressing the simpler one-person stimulus response interface questions, we have not developed techniques to address multiperson interaction problems such as distributed decision making. He believes that the multi-person interaction will become more important as technological systems grow and become more interconnected. "Interconnectedness" is no longer a fanciful thought, but it is here, and the information highway promises more (consider the exponential growth rate of INTERNET). Sheridan (1991, p.3) describes the dilemma with respect to human factors theory as:

> **". . . how to keep what is simple and what works for problems at the micro level and add to the paradigm that which is necessary to achieve the best characterization of data, make the best predictions, or contribute the most to understanding or design."**

Meister's concern about the future of human factors is reflected in his (1989) book, *Conceptual Aspects of Human Factors.* He describes the goals of human factors as to "describe incisively, predict with precision, control with strength" (p 243). He feels that, while we are growing as a profession, we have a long way to go as a discipline if we are to achieve the aforementioned goals. Within a systems context, he addresses the broader issues of human factors including the requirements of human factors research, and measurement problems (see also Meister and Enderwick, 1992). He also argues for the development of a human performance data base which would allow us to predict human performance in a systems context. Meister bemoans our inability to establish the worth of human factors. Readers of his text will benefit from a much broader perspective of human factors in systems, appreciate his challenging questions and may be discomforted by some of his positions.

Moray (1993), Van Cott and Huey (1992), and Meister (1989) foresee human factors personnel as members of interdisciplinary teams that include not only engineers and designers but market analysts, sociologists, economists and political scientists. Moray includes the following areas as requiring the attention of human factors: population, water, energy, transportation, health care, accidents, pollution and aging. He struck a resonant chord when he discussed transportation: specifically the development of and head-up displays for use in automobiles, and asked are these really the places where we should invest our time and energy ? He chides that perhaps, rather than encouraging more vehicles per mile, we should be addressing broader transportation issues including how and when people should travel.

Nickerson (1992) provides considerable food for thought in his 1992 book entitled: *Looking Ahead: Human Factors Challenges in a Changing World*. He avoids the linguistic quagmire by broadly defining Human Factors, as I did in this chapter. In the continuum of human factors literature, Nickerson's work is at one end, while specifications and standards are at the other. He reflects the position taken by Laughery, in his 1991 (p.2) President's Message to the Human Factors Society, that human factors professionals "need to think beyond the boundaries of our own membership, beyond the traditional problems that we work on, and beyond the usual way we do things". Nickerson's book contains chapters on topics as diverse as industry, energy, environmental change, education, transportation, space exploration, biotechnology, information technology, HCI, work and the quality of life. These areas are examined from a HF perspective, in an honest, insightful, carefully balanced fashion. For example, his chapter on transportation contains some chilling data: e.g. by the year 2005, there will be 50 percent more cars on US roads than there were in 1988. Barring major adjustments in transportation utilization, this will lead to an increase in the number of accidents and according to Ervine and Chen (1988-1989, cited in Nickerson) will also result in a fivefold increase in congestion (measured as vehicle hours of delay). It is interesting to juxtapose this prospect with the 1990 report of the Transportation Research Board that despite the long history of developing standards for highway safety, relatively little is known about the cost/benefit ratio of specific improvements. This leaves designers with inadequate data on which to evaluate alternate strategies. Obviously, this is an area in which the skills of HF personnel could contribute significantly. Nickerson's (1993) chapter entitled "Quality of Life" overlaps with the areas cited by Moray (1993) and includes material on designing for special populations, aging, personal safety and health, population growth and increased urbanization, and equity and international cooperation.

The world has been described as a global village within which we all must interact. At least part of that interaction involves the transfer of technology between countries. Meshkati (1989a and b) addresses the issue of technology transfer to developing countries and cautions that technology transfer without consideration of micro- and macroergonomics is doomed to failure. He emphasizes the need to integrate the technology with the local resources and infrastructure. On the micro-ergonomic level he calls for consideration of not only workplace design issues (anthropometry, strength, etc) but also the cognitive aspects of work (stereotypes, the concept of mental models, information processing and decision making). At the macro-ergonomic level, he addresses the effect of cultural variables on technology transfer. These include attitudes towards work, technology, organizations, group dynamics and motivation. He notes that organizational and management structures which work in western cultures may not work in cultures with different historical experiences. Based on the findings of

Meshkati and related comments by Moroney and Reising (1992), the impact of cultural and individual differences should be considered when selecting subjects for experiments, and system test and evaluation.

The chapters of this book provide domain specific information on what the authors perceive as important to the present and future activities of our profession and our discipline. They address the traditional areas of aerospace, automotive, communication systems, military systems, training, and industrial ergonomics and provide new vistas in both the traditional and emerging areas. Some of the perceived trends include:

- Improving consumer products as a result of increased awareness of the importance of "quality" in a more competitive, international market.
- An increased emphasis on the importance of effective training in the more competitive international civilian marketplace.
- Shifts in the role of human factors in the military from supporting the development of new systems to modifying existing systems and improved training of military personnel.
- Designing for an aging population.
- Designing to improve both the efficiency and acceptance of emerging technologies in the areas of communication, computing systems, and medical systems.
- An increased awareness of the role of industrial ergonomics in injury prevention due to work related injuries.

Taken as a whole, human factors has much to offer in many areas and can have significant economic and social impact.

Clearly, there are and will be sufficient challenges for human factors enginnering personnel as technology progresses and the world "shrinks". Historically, like other professions, we have responded to the needs of the marketplace. Indeed, Sheridan (1991) suggests that we have become reactive when we should be proactive within the market place. Laughery (1991, p.2), encourages outreaching i.e. "we need to think beyond the traditional problems that we work on, and beyond the usual way we do things.". In addition to broadening our horizons and becoming more proactive, I would like to make a modest proposal. I propose that before becoming immersed in a problem, we make a special effort to ascertain, that the "right question" is being asked. Indeed, when we realize that the "right question" is not being asked, then as a minimum, we should pose our version of the "right question" to the decision makers. Thus, perhaps we can focus human factors on what Moray (1993) has termed "humane factors".

7.0 Biography

Dr. Moroney served as a US Navy Aerospace Experimental Psychologist for more than 22 years in the area of human factors engineering. He has authored scientific and technical publications dealing with topics as diverse as motion sickness, helmet mounted displays, laser designator systems, simulation, selection and training. He has supported the development and upgrading of a variety of advanced aircraft and systems. and taught in the Operations Research Department at the Naval Postgraduate School, the Naval Aviation Safety School, and the Navy Test Pilot School. He is a founding member of the Department of Defense Human Factors Engineering Technical Group for Test and Evaluation and has served in a variety of positions in DOD, national, and international human factors groups. As an Associate Professor of Psychology at the University of Dayton, he continues his research in simulation, workload, cockpit design, displays, and anthropometry. He is presently Chair of both the Test and Evaluation Technical Group and the Accreditation Review Committee of the Human Factors and Ergonomics Society. His E-mail address is: Moroney@udavxb.oca.udayton.edu

ACKNOWLEDGEMENTS

I gratefully acknowledge the suggestions of my colleagues and students at the University of Dayton and A.C. Bittner in the preparation of this chapter.

REFERENCES

Adams, J. A. (1989). *Human Factors Engineering.* New York: Macmillan.

Bailey, R. W. (1989). *Human Performance Engineering: Using Human Factors/Ergonomics to Achieve Computer System Useability* (2nd ed.). Englewood Cliffs,NJ: Prentice-Hall.

Barton, T. C., & Weybrew, B. B. (1957). *A Short Summary of the Findings of the 265 Hour Completely Submerged Habitability Cruise Made by the USS NAUTILUS (SSN 571). MRL RPT 280.* Groton,CN: U.S. Naval Medical Research Laboratory.

Boehm-Davis, D. (1994). Human-computer inteface techniques. In J. Weimer (Ed.) *Research Techniques in Human Engineering.* Prentice-Hall: Englewood Cliffs, NJ.

Boff, K. R., Kaufman, L., & Thomas, J. P. (1986). *Handbook of Perception and Human Performance (Vol. 1 & 2).* New York: John Wiley.

Boff, K. R., & Lincoln, J. E. (Eds.). (1988). *Engineering Data Compendium: Human Performance and Perception.* Wright Patterson AFB, Dayton OH: Harry G Armstrong Aerospace Medical Research Laboratory.

Booher, H. R. (Ed.). (1990). *Manprint, An Approach to Systems Integration.* New York: Van Nostrand Reinhold.

Card, S. K., Moran, T. P., & Newell, A. (1983). *The Psychology of Human Computer Interaction.* Hillsdale, NJ: Lawrence Erlbaum Associates.

Casey, S. (1993). *Set Phasers on Stun and other True Tales of Design, Technology, and Human Error.* Santa Barbara, CA: Aegean.

Chapanis, A., Garner, W. R., Morgan, C. T., & Sanford, F. H. (1947). *Lectures on Men and Machines: An Introduction to Human Engineering.* Baltimore: Systems Research Laboratory.

Christensen, J. M. (1987). The human factors profession. In G. Salvendy (Ed.), *Handbook of Human Factors* (pp. 3-16). New York: John Wiley & Sons.

Clauser, C. E., Tucker, P. E., McConville, J. T., Churchill, E., Laubach, L. L., & Reardon, J. A. (1972). *Anthropometry of Air Force Women.* Wright-Patterson Air Force Base, OH: Armstrong Aerospace Medical Research Laboratory.

Cobb, P. W. (1938). Selecting the accident prone driver by means of tests. *Presented at Annual Meeting of Highway Research Board.*

Deaton, J. E., & Hitchcock, E. M. (1991). *Human Performance Under High G Environments: A Comparison of Upright and Reclined Seat Configurations.* Warminster, PA: Naval Air Development Center.

Dempsey, C. A. (1985). *50 years of Research on Man in Flight.* Wright-Patterson AFB, Ohio: United States Air Force.

Department of Defense. (1991). *DODI 5000.2. Defense Acquisition Management Policies and Procedures, Part 7, Section B, Human Systems Integration.* Washington, D.C.: Pentagon.

Driskell, J. E., & Olmstead, B. (1989). Psychology and the military. *American Psychologist*, 44(1), 43-54.

Edholm, O. G., & Murrell, K. F. H. (1973). *The Ergonomics Research Society: A history 1949-1970.* Winchester, Hampshire,England: Warren & Son,Ltd.

Ervine, R. D., & Chen, K. (1988-1989). Toward motoring smart. *Issues in Science and Technology*, 5(2), 92-97.

Federal Aviation Authority. (1990). *The National Plan for Aviation Human Factors (Vol. I & II) PB91-100347.* Washington, D.C.: Department of Transportation.

Fischetti, M. A., & Truxal, C. (1985). Simulating "The right stuff". *IEEE Spectrum*, 38-47.

Forbes, T. W. (1939). The normal automobile driver as a traffic problem. *Journal of General Psychology*, 20, 471-474.

Forbes, T. W. (Ed.). (1981). *Human Factors in Highway Traffic Safety Research.* Malabar, FL: Robert E. Krieger.

General Accounting Office. (1981). *Effectiveness of U.S. Forces Can be Increased Through Improved Weapon System Design. PSAD-81-17.* Washington, D.C.: U.S. General Accounting Office.

Howell, W. C. (1993). Engineering psychology in a changing world. *Annual Review of Psychology,* 44, 231-263.

Huchingson, R. D. (1981). *New Horizons for Human Factors in Design.* New York: McGraw-Hill.

Huey, B. M., & Wickens, C. D. (Eds.). (1993). *Workload Transition: Implications for Individual and Team Performance.* Washington, DC: National Academy Press.

Human Factors Society. (1991). *1991 Directory and Yearbook.* Santa Monica, CA: Human Factors Society.

Jones, E., Hennessy, R., & Deutsch, S. (1985). *Human Factors Aspects of Simulation.* Washington, DC: National Academy Press.

Kemeny, J. R. (1979). *Report of the Presidents Commission on Three Mile Island.* Washington, DC: Government Printing Office.

Klemmer, E. T. (1989). *Ergonomics: Harness the Power of Human Factors in Your Business.* Norwood,N.J.: Ablex.

Kroemer, K. H. E., Kroemer, H. B., & Kroemer-Elbert, K. E. (1994). *Ergonomics: How to Design for Ease and Efficiency.* Englewood Cliffs, NJ: Prentice-Hall.

Lauer, A. R., & Helwig, D. (1932). Improvement in highway signs. *American Highways,* 11, 14,15,19.

Laughery, K. R. (1991). President's message. *Human Factors Society Bulletin,* 34 (12), 1-2.

Licht, D. M., Polzella, D. J., & Boff, K. (1989). *Human Factors, Ergonomics, and Human Factors Engineering: An Analysis of Definitions. CSERIAC-89-01.* Wright Patterson AFB, Dayton, OH: CSERIAC.

Malone, T. B., Kirkpratrick, K., Eike, D., Johnson, J. H., & Walker, R. J. (1980). *Human Factors Evaluation of Control Room Design and Operator Performance at Three Mile Island. NUREG/CR-1270.* Washington DC: U.S. Nuclear Regulatory Commission.

Martin J. (1972). *Design of Man-Computer Dialogues.* Englewood Cliffs, NJ: Prentice-Hall.

McCauley, M. E. (Ed.). (1984). *Research Issues in Simulator Sickness.* Washington,DC: National Academy Press.

McFarland, R. A. (1946). *Human Factors in Air Transport Design.* New York: McGraw-Hill.

McFarland, R. A. (1953). *Human Factors in Air Transportation.* New York: McGraw-Hill.

McFarland, R. A., & Moseley.AL. (1954). Human Factors in Highway Transport Safety. Boston, MA: Harvard School of Public Health.

Medvedev, G. (1991). The Truth About Chernobyl. New York: Basic Books.

Meister, D. (1976). *Behavior Foundations of System Development.* New York: John Wiley & Sons.

Meister, D. (1989). *Conceptual Aspects of Human Factors.* Baltimore: The Johns Hopkins University Press.

Meister, D., Enderwick, T. P.,(EDs). (1992). Measurement in human factors. *Human Factors*, 34, 383-506.

Meshkati, N. (1989a). An etiological investigation of micro- and macroergonomic factors in the Bhopal disaster: Lessons for industries in both industrialized and developing countries. *International Journal of Industrial Ergonomics*, 4, 161-175.

Meshkati, N. (1989b). Technology transfer to developing countries: A tripartite micro- and macroergonomic analysis of human-organization-technology interfaces. *International Journal of Industrial Ergonomics*, 4, 101-115.

Mills, F. W. (1933). The comparative visability of standard luminous and non-luminous highway signs. *Public Roads*, 14, 109-128.

Moray, N. (1993, October). Technosophy and humane factors. *Ergonomics in Design*, 33-39.

Morgan, C. T., Cook, J. S., Chapanis, A., & Lund, M. W. (Eds.). (1963). *Human Engineering Guide to Equipment Design.* New York: McGraw-Hill Book Co.

Moroney, W. F., & Reising, J. (1992). Subjects in human factors: Just who are they? *Proceedings of the Human Factors Society 36th Annual Meeting*, 1227-1231.

Monod, H., & Valentin, M. (1979). The predecessors of ergonomy (in French).. *Ergonomics*, 22,673-680.

National Research Council. (1949). *A Survey Report on Human Factors in Undersea Warfare.* Washington, DC: National Research Council.

Naval Training Devices Center. (1949). Handbook of Human Engineering Data for Design Engineers. Port Washington, NY: Naval Training Devices Center.

Nickerson, R. S. (1992). *Looking Ahead: Human Factors Challenges in a Changing World.* Hillsdale,NJ: Lawrence Erlbaum Associates.

Orlansky, J., & String, J. (1980). *Cost-Effectiveness of Flight Simulators for Military Training. AGARD-CP-268.* Arlington, VA: Institute for Defense Analysis.

Parsons, H. M. (1972). *Man-Machine System Experiments.* Baltimore: The Johns Hopkins Press.

Perrow, C. (1984). *Normal Accidents: Living with High Risk Technologies.* New York: Basic Books.

Ramsey, H. R., & Atwood, M. E. (1979). *Human Factors in Computer Systems: A Review of the Literature.* Englewood, CO (ADA075679): Science Applications Inc.

Sanders, M. S., & McCormick, E. J. (1993). *Human Factors in Engineering and Design (7th ed.).* New York: McGraw-Hill.

Sheridan, T. (1991). New realities of human factors. *Human Factors Society Bulletin*, 34 (2), 1-3.

Shilling, C. W., Werts, M. F., & Schandelmeier, N. R. (1976). *The Underwater Handbook: A Guide to Physiology and Performance for the Engineer*. New York: Plenum Press.

Shneiderman, B. (1987). *Designing the User Interface: Strategies for Effective Human-Computer Interaction.* Reading,MA: Addision-Wesley.

Shneiderman, B. (1980). *Software Psychology: Human Factors in Computers and Information Systems.* Cambridge,MA: Winthrop Publishers, Inc.

Smith, S. L., & Mosier, J. N. (1986). *Guidelines for Designing User Interface Software. ESD-TR-86-278.* Hanscon AFB, MA: Electronics Systems Division.

Steege, F. W. (1991). Selection, classification and placement in military services. In R. Gal & A. D. Mangelsdorff (Eds.), *Handbook of Military Psychology* (pp. 1-149). New York: John Wiley & Sons.

Taylor, H. L., & Alluisi, E. A. (1993). Military psychology. In V. S. Ramachandran (Ed.), *Encyclopedia of Human Behavior*. San Diego,CA: Academic Press.

Transportation Research Board. (1990). *Safety Research for a Changing Highway Environment* (Special Report # 229). Washington, DC: National Academy Press.

Van Cott, H. P., & Huey, B. M. (1992). *Human Factors Specialists' Education and Utilization: Results of a Study*. Washington, D.C.: National Academy Press.

Wasserman, A. S. (1989). Redesigning Xerox: A design strategy based on operability. In Klemmer (Ed.), *Ergonomics: Harnessing the Power of Human Factors in Your Business* (p. 218). Norwood,NJ: Ablex.

Weinberg, G.M. (1971). *The Psychology of Computer Programming.* New York: Van Nostrand Reinhold.

Chapter 2
Developing a Research Project

Jon Weimer
General Motors Corporation

1.0 Where Do I Start?

Most people don't undertake their first research project of their own accord. More often than not the research project is a requirement for completing a research course or a graduate degree. Upon finding out that they must complete a formal research project, most people typically have the same reaction: Panic. This panic is usually followed by the question: Where do I start?

Since human engineering is a very applied discipline, this decision is somewhat easier than in a more general discipline such as chemistry. Merely ask yourself: What am I interested in? Cars? Airplanes? Medical Equipment? Computers? Telecommunication? Consumer Products? Answering this question will help you narrow your focus to a particular subdiscipline.

Once you've decided what type of subdiscipline you want to do research in, the next question is somewhat more problematic. Do you want to do basic or applied research? Basic research is the acquisition of knowledge for supporting or formulating a theory and not necessarily practical application (Mason and Bramble, 1978). Applied research, on the other hand, is more concerned with finding answers to practical problems than theory development.

1.1 Basic Human Engineering Research

While human factors and ergonomics are applied fields, making the distinction between basic and applied research is difficult at times. This doesn't mean that basic research is not conducted[1]. It means that human factors theories have a more applied flavor than a more theory-based discipline (e.g., personality psychology). However, it is not always easy to tell from the title whether a journal article is an example of basic or applied research.

---

[1]However, there is little agreement on what the ratio of applied to basic research should be. The controversy over this topic is beyond the scope of this chapter. The interested reader is referred to a series of letters and articles by Flach (1989), Boff (1988), Rouse (1987), Smith (1987), Simon (1987), Klein and Brezovic (1986), Kantowitz (1985), Wickens (1984), and Meister (1984).

Consider the journal article: *Optimal Symbol Set Selection: A Semiautomated Procedure.* (Fisher and Tanner, 1992). In spite of a title that would lead you to believe that the article is an example of applied research, this is a good example of basic human engineering research. The authors clearly state in their abstract that the purpose of the experiment was to determine if experimentally-derived data are better explained by one theory or another, thus putting it in the domain of basic research:

> **"An experiment was developed to determine whether the new, componential model or an already existing, discriminability model better explains visual search behavior. The results were consistent with the componential model."**

Basic research in human engineering advances the understanding of the factors that influence human performance in man-machine systems. Since most corporations frown on the pursuit of knowledge for knowledge's sake, most basic research is performed at universities in well controlled and sometimes artificial situations. As knowledge about a particular problem domain grows, researchers attempt to integrate that knowledge into a theory that explains the phenomenon.

For example, Mackworth, in response to a request from the Royal Air Force, set up a series of experiments to study why radar observers missed U-boats contacts. To simulate a radar display, Mackworth created the so-called "clock test". Observers were asked to monitor the movements of a black pointer along the face of a blank clock. Once each second, the pointer would move 0.3 inches. At random intervals, the pointer would move 0.6 inches (a double jump), at which time the subjects were supposed to depress a button to indicate that they had observed the target signal. Mackworth's studies were the essence of applied research. However, in the ensuing 48 years, more than a dozen theories have been offered to explain a relatively simple phenomenon[2] (i.e., when a task involves monitoring a display for infrequent target signals, missed targets increase as time on task increases).

Thus, while theoretical propositions gleaned from basic research often provide the basis for making predictions about human performance in practical settings (Mason and Bramble, 1978), the evolution of vigilance research shows that the process can flow the opposite way too.

1.2 Applied Human Engineering Research

Since the field of human engineering is by its nature applied, it should be no surprise that much of the research performed involves taking findings from basic research in cognition, perception, and physiology and applying them to the evaluation of man-machine systems in practical settings. Mackworth's "clock test" study is an example of pure applied research.

[2]After 45 years, it is amazing that vigilance continues to be fertile ground for research ideas. If you're interested in learning more about the vigilance decrement, and the various theories surrounding it, read Joel S. Warm's excellent book (Warm, 1984) as a starting point.

Mackworth was responding to the Royal Air Force's request to solve a particular practical problem, not to develop a theory of vigilance. The theories came later.

A good rule of thumb for determining if a study is an example of applied research is: The specificity of the hypotheses and the absence of general knowledge or theory advancement identify a study as an example of applied research.

Corporations and government agencies have a greater incentive to fund applied research, since the outcomes may directly impact them or the way they do business (Mason and Bramble, 1978). For example, the Department of Transportation would probably be more inclined to fund a study of obstacle detection during periods of sustained driving than an investigation of electrocortical indicators of arousal[3]; this is because the first study is more directly applicable to highway safety, even though they both deal with vigilance. Applied research is also easier to sell to bureaucrats, executives, politicians, and tax payers, because the concrete goals of applied research are often more easily understood by the lay person. However, this isn't to say that basic research is never funded by large corporations or government agencies. Most funding agencies realize that overemphasizing applied research results in a languishing of basic research at universities and research facilities (Mason and Bramble, 1978). Without a foundation in basic research, applied research is as stable as a house of cards.

2.0 Finding a Problem

Probably the single largest obstacle that new researchers face is finding an appropriate research problem. I've found that most novice researchers -- I was no exception -- have the unconscious expectation that any research problem worth studying should be worthy of a Nobel laureate. This is an unrealistic expectation for the majority of professional researchers -- let alone a graduate or undergraduate student. While Copernican epiphanies have resulted in scientific revolutions, science tends to advance in baby steps rather than quantum leaps.

Take Ivan Petrovich Pavlov for example. If you'd ask most people what Pavlov won the Nobel prize for, they'd probably say learning, classical conditioning, or something like that. The truth is, Pavlov was a physiologist, not a psychologist, and he won the Nobel Prize for studying the digestive processes of living animals. In that study, Pavlov found -- to his dismay -- that his dogs had begun to salivate before they had been given meat powder. It was his investigation into what extraneous variables were corrupting his experiment (i.e., causing the dogs to salivate prior to the administration of the meat powder) that led to the discovery of classical conditioning: The mere sight of the experimenter was causing the dogs to salivate, because they associated his presence with the presentation of the meat powder. Hence,

[3]Thanks to Mark Scerbo for this example.

classical conditioning was discovered by attempting to control nuisance variation within the context of a physiology experiment, rather than through an attempt to formulate a new theory of learning. Likewise, Henri Becquerel's goal was to determine what was clouding his photographic film, not to discover radioactivity and share the Nobel prize with the Curies.

Most day to day research doesn't set the scientific community on its ear. Rather, it sets out to solve simple problems (e.g., why a piece of film becomes clouded), and sometimes ends up answering big questions (e.g., because uranium placed near the film emits radioactivity). Most professional researchers get their ideas from a thorough reading of the scientific literature (i.e., journals, technical papers, and conference proceedings), networking with colleagues, observing a novel problem, trying to control or explain nuisance variation in an experiment, or by following up on their own or someone else's research. In general, scientific problems fall into 3 distinct categories: (1) a gap in the research on a specific topic or area, (2) contradictory experimental results, or (3) the occurrence of an unexplained fact.

2.1 Filling a Gap in Existing Research

Unexplained gaps in scientific knowledge are probably the most obvious source of research problems. However, nothing is free. Gaps in scientific knowledge often exist for a good reason. Ill-developed technology, variables that defy operationalization, ethics, political opposition, unavailability of prototypes, or enormous data collection costs are just some of the factors that can cause knowledge gaps.

I find review articles to be an invaluable source of research ideas. Review articles, if they are well written, outline the problem domain of a particular topic, telling you what is currently known about a particular area. More importantly, review articles tell you what is <u>not</u> known; the authors almost invariably allude, overtly or covertly, to questions that still need to be answered. If no review articles exist in a given area, you can scan the table of contents of related journals for the past ten years or so and read all the articles that appear to be related to your topic of interest. Use the references of those articles to find additional related references.

Without the guidance of a review article, it's difficult to glean the existence of a knowledge gap by wading through a dozen journal articles, many with conflicting results. After all, different researchers study a problem in different ways. Researchers try to build on existing knowledge, often leaving the questions raised in the originating paper unanswered. The whole process can seem confusing to the casual reader. Critical reading[4] and conceptual integration of prior research is required to determine where a knowledge gap may exist. Often there are many.

---

[4]For information on how to improve your critical, journal reading skills, read Huck, Cormier, and Bounds (1974) and Katzer, Cook, and Crouch (1991)

2.2 Resolving Contradictory Experimental Results

Carefully reading the literature in a problem area will often reveal contradictory experimental results. Use Table 2-1 as a guide when reading such articles. McGuigan (1993) points out that the most common methodological error, resulting in conflicting results, is a failure by one or more of the authors to control the influence of relevant extraneous variables (e.g., prior experience with the task, fatigue, etc.). See Table 2-1.

Table 2-1: Questions to Ask When Article Results are in Conflict

Introduction	
1.	Do the authors share the same goal(s)?
2.	Have both authors adequately interpreted past research in their reviews?
3.	Are both authors testing the same hypotheses?
Method	
4a.	Is one author's methodology better than the other's?
4b.	Are the methods of each author actually testing their hypotheses?
4c.	Are both authors measuring the same independent, dependent, and control variables?
4d.	Are they using the same operational definitions?
4e.	Are extraneous variables being adequately controlled by both authors?
4f.	Are the subjects from the same population in both studies?
4g.	Are both authors using the same type/model/version apparatus?
5.	Are there extraneous variables that may have effected one study but not the other?
6.	Did one of the authors use the appropriate statistical test for the type of data generated?
7.	Did each author correctly interpret the results?
8.	Are the findings of the authors in the same or a different direction?
9a.	Was the difference in their findings large or small?
9b.	Would adding more subjects to one study increase its power enough to obtain significance?
Discussion	
10.	Does the interpretation of the data by one author better fit the existing body of data than the other author?

When reviewing articles that have conflicting results, it's important to determine whether or not the authors share the same goal(s). While authors sometimes make their goals and theoretical perspectives explicit, most times they don't, leaving the reader to infer them from the text. That's why it's important to decide whether or not both authors have adequately interpreted past research in their introductions. If the authors are interpreting past research differently, or approaching the experimental situation in different ways -- as is often the case when authors from two opposing schools of thought approach the study of the same problem -- then they may have differing goals or hypotheses. It's very important to distinguish whether an author is misinterpreting past data or reinterpreting it. If the author has misinterpreted past research, then their hypotheses could be wrong, and they could be studying one thing while thinking they're studying something else. However, if the research is coming from an opposing viewpoint, the author may formulate their hypotheses within the framework of their theoretical model, using the language of that model. Their hypotheses aren't wrong, they're just different. Thus, it's very important to determine whether or not two different investigators are using the same hypotheses. If they aren't, then they're probably studying two different things. That's not a problem, so long as you realize it and, more importantly, they realize it. Beware of situations where two different authors investigate two different hypotheses, but interpret the data as though the same hypotheses were tested.

If the authors have the same basic goals and the same basic hypotheses, but still get differing outcomes, then you have to ask whether each author's method is actually testing their hypotheses. If your answer is yes, then you must decide whether one author's methodology is better suited for testing the hypotheses than the other author's. To evaluate the adequacy of a particular author's methodology, there are a number of questions you must ask. Are both authors measuring the same independent, dependent, and control variables? Are both authors adequately controlling all of the relevant extraneous variables? Remember: If the two authors have operationally defined the independent, dependent, and controlled variables differently, then not only are they not measuring the same variables, but they're probably not testing the same hypotheses.

Another very important difference may be in the selection of their subjects. Are the subjects in both studies drawn from the same population? Are the sampling techniques (e.g., random selection of subjects) the same for both studies? Are roughly the same numbers of subjects being used? Are different subjects being used in each treatment condition (between groups design), or are the same subjects being used in multiple treatment conditions (within groups/repeated measures design)?

The apparatus used is as important as the type of subjects. Are both authors using the same type/model/version apparatus? Different manufacturers may use different techniques for measuring certain types of phenomena that could effect the outcome of the study (e.g., weight can be measured by springs, sensors, counter-balanced weights, or displacement, resulting in varying degrees of accuracy). Similarly, different models often have different features (i.e., more expensive models are sometimes more sensitive than less expensive models). For example, if audio output is being delivered to a subject, then signal-to-noise ratio may make a big difference in your results. If you compare the signal-to-noise ratio and dynamic range of a $300 Pioneer "boom box" with a top-end unit of well over $1000, you may find a big difference in their acoustical properties. Likewise, software comes in different versions, and later versions tend to have augmented features, which could make a big difference if one author is using the older version.

Far too often, authors will use the wrong experimental test when evaluating their data. For example, was an ANOVA used to analyze ordinal data? ["Some statisticians . . . require that the data be of interval or ratio scaling in order to use the z-test, Student's t test, and the analysis of variance." (Pagano, 1981; pg. 335)]. Did each author correctly interpret the results of whatever statistical test was performed? Did either author try to generalize the results to a larger population than the one from which the sample was drawn? If the findings of both authors were in the same direction, then perhaps one of the authors did not include enough subjects in his experiment, resulting in insufficient power to detect the effect observed by the other investigator. Look at the differences between the means in each experiment and try to decide whether the observed effect size is large or small. While a discussion of effect size is beyond the scope of this chapter, it's a very important topic. The calculation of effect size is simple, and the reader is encouraged to read Weimer and Hart (1989)[5].

Finally, after reading the results of both articles, weigh the arguments of both authors. Does the interpretation of the data by one of them better fit the existing body of data than the other's? Does one author's interpretation of the data seem to fit with your interpretation? After having evaluated the strengths and weaknesses of the authors' studies, design your own study. Consider it a tie breaker. Design your study to be stronger than those you've just read by clearly operationalizing your variables, rigidly controlling extraneous variation, and making sure that your measurements are measuring what they're supposed to be measuring.

2.3 Explaining the Occurrence of an Unexplained Fact

In 1978, doctors at the Claude-Bernard Hospital in Paris noticed an outbreak of a rare type of pneumonia: *Pneumocystis carinii* (Shilts, 1987). The outbreak was troubling because it was accompanied by a complete breakdown of the immune system and bizarre, opportunistic infections (e.g.,

[5]Effect size refers to proportion of the total variance accounted for by each treatment. Unfortunately, increased printing costs have forced journal editors to reduce the number of journal pages. Too often, journal editors omit raw data and descriptive statistics, making it impossible to compute effect sizes or the accuracy of an author's calculations. However, I've had a great deal of success calling authors directly and asking them to fax me the descriptive statistics associated with a particular study.

toxoplasmosis, a cat's disease, and Kaposi's Sarcoma, a rare form of skin cancer). Several years would pass before epidemiologists would find enough pieces of the puzzle to identify the disease as a retrovirus, HIV, and its means of transmission (shared bodily fluids).

Ironically, since the preponderance of early AIDS victims were gay men, AIDS was labeled a "gay" men's disease, when in fact the first reported victim was a woman in Hjardemaal, Denmark[6]. Unfortunately, such mistakes are common in science. In a fervor to find an explanation for some phenomenon, scientists looking for commonalties (a large number of victims are gay) may overlook important specifics (women are getting the disease as well), resulting in dangerously false conclusions (the disease cannot be spread to heterosexuals or the blood supply). Such mistakes may mislead scientists for decades. AIDS still holds the stigma of being a gay men's disease over a decade and a half after the first case (a heterosexual female) was identified.

When scientists become aware of a fact that does not seem to have any explanation (e.g., why individuals are dying from a rare form of pneumonia and opportunistic infections), the first thing they do is attempt to relate aspects of the problem to a body of related literature. In the case of AIDS, Dr. Don Francis at the Centers for Disease Control observed that some aspects of the pneumocystis were similar to symptoms of hepatitis B (e.g., delayed onset of symptoms), while other symptoms were similar to feline leukemia (i.e., total breakdown of the immune system). By making a connection between pneumocystis, hepatitis B and feline leukemia, Francis was able to postulate the existence of a blood-borne virus (similar to hepatitis B) with symptoms similar to feline leukemia; which in turn led to the development of the first HIV test, based upon the existing hepatitis B test.

However, there are times when a fact flies in the face of traditional knowledge (Why is there an outbreak of GRID[7] among heterosexual Haitians when it's a disease of gay men?). When a fact does not fit the existing body of knowledge, a research problem is created. If the problem runs counter to a currently fashionable theory or school of thought, then it is incumbent upon proponents of the conflicting theory to explain the phenomenon or integrate it into their theory (e.g., a possible explanation for the outbreak of AIDS among heterosexual Haitians is the use of shared blood during voodoo rituals).

Often a phenomenon is not easily integrated into the existing body of knowledge. To aid in integration, researchers collect more information. For example, it was not enough for the epidemiologists at the Centers for Disease Control to theorize that HIV -- like hepatitis B -- was transmitted through

---

[6]The first victim was a woman named Grethe Rask, and she was not gay. Grethe Rask was a physician who'd been working in Abumombazi, Zaire. In that region of Africa, rubber gloves were considered a luxury. Consequently, most of the surgeons in the area would stick their bare hands into a patient when performing surgery -- submersing their hands in the patient's blood (Shilts, 1987). This was probably how Dr. Rask contracted the disease.

[7]GRID, or Gay Related Immune Deficiency, was the initial name given to the AIDS epidemic, when it was still thought that the disease was only contracted by gay men. The name Acquired Immune Deficiency Syndrome (AIDS) came later.

bodily fluids, they had to gather information that would establish a link between the proposed HIV virus and hepatitis B. To establish the link, the CDC scientists gathered information on the rate of occurrence of HIV-related symptoms in intravenous drug users, since there is a high incidence of hepatitis B in intravenous drug users due to the sharing of needles.

Remember, when altering a theory to accommodate a novel phenomenon, the new theory must not only account for the new phenomenon but previously supported phenomena as well. That's why the discovery of a new phenomenon normally generates more questions than it answers. It's rare that a new discovery is a *rosetta stone*, mending the schism between conflicting theories. More often, such phenomena further widen schisms, which in turn can result in the generation of additional research problems. Ask yourself the following questions: Why doesn't the new phenomenon resolve the schism? What are the underlying dynamics that make the phenomenon easier to reconcile with one theory as opposed to another? Can the phenomenon be explained better by still another theory? Can the new phenomenon explain phenomena that cannot be explained by other theories?

McGuigan (1993), discussing the implications of discovering new phenomena, states:

> **"One of the most engaging aspects of the scientific enterprise is to tease out the implications of a general theory and subject those implications to additional empirical tests." (Page 20)**

Finally, it's important to mention that applied researchers sometimes get problems from a "bug" list[8]. A "bug" list is a list of unexplained usability problems with a particular system. Mackworth's investigation into why radar operators were missing U-boats could be considered a bug list with 1 item. Bug lists are particularly common in private industry, where usability researchers are called on not only to explain why users' performance is suboptimal, but also to recommend what system changes need to be made to increase performance.

2.4 Reading for Problems

In the absence of a bug list, you must immerse yourself in the literature to find a research problem. It's not enough to just read the articles; you must learn to read them critically. Critical reading takes practice, but you can increase your critical reading ability right away by doing the following.

Collect all the articles you can find in a particular area. Casually read each one, jotting down the author's goals, hypotheses, methods, variables, results, and whether or not they accepted their hypotheses. When you've read all of them and compiled your notes, pick up the first article again. Slowly and carefully read through it, referring to the notes you made during

---

[8]Thanks to Mark Scerbo for the example of the bug list. If you're interested in usability testing, read Mark's excellent chapter in this book.

the casual reading. Do this for each of the articles. Kantowitz, Roediger, and Elmes (1991) suggest that you avoid rushing through an article, stopping after each section to write to answer the questions in Table 2-2.

The *authors' goal* is the reason they performe did the experiment. In the introduction, authors discuss past research, conflicting theories, predictions those theories make, and why they think their approach is better than those of other researchers. When authors discuss why they think other theories don't adequately predict the observed phenomenon, you usually get a flavor for their approach to the problem and their biases. The *hypotheses that will be tested* should arise out of the authors' theoretical background, though they may not always explicitly state them; incompatibility between the authors' hypotheses and their goals or theoretical model is a warning sign that the test results may not agree with the authors' theoretical model and could explain conflicts within the larger body of research.

As you read an article, continually ask: *What would I do if I were conducting the experiment?* This will help you maintain a critical eye. Hard as it to believe, mistakes are published in journals every year, in spite of peer review. Talented writers can be very persuasive, directing your attention away from the weaknesses of their approach; you can find yourself accepting the authors' point-of-view, hypotheses, and conclusions without having critically evaluated them. Asking yourself what you'd do forces you to draw your own conclusions, rather than blindly accepting the author's.

Part of asking yourself what you would do is to propose your own method of studying the problem and ask yourself (honestly): *Is my proposed method is better than that of the authors?* In order to decide, you have to ask: *Does the method actually tests the hypotheses* ? That refers not only to your method, but the authors' method too. *What are the [authors'] independent, dependent, and control variables?* List them. Are they the same as yours? Are you and the author using the same operational definitions? Are you and the author manipulating the variables in the same way?

Once you've laid out your method of testing the authors' hypotheses, ask yourself: *Using the subjects, apparatus, and procedures described by the authors, what results would I expect for this experiment?* Remember to ask this question before you look at the Results section. This will increase your ability to predict the outcome of experiments. Also remember, that most authors' don't anticipate the occurrence of interactions unless their hypotheses specifically predict them[9]. Thus, when making your predictions, don't forget to ask if there could be an interaction among variables that was not anticipated by the authors.

---

[9]In other words, authors often phrase their hypotheses only in terms of anticipated main effects (i.e., a treatment effect only with no interaction among treatments). Thus, when an interaction does occur, the experimenter may be hard pressed to account for it since it was not accounted for in his or her original hypotheses.

Table 2-2: Questions for Critical Readers

Introduction

1. What is the author's goal?
1a. Introduction of new theories?
1b. Review of a particular problem area?
2. How comprehensive is the literature review?
2a. Have any important articles or areas been neglected?
3. What hypotheses will be tested in the experiment?
4. Have all concepts been adequately operationalized? (See Section 3.1.1)
5. If I had to design an experiment to test these hypotheses, what would I do?

Method

6. Who are the subjects?
6a. How adequate are the selection procedures with respect to number and type of subjects?
6b. If this is consumer or usability research, do the demographics and psychographics match those of the target population of users/consumers?
6c. Given the characteristics of the subject sample, can the results be generalized to larger populations?
7. What are the independent, dependent, and control variables?
8. Is the experimental design appropriate?
8a. Would a different experimental design be more appropriate?
8b. Is adequate control of nuisance variables being used?
9. How appropriate are the stimuli, materials, test questions, and apparati?
9a. Are the stimuli representative of the operationalized problem? (See 3.1.1)
10. How appropriate are the procedures?
10a. Are tasks being properly sequenced?
10b. Where appropriate, has adequate practice been given to subjects?
10c. Are instructions leading or misleading?
10d. Where appropriate, have subjects been given adequate rest periods?
10e. Are contamination effects possible?

Table 2-2: Questions for Critical Readers (Continued)

11. Does the author's method actually test his/her hypotheses?
12. Have enough observations been made?
13. Is my proposed method better than the author's?
14. Using the same subjects, apparati, and procedures, what results would I expect?

Results

15. How has the data been collected?
15a. How has it been coded?
15b. How has it been reduced?
16. Has the data been properly analyzed?
16a. Have critical analyses been neglected?
16b. Could alternative or additional analyses be performed?
17. Have the tables and figures been properly prepared?
17a. Are they misleading?
18. Did the author get the "wrong" results?
19. How would I interpret the results?

Discussion

20. Have the results been properly interpreted?
21. Do the results support the hypotheses?
21a. If not, are adequate explanations offered?
22. Are there alternative explanations for the findings? (See Huck and Sandler, 1979)
23. Is my interpretation better than the author's?
24. Do the findings have any practical significance?
25. What additional research might be performed to increase understanding of the problem?

Adapted from Kantowitz, Roediger, and Elmes (1991) and Scerbo (1993)

Now compare the results to your predictions. If they don't match then ask: *Did the authors get the wrong results?* Go back and reexamine your prediction. Could you have made a mistake in your prediction? If your answer is no, then critically reevaluate the methods used by the authors. Can you think of an uncontrolled source of variation that could account for the results? Are the authors manipulating the independent variable or something else? Are the authors' operational definitions adequate and appropriate? Are the authors' methods really testing the stated hypotheses.

If the answer to any of these questions is no, then you may have the answer to why your predictions do not match the authors' results.

If your predicted outcome matches the outcome of the experiment, then -- before you read the discussion -- you should ask: *How would I interpret these results?* By interpreting the results yourself, you're honing your analytic skills. Now read the discussion and (honestly) ask: *Is my interpretation "better" than the authors'?* By better, I mean: Does your interpretation of the results better match the data than the authors'? If you find that your interpretation of the data is not as good as theirs, reread the introduction and the methods section. Try to determine where you went wrong in your analysis.

If your interpretation of the data is a better fit than theirs, ask: Why didn't they reach the same conclusion? Again, ask the following questions. Are the authors over looking my interpretation because they're trying to fit data into an incorrect theoretical model? Are they merely misinterpreting the data? Could some intervening variable(s) influencing the results? Could there be yet a third interpretation of the data?

Don't get discouraged. Reading and interpreting the research of others is often a difficult and frustrating endeavor; this is particularly true when your interpretation of the results don't match those of the authors. Remember:

> **"The discussion section is the most difficult to evaluate. Often only future research can decide if it is correct." (Kantowitz, Roediger, and Elmes, 1991)**

Now, go back and do this for each of the articles that you collected. When you have gone through this process for all of the articles, compare the notes that you took on each article. Are there questions that still remain unanswered or aspects of the problem that have not yet been studied (knowledge gaps)? Are there one or more articles, with sound methodologies and interpretations, yet their results and/or interpretations differ (conflicting results)? Was some artifact found that could not be explained (occurrence of an unexplained phenomenon)? If the answer to any of these questions is yes, then you have the beginning of a research problem. If the answer is no, then read the articles again and ask yourself if you know of any related theory or discipline could shed new light on this area. For example, vigilance has been studied for over 4 decades, but people are still finding new ways to investigate it.

2.5 Summary

Research can be both basic and applied. Basic research is the acquisition of knowledge for developing or supporting a theory, while applied research is concerned with finding answers to practical problems. Whether basic or applied, research problems fall into 3 distinct categories:

(1) a knowledge gap, (2) contradictory research results, or (3) the occurrence of an unexplained fact. When trying to find a problem to research, read critically using the information in section 2.4 and the checklists in Tables 2-1 and 2-2.

3.0 Turning a Problem Into a Testable Hypothesis

Problems, while interesting, are not very useful. Why? Because a problem is just a question that may or may not have an answer. Not every problem is solvable. For example:

1. How can God exist when there is so much suffering?
2. Does life start at conception or at some later point in time?
3. Does extraterrestrial life exist?
4. Is there such a thing as ESP?
5. Is there life after death?

While each of these problems is interesting, there are no good techniques for answering them (e.g., the point at which life starts or the presence of extraterrestrial life). In order to be useful, a problem must translatable into a hypothesis that can be tested. McGuigan (1993) states that an appropriate research problem is:

> **"A problem [that] is solvable if, and only if, one can empirically test its tentative solution (which is offered in the form of a hypothesis) . . . A hypothesis is testable, if and only if, it is possible to determine that it is either true or false. . . [Stated differently,] if it is possible to determine that a hypothesis, stated as a proposition, is either true or false, then the hypothesis is testable. If it is not possible to determine that the proposition is either true or false, then the hypothesis is *not* testable [in its current form] and should be discarded [or restated]. . ."**

Hypotheses are stated in the form of propositions that can be shown to be true or false. Often, these statements are of the form: If A then B. In other words, a change in A is accompanied by a change in B. Notice that I didn't say that a change in A *causes* a change in B. That's because sometimes the hypothesis you want to test is correlational, and hence a proposition stating causation would be inappropriate. The important point to remember is that the hypothesis must be stated in such a way that it can be evaluated to be true or false[10]. You can never, with absolute certainty, say

---

[10]Although a hypothesis is a true or false proposition, we never prove a hypothesis to be true or false. Whether or not we accept or reject a hypothesis can change with the probability value we choose (e.g., increasing a p value from .05 to .01 means that you're making it more difficult to accept the tested hypothesis, because you're a choosing a smaller margin of error for the test). Thus, you are decreasing the likelihood of rejecting the null hypothesis when the null hypothesis is true (i.e., you are reducing the number of "false" alarms). Sometimes, when high risk is associated with falsely accepting the null hypothesis, it is more prudent to make the probability more liberal (e.g., increase the p value from .05 to .2). For a more in depth discussion of this topic, see section 4.0 in chapter 5.

that a hypothesis is true. You can merely state, on the basis of a statistical test, your degree of certainty that the hypothesis is true. Thus, a more correct definition would be:

> **A hypothesis is testable, if and only if, it is possible to determine the probability that it is true or false.**

Taking this definition and combining it with the previous one, we get the following definition of a testable problem:

> **A problem is testable if (1) it can be stated in the form of a hypothesis, and (2) the probability of true or falsity of that hypothesis can be determined.**

So why are some problems capable of being tested while others aren't?

3.1 Some Reasons for Problems that Aren't Testable

Oftentimes some hypotheses may seem to be testable, but they really aren't (pseudohypotheses). Perhaps the technology doesn't yet exist to test the hypothesis, some essential piece of the puzzle is missing, or the problem has been inadequately defined. While there are many reasons for unsolveable problems, the most common are:

1. Problem is inadequately structured
2. Data cannot be collected
3. Impasse problem
4. Ethical problems

These four problems form the core of all problems with testability. While all of these problems can be overcome to some degree, problem 1 is probably the easiest to overcome, while problems 2, 3, and 4 require some ingenuity on the part of the researcher.

3.1.1 The problem is inadequately structured. Problems of structure refer to problems that have not been put into the form of a testable hypothesis. Some examples of ill-structured problems are:

1. Why is my mother crazy?
2. Why is my E-mail program so hard to use?
3. Why is it difficult for people to program their VCR?
4. Why can some people see red, while others cannot?

These questions are not phrased in a manner that can be tested. Vague words (e.g., crazy, hard, and difficult) are used that do not lend themselves to being measured. Fortunately, vaguely worded questions can often be rephrased so they are more easily testable.

Vagueness comes from using terms that have not been operationally defined adequately. Operational definitions unambiguously describe the nature of the observed phenomenon by specifying how and in what units it can be measured. The definition of an operational definition is slippery, in itself, as seen in the following formal definitions[11].

> **"An operational definition completely specifies the meaning of the term by identifying the operations involved in its measurement." (Neale & Liebert, 1986)**

> **"An operational definition is one in which a term is defined by the operations used to measure them." (Robinson, 1981)**

> **"Operational definitions describe the procedures used to produce a concept and allow us to communicate successfully about the concepts we are studying . . . An operational definition is a formula for building a construct in a way that other scientists can duplicate, by specifying the operations used to produce and measure it." (Kantowitz, Roediger, and Elmes, 1991)**

> **"An operational definition is a recipe for specifying how a construct, such as reading, is produced and measured. The conditions that produce the concept are carefully specified, and the ways in which the concept is to be measured are defined . . . An operational definition is a formula for building a construct in a way that other scientists can duplicate." (Elmes, Kantowitz, and Roediger, 1992)**

> **". . . an operational definition is one that indicates that a certain phenomenon exists, and does so by specifying precisely how (and preferably in what units) the phenomenon is measured." (McGuigan, 1993)**

In my opinion, there are good and bad points about each of these definitions. I guess my problem with the above definitions center around the use of the word operation itself; *Webster's Ninth New Collegiate Dictionary* lists 8 entries for the term operation. Thus, I would posit the following definition, which incorporates aspects from all of the definitions:

> **An operational definition defines a concept in terms of the methods used to produce and/or measure it -- procedures and measurements that are specific enough to allow scientists to exactly duplicate the concept.**

---

[11] The definition of operational definition even changes between different publications by the same author. Compare the definition offered by Kantowitz, Roediger, and Elmes (1991) with that offered by Elmes, Kantowitz, and Roediger (1992).

Consider the word red. Red is a vague concept. While you have a mental image of red, but my image may be more crimson and yours may be more vermilion. By operationally defining red as reflected light of 640 nm wavelength, I have not only unambiguously defined the concept, but I have also defined it in a manner that allows others to recreate *my* version of red.

However, most concepts are not as easily defined. How do you define learning? Motivation? Attention? Attraction? Love? The more abstract the concept, the more difficulty you'll have deriving an operational definition. Note, however, that operational definitions are not arbitrary. For example, while the operational definitions you use for learning can differ somewhat from traditional operational definitions, you need to justify this departure, and your rationale must follow from your theoretical model. In general, the more abstract the concept, the more likely you will be to get a number of different, conflicting operational definitions of the same concept. Recall that I mentioned earlier that researchers may sometimes have conflicts because they are looking at the same thing in different ways? There are times when authors are looking at a concept in slightly different ways, merely because they have operationally defined the concept in subtly different ways. For example, there is no good agreement in the literature concerning the definition of what boredom is and how it is best measured[12].

In order to have a testable problem, you must be able to operationally define all critical concepts that describe it. Operational definition dictates that concepts are specified in terms of the methods used to produce and/or measure them. If you're having difficulty deriving a testable problem, then perhaps you have not operationally defined one or more important concepts adequately. If you cannot operationally defined the concepts comprising the problem, then you have an inadequately structured problem. Approach the problem from a different tact. If the problem continues to defy being operationally defined, then perhaps you have a problem that cannot be studied for some reason. Perhaps you're having problems operationalizing your concepts in terms of the data collection methods, because data cannot be collected on this problem.

3.1.2 Data cannot be collected. Sometimes you can precisely state your problem, but you just can't find a way to collect the necessary data. There are many reasons why data cannot be collected for a certain type of problem. The technology does not yet exist to measure the phenomenon you're trying to study, the technology exits but it's too expensive, or it's unethical to collect the type of data you wish to collect. For example, biological explanations have been posited for both schizophrenia and homosexuality, yet biological indicators for both continue to elude scientists[13].

---

[12]Thanks to Mark Scerbo for this example.

[13]This is not entirely true. Promising research has been conducted using the psychotropic drug Clozaril. CAT scans of the brains of schizophrenics taken before and after treatment with Clozaril show alterations in brain metabolism. However, the drug's physiological mechanism of action is not clear.

3.1.3 Impasse problem. An impasse problem occurs when a body of literature develops, with adequately stated problems and terms, yet the results are contradictory or inconclusive for no apparent reason. In cases such as these, performing another experiment may simply add to the confusion. If you're interested in an area where an impasse exists, you should try to take a novel approach, rather than trying to see where the others have failed; try a different theoretical model or introduce techniques and models from another discipline into the problems space (e.g., the application of signal detection theory to the study of vigilance).

3.1.4 Ethical problems. Sometimes a problem, no matter how interesting, simply cannot be studied. If there is any reason to suspect that physical or psychological damage will be inflicted on subjects, then you should either not study the problem or find some other way to gather the data. Some examples of unethical experiments would be:

1. To determine the heterosexual transmissivity of AIDS, individuals are asked to engage in unprotected sex with HIV positive partners.
2. To test the G-stress limits that pilots can endure, G's are increased until the death of the subject.
3. Military personnel are exposed to chemical weapons without protective clothing.
4. Subjects are injected with harmful substances without their knowledge.

The irony is that while examples 1 & 2 are fictitious, examples 3 & 4 are not. During World War II, soldiers were subjected to mustard gas, while they put on their gas masks, to test the effects of short-term exposure to the gas. Many of them have neurological damage today.

In 1945, as part of the Manhattan Project, doctors at the University of Rochester's Strong Hospital injected 17 unsuspecting patients with .3 microcuries of plutonium-239 (47 times the safe lifetime limit) (Susan Miller, 1993). The purpose of the experiment was to show how quickly the body rids itself of plutonium. Even though follow ups were continued for several years, the patients were not told of their participation until 1974.

4.0 Conducting the Experiment

Definition of variables, experimental design, and the execution of experiments are covered in Robert Williges' overview of experimental design (Chapter 3). If you're interested in additional information, read chapters 3-6 in Robinson (1981), chapters 2-3 in Kantowitz, Roediger, and Elmes (1991), chapters 4-5 in McGuigan (1993), or Kerlinger (1973). If you're looking for a more detailed treatment of designing experiments, read chapters 6-12 of McGuigan (1993), chapters 7-11 of Neale and Liebert (1986), or chapters 7-12 of Robinson (1981). For a rigorous treatment of the design and analysis of experiments, read Keppel (1982) or Kerlinger (1973) for a conceptual approach, or Kirk (1982), Winer (1971), Montgomery (1991), or Cochran and Cox (1957) for a mathematical one. If you're interested in the design of multivariate experiments, read Tabachnick and Fidell (1983) for a conceptual approach, or Marascuilo and Levin (1983) for a more mathematical one. Finally, if you're interested in quasi-experimental designs, read Cook and Campbell (1979) for a complete treatment and Campbell and Stanley (1963) for a quick overview.

5.0 Threats to Research Validity

Once you've found a problem, developed a set of hypotheses, and selected an experimental design, you're ready to collect data. Right? Not exactly. There's a final question you must ask before you collect that first data point. Is the change in the independent variable the <u>only</u> possible explanation for observed changes in the dependent variable?

Unfortunately, validity is often omitted in discussions of methodology. Validity refers to whether or not the experimental design answers the research question, and is threatened when factors -- if left uncontrolled -- can confound (i.e., become inseparably enmeshed with) the treatment effects in the experiment. There are 2 types of validity: internal and external.

5.1 Threats to Internal Validity

Internal validity refers to the degree to which you can conclude that the manipulation of the independent variable, and <u>only</u> that manipulation, has caused the observed change in the dependent variable. Without internal validity, your results are uninterpretable. Campbell and Stanley (1963) have identified 8 threats to the internal validity of an experiment:

1. History
2. Maturation
3. Testing
4. Statistical Regression
5. Mortality
6. Instrumentation
7. Selection
8. Interactions Among Factors

5.1.1 History. History refers to events, other than the experimental treatment, that occur in the elapsed time between two measurements. For example, suppose you're evaluating the effect of adding a midnight to 6 AM shift on the number of defective parts produced in a month at a stamping plant. First you evaluate the number of defective parts before the new shift is added (baseline measurement). Now you take some of the workers and form a midnight to 6 AM shift. Suppose, however that the company tells half of the workers on the new shift that they will be laid off at the end of the month, but no one tells you. When you collect the next set of data (treatment measurement), you notice that the number of defective parts in the midnight shift has dramatically increased. Is the change due to sleep loss or the announced layoff?

The easiest way to prevent the influence of history effects is to decrease the elapsed time between successive measurements. History effects are most likely to occur in experiments where measurement of the same subject's behavior are taken at separate times (within groups/repeated measures designs).

5.1.2 Maturation. Maturation refers to a subject's physiological or psychological characteristics that systematically change during the experiment. Subjects can become bored, frustrated, hungry, thirsty, or fatigued. Maturation, like history effects, are most likely to occur in experiments where measurements of the same subject's behavior are taken at separate times (within groups/repeated measures designs).

For example, suppose you want to compare two different types of simulators. Subjects who have never used a simulator are placed in simulator 1 and asked to perform a given task. When the task has been completed, the subject is escorted to simulator 2 and asked to perform the same task. The results of the experiment show that subjects make fewer errors in simulator 2 than in simulator 1. Does that mean simulator 2 is better than simulator 1, or have the subjects merely improved with practice? There's no way to tell. The observed effects may simply be the result of subjects having become accustomed to the novelty of the simulator.

Maturation effects, like history effects, become more likely as the amount of time between successive measurements increases. Maturation effects are controlled insofar as the chosen experimental design guarantees that the maturation effect is manifested equally in experimental and control groups. Treatment counter-balancing, use of Latin squares designs, reducing the time between successive measurements, and allowing subjects to take frequent breaks, are just some of the ways to reduce that maturation effects.

5.1.3 Testing. Testing refers to the effect of the first measurement on the second measurement. Like maturation and history effects, testing effects are most likely to occur in experiments in which measurement of the same subject's behavior are taken at separate times (within groups/repeated measures designs). Testing effects occur most often in pretest-posttest situations, where the mere practice of taking the pretest can cause the subjects to perform better on the posttest. A possible solution is to allow subjects to take practice tests before the actual measurement begins. Testing effects can also be controlled by choosing an experimental design that guarantees the testing effect is manifested equally in experimental and control groups.

5.1.4 Statistical regression. Statistical regression refers to the tendency of extreme scores (outliers) to become less extreme (regress towards the mean) with repeated testing. Statistical regression is a problem when subjects are selected for participation in a study based upon their extreme scores on some pretest.

Individual variation is inevitable in behavioral science research. Any number of organismic variables, such as a subject's mood, can effect their performance from one testing condition to the next. Normally, when data is statistically analyzed, the averaging of high and low scorers tends to cancel this "noise". Unfortunately, when subjects are selected based on extreme scores, this noise can become magnified in the direction of the score. Hence, extreme high scores may have higher than normal amounts of "noise", while extreme lower scores may have lower than normal. Over repeated testing, however, the influence of this "noise" variance will disappear, making the extreme scores appear to move (regress) toward the mean.

One possible solution to this problem is to not select by extreme scores when more than one measurement per subject will be taken (within groups/repeated measures designs). Regression effects can also be controlled if subjects are randomly assigned to treatment and control conditions from the same extreme pool of subjects (Campbell and Stanley, 1963). Thus, subjects in the control group and the experimental group regress to the same degree, canceling the effect (Campbell and Stanley, 1963).

5.1.5 Mortality. Experimental mortality occurs when subjects drop out of comparison groups at different rates. For example, suppose that we are evaluating the effect of gender on lane keeping[14] in an automotive simulator task. If more women develop simulator sickness[15] , withdrawing from participation, then the groups will no longer be equivalent, invalidating the comparison of the groups.

Longitudinal studies can prove to be quite troublesome due to subjects dropping out because they're "tired" of showing up for the experimental sessions. One possible alternative is to randomly discard subjects from the comparison group for each mortality.

5.1.6 Instrumentation. Instrumentation refers to changes in measurement or observation that occur during the data collection. Instrumentation can occur because observers become bored, tired, or fatigued, or because the experimental apparatus overheats, becomes

[14]Lane keeping is a task, similar to tracking, that refers to the ability of a subject to keep the experimental vehicle within their lane. Lane keeping can be measured in a number of ways, but one of the simplest measures is the number of times the center lane is crossed.

[15]Some anecdotal evidence suggests that novice female subjects may be more susceptible to simulator sickness than novice males.

uncalibrated, or malfunctions. For example, my eyetracker[16] can become uncalibrated by only a slight bump to the headset. Frequent rests and short testing sessions will reduce the likelihood of instrumentation effects by reducing the wear and tear on the observers and apparatus. In addition, automated data collection can reduce the possibility of instrumentation effects that might occur due to observer fatigue or boredom.

5.1.7 Selection. When two groups are assumed to be equivalent, but actually differ on a significant characteristic before the experiment begins, then you run the danger of having your measurements corrupted by selection effects. For example, suppose you want to evaluate the effect of safety training on the performance of machinists who have completed a formal trade school program vs. machinists who have completed an apprenticeship program. However, in order to obtain enough subjects to fill each group, you have to get the trade school machinists from one plant and the apprenticed machinists from another. However, the plant employing the trade school graduates have a managerial philosophy that training is a waste of valuable work time, while the plant employing the apprentice graduates is indifferent. Managerial philosophy toward training can influence the success of the training (See Chapter 14). Hence, the two groups of machinists may not be equivalent prior to the presentation of the training.

Matching and blocking type designs are particularly sensitive to this type of threat. Randomization of subjects can help to eliminate the possibility of selection influence.

5.1.8 Interactions among factors. Of course, each of the other 7 threats can act in concert to jointly influence the dependent measures.

5.2 Threats to External Validity

Threats to internal validity effect the dependent variable in ways that can be confused with the effects of the independent variable. Inasmuch as the threats to internal validity could be described -- in the language of ANOVA -- as main effects, threats to external validity could be characterized as interaction effects (i.e., an interaction between the independent variable and some other variable) (Campbell and Stanley, 1963).

External validity refers to the ability to generalize the results of an experiment to the population from which the samples were taken. Unfortunately, most populations are so large that you're almost never capable of studying them with absolute certainty due to resource limitations[17]. Thus, it is difficult, if not impossible in most cases, to assess the true external validity of an experiment.

---

[16]An eyetracker is a device that bounces infrared light off the surface of a subject's eyes, recording their eye movements, and superimposing cross hairs, representing eye fixations, on a videotape of the scene in front of the subject. Eyetrackers are used to study where in visual space a user may be looking at any given time.

[17]One exception is in industrial research where a "lot" or a production run is considered to be a population.

Campbell and Stanley (1963) list the following four threats to external validity:

1. Interaction Between Testing and the Independent Variable
2. Interaction Between Selection of the Independent Variable
3. Reactive Effects of Experimental Arrangements
4. Multiple Treatment Interference

5.2.1 Interaction between testing and the independent variable. In this situation, the pretest sensitizes subjects to the independent variable, making it impossible to generalize any treatment effects to situations in which the pretest is not administered.

For example, suppose you're studying the effect of human relations training on attitudes toward work place diversity issues (e.g., gay rights, minority issues, etc.) in a conservative corporation. Pretesting the attitudes of the executives prior to administering the training might give them the tacit message that the training is being offered because higher level executives are taking diversity issues seriously. Hence, fearing that their promotions may depend on them taking the training to heart, the trainees might show more attitude change than had they not been pretested. Thus, the results of the study would not be generalizable to situations in which a pretest is not administered.

Campbell and Stanley (1963) offer this advice for reducing the interactions between independent variables and pretests:

> **"In research [on training], one is interested in generalizing to a setting in which testing is a regular phenomenon. Especially if the experiment can use regular classroom examinations as [tests], but probably also if experimental [tests can be made to be] similar to those usually used, no undesirable interaction of testing and [the independent variables] [should] be present. Where highly unlikely test procedures are used, or where the test procedure involves deception, perceptual or cognitive restructuring, surprise, stress, etc., designs having unpretested groups remain highly desirable if not essential."**

5.2.2 Interaction between selection and the independent variable. If you have reason to suspect that the test subject might be unusually sensitive to the effects of the independent variable, you may be unable to generalize your results to the larger population because of a subjects-by-treatment interaction. In this situation, the subjects assigned to experimental groups are special in some way that sets them apart from the general population. Whatever makes them "special" makes it impossible to generalize to a larger population.

Let's return to the example of work place diversity issues. Suppose you have gone to 10 corporations, offered them your training course for free, and have been turned down my 9 of them. The 10th accepts your offer. Could there be something unusual about that 10th corporation? Could they have more liberal personnel policies? Could diversity issues be of particular interest to them? Is this a reaction to recent sexual harassment or affirmative action litigation against the corporation? Any of these special cases could influence the effectiveness of the training in ways that would not appear in the larger population of corporations.

The best way to insure that selection-by-treatment interactions doe not occur is to broaden the scope of your sampling. Could you sample more than 10 corporations? Only rigorous adherence to proper sampling procedures can insure the absence of a sampling by treatment interaction. For more information on sampling techniques, see Cochran (1963).

5.2.3 Reactive effects of experimental arrangements. Reactive effects of experimental arrangements, refer to the influence of the experimental setting on the effectiveness of the independent variable. This is the old "field work is more representative than lab work" argument. The argument is not without merit. It's easy to be assertive while role playing in assertiveness training, but the situation changes dramatically when you're facing down your boss for a raise -- particularly if he's in a bad mood. Similarly, the argument that driving simulators are not indicative of true driving performance is also often made. Again, the argument is not without merit. In a driving simulator, what are the consequences if you mow down an old lady in the cross walk or plow head on into a computer-generated truck? The consequences in the real world are imprisonment or death, which raises the stakes considerably.

Subjects may react differently merely because they realize that they are part of an experiment. This is known as the *Hawthorne* effect. Experiments in which the setting is highly artificial or totally unfamiliar to the subject are particularly susceptible to Hawthorne effects. Thus, reactive arrangement-by-treatment interactions may seem impossible to overcome, but Campbell and Stanley (1963) offer this advice:

> **"Where *reactive arrangements* are unavoidable [e.g., simulator studies], internally valid experiments of this type should by all means be continued. But if they can be avoided, they obviously should be . . . Any aspect of the experimental procedure may produce this reactive effect . . . The more obvious the connection between the experimental treatment and the [dependent variable] the more likely this effect becomes."**

5.2.4 Multiple treatment interference. When multiple treatments are sequentially delivered to a subject, it sometimes becomes difficult to separate the effects of single treatments from the cumulative effects of all administered treatments. This problem is particularly troublesome in repeated measures designs, where the same subjects are exposed to all treatment conditions. The most common occurrence of this threat is the so-called practice effect, where performance on the final measurement is better than on the initial measurement purely by virtue of repeated practice. Drug carry-over effects are also troublesome in repeated measures designs. The only way to avoid this difficulty is to redesign your experiment to be a between groups design, or only use variables that you know will not have cumulative effects.

5.3 Summary

The validity of an experiment can be challenged by internal and external factors. Internal threats challenge the validity of drawing the conclusion of a causal relationship between the independent and dependent variables by confounding the effects of the independent variable. External threats challenge your ability to generalize an experiment's results to a larger population by interacting with the independent variable. Threats to internal and external validity can often be obviated through careful selection and execution of your experimental design.

6.0 Suggestions for Further Reading

If you want more information on how to improve your critical reading skills, read Huck, Cormier, and Bounds (1974) and Katzer, Cook, and Crouch (1991). Likewise, if you would like some exercises to increase your analytical research skills, read Huck and Sandler (1979). For additional reading on the evaluation of data from multivariate experiments, read Cliff (1987). Research results are not always definitive, and sometimes require experimenters to make educated guesses, or judgment calls; I would suggest that all readers of this book read a monograph on judgment calls in research by McGrath, Martin, and Kulka (1982).

Applied psychology and human engineering employ unique measurement techniques. Meister (1985) presents an excellent, rigorous treatment of the different data collection and evaluation methods available to the applied experimental psychologist and the human engineering professional. While slightly dated now, Chapanis (1959) describes some techniques, such as critical incidents reporting, that are still used today and that you might find useful. For more information on ethical conduct in research, read the American Psychological Association's guide to ethical research (APA, 1982).

As an applied discipline, the research problems of human engineering do not always lend themselves to the collection of neat data that can fit nicely into a traditional analysis of variance. Oftentimes, researchers find themselves with data that they're not quite sure how to analyze. A book on non-parametric statistics that I've found extremely useful is Siegel (1956). This book presents a terse, but invaluable treatment of non-parametric statistical techniques, including a very valuable chart on the inside and back covers for helping you to decide what technique you need. Most of us are taught in statistics class to blindly use random sampling, however there are cases in which random sampling is not appropriate. Cochran (1963) presents a comprehensive description of the different types of sampling techniques that are available to the applied researcher.

As you can tell from looking at the table of contents of this book, human engineering is an interdisciplinary science that becomes increasingly interdisciplinary as technology diversifies. Human engineering should be considered as one or more poles on a series of multidimensional axes. On the other end of one of those axes is market research. In their simplest forms, human engineering studies human performance while market research studies human preference[18]. Viewed as opposing poles on a continuum, it is easy to see why there is overlap among these disciplines. In a typical usability study, it's not uncommon to ask a subject how much they liked a system or how likely they would be to buy it; this does not make the usability researcher a market researcher. Likewise, it's not uncommon for market researchers, while conducting a focus group or clinic, to observe difficulties that typical users of a product may have when interacting with a product; this does not make them human engineers. If you are contemplating a career in private industry (e.g., usability, medical devices, or consumer products), I would strongly suggest that you read Schwartz (1987) and Worchester and Downham (1978); this is because human engineering professionals are often included as part of a market research organization or are called upon to frequently interact with market researchers.

7.0 Biography

I received my Ph.D. in Experimental Psychology from Texas Tech University in May of 1988. I specialize in human-computer interaction and experimental design. I've worked for AT&T's Network Operations, PRODIGY's usability lab, and General Motors' Advanced Product Engineering. I've designed, evaluated, and prototyped interfaces for corporate budgetary software, videotext, technical memory, online purchasing and advertising, interactive conferencing, Intelligent Vehicle and Highway Systems, and service information software. In addition to a number of articles, I'm the author of two other Prentice-Hall books: *Effective Computer Display Design* and *Handbook of Ergonomic and Human Factors Tables*. I'm also a feelance writer and film critic for *Encore Magazine*. If you have questions or comments about this chapter or book, I'd love to hear from you. E-mail me at: weimerj@aol.com.

REFERENCES

American Psychological Association. (1982). *Ethical Principles in the Conduct of Research with Human Subjects*. American Psychological Association: Washington, D.C.

[18]Thanks to Nick Simonelli for this example.

Boff, K.R. (1988). The value of research is in the eye of the beholder. *Human Factors Society Bulletin*, 31(6), 1-4.

Campbell, D.T., & Stanley, J.C. (1963). *Experimental and Quasi-Experimental Designs for Research*. Houghton-Mifflin: Boston.

Chapanis, A. (1959). *Research Techniques in Human Engineering.* Johns Hopkins Press: Baltimore.

Cliff, N. (1987). *Analyzing Multivariate Data.* Harcourt Brace Javonovich, Publishers: New York.

Cochran, W.G. (1963). *Sampling Techniques.* John Wiley: New York.

Cochran, W.G., & Cox, G. (1957). *Experimental Designs.* Wiley: New York.

Cook, T.D., & Campbell, D.T. (1979). *Quasi Experimentation: Design and Analysis Issues for Field Settings.* Houghton-Mifflin: Boston.

Elmes, D.G., Kantowitz, B.H., & Roediger, H.L. (1992). *Research Methods in Experimental Psychology.* (4th ed.). West Publishing Company: St. Paul, MN.

Fisher, D.L., and Tanner, N.S. (1992). Optimal symbol set selection: A semiautomated procedure. *Human Factors*, 34 (1), 79-96.

Flach, J.M. (1989). An ecological alternative to egg-sucking. *Human Factors Society Bulletin,* 32(9), 4-6.

Huck, S.W., Cormier, W.H., & Bounds, W.G. (1974). *Reading Statistics in Research.* Harper & Row: New York.

Huck, S.W., & Sandler, H.M. (1979). *Rival Hypotheses : Alternative Interpretations of Data Based Conclusions.* Harper & Row: New York.

Kantowitz, B.H. (1985). Letter. *Human Factors Society Bulletin*, 28(1), 4.

Kantowitz, B.H., Roediger, H.L., & Elmes, D.G. (1991). *Experimental Psychology: Understanding Psychological Research.* (4th ed.). West Publishing Company: St. Paul, MN.

Katzer, J., Cook, K.H., & Crouch, W.W. (1991). *Evaluating Research: A Guide for Users of Social Science Research.* (3rd ed.). McGraw Hill: New York.

Kirk, R.E. (1982). *Experimental Design.* (2nd ed.). Brooks/Cole: Belmont, CA.

Keppel, G. (1982). *Design and Analysis: A Researcher's Handbook.* Prentice-Hall: Englewood Cliffs, NJ.

Kerlinger, F.N. (1973). *Foundations of Behavioral Research.* (2nd ed.) Holt, Reinhart, and Winston: New York.

Klein, G.A., & Brezovic, C.P. (1986). Design engineers and the design process: Decision strategies and human factors literature. *Proceedings of the Human Factors Society 30th Annual Meeting* (pp. 771-775). Santa Monica, CA: Human Factors Society.

Loeb, M. & Alluisi, E. A. (1984). Theories of vigilance. In J.S. Warm (Ed.) *Sustained Attention in Human Performance.* John Wiley and Sons: New York.

Marascuilo, L.A., & Levin, J.R. (1983). *Multivariate Statistics In the Social Sciences: A Researcher's Guide.* Brooks/Cole: Belmont, CA.

Mason, E.J., & Bramble, W.J. (1978). *Understanding and Conducting Research / Applications in Education and the Behavioral Sciences.* McGraw-Hill: New York.

McGrath, J.E., Martin, J., & Kulka, R.A. (1982). *Judgment Calls in Research.* Sage Publications: Newbury Park, CA.

McGuigan, F.J., (1993). *Experimental Psychology: Methods of Research.* (6th ed.). Prentice-Hall: Englewood Cliffs, NJ.

Meister, D. (1985). *Behavioral Analysis and Measurement Methods.* John Wiley & Sons: New York.

Meister, D. (1984). Letter. *Human Factors Society Bulletin*, 27(10), 2.

Miller, S. (1993, December 17). A human horror story. Plutonium: What doctors didn't tell Eda Charlton. *Newsweek*, 122(26), 17.

Montgomery, D.C. (1991). *Design and Analysis of Experiments.* (3rd ed.) John Wiley & Sons: New York.

Neil, J.M., & Liebert, R.M. (1986). *Science and Behavior* (3rd Ed.) Prentice-Hall: Englewood Cliffs, NJ.

Pagano, R.P. (1981). *Understanding Statistics in the Behavioral Sciences.* West Publishing Company: St. Paul, MN.

Robinson, P.W., (1981). *Fundamentals of Experimental Psychology.* (2nd ed.). Prentice-Hall: Englewood Cliffs, NJ.

Rouse, W.B. (1987). Much ado about data. *Human Factors Society Bulletin*, 30(9), 1-3.

Scerbo, M.W. (1993). *Elements of a Good Critique.* Class notes for Perception 741/841.

Shilts, R. (1987). *And the Band Played On: Politics, People, and the AIDS Epidemic.* St. Martin's Press: New York.

Siegel, S. (1956). *Non-parametric Statistics for the Behavioral Sciences.* McGraw-Hill: New York.

Simon, C.W. (1987). Will egg-sucking ever become a science. *Human Factors Society Bulletin*, 30(6), 1-4.

Schwartz, D. (1987). *Concept Testing.* American Management Association: New York.

Smith, L.L. (1987). Whyfore human factors? *Human Factors Society Bulletin*, 30(2), 6-7.

Tabachnick, B.G., & Fidell, L.S. (1983). *Using Multivariate Statistics.* Harper & Row: New York.

Warm, J.S. (1984). An introduction to vigilance. In J.S. Warm (Ed.) *Sustained Attention in Human Performance*. John Wiley and Sons: New York.

Webster's Ninth New Collegiate Dictionary. (1983). Myriam Webster, Inc., Publishers: Springfield, MA.

Weimer, J. & Hart, A. (1989). Dollars & sense: Using effect size estimates to make design decisions. *Proceedings of the Human Factors Society's 33rd Meeting*, pgs 602-605.

Winer, B.J. (1971). *Statistical Principles in Experimental Design*. (2nd ed.) McGraw-Hill: New York.

Wickens, C.D. (1984). Letter. *Human Factors Society Bulletin*, 27(11), 3.

Worchester, R., & Downham, J. (Eds.) (1978). *Consumer Market Research Handbook*. Van Nostrand Reinhold Company: New York.

Chapter 3
Review of Experimental Design

Robert C. Williges
Virginia Polytechnic Institute and
State University

1.0 Introduction

Experimental design is an important tool for the human factors engineer during initial systems design, development testing, and final field evaluation. These procedures are used in the laboratory, in simulation environments, and in actual operating system conditions. Because several controls can be employed by the appropriate experimental designs, these procedures offer many advantages in terms of meaningful interpretation over the counterpart direct observation techniques in which no controls are present. Experimental design and statistical analysis textbooks by Box and Draper (1987), Box Hunter, and Hunter (1978), Keppel (1992), Montgomery (1991), Myers (1990), and Winer, Brown, and Michels (1991) provide details on experimental designs useful in human factors engineering research, while Chapter 13, section 3.3, of this book discusses statistical and methodological issues encountered in human factors research.

2.0 Stages in Experimental Research

Empirical research can be viewed as a process composed of five stages. These stages are problem definition, planning, conduct of research, analysis, and interpretation. Figure 3-1 presents a flow diagram of the steps involved in each of these five stages. Often these steps do not occur in the same order for every researcher, but generally each of these steps is included in the process. The major advantage of the flow diagram is to underscore the dynamic, iterative process of research. Each step throughout each of the stages has implications for the other steps in the process.

2.1 Stage 1: Problem Definition

2.1.1 Research Idea. Research ideas come from a number of sources (from real-world problems such as teaching someone to fly an airplane to tests of theories and models). Human factors research issues are primarily concerned with the relationship between observable behavioral events and the external and internal conditions responsible for these events. Specific research ideas can arise from a gap in existing knowledge, a need to explain a particular fact, or a need to resolve competing alternative explanations.

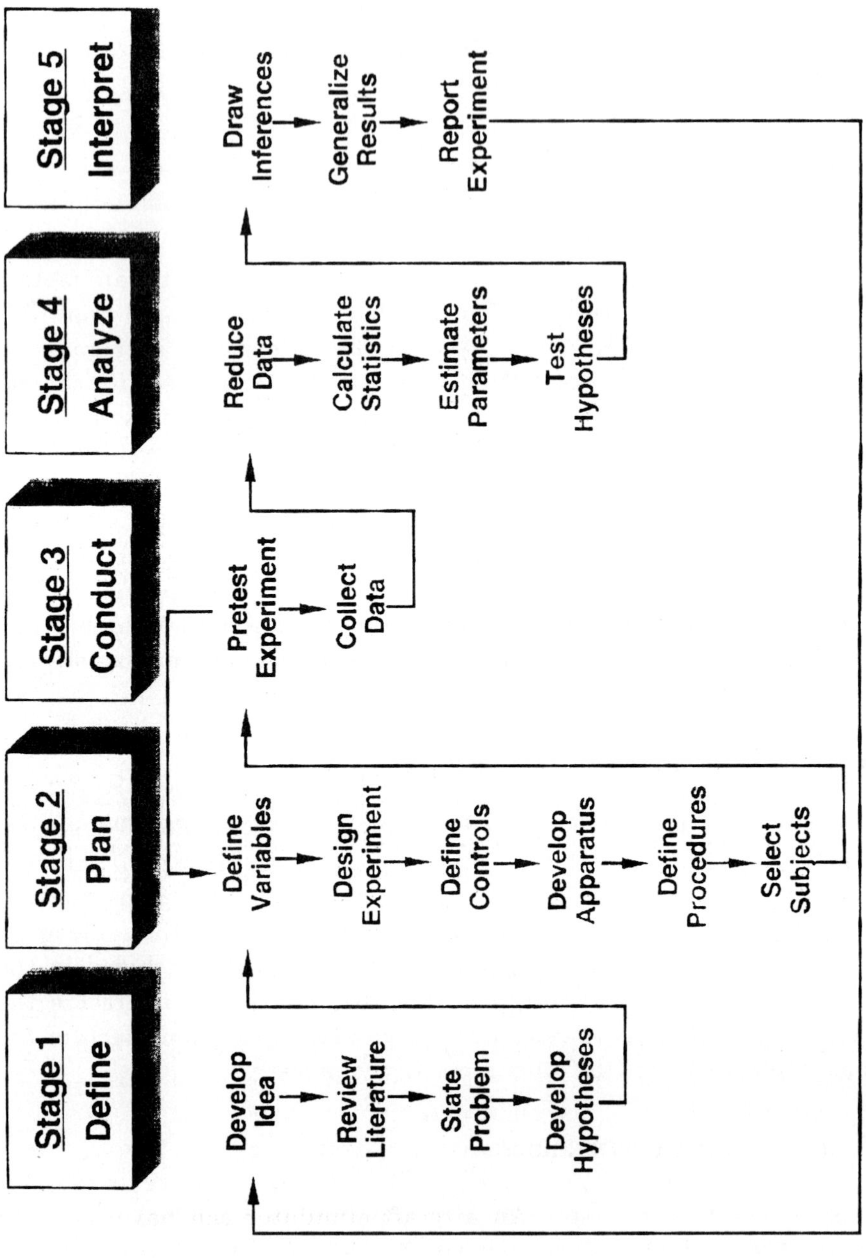

Figure 3-1. Flow Diagram of the Stages in Experimental Research

2.1.2 Literature review. Research is not done in isolation from the existing body of knowledge. Relevant scientific literature must be consulted to determine the current state of knowledge in a problem area, to gain insights on previous approaches, and to ascertain existing alternative explanations for research issues. Meaningful research extends and complements existing literature, rather than merely duplicating findings.

2.1.3 Statement of problem[1]. Once a research idea has been crystallized and placed in the context of the existing research literature, you should be able to make a precise statement of the problem. This includes a description of the general problem area as well as a statement of the specific research issue of the proposed empirical study.

2.1.4 Hypothesis development. A testable hypothesis is simply a formal statement of a possible solution to the research problem. The hypothesis is the central focus of the study. The subsequent experiment provides information in the form of data that can be used to test the plausibility of the hypothesis. Specifying the hypothesis to be tested in the experiment is the final step in the definition of the research problem.

As an example of the problem definition stage, consider the real-world problem of teaching someone to fly an airplane. You have an idea that pretraining on a synthetic device will improve pilot training. A review of the existing literature on transfer of training from aircraft simulators shows that little is known about the effect of the fidelity of simulator motion on positive transfer. Subsequently, you develop a hypothesis stating that motion simulation results in a higher degree of positive transfer of training than a synthetic flight trainer without motion.

2.2 Stage 2: Planning

2.2.1 Definition of variables. Planning begins once you define a research problem. Initially, you must define your variables. There are three categories of variables to be considered. First, define the <u>independent variables</u> that are the factors of interest or conditions in the experiment. These variables are manipulated by you, and their specific values are <u>independent</u> of the subject's performance. Usually independent variables are referred to as X's in design presentations and data analysis procedures. The independent variables in the pilot training example might include various values of motion in the flight trainer, ranging from no motion through 6 degrees of freedom of motion. (An aircraft simulator can have 3 linear motions, vertical, horizontal, and longitudinal, and 3 rotational motions, pitch, yaw, and roll.)

---

[1] For a more detailed treatment of finding and operationalizing a research problem, see Chapter 2.

Second, you must define the dependent variables. These are the variables that measure the subject's performance and, consequently, are dependent upon the subject. The dependent variable is usually referred to as the Y variable. In the simulator experiment example, the dependent variable may be time or trials to some criterion of performance or it may be the amount of transfer from the trainer to the aircraft. The values of these independent variables provide the data for subsequent statistical analysis.

Third, you must consider the subject variables present in the experiment. One of the largest sources of variation in any behavioral study is the individual difference among subjects. Procedures need to be considered for the control of these subject differences.

2.2.2 Experimental design. Usually all the planning involved in an experiment culminates in a formal experimental design or plan that specifies the particular treatment conditions of the experiment, the assignment of subjects to conditions, the order of testing of subjects, and the appropriate statistical analyses. Obviously, all the planning constraints cannot be maximized individually in an experiment, and you must trade off some constraints against others.

2.2.3 Controls. You should make every attempt to control all other variables in the experimental environment other than the specific independent variables of interest. In this way you can guard against systematic biases in the data and can draw the appropriate inferences. Most of these extraneous variables are controlled by maintaining them at a constant level. Alternatively, extraneous variables can be controlled through randomization or blocking.

In the case of subject variables, you can control for individual differences through randomization, blocking, or using subjects as their own control. Through randomization each subject is equally likely to be assigned to any treatment condition defined by the independent variables. Although this approach is fundamental to experimental design, it is often difficult to accomplish in actual practice due to constraints of equal sample size and subject attrition[2]. You also have the option to match subjects if variables affecting individual differences are known. Finally, you can control the subject variables by having subjects serve as their own control by obtaining repeated observations on the same subjects.

2.2.4 Apparatus. You must choose the appropriate apparatus to manipulate the independent variables and measure the dependent variables in the experiment. For instance, in the pilot training study you must choose the proper type and configuration of the aircraft simulator as well as the various methods of recording performance.

[2]See Chapter 2, section 5.1.5 for more information on subject attrition as a threat to experimental validity.

2.2.5 Procedures. Questions concerning the order of testing subjects, the types of instructions to provide, the amount of practice, the number of rest periods, etc., need to be specified before the experiment is conducted.

2.2.6 Selection of subjects[3]. It is important to consider the characteristics of the subject population so that an appropriate sample can be drawn to allow the necessary inferences. Many areas of investigation clearly define a population. In the hypothetical pilot training experiment, you would choose completely flight-naive subjects or subjects with previous flight experience depending on the exact nature of your experimental problem.

2.3 Stage 3: Conduct of Research

2.3.1 Preliminary testing. To the inexperienced investigator, this is often the least important and most often overlooked step in the research process. This is probably because the novice experimenter is eager to collect data and analyze it after going through the tedious procedures of defining a research problem and planning an experiment. To the experienced investigator, on the other hand, this is probably the most time-consuming aspect of research. As shown by the feedback line in Figure 3-1, preliminary testing often has implications for redesigning all or part of the experimental plan. The appropriate levels of the independent variable must be determined, the adequacy of the instructions must be tested, the reliability of the apparatus must be checked, the appropriateness of repeated measures on subjects must be reviewed, and the overall procedures must be pretested. If you fail to complete this step, a great deal of time, money, and effort may be wasted in continuing with an ill-defined and ill-planned study.

2.3.2 Data collection. After the completion of a rigorous pretesting and possible re-planning of the experiment, collect the data according to the experimental plan, taking care to maintain the appropriate controls and to check the reliability of the apparatus.

2.4 Stage 4: Data Analysis

2.4.1 Data reduction. Before any analysis can be made on the data, it must be formatted properly. This process includes both hand and automatic computation procedures for obtaining the raw scores and derived scores necessary for statistical analysis. Careful preplanning can eliminate much of the physical effort involved in this step.

2.4.2 Statistics. Data analyses are statistical in nature. Descriptive statistics such as means and variances are used to make inferences about various population parameters from sample data.

---

[3]See Chapter 2, sections 5.1.7 and 5.2.2 for a discussion of selection as a threat to experimental validity.

Inferential statistical procedures are primarily multi-factor univariate as opposed to multivariate procedures. Univariate procedures are defined as statistical techniques employing only one dependent variable across one or several independent variables, whereas multivariate techniques use more than one dependent variable in the analysis.

2.4.3 Parameter estimates. Part of the analysis of data may include estimates of population parameters from sample data. These estimates can be either point estimates or confidence intervals of the parameter.

2.4.4 Statistical hypothesis testing. Most statistical analyses deal directly with testing a variety of statistical hypotheses concerning population parameters and follow a formal logic of statistical hypotheses testing.

2.5 Stage 5: Interpretation

2.5.1 Inferences. Statistical analyses allow you to make inferences concerning causal relationships between the manipulation of the independent variables and measured changes in the dependent variables. The statistical analyses are interpreted with regard to the hypotheses developed during the problem definition stage. For example, the statistical analyses in the flight simulator experiment would be interpreted in terms of whether the results support the hypothesis that simulator motion enhances positive transfer.

2.5.2 Generalizations. All inferences drawn from the data analyses are limited to some extent in terms of generalizability[4]. Often the controls used in the study directly determine the limits on generalizations. For example, if the transfer of training study were conducted on flight-naive students, would the results generalize to transition training for experienced pilots? Would the results generalize to all simulators and to all aircraft? You must be careful not to over-generalize the results of this empirical research.

2.5.3 Reporting. Research conducted in a vacuum does little to advance the body of knowledge. You should feel obligated to report the results to the scientific community. A written report should provide not only a careful description of the problem, methods, and results, but also it should include a discussion of the interpretation of the data. This discussion can provide the research ideas for the next study or series of experiments as shown by the feedback loop in Figure 3-1.

[4]See Chapter 2, section 5.2 on the threats to external validity (i.e., generalizability of results).

3.0 Some Experimental Designs

3.1 Two Group Designs

Suppose you were interested in determining the potential reduction in ship navigation error using a predictor display. You would probably make an experimental comparison between the standard display and the new predictor display. Because different people may react differently to the displays due to previous training, biases, etc., it is important to test the two displays with a variety of subjects who navigate these ships to estimate the average performance of ship navigators using standard versus predictor displays. Table 3-1 shows a breakdown of this design where "s" refers to the individual subjects who are randomly assigned to the two groups.

Table 3-1. Two Group Experimental Design

Standard Display	Predictor Display
s_1	s_7
s_2	s_8
s_3	s_9
s_4	s_{10}
s_5	s_{11}
s_6	s_{12}

Note that in this case the standard display serves as a control condition to which the experimental predictor display can be compared. By calculating the average (mean) error performance and a measure of variability (standard deviation), the two conditions can be statistically compared by means of a t-test or one-way analysis of variance[5] to determine if there is a statistically significant reduction in ship navigation error using the predictor display[6].

3.2 Multiple Group Designs.

One of the most useful designs is the analysis of variance. This design is used when there are more than 2 conditions in an experiment (e.g., you may be interested in studying the number of eye fixations of a machine operator as a function of 3 sizes of an object in the visual field). The analysis of variance conducted on the data from this experiment provides an overall test of reliability of all paired differences among the 3 sizes of an object. You may also be interested in investigating the differential effects of the color of

---

[5] "Some statisticians . . . require that the data be of interval or ratio scaling in order to use the z-test, Student's t test, and the analysis of variance." (Pagano, 1981; pg. 335)

[6] See Chapter 13, section 3.3, for a discussion of the special issue of new and standard systems with different learning curves.

the object as well as size on the worker's eye fixations. If 2 colors and 3 sizes are chosen, observations of eye fixations can be made under the six treatment conditions resulting from the pairing of each colored object with each object size. A subsequent ANOVA can test the data collected from these 6 treatment conditions for significant differences in eye fixations due to the object's color, size, and the differential effects of color and size combinations.

The popularity of ANOVA designs is related to the numerous advantages it offers you. First, they provide a convenient way of conceptualizing research hypotheses into an efficient data collection scheme. Several hypotheses concerning the effects of an object's size, color, and combinations of size and color on a worker's eye fixations can be tested in one experiment using an ANOVA design. Second, a composite statistical test of significance is made on all comparisons simultaneously. Third, you can readily examine the possible interactions among the various independent variables. For example, object size may affect a worker's perceptions when the color is familiar, but size may have no effect on eye fixations when the color is unfamiliar. By increasing the number of independent variables, interactions of two, three, four, or more variables can be tested simultaneously. Finally, ANOVA provides a broader baseline for generalizing research results. Including a number of independent variables as well as a number of different values of each independent variable, enable you to examine a phenomenon over a variety of conditions that are, hopefully, more reflective of the complex nature of human behavior.

3.2.1 Basic terms. Several basic terms are used to describe any ANOVA.

1. Factor. This is the independent variable in the experiment and is tested at several values or levels.
2. Factor Level. Refers to a specific value of a factor. There are as many factor levels as there are treatments of an independent variable.
3. Factorial Design. An experiment consisting of more than one factor in which the levels of each factor are balanced, or appear equally, across the levels of other factors.
4. Cell. A specific combination of levels of factors observed across subjects in the factorial design. Cells define the treatment combinations in the experiment.
5. Crossed Factors. Each level of a particular factor occurs with each level of another factor. In completely crossed factorial designs, the number of cells is determined simply by multiplying the levels of the factors in the design.
6. Nested Factors. A particular level of one factor occurs only with one level of another factor.
7. Interaction. The effects one factor's levels are differentially affected by the levels of another factor. Factors must be crossed to interact Thus, a nested factor cannot interact with the factor(s) within which it is nested. Figure 3-2 shows a hypothetical interaction between font type and number of words per line on reading comprehension.

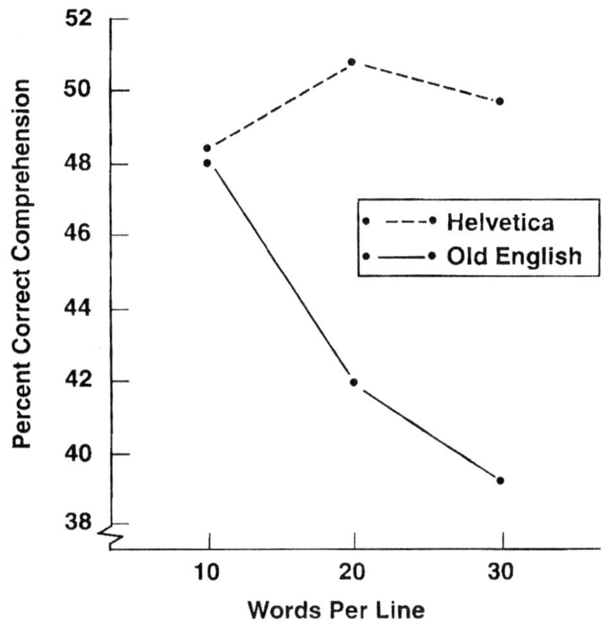

Figure 3-2. Hypothetical Example of a Two-way Interaction.

3.2.2 Design classification. Every analysis of variance design in behavioral research can be conveniently classified by the way subjects are assigned to treatment combinations. Three subject-assignment classifications are possible: between-subjects designs, within-subject designs, and mixed-factor designs.

3.2.2.1 Between-subjects design. This design occurs when each subject receives only one treatment combination in the analysis of variance design. Subjects are assigned at random to the various cells, and usually an equal number appear in each cell. Often this design is referred to as a completely randomized design. The factors in these designs are referred to as between-subjects factors. Subjects are always completely nested within the factors of the design.

3.2.2.2 Within-subject design. This design occurs when each subject receives every treatment combination in the experiment. Consequently, each subject is observed in each cell of the resulting design. Because each subject is observed more than once, within-subject designs are often referred to as repeated measures designs. The factors in this design are called within-subject factors. Subjects can interact with every factor in the within-subject design, because subjects are completely crossed with all the factors[7].

[7]Within-groups experiments are particularly sensitive to validity threats (See sections 5.1 & 5.2 of Chapter 2 and section 3.3 of Chapter 13).

3.2.2.3 Mixed-factor design. This design occurs when some factors of the design are within-subject factors and some factors are between-subjects factors. Subjects are nested within the between-subjects factors so they cannot interact, but subjects can interact with the within-subjects factors. Mixed-factor designs are quite useful in behavioral research and are most common in large multi-factor analysis of variance designs.

Table 3-2 compares the three classifications in a 2x2 factorial design in which three subjects are observed in each cell. Different subjects are denoted by different subscripts. The between-subjects version of the factorial design requires twelve subjects because three different subjects are needed in each of the four resulting treatment combinations. The within-subject design requires only three different subjects for the entire experiment. The mixed-factor version, on the other hand, requires six different subjects (three in each of the two levels of the between-subjects factor, A).

Before choosing among these three design classes, you must consider the particular variables of interest in the experiment. Many variables in human factors are amenable to either between-subjects or within-subject manipulation. Highly practiced subjects, for example, may either observe one or all the display formats in an experiment on visual display. When practice trials are included in an experiment, this variable must be manipulated as a within-subject factor. Likewise, various training procedures can only be used as between-subjects variables because of baseline considerations. Once a subject has been trained to criterion using one procedure, that individual cannot be forced effectively to forget the material completely before relearning it under another training procedure.

Often you must use a design in which some factors are between-subjects and some factors are within-subjects. This category of design, the mixed-factors design, is one of the most widely used complex multi-factor ANOVA designs in human factors. It often is used when the between-subjects factors are investigated in terms of some time-dependent factor requiring repeated measures. For example, a human factors specialist may be interested in reduction of tracking error as a function of training condition and practice trials. In this experiment, the two training conditions (fixed difficulty and computer-adaptive difficulty) would be manipulated as a between-subjects variable and 25, two-minute training trials on a pursuit tracking task would be manipulated as a within-subject factor.

3.2.3 Between-subjects design considerations. One difficulty with a between-subjects design is that the error estimate in the analysis of variance is largely affected by individual differences of subjects within groups. Even though subjects are randomly assigned to treatment conditions, it is possible to assign more good subjects to one condition than to another quite by random. One approach is to match the subjects in each treatment condition as closely as possible on certain given characteristics that affect variability of the dependent variable. The concomitant variable affecting individual differences is removed; and the overall design becomes more sensitive.

Table 3-2. Comparison of Analysis of Variance Design Classifications

Between-Subjects Design:

		A (Between-Subjects) a_1	A (Between-Subjects) a_2
B (Between-Subjects)	b_1	s_1 s_2 s_3	s_7 s_8 s_9
	b_2	s_4 s_5 s_6	s_{10} s_{11} s_{12}

Within-Subjects Design:

		A (Within-Subjects) a_1	A (Within-Subjects) a_2
B (Within-Subjects)	b_1	s_1 s_2 s_3	s_1 s_2 s_3
	b_2	s_1 s_2 s_3	s_1 s_2 s_3

Mixed-Factor Design:

		A (Between-Subjects) a_1	A (Between-Subjects) a_2
B (Within-Subjects)	b_1	s_1 s_2 s_3	s_4 s_5 s_6
	b_2	s_1 s_2 s_3	s_4 s_5 s_6

A randomized-block design is a special between-subjects design that allows for a more homogeneous grouping of subjects providing you are aware of some variable relating to individual differences that is correlated with the dependent variable. The design is constructed by a simple two-step procedure. First, subjects are classified into different levels (i.e., blocked on a variable that is correlated with the dependent variable) before the experiment is conducted. Blocking variables include such things as sex, religious affiliation, socioeconomic status, IQ, racial background, or scores on a pretest, etc. Correlation with the dependent variable is determined either through preliminary experimentation or research literature. Usually a blocking variable is merely a way of classifying, rather than manipulating subjects; it is only included as a means of increasing experimental precision by decreasing between-subject variability. Second, an equal number of subjects, from each level of the blocking variable, is randomly assigned to the treatment conditions, resulting in the name randomized-blocks design.

3.2.4 Within-subject design considerations. These designs require fewer subjects and help reduce the variability within each cell of the design. This is because each subject serves in each condition thereby controlling for individual differences. Within-subject designs also provide a procedure for systematically investigating time-dependent factors such as practice effects and time on task. Presentation order of conditions, however, must be counterbalanced to avoid biasing the results by order effects.

In all within-subject designs, each subject is observed more than once in the experiment. Often there are carry-over effects from one condition to the next. In learning and transfer experiments these carry-over effects are the object of investigation in the study. In other studies, these carry-over effects become a nuisance variable and must by controlled. If, for example, you were investigating the effect of 3 different target sizes on detection latency in a within-subject design, you would be careful not to confound the order of testing with the three treatments. If the order of testing and the treatments are confounded (i.e., each subject is tested under target size a_1, and then a_3), you would not be able to determine whether a reliable treatment effect in the ANOVA is due to the treatment effect of target size, the carry-over effect of improvement with practice, or an interaction of these 2 factors.

The general approach is to counterbalance the effect of order of testing with treatments to eliminate this confounding. There are 6 possible orders of testing subjects on the 3 target sizes. If 6 subjects are used, as shown in Table 3-3, and each received one of these testing orders, the design is completely counterbalanced (i.e., order of testing and treatments is unconfounded). Select a sample size in multiples of 6 so that counterbalancing can be maintained throughout the experiment.

Table 3-3. Completely Counterbalanced Design (Treatments a_1, a_2, and a_3)

		Subjects					
		s_1	s_2	s_3	s_4	s_5	s_6
Presentation	1	a_1	a_3	a_2	a_1	a_2	a_3
Order	2	a_2	a_1	a_3	a_3	a_1	a_2
	3	a_3	a_2	a_1	a_2	a_3	a_1

Often it is not possible to counterbalance the design completely because the total number of possible testing orders is too large. This fact becomes readily apparent as more factors and/or levels of each factor are added to the within-subject design. In these instances, you can use a Balanced Latin Square design to assign treatment conditions to subjects. An example of such an approach is shown in Table 3-4 in which four treatment conditions occur. To completely counterbalance the design, 24 subjects are required, but only multiples of 4 are needed in the Balanced Latin Square assignment. Notice that this type of Latin Square insures that every treatment condition is immediately preceded and followed once by each of the other treatments.

Table 3-4. Balancing Order of Presentation Using a Balanced Latin Square (Treatments a_1, a_2, and a_3)

		Subjects.			
		s_1	s_2	s_3	s_4
	1	a_1	a_2	a_3	a_4
Presentation	2	a_2	a_3	a_4	a_1
Order	3	a_4	a_1	a_2	a_3
	4	a_3	a_4	a_1	a_2

3.3 Data Reduction Designs.

Many human factors research problems include additional constraints that must be considered in the experimental design. Some factors cannot be crossed in the real world. For example, supervisors cannot be crossed with industrial plants because they only work in one location. In addition, many human factors problems require the simultaneous investigation of several factors thereby making a completely crossed factorial design unwieldy due to the extremely large number of resulting treatment combinations. Several experimental design procedures have been developed to help you overcome these constraints.

3.3.1 Hierarchical designs. In many human factors situations the environmental constraints do not allow various classification variables and experimenter-related variables to be crossed with the independent variables of interest. For instance, it may not be possible to manipulate all the treatment conditions in an experimental evaluation of various aids provided to human inspectors on the production line in one plant due to the set-up costs on the inspection line. Consequently, each of two inspectors' aids is set-up separately in separate plants. Nonetheless, unique characteristics of the plants, which are now nested within treatment conditions (inspection aids), may affect the research outcomes. Whenever factors other than subjects are nested, the design is called a hierarchical design because of the hierarchical, or pyramidal, shape of the treatment conditions. Table 3-5 shows a complete hierarchical design in which factors B and C are nested within A. Any hierarchical design must have at least two levels of one factor nested within a level of another factor to avoid complete confounding.

Table 3-5. Design Matrix for a Three-Factor, Between-Subjects, Complete Hierarchical Design.

A_1				A_2			
B_1		B_2		B_3		B_4	
C_1	C_2	C_3	C_4	C_5	C_6	C_7	C_8
n=10	n=10	n=10	n=10	n=10	n=10	n=10	n=10

3.3.2 Blocking designs. Often it is not possible to obtain data from the entire factorial design all at one time, and the researcher is forced to collect data in stages or blocks. In human factors research these blocks can be different testing times or different experimenters collecting subsets of data. Obviously, there could be a great deal of variation among blocks, and certain aspects of the factorial design must be confounded with these block differences. Procedures are available whereby you can systematically confound only certain components of the experimental design with block differences while balancing the remaining aspects of the design within each block (Winer, Brown, and Michels, 1991). In most cases, you need only sacrifice all, or part, of a higher-order interaction while keeping the rest of the design balanced.

Consider an example in which the human factors specialist is evaluating two data entry procedures (Factor A) under two levels of pilot workload (Factor B) in two different area navigation displays (Factor C). The tests are being conducted in an aircraft simulator, and it is not possible to collect the data on all eight treatment conditions resulting from the design in one flight. Only four conditions can be evaluated each flight. Figure 3-3 shows how the design can be blocked into two flights of four treatment conditions such that the main effects and two-way interactions of the three factors will not be confounded with possible flight differences. Only the three-way interaction is completely confounded with the two flight effects.

At times it is desirable to make all comparisons with equal precision and not sacrifice entire effects to blocking as the three-way interaction was in Figure 3-3. Alternative procedures referred to as balanced and partially balanced incomplete block designs have been developed for this purpose when one factor consisting of several levels is being investigated. Designs of this type can include a variety of treatment levels and block sizes with the restriction that the number of treatment levels exceeds the block size.

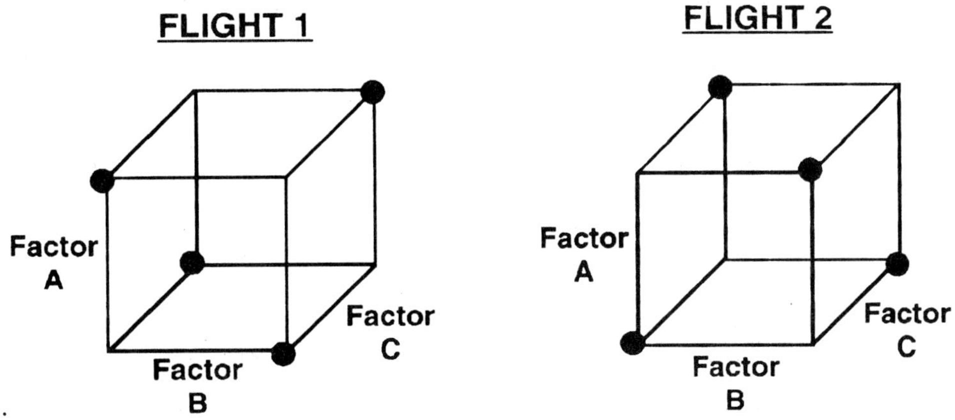

Conditions (Flight 1)	Conditions (Flight 2)
A_1, B_2, C_1	A_1, B_1, C_1
A_1, B_1, C_2	A_1, B_2, C_2
A_2, B_1, C_1	A_2, B_2, C_1
A_2, B_2, C_2	A_2, B_1, C_2

Figure 3-3. Blocked 2x2x2 Factorial Design.

3.3.3 Fractional factorial designs. Sometimes, time or budget constraints make it impossible to collect all the data from a higher-order factorial design. Information on some effects will be lost and some effects will be confounded if data from the complete factorial design are not collected. The fractional-replication procedure enables you to systematically determine the extent and nature of this confounding. By making this decision judiciously, you can still obtain a great deal of useful information from the data subset you choose to collect.

For example, if only enough time was available on the aircraft simulator to collect data on 4 of the treatment conditions, you could choose to collect data in either Flight 1 or Flight 2 as shown in Figure 3-3. Each flight represents a one-half replicate of the complete factorial design such that either half will allow an evaluation of the 3 unconfounded main effects.

3.3.4 Central-composite designs. Often, you want to determine a quantitative relationship between human performance and several quantitative systems parameters. A convenient way to specify this relationship is through a polynomial regression equation in which Y, the operator's performance, varies as a function of X variables or system parameters. A second-order polynomial including 3 X variables would be:

$$Y = b_0 + b_1X_1 + b_2X_2 + b_3X_3 + b_4X_1^2 + b_5X_2^2 + b_6X_3^2 + b_7X_1X_2 + b_8X_2X_3 + b_9X_1X_3$$

where:

b's = the partial regression weights estimated from the data using a minimized sum of least squares criterion.

Central-composite designs are used as an efficient and economical procedure for collecting the data necessary to solve the polynomial prediction equations. Box and Draper (1987); Box, Hunter, and Hunter (1978); and Myers (1970) provide details on the design and analysis of central-composite designs. These designs require fewer data points than comparable factorial designs thereby allowing for the inclusion of more factors in the design. The design itself is a composite of two-level factorial designs augmented by a center point and 2K additional points. Each of the K factors in the design occurs at five levels as shown in the three-factor, central-composite design depicted in Figure 3-4. Such a design, for example, might be used to assess the human operator's target detection latency (Y) on a visually, time-compressed radar display as a function of target velocity (X_1), number of stored frames (X_2), and the amount of clutter (X_3). This polynomial expression, in turn, can be used to trade off the three display parameters, to predict operator performance, and to determine the system variables necessary to maintain a designated performance level.

Actually, central-composite designs are part of a larger set of research designs included in <u>response surface methodology</u> (Myers, 1971). These procedures provide a strategy for conducting multi-factor research to seek an optimal level of performance. The strategy includes designs for initial pretesting, for collecting and analyzing data in stages to add and subtract variables of importance, and for determining the point or points of optimal performance.

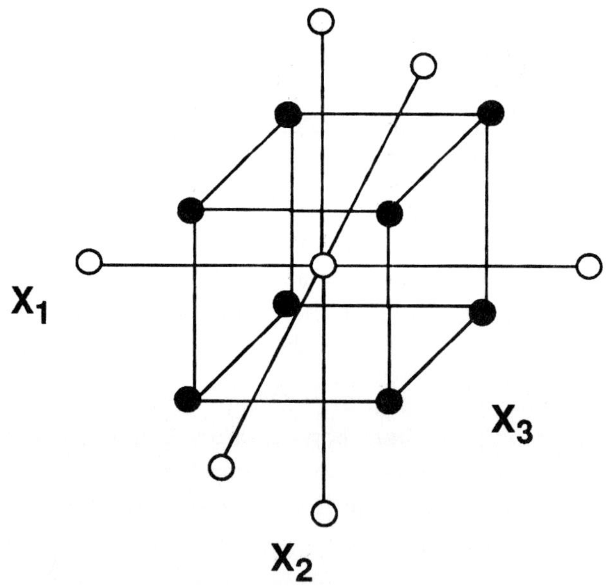

Figure 3-4. Second-order, Central-composite Design in 3 Variables, X_1, X_2, X_3.

3.4 Sequential Experimentation

Williges and Williges (1989) proposed a sequential research paradigm that addresses the three major steps of selecting, describing, and optimizing independent variables affecting interface design. Figure 3-1 summarizes many of the issues and research methods that need to be considered in their paradigm. Several methods that already exist can be used effectively in each of these three major steps. The resulting procedure is systematic, but it may not always involve elaborate experimental designs. In fact, the procedure is characterized by using a series of integrated, small experiments as opposed to one large study. Since the emphasis is on combing data from sequential experiments, the replication within each experiment is minimized. Expert opinion and user ratings are used in the beginning stage to select independent variables, and the data resulting from previous studies in the series are combined with follow-on experiments as necessary to result in a truly integrated database that can be interrogated through the use of empirical models. These empirical models provide one source for design decisions during the iterative design process.

This sequential research strategy is designed to obtain approximate responses of the true functional relationships in an efficient and systematic manner by integrating several small experiments in the form of second-order models. This approach is useful when the researcher does not know about the true relationships among independent variables and wants to have a quantitative evaluation of the system of interest. In addition, this approach can be used to provide the designer with empirical data of system performance. As a result, these resulting empirical data could provide a basis of inferring the true relationships among the independent variables (e.g., theoretical models) as well as practical implications to the interface design. Additionally, these empirical models can form the basis of quantitative design guidelines (Williges, Williges, and Han, 1992).

3.4.1 Selection. The first stage in a systematic research strategy shown in Figure 3-5 involves the identification of all variables that may affect human performance when using the system. A variety of non-experimental techniques including brainstorming, prototyping, feasibility and relevance analyses, subjective ratings, and a literature review can be used as the basis for selecting a subset of the independent variables that require subsequent experimental investigation. Merkle, Beaudet, Williges, Herlong, and Williges (1988) describe several procedures that can be used for the initial selection of independent variables. Efficient screening studies can then be used to isolate the main effects of these key independent variables that require follow-on experiments to describe functional relationships.

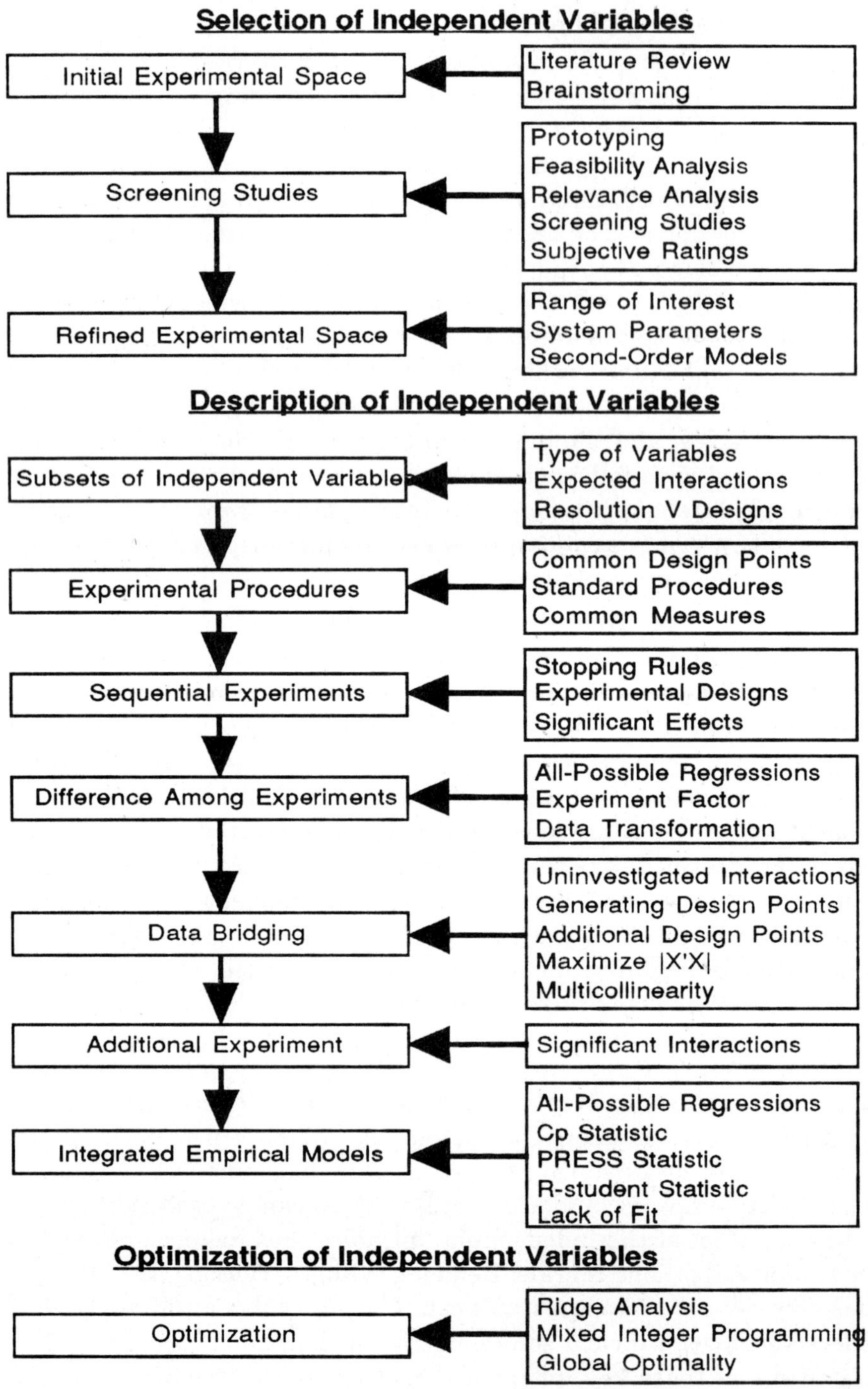

Figure 3-5. Summary of Sequential Experimentation Issues and Methods

3.4.2 Description. A series of small experiments can be used to gather data in order to describe the effects of the independent variables selected during the screening studies. Important independent variables referred to as parameters are include in each sequential experiment. The effect of these parameters as well as common data points can be used to evaluate the comparability of data across experiments and possible interactions with other independent variables. The experimental designs used in this description stage are chosen to estimate main effects and two-way interactions. Efficient experimental designs for each sequential study should be selected to provide data collection economy. If one can assume that main effects and two-way interactions are of primary importance to human factors research and higher-order effects are negligible, two-level factorial or fractional-factorial designs can be used to evaluate dichotomous variables; whereas central-composite designs can be used to evaluate continuous variables.

Since many discontinuous factors in human factors research are dichotomous (e.g., gender, availability of specific features, etc.), 2^k complete factorial designs are often used for data collection. When the researcher finds it impossible to collect all the data from a higher-order factorial design due to time and/or budget constraints or, when the researcher can assume higher-order interactions are not present, fractional-factorial designs provide an efficient alternative for considering multiple factors simultaneously.

A fractional factorial, as the name implies, is a design consisting of a fraction of a complete factorial experiment. Although some information will be lost and some effects will be confounded, the fractional replication procedure enables the researcher to systematically determine the confounding structures so that an appropriate subset of treatment combinations can be tested. Choice of the appropriate 2^{k-p} fractional factorial design depends on the degree of information resolution required. A Resolution V fractional-factorial design, which allows all main effects and two-way interactions to remain unconfounded, is needed in the description stage of sequential experimentation. Consequently, at least 5 factors need to be investigated simultaneously before 2^{k-p} fractional factorial designs of Resolution V can be constructed (Box and Draper, 1987).

A central-composite design provides an experimental plan that allows for efficient estimation of a second-order model including main effects, pure quadratics, and two-way interactions. This design consists of 3 portions: (1) a 2^k or 2^{k-p} factorial portion; (2) an axial portion; and (3) a center point (Box, Hunter, and Hunter, 1978; Box and Draper, 1987). Spherical, second-order, central-composite designs represent 5 levels of each factor in coded form of $-\alpha$, -1, 0, +1, and $+\alpha$. Williges (1981) discusses the construction of central-composite designs, the choices for α, and the use of these designs for describing the effects of continuous variables in behavioral research.

Additional data collection is needed to bridge across the sequential experiments to evaluate uninvestigated interactions. Integrated empirical models based on polynomial regression can then be built from the combined data set of all the sequential experiments. Han (1991) describes the mathematical criteria used during data bridging and statistics from modern regression (Myers, 1990), which can be used to minimize multicollinearity effects in the integrated empirical models.

3.4.3 Optimization. The final stage of the Williges and Williges (1989) sequential design procedure is to determine the optimum combination of levels of the important independent variables. An integrated empirical model is developed using polynomial regression procedures. The integrated model describes the interrelationships among the key independent variables. Equation 1 shows the general form of a complete second-order, integrated empirical model[8]:

$$Y = \beta_0 + \Sigma_i \beta_i X_i + \Sigma_{i<j} \beta_{ij} X_i X_j + \Sigma_i \beta_{ii} X_i^2 + \varepsilon \qquad (1)$$

where:

Y = a performance measure
β's = are the coefficients of model items
X_i = the main effect of i-th variable
$X_i X_j$ = the interaction effect between the i-th and the j-th variables
X_i^2 = the pure quadratic effect of the i-th variable
ε = experimental error.

3.4.4 Guidelines for sequential experimentation. Williges, Williges, and Han (1993) provide an example of sequential experimentation in the design of a telephone-based, computer, information system. In addition, they propose general guidelines that can be summarized for planning and conducting sequential experimentation. These guidelines are listed in Table 3-6 and are grouped around the major considerations of determining a sequential research plan, selection of independent variables, the description of independent variables, and the optimization of independent variables.

4.0 Conclusion

Although the research problem rather than the experimental design procedures should be the driving force in human factors research, the researcher should be aware of the various statistical tools available. In designing research, several key design points should be considered:

1. Design the experiment before collecting data.
2. Determine real-world constraints dictated by the research problem.
3. Select design modifications based on real-world constraints.
4. Complete a thorough and careful pretesting.
5. If in doubt, consult a research design expert before starting.

---

[8] Optimization procedures using response surface methodology (Myers, 1971), as well as ridge analysis and mixed integer programming (Han, 1991), are appropriate.

Table 3-6. Guidelines for Conducting Sequential Experimentation

1. Sequential Research Plan
- 1.1. Assumption
- 1.2. Parameters
- 1.3. Common Data Point
- 1.4. Stopping Criteria
- 1.5. Data Collection Strategy
- 1.6. Amount of Data
- 1.7. Replication
- 1.8. Benchmark Task
- 1.9. Experimental Procedures
- 1.10. Data Recording

2. Selection of Independent Variables
- 2.1. List of Factors
  - 2.1.1. Literature Review
  - 2.1.2. Selection Criteria
- 2.2. Analytical Methods
- 2.3. Prototyping
- 2.4. Initial Selection Studies
- 2.5. Screening Studies

3. Description of Independent Variables
- 3.1. Two Level Designs
  - 3.1.1 Factor Levels
  - 3.1.2. Complete Factorials
  - 3.1.3. Fractional Factorials
- 3.2. Central-Composite Designs
  - 3.2.1. Coded Values
  - 3.2.2. Spherical Designs
  - 3.2.3. Cuboidal Designs
- 3.3. Data Bridging
  - 3.3.1. Selection Criterion
  - 3.3.2. Multicollinearity
- 3.4. Integrated Empirical Models
  - 3.4.1. Polynomial Regression
  - 3.4.2 Predictors
  - 3.4.3. Experiments
  - 3.4.4. Lack of Fit

4. Optimization of Independent Variables
- 4.1. Discrete Variables
- 4.2. Continuous Variables
- 4.3. Combination of Variables
- 4.4. Range of Interest

5.0 Biography

Robert C. Williges is currently Professor of Industrial and Systems Engineering, Professor of Psychology, and Professor of Computer Science at Virginia Polytechnic Institute and State University where he manages the research activities in the Human-Computer Interface Laboratory and the Usability Methods Research Laboratory. He has over 25 years experience in directing human factors engineering research dealing with topics including human-computer interaction, computer-based training procedures, and human factors research methodology. Before joining the faculty at Virginia Tech, Dr. Williges was on the faculty of the Department of Psychology at the University of Illinois at Urbana-Champaign and was the associate head of the Aviation Research Laboratory. He received the M.A. and Ph.D. degrees in engineering psychology from The Ohio State University.

He is a fellow of both the Human Factors and Ergonomics Society and the American Psychological Association. He has served as president of the Human Factors and Ergonomics Society and as president of Division 21 of the American Psychological Association. In addition, he has served on several professional committees including the U.S. Navy Task Force on Basic Research Needs, the National Research Council Working Group on Simulation, the Army Science Board, the International Commission of Human Aspects in Computing, the Board of Directors of the Virginia Tech Corporate Research Center, and the National Research Council Committee on Human Factors. In 1989, he won the Franklin V. Taylor Award from the American Psychological Association for outstanding contributions to the field of engineering psychology and the President's Career Achievement Award from the Human Factors and Ergonomics Society.

Dr. Williges is a past editor of *Human Factors* and has served on the editorial board of the *International Journal of Man-Machine Studies.* He has over 150 scientific publications and has made over 125 technical presentations at national and international scientific meetings. He received the 1974 and the 1993 Jerome H. Ely Awards for the best papers published in *Human Factors*. He has conducted and managed over $6.5M of research on a variety of human factors engineering topics. His three current research interests include developing methods for usability evaluation, improving multimedia information presentation, and designing computer-based assistive technology for computer users with disabilities.

REFERENCES

Box, G.E.P. and Draper, N.R. (1987). *Empirical model building and response surfaces*. New York: Wiley.

Box, G.E.P., Hunter, W. G., and Hunter, J. S. (1978) *Statistics for experimenters: An introduction to design, data analysis, and model building*. New York: Wiley.

Han, S.H. (1991). Integrated empirical models based on a sequential research strategy. Unpublished doctoral dissertation. Virginia Polytechnic Institute and State University, Blacksburg, Virginia.

Keppel, G. (1992). *Design and analysis: A researcher's handbook*. (3rd. Ed.). Englewood Cliffs, NJ: Prentice-Hall.

Merkle, P.J., Jr. Beaudet, D.B., Williges, R.C., Herlong, D.W., and Williges, B.H. (1988). A systematic method for the selection of independent variables in the investigation of complex systems. *Proceedings of the Human Factors Society 32nd annual meeting.* Santa Monica, CA: Human Factors Society, 1179-1182.

Montgomery, D.C. (1991). *Design and analysis of experiments*. (3rd. Ed.). New York: Wiley.

Myers, R.H. (1971). *Response surface methodology*. Boston: Allyn and Bacon, Inc.

Myers, R. H. (1990). *Classical and modern regression with applications* (2nd. Ed.). Boston, MA: PWS-Kent.

Pagano, R.P. (1981). *Understanding Statistics in the Behavioral Sciences*. West Publishing Company: St. Paul, MN.

Winer, B.J., Brown, D.R., Michels, K.M. (1991) *Statistical principles in experimental design* (3rd Ed.). New York: McGraw-Hill.

Williges, R.C. (1981). Development and use of research methodologies for complex systems/simulation experimentations. In J. Moraal and K.F.

Krais (Eds.) *Manned system design, methods, equipment, and applications*. New York: Plenum, pp. 59-87.

Williges, R.C. and Williges, B.H. (1989). Integrated research paradigm for complex experimentation. In *Proceedings of the Human Factors Society 33rd annual meeting*. (pp. 606-610). Santa Monica, California: Human Factors Society.

Williges, R.C., Williges, B.H., and Han, S.H. (1992). Developing quantitative guidelines using integrated data from sequential experiments. *Human Factors*, 34, 399-408.

Williges, R.C., Williges, B.H., Han, S.H. (1993). Sequential experimentation in human-computer interface design. In R. Hartson and D. Hix (Eds.), *Volume IV, Advances in human-computer interaction*. New York: Ablex, pp. 1-30.

Chapter 4
Usability Testing

Mark W. Scerbo
Department of Psychology
Old Dominion University

1.0 Usability

Almost everyone, at one time or another, has bought something that was supposed to be easy to use but turned out to be a nightmare. Perhaps, it was the "easy-to-assemble" children's toy or the "no programming necessary" spreadsheet package. Usually, these products end up being donated anonymously to the local garage sale or stuffed in a brown paper bag and discarded. Rarely, do people return these products for a refund, because they would have to admit they were incapable of using them. What most people do not realize is that there are probably many others, like themselves, who also cannot use the products.

Products such as these represent failures in usability. It is important to understand that a product can be completely functional, pass rigorous quality control tests, and still be unusable. Thus, much of the success of a product rests with whether an individual can <u>use</u> it.

<u>Usability</u> refers to how well an individual can interact with a product or operate a piece of equipment. A highly usable product compliments one's style or facilitates one's performance. Further, Bennett (1984) argues that usability is achieved when one makes effective use of a product's full potential and does so willingly. Accordingly, products with usability problems interfere with one's performance and would be considered annoying or frustrating to work with. Further, a product that is used for only a small fraction of the tasks for which it was designed might be considered a usability failure as well.

Usability is not functionality, although the two concepts are related. Functionality refers to what a product can do, whereas usability is tied to <u>how</u> the functionality is implemented. For instance, a software product may support interaction via keyboard or mouse. Either method will execute the program's functions; however, the user may find one method easier and more palatable than the other and, therefore, more usable.

Although usability problems may seem like some of life's little inconveniences, they may have more serious ramifications. From a marketing perspective, customers who feel frustrated or overwhelmed by a product are unlikely to buy another one from that manufacturer. From a business perspective, employees who cannot or will not use products, offset the potential gains in productivity which may have prompted the acquisition or creation of the product in the first place. Thus, the need to understand and -- more importantly -- measure usability is critical to the success of any business.

Usability testing, or usability engineering, is a process that allows you to assess the usability aspects of products. What distinguishes usability engineering from other human factors techniques is the emphasis on operationalizing usability. Traditionally, human factors practitioners have argued that their efforts to improve the "look and feel" of products have helped create products that are "user friendly". Until recently, however, there was little that anyone could do to verify that these objectives had been met. Usability engineering addresses this issue by providing a mechanism for assessing the impact of human factors contributions to the product development process.

The usability engineering process allows you to define, measure, assess, and set goals for usability (Good, Spine, Whiteside, and George, 1986). Further, these objectives can be communicated accurately to all members of the design team, management, and end users. Moreover, this allows all members of a design team to establish mutually agreed upon standards against which they can measure the success of their efforts (Whiteside, Bennett, and Holtzblatt, 1988).

The methods for usability testing described below borrow heavily from those of experimental research. Unfortunately, this has led some to believe they are one in the same, which they are not. Although experiments are performed in each venue, the objectives of usability testing and scientific research are different.

To understand the distinction, you must consider the nature of science and technology. Science impacts technology in three stages. In the first stage, scientists attempt to uncover and <u>understand</u> lawful relationships among events. In the second stage, an understanding of these underlying relationships allows you to <u>predict</u> the likelihood of events in the future. In the last stage, the ability to predict enables you to exert some degree of <u>control</u> over future events. The vast majority of scientific or basic research contributes to the first two stages. Usability testing, on the other hand, is tied more closely to the second and third stages where scientific knowledge is applied to technology.

Finally, although most of the ideas and examples discussed in this chapter pertain to computer systems, the process can be applied to a much wider range of products (See, for example, Chapter 9). In fact, Whiteside, Bennett, and Holtzblatt (1988) argue that their usability engineering method is derived largely from standard techniques used in civil, electrical, and mechanical engineering. Alternatively, usability engineering should not be used to the exclusion of other methods for generating interfaces.

2.0 History

Usability engineering has a relatively brief history. Although manufacturers have always been concerned about whether consumers like and can use their products, orchestrated efforts aimed at improving usability -- as opposed to -- functionality have been slow to evolve.

The usability testing methods described in this chapter grew out of a relationship between psychologists and engineers that began in the 1970s, though the collaboration has not always been a pleasant one. As Scerbo (1991) indicated, during that period numerous psychologists were courted by the computer industry to help make complex computing accessible to a wider audience. The psychologists, unaccustomed to the engineering process, did what they were trained to do. They designed and conducted experiments to understand the intricacies of human-computer interaction. In turn, the industry was rewarded with volumes of papers, articles, and books addressing every facet of how humans interact with computers.

Despite this burgeoning wealth of knowledge, there existed a dilemma. Many designers found little information in the literature that addressed their particular needs. The source of the dilemma lay not so much with the content of the literature, but with how the information was "packaged". There existed a communication gap as fundamental as the difference between engineering and behavioral science.

Engineering is a deterministic discipline. Engineers are taught to solve equations and find optimal solutions to problems. Behavioral science, on the other hand, is probabilistic. Behavioral scientists (e.g., sociologists, psychologists) are trained to assess the likelihood of different solutions. For years, psychologists in industry had been assessing the statistical significance of various theories regarding human-machine interaction while engineers had been searching for the ideal way to design machines for people to use.

Until recently, this state of affairs had all but polarized practitioners and researchers within the human factors community. Practitioners complained that the results of published experiments failed to address their particular needs and were therefore of questionable value in the design process (Klein and Brezovic, 1986; Smith, 1987). Standards and guidelines were published that appeared straight forward, but were difficult to apply in practice (Chapanis, 1988; Grudin, 1989). On the other hand, some researchers argued that even designers with good intentions failed to follow or implement recommendations based upon human factors research (Gould and Lewis, 1983; Grimes, Ehrlich, and Vaske, 1986).

The gap between researchers and practitioners may become more narrow as usability engineering gains greater acceptance. Researchers will find that they can work with designers to plan and conduct studies aimed at meeting usability objectives. Designers, in turn, will find that they can more readily apply the results of usability studies to the product at hand.

3.0 Rationale

The need for usability testing arises from two primary areas, both grounded in economics. One of these is the commercial market. In the mid to late 1980s, a shift in American business philosophy became apparent. Businesses started to become more customer oriented (Peters and Austin, 1985). There are several reasons for this paradigm shift. One of these is the expanding global economy. There were more markets for American goods than ever before. However, there are more foreign competitors seeking access to those same markets as well as to the American market. Thus, American companies must compete with a growing number of foreign companies to retain their market share. Moreover, the success with which foreign competitors have implemented quality control and quality improvement processes has meant that better products could be obtained from outside of our borders (Deming, 1986). Another reason for the shift can be attributed to the growing number of small businesses. Large companies have seen their market share eroded by small businesses that can move quickly to meet customer needs. Thus, more and more American businesses are beginning to ask "What does the customer want?" instead of "What will the customer buy?"

A second impetus for usability testing arises from the efforts of companies to streamline business processes. In order to become more efficient, businesses have had to reexamine how they operate. In particular, equipment or software that is difficult to use adds to operations costs because it wastes time. Therefore, it has become critical that the tools, methods and techniques that employees have available to them are cost effective and operate as efficiently as possible. Thus, issues regarding the usability of internal products and tools, that were once overlooked, are now seen as critical to the success of cost reduction efforts (Nickerson, 1992).

4.0 Conducting a Usability Test

The first step in usability testing is to operationalize <u>usability</u>. Unfortunately, the concept, usability, means many things to many people. Thus, any attempt at a single definition would be futile. A better approach would be to consider the many facets of usability.

Whiteside, Bennett, and Holtzblatt (1988) describe a process that has evolved from ideas originally discussed by Bennett (1984) and Gilb (1981, as cited in Bennett, 1984). According to this approach usability is characterized by multiple <u>attributes</u>. An attribute is a particular component of usability. Learnability, for example, describes how well a system can be mastered. According to Bennett (1984), four attributes are likely to be common to most products: learnability, throughput, flexibility, and attitude. Other examples of attributes might include: availability of help, consistency, flexibility, likability, maintainability, memory demand, etc. However, some attributes may be unique to certain types of products. For example, durability may be an important attribute of hardware but is not applicable to software.

Once the relevant attributes are identified, a method or measuring concept for assessing each attribute must be considered. The concept represents a general plan for measuring the attribute. Consider the attribute, learnability. The measuring concept for this attribute might be a benchmark task where the user would perform several fundamental activities with the system. Alternatively, a retention test could be used to assess how well the system was learned. Specifying the measuring concept demonstrates that the attribute can indeed be assessed.

When the project team agrees upon a measuring concept, a measuring method is then specified. The method is the particular metric that will be used to assess the attribute. Regarding learnability, this attribute could be measured by the time it takes to complete the benchmark task. On the other hand, you could also measure accuracy, the number of tasks completed in a given time period, or the number of correct responses on a retention test. Again, the project team would decide which methods are needed to assess the attribute.

Once the measuring concept and method have been specified, several criteria are established to gauge performance on each of the attributes. The first criterion is the planned level. This represents the level of performance the project team wishes to achieve. In addition, a worst case scenario is specified. This level represents the lowest acceptable value for the attribute. If the users cannot meet the worst case level, the product must be reengineered. The third criterion is the optimal level. This represents a level of performance that might be realized with unlimited resources. It is not science fiction, but a level that is technically feasible in the present, yet unattainable given current constraints. This criterion is included in the usability plan to help establish goals for future iterations. The fourth criterion is the current level and specifies the present level of performance for the attribute. In many instances, the present level may be unknown but will become apparent after the first usability test.

When multiple attributes are considered collectively they can be grouped together in an attribute specification table. A sample is shown in Table 4-1. This table specifies the measuring concepts, methods, and performance criteria for four attributes.

Consider learnability. This attribute is assessed by having the users complete an on-line tutorial. Success is determined by how long it takes the users to complete the tutorial. The plan calls for a 2 hour completion time. If the users take more than 3 hours to finish, then the system as a whole fails to meet the worst case level and must be redesigned and reevaluated. Notice that the criterion for the worst case level exceeds that of the current level. This strategy guarantees that the new system will outperform the present one and forces continuous product improvement into the design plan. Finally, the optimal level for this attribute indicates that a completion time of 1 hour might be achieved if, perhaps, a coaching system was added to the tutorial.

Table 4-1. A Sample Attribute Specification Table.

Attribute	Measuring Concept	Measuring Method	Planned Level	Worst Case	Optimal Level	Current Level
Learnability	On-line Tutorial	Completion Time	2 hrs	3 hrs	1 hr	4 hrs
Flexibility	Change Default Values	Number of Errors	<3	>6	0	4
Intuitiveness	Use of Help	Frequency of Access	5	>10	2	?
Likeability	Attitude Survey	Likert Scale	5 Positive	<4 Negative	7 Very Positive	3 Negative

Adapted from Whiteside, Bennett, and Holtzblatt (1988).

The next step in the usability process is to conduct the test. Individuals are asked to use the product and performance is measured on each attribute. In addition, any other factors that impact the usability of the product are recorded as well. Afterward, the results of the test sessions are analyzed and assessed against the predefined criteria.

Rarely, will the objectives for all attributes be met after the initial test. Under such conditions, Whiteside et al., argue that resources should only be allocated to those attributes which fail to meet the planned levels. Once identified, portions of the system that impact the attributes in question will have to be redesigned. In some instances, the appropriate action may be straight forward. For example, where users had trouble completing a task because they could not find the information they sought, it may be necessary to provide them with additional information. On the other hand, alternative methods to access the available information may need to be considered.

In other situations, however, ideas about how to address attributes that come up short may be less obvious. In such cases, the first issue to consider is whether the original criteria were realistic. If they are inappropriate they should be adjusted. On the other hand, if they are appropriate, then the product as a whole may have to be reexamined to meet the objectives for that attribute. For example, if a 60 minute criterion is desired to learn the fundamentals of a product and the best that can be predicted after obvious usability problems have been addressed is 90 minutes, then new ways to achieve learnability must be considered. Situations such as these will call for some creative problem solving. For example, instead of a user manual, perhaps users should be given a job aid that lists only the required sequence of steps to execute the fundamental activities. On the other hand, a tutoring system might be developed to augment the tutorial. Obviously, adoption of any of these radical proposals would have to be weighed against the availability of resources.

It is important to understand that if the product is modified, another test will be required. There are good reasons for this. First, a subsequent usability test validates the modifications. This not only allows the designer to check the appropriateness of the changes, but also provides important information that can be used to calculate the dollar value of improvements in performance. Second, it is likely that a follow up study may reveal some usability problems that were undetected in the first test. Third, any changes in features may result in performance modifying interactions between features.

It may be necessary to perform several usability tests before all objectives are met. Thus, usability testing should be viewed as a continual process of testing, modifying and refining, and retesting. In fact, Whiteside et al. (1988) estimate that usability may be improved by as much as 30% with each iteration.

Others have also stressed the importance of early and continual testing throughout the development process (Hewett and Meadow, 1986; Wixon and Whiteside, 1985). In fact, Gould and his colleagues (1987) claim that the user guides for the 1984 Olympic Messaging System may have gone through as many as 200 iterations prior to being distributed at the Olympics.

Some might think that extensive testing would delay product development indefinitely, but evidence suggests that these concerns are unfounded. For instance, Gould (1988) describes numerous testing techniques that can be used at each stage of development. In the early stages, the appearance of the product can be evaluated from sketches or crude facsimiles. Functional aspects can be simulated with rapid prototyping tools. In later stages, more formal prototypes can be developed to assess refinements in functionality. Moreover, user documentation can be written and revised in parallel with the usability tests. Thus, there is <u>no need</u> to wait until a fully functional system is available to prepare the user manuals.

In a study designed to examine the impact of prototyping on system development, Boehm, Gray, and Seewaldt (1984) compared the traditional system specification approach with a prototyping approach. They found that prototyping and iterative testing <u>did not</u> have an adverse effect on the development cycle. Instead, they found several advantages to the prototyping approach. First, this technique produced systems containing fewer lines of code. Second, the system development effort was distributed more uniformly across the development period. Thus, it was less likely that a project would enter a crisis mode in the final days before the scheduled delivery date. Third, if for some unexpected reason the development period had to be cut short, a scaled down version of the system would still be available if the prototyping approach had been followed.

5.0 Error Analysis

Performing a usability test with a benchmark task will highlight aspects of the system that work well and those that are problematic. Examining the types and frequencies of problems users encounter can be a rich source of information about where to target resources for the next iteration.

Consider an example of a usability test performed on a software product designed to generate graphs and charts from numerical data. Users, unfamiliar with the product, were supplied with the software and the documentation and asked to perform a variety of tasks, e.g., installing the software, entering sample data, creating a bar graph, etc. The users were asked to complete as many of the tasks as they could in one hour. Analysis of the data revealed the following 9 categories of problems (labeled A - I) and the corresponding amount of time it took the users to recover from those problems. Collectively, the users spent 22 minutes on average recovering from these errors. Thus, 37% of the one hour session was unproductive time.

Table 4-2 . Problem Categories Uncovered in a Usability Test of a Graphics Package.

Problem	Time
A) Rescaling an axis	6.0 min.
B) Plotting wrong data type	5.0 min.
C) Grouping bars	3.5 min. *
D) Selecting X and Y axes	2.5 min.
E) Saving the graph to disk	2.0 min.
F) Removing scale marks	1.0 min.
G) Changing bar colors	1.0 min.
H) Exiting spread sheet	0.5 min. *
I) Removing a second graph	0.5 min.
Total time	22.0 min.

The next step is to determine the source of those errors. In most instances, the cause will be obvious to those conducting the usability test, e.g., pressing ALT-Q to exit instead of ALT-X. However, there may be times when it is necessary for the entire project team to review the records and determine the source of an error.

Once the causes of the errors are identified, you must decide how to address the problem areas. Ideally, you would like to fix all problem areas. However, budgetary or scheduling constraints may force the team to compromise and select a subset of problems to be addressed by the next iteration. For instance, in this example it was determined that the programmer could address most of the problems in one day. However, the problems labeled C and H (denoted by the asterisk) might take two to three weeks to remedy. Thus, the team decided to address these at a later date.

Whiteside et al. (1988) suggest using a Pareto chart to facilitate this process. In a Pareto chart, the categories of problems would be shown along the X axis and the amount of time spent recovering from the problems would be plotted along the Y axis on the left hand side of the chart. Figure 4-1 shows a Pareto diagram created for the data from this example. The nine categories of problems are rank ordered along the X axis from the most to least time consuming. In addition, the Pareto diagram displays a cumulative plot of the error recovery time for all of the problems. In Figure 4-1, this is the line with filled circles.

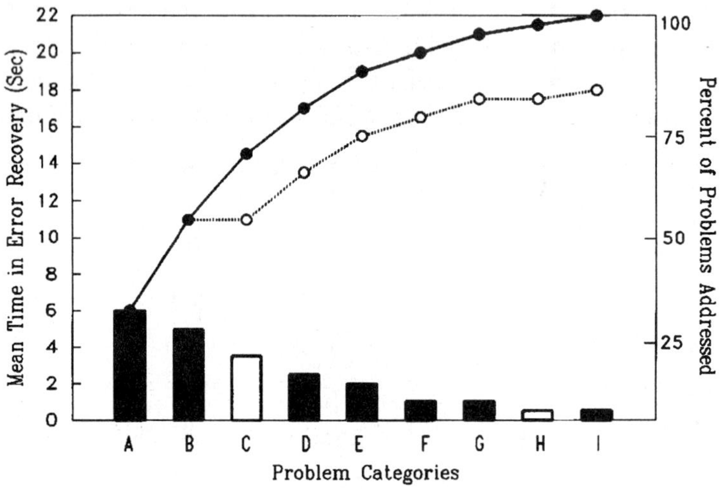

Figure 4-1. A Pareto Chart

There are several other features of Figure 4-1 that should be noted. First, this particular diagram has two cumulative plots. To understand the basis for the second plot, recall that problem categories C and H were to be addressed at a later date. This is depicted by the white bars in the chart. The second line with the white circles, therefore, shows a cumulative plot of only those problems currently being addressed. Notice also that there is a second axis on the right hand side of the figure. This axis shows the percentage of time spent recovering from errors. In this example, by addressing 7 of the 9 problem categories, approximately 82% of the time spent recovering from errors should be eliminated by the next iteration. If the team had decided to fix all of the problems, then a full 100% of the problem time revealed by this usability test would have been eliminated.

6.0 Test Subjects

6.1 Who are the users?

Nearly all human factors texts speak to the importance of knowing the users. The most efficient way to achieve planned usability objectives is to understand the user population and to design for them. For example, if you were to design a product to be used by a bank teller, you would want to know a little about a teller's responsibilities. What kinds of activities and how many activities do tellers perform? Which activities will the product affect? It is also important to know some demographics about the bank tellers who will use the product. What is the extent of their formal education? What are their reading levels? How many speak English as their primary language? What is their turnover rate? In some instances, it may be equally important to understand some psychographics of prospective users (i.e., user attitudes and lifestyles; see for example Riche, 1989; Wells, 1974). The answers to questions such as these will place unique constraints on both the functionality and usability of the product.

Collecting demographic or psychographic information about users can be facilitated by using standardized forms to compile user profiles. An example of a user profile developed by Weimer and Banks (1992) appears in Appendix 4-1. This particular form separates user information into five categories; physical characteristics, educational background, work-related experience, computer experience, and job characteristics. Blank user profile worksheets appear in Appendix 4-2 for your use.

It is crucial to gather as much information about the users as possible prior to the design phase of the development cycle. There are several reasons for this. First, data about the users will help determine some of the planned levels for the usability attributes. Second, the effort expended to learn about the user population early in the development process can significantly reduce the number of iterations needed to meet usability objectives.

It follows that test subjects should be drawn from a pool of the intended users. This ensures that recommendations based on data from testing will meet the usability objectives of the target population. This is particularly important when designing for a select class of users (e.g., programmers, pilots, executives, etc.). There may be an additional benefit to testing with the intended users. Having future users become involved in the design and testing process can increase the level of user acceptance for the finished product. In fact, Gould (1988) advocates including a user on the design team.

Although you should strive to test with users from the target population, in practice, it may not always be possible. The intended users could be located some distance away and would therefore be geographically inaccessible. It is also possible (even likely) that the users may belong to another organization whose management is unwilling to let them participate. Under these circumstances, you should try to use test subjects who are representative of the intended users in terms of demographics and job description. You should understand that testing with subjects other than the intended users will undoubtedly place some restrictions on the generalizability of results, but it does not necessarily invalidate the study. Kantowitz (1992) has argued that it may be perfectly reasonable to draw upon a more convenient subject pool when only a short period of time is needed to develop the skills and strategies necessary to test the product. You should not, however, attempt to use "substitute" test subjects when designing for a select class of users.

It is important to note that there are also situations when it is advisable to test with a less homogeneous group of subjects. As Chapanis (1988) has indicated, the generalizability of results is enhanced when data are gathered from heterogeneous samples. Thus, if you are designing for the general population or you cannot identify a target user group, you should include as wide a variety of subjects as possible. Moreover, as Flemming, Morrissey, and Kinghorn (1992) argue, recent passage of the Americans with Disabilities Act will undoubtedly force designers to consider individuals with a broader range of skills and needs in all of their testing.

One final word about test subjects is in order. It is important for those who come from a behavioral sciences background to understand that not everyone has had the experience of being an experimental subject. For many individuals, participating in a usability test is their introduction to the behavioral research process. Consequently, experimenters must make an extra effort to explain the testing process to participants and to make them feel comfortable. At a minimum, anyone conducting research with human subjects should be familiar with guidelines for the ethical treatment of subjects outlined by the American Psychological Association or the code of ethics for members of the Human Factors and Ergonomics Society. In addition, Schrier (1992) has discussed several good ideas for reducing the potential stress of test subjects in industrial research.

6.2 How many?

One of the most difficult decisions to be made when conducting a usability study concerns the number of subjects to be tested. Unfortunately, there are no easy solutions. From a statistical perspective, you would want to run as many test subjects as possible. The greater the number of subjects, the more confidence you can have in the results. From a business perspective, however, there may be many forces at work to reduce the number of subjects to as few as possible. Fewer subjects means lower costs and shorter development times. Thus, the number of test subjects will always be a compromise between thoroughness and available resources.

Virzi (1992) has recently provided some help with this dilemma. In a series of experiments, Virzi set about to determine how many subjects would be necessary to identify usability problems in three different products. Based upon experimental data and the results of several Monte Carlo studies, he derived a function relating the proportion of problems identified to the number of subjects in a test session. Virzi found that the majority of problems were detected by the first few subjects and that the likelihood that other problems would be uncovered decreased with each additional subject. Further, as Figure 4-2 shows, the more severe problems are likely to be detected with fewer subjects. Consequently, greater numbers of subjects increase the likelihood of detecting the less critical problems. Virzi concluded that -- in most -- situations 5 subjects would be able to detect approximately 80% of the most important usability problems in a test session.

Virzi's data may provide some guidance in selecting the appropriate number of test subjects for a study. It is important to realize, however, that these data were generated from studies that exhausted the functionality of product. Obviously, if care is not exercised in designing a comprehensive benchmark task, usability problems will go unnoticed.

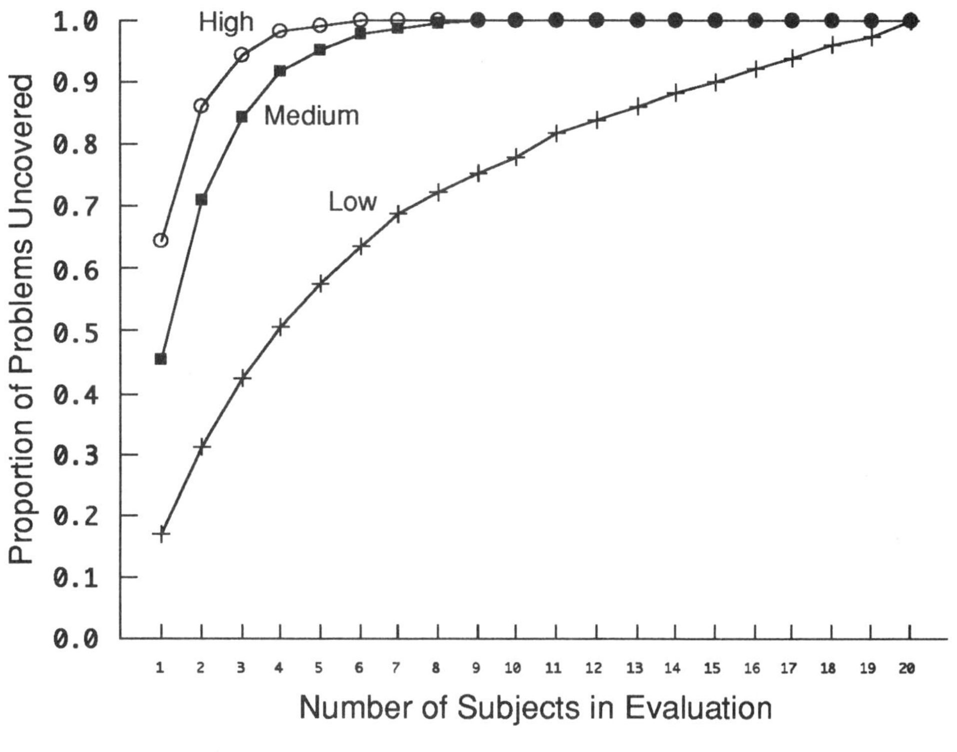

Figure 4-2. Proportion of Usability Problems Detected as a Function of the Number of Subjects for All Problems at 3 Levels of Severity (high, medium, and low). (Virzi, 1992)

(Reprinted with permission of the Human Factors and Ergonomics Society)

Those schooled in experimental methods will notice that Virzi's ideas for estimating sample size differ from more traditional approaches. For example, many statistical references and experimental design books describe procedures for estimating the magnitude of some effect in the population and calculating sample size based upon a power analysis (see for example, Cohen, 1988; Keppel, 1982). These methods are appropriate when your interest lies in comparing samples drawn from a population. As noted, however, the objectives differ for usability testing and behavioral science. The goal of usability testing is to determine what works and what doesn't. Therefore, the use of Virzi's procedures for selecting a sample size may be appropriate for estimating the likelihood that problems will be detected. They should not, however, be used if your objective is to reject the null hypothesis.

7.0 Tools of the Trade

There are several tools and types of equipment that are common in usability laboratories. Obviously, the product to be tested and a place in which to work are needed. Video cameras and microphones are often used to record the user's actions and comments. Also, flexible lighting arrangements in the test rooms help to produce good video images and limit the amount of glare on VDTs. Figure 4-3 shows a test subject seated at a computer work station with the video and audio recording equipment in place. Some usability labs have a separate room that provides the experimenter with remote control of all camera adjustments and other equipment that can be used to analyze the video and computer records generated in a test session. Figure 4-4 shows the configuration of one such control room.

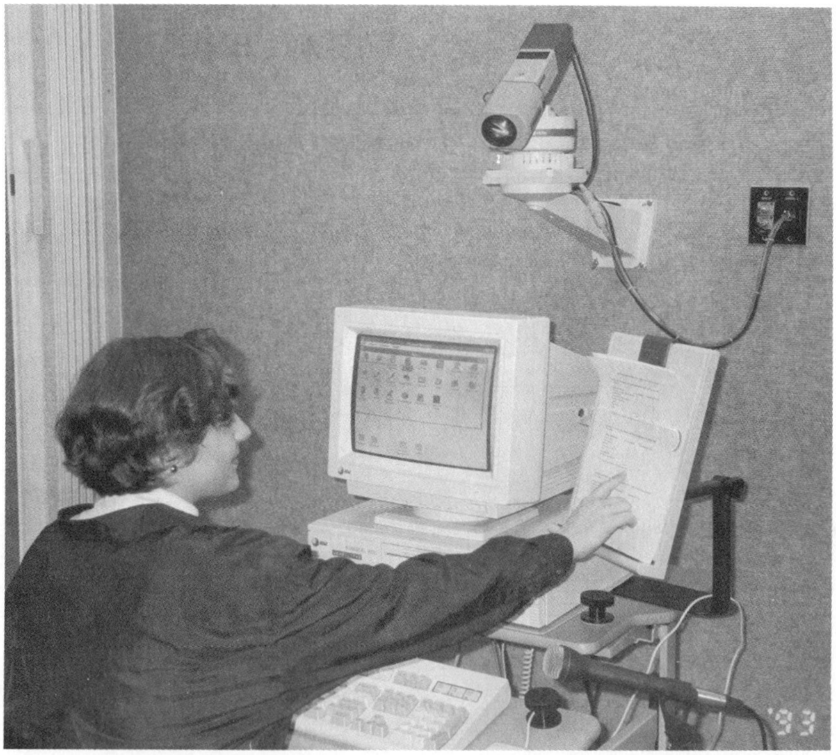

Figure 4-3. A Usability Laboratory Test Station
(Courtesy of the AT&T Human Resources Information Systems Organization Human Performance Laboratory , Greensboro, NC.)

Figure 4-4. A Usability Laboratory Control Room.
(Photographs provided courtesy of the AT&T Human Resources Information Systems Organization Human Performance Laboratory ,Greensboro, NC.)

7.1 Keystroke records

A valuable aid to the usability process is a keystroke record. Many usability laboratories rely on software to create a record of every keystroke made by the user. These records often include time stamps as well. Some systems also record codes entered by the experimenter for various user behaviors such as asking for assistance or taking a break (Neal and Simons, 1984).

Keystroke records are typically used when it is paramount to generate a precise chronology of command usage. A sample from a keystroke record appears in Table 4-3. The first column shows the keyboard character pressed and the second column displays the decimal scan code for that character. The third column contains the elapsed time in milliseconds since the last key press and the fourth column displays a cumulative time record of each key press for the session.

There are several advantages to this process. First, an accurate record of all interactions with the keyboard is created for each session. This record can then be searched for instances of critical character strings, e.g., commands, use of Function keys, etc. Tallies of the frequencies of command usage can be generated very quickly. Typographical errors can be obviated readily. The time coded data produce a chronological record of the session. Further, the elapsed time between keystrokes or commands can be easily computed to provide a rudimentary estimate of mental processing time. Thus, many preliminary analyses can be derived from a usability test session with a minimal amount of effort.

Table 4-3 . Sample Output From a Keystroke Logging Package.

Cumulative Keystroke	Code	Scan Time	Elapsed Time
c	46	660	660
d	32	110	770
SPC	57	220	990
c	46	495	1485
lshift	42	275	1760
:	39	55	1815
\	43	275	2090
w	17	550	2640
p	25	165	2805
5	6	165	2970
1	2	110	3080
CR	28	165	3245
w	17	1045	4290
p	25	220	4510
CR	28	165	4675

There are drawbacks to this technique. First, it may be difficult to obtain a keystroke logging package commercially. Most of the products used in laboratories are developed internally. As a result, many of these packages are system specific and may not be very portable (e.g., a keystroke logging package developed on the IBM PC may not work on Apple or mainframe applications). Also, many of these products are less useful when attempting to capture interactions with alternative input devices, e.g., a mouse, track ball, joystick, etc. Although it may be easy to record a button press on a mouse from a technical standpoint, without knowing what function was executed, the record is of little utility. Despite these disadvantages, keystroke logging packages can significantly reduce the labor involved in analyzing data from usability test sessions in which they are applicable.

7.2 Video Records

Users can exhibit a wide variety of behaviors in even a brief testing session. Ultimately, this rich source of information must be structured in some way to permit analysis of the session. Considerable attention must be paid to categories of events and behaviors so that they may be coded accurately and efficiently. Some investigators have devised methods for facilitating the coding of behaviors in real time (Philips and Dumas, 1990). However, in recent years it has become popular to videotape test sessions.

Video recording is often used when it is important to capture a wider variety of user interaction than can be obtained with keystroke records. However, the ability to record this richer source of information does have its costs. Typically, there is reduction in the quality of key press data recorded as well as the precision of keystroke time stamps.

If you can live with a little less precision, then there are some important advantages to this medium to consider. First, video provides a permanent record of the session which can then be analyzed at a later time. This eliminates the difficulties of attempting to code all user behavior in real time. Second, video is not technology dependent. Records of interactions with almost any device can be recorded. In fact, it is often possible to record usable images from the screens of various VDTs. In some cases, the electronic signal from a VDT can be recorded to video tape directly thereby circumventing some of the drawbacks of keystroke logging packages noted above. Finally, and most important, the video record can be a very effective format for illustrating usability problems. Brief episodes of user frustration or even anger are apt to have a greater impact on the decisions of team members and managers who might be inclined to dismiss data and statistics, or even deny that usability problems exist with "their" system.

Video configurations can be simple (e.g., a single hand held camera) or quite elaborate (e.g., a video production center). However, more elaborate configurations offer greater flexibility in the kinds and quality of the video images that can be recorded. For example, in Figure 4-3 a subject is seated at a work station operating a computer. The camera is aimed at the user to record head and, perhaps, gross eye movements. A second camera could be set up behind the user to record an image of what appears on the VDT. The signals from each camera can be sent to a video special effects generator to produce a composite image. A microphone is also present to record user comments.

Obviously, other configurations are possible. For instance, if keystroke logging software is available this would permit one of the cameras to record page numbers from user documentation. Images from different cameras can be superimposed on one another or displayed in separate windows using a special effects generator. The date and a running chronometer can also be added to the video image. In the end, however, decisions regarding the video configuration should be driven by the nature of the research as well as the equipment being studied.

7.2.1 Analyzing video data. Video records can provide a rich and extensive source of information. Unfortunately, this also places an enormous burden on the researcher who must subsequently reduce this wealth of information to meaningful data. Video analysis/reduction is a labor intensive activity which can often be the bottle neck in the usability assessment process.

There are, however, some tools which can facilitate this process. For instance, when choosing a VCR, you should select a deck with editing capabilities. These units include two valuable features. The first feature is a controller which allows you to adjust the speed of playback, in either direction, from up to 10 times normal to a single frame at a time. Second, they also allow the user to electronically mark individual frames of video which can later be used to search and tally key behaviors as well as calculate elapsed time between behaviors.

Unfortunately, many designers of usability laboratories often overlook the utility of such equipment in their efforts to maximize the quality and quantity of information recorded on tape. You would be well advised to allocate resources equally between the recording and analyses functions of the video equipment for the lab.

7.2.2 Coding behavior. The nature of the product being tested and the tasks users are asked to perform often dictate the kinds of behaviors that can be coded. In addition, the kinds of resources and equipment that are available will have an impact upon the precision of coding (e.g., knowing where a user's eyes are directed vs. which direction their head is pointed).

The types of behaviors that can be coded vary greatly. Often, interest lies in where the user is looking at any point in time (e.g., knowing when the user is working with the product or reading the user manual). Interest may also lie with hand movements (e.g., periods when the user works with the keyboard, the mouse, or a pencil and paper). On the other hand, important behaviors required to perform certain activities might be recorded. For example, in a study examining the use of reference materials, Scerbo and Fisk (1990) observed that each activity was comprised of primarily three behaviors; reading the task description, searching for the appropriate reference aid, and locating the requested information. A similar categorization scheme would apply to benchmark tasks as well. For example, an activity in a benchmark task addressing the usability of a word processor might require the user to move a paragraph of text. The behaviors associated with this activity would include; a) reading the activity description, b) searching the user manual for information about "moving text", c) reading the instructions, d) performing the activity, and e) verifying the result.

Other portions of a test session are also important to code. Obviously, any and all errors committed by the users as well as their attempts to get back on track should be noted. In addition, instances where the users took a rest or asked for assistance would need to be distinguished from time on task.

Regardless of whether behavior is coded in real time or from a video tape, the coding process should be given serious consideration. Laws and Barber (1989) argue that much effort is needed to establish and refine the behavioral classification scheme prior to collecting data. Otherwise, problems may arise later in the analysis process (e.g., how to code unanticipated behaviors or behaviors that fall into more than one category).

It may be necessary to "usability test" the classification scheme prior to the formal test session to ensure the integrity of the data. Further, Laws and Barber argue that the data should be scored by more than one individual. At best, this method helps to eliminate individual bias from the coding process by revealing differences among raters' analyses and allowing the discrepancies to be resolved. At worst, however, the inter-rater reliability indices can be computed and reported along with the analyses.

7.3 Eye Movement Tracking

In recent years the ability to record eye movements has become a more viable technology. Reductions in the size and weight of components has made the data gathering *process* less disruptive and invasive. This technology has been applied successfully in laboratory environments, field studies, and even inside a moving automobile. Moreover, cost reductions have placed them within reach of most usability labs.

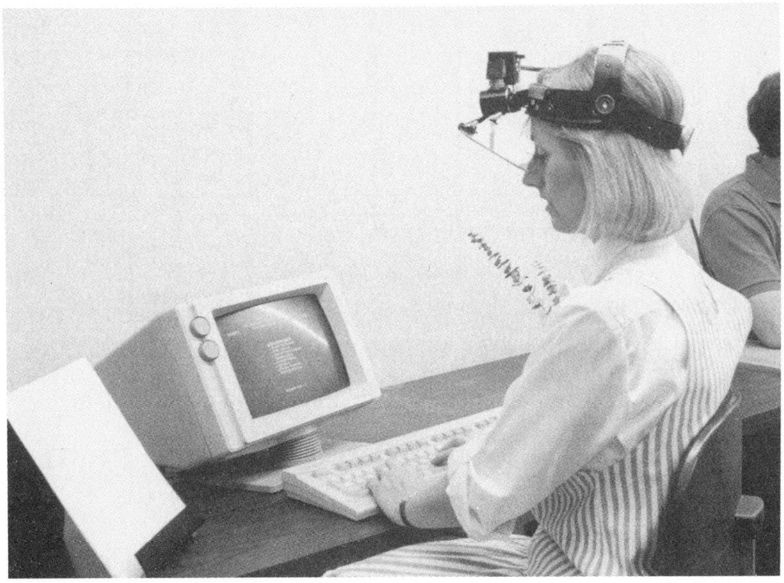

Figure 4-5. ASL 4100H Head Mounted Eye Movement Tracker
(Courtesy of Applied Science Laboratories)

Eye movement tracking allows you to record where a user's eyes are fixating as well as the pattern of eye movements made when viewing visual information (e.g., Figure 4-5 shows a head mounted eye movement tracking system being used to record the pattern of eye fixations produced by a VDT user). Unfortunately, eye trackers vary widely (See Appendix 4-3) in sophistication, reliability, size, robustness, and price; some *require* the placement of an instrumented hard contact on the user's eye, some require users to wear a helmet or headband (See Figure 4-5), while others are relatively free of user constraints by using wall or floor mounted optics.

In general, eye trackers measure the movement of a user's dominant eye relative to a set of optics. Their relative non-intrusiveness, measurement robustness, and moderate price, make pupil-to-corneal reflex eye trackers well suited for most usability settings. Figure 4-6 shows a schematic of a helmet-mounted pupil to-corneal reflex vector system similar to the one shown in Figure 4-5.

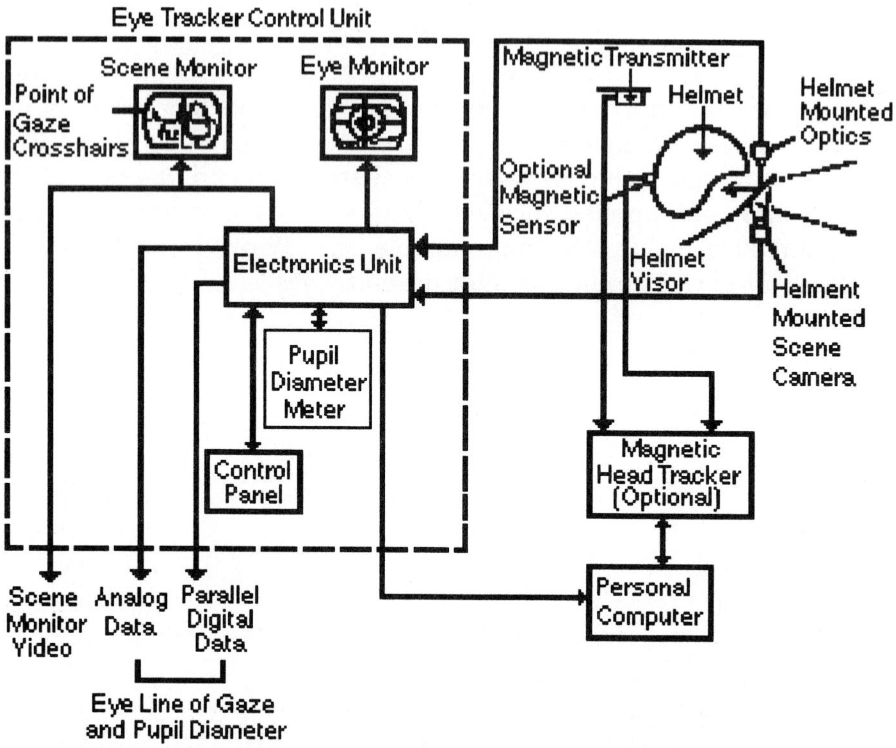

Figure 4-6. Head Mounted Pupil to Corneal Reflex Eye Tracker
(Courtesy of Applied Science Laboratories)

Figures 4-5 and 4-6 show a typic head-mounted system, where 2 minature cameras are mounted to either a helmet or a headband. In this particular system, an infrared light source, mounted to the headgear, bounces infrared light off the surface of the user's eye with a mirrored visor. Some of the light is absorbed by the pupil, while some is reflected off the cornea. Light reflected off the cornea is called the corneal reflex. The camera (eye camera) mounted above the user's eye, records the corneal reflex. The degree of separation between the pupil and the corneal reflex varies with a change in eye rotation (i.e., a change in the user's point of gaze).

The visor is mirrored to reflect infrared on both sides, but transparent to the user. A second camera (scene camera) is mounted on an armature attached to the side of the helmet or headband (See Figure 4-6). The armature is positioned so that the user's visual space is reflected off the surface of the visor and into the scene camera. Mirroring both surfaces of the visor allows the scene and eye cameras to be collimated. Pupil-to-corneal reflex is recorded by the scene camera and fed into the eye tracker control unit (Figure 4-6). This information is then used to position a cross hair onto the image of the user's visual space recorded by the scene camera. As the user's eye moves (corresponding to a change in fixation), the pupil-to-corneal reflex measurement is recalculated, changing the positioning of the cross hairs on the visual scene. The result is a video image showing the pattern of fixations superimposed on the user's visual scene. (See Figure 4-7).

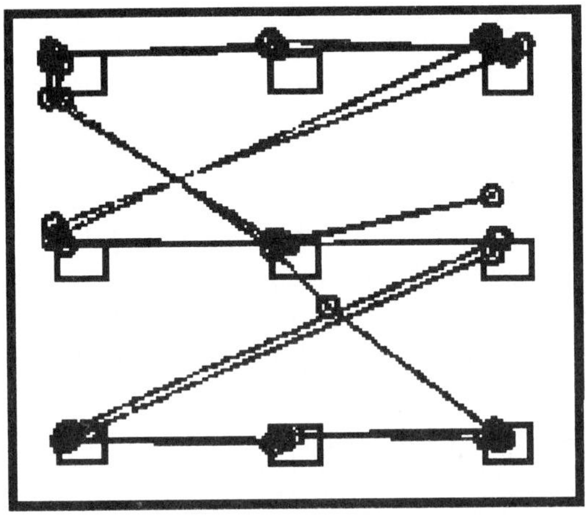

Figure 4-7. Eye Fixations on a 9 Square Grid
(Courtesy of Applied Science Laboratories)

7.4 Think Aloud Protocols

Another technique often employed in usability tests is to encourage users to think aloud as they work their way through an activity. Human factors practitioners have adopted this procedure from psychologists who were originally interested in studying human problem solving behavior (Ericsson and Simon, 1980). The rationale behind this technique is that when users verbalize their thoughts, they reveal the strategies they employ to accomplish a given task. This information can be very helpful in highlighting discrepancies between the product design and a user's knowledge and expectations about the product's operation.

Typically, users are asked to perform a benchmark task, describing what they are doing and why they are doing it at each step. For instance, at the end of a session a user might say: "I'm now finished, so I will press ALT-X to exit. Oh, that's funny, I'm still in the system. It didn't exit." This brief discourse illustrates one advantage of verbal protocols; they reveal the user's intentions (e.g., the user planned to terminate the session, but instead entered an incorrect key sequence which placed her in another area of the system). With only a keystroke record of the session, you would not be able to determine whether pressing the ALT-X key sequence was intentional. Thus, verbal protocols help to resolve ambiguities in the performance record.

Moreover, Wright and Monk (1991) found that the think aloud procedure was useful for identifying usability problems in the early stages of testing.

At present there is still much debate surrounding the use of think aloud protocols in usability testing. Some experimenters leave the subject alone to volunteer information while others advocate a more interactive discourse between the subject and the experimenter (Carroll and Mack, 1984; Wright and Monk, 1991)[1]. Some argue that verbal protocols may not be true representations of underlying cognitive processes (Nisbett and Wilson, 1977). Still, others have reservations about the procedure itself because the requirement to describe one's thought process may contaminate task performance (Holleran, 1991). As noted above, however, the objectives of usability testing are not identical to those of experimental research. If your interest lies in understanding human-computer behavior, then you should be cautious about the potential impact of concurrent verbal protocols on that behavior. On the other hand, if your objective is to identify usability problems in a given product, then you should be more concerned with selecting those methods which improve the chances of revealing problems and less concerned about the quality of human-computer behavior.

7.5 User Surveys and Checklists

A great deal of information about usability can be obtained by asking the user about the product. You can use of surveys or questionnaires to gather information and opinions about a product in a short period of time. Surveys can be made up of several types of questions, each designed to elicit certain kinds of information. For example, multiple choice questions force the user to select from a limited number of options that the experimenter believes are relevant. Rating scales allow users to express their opinions along a numerical scale. Ranking scales combine aspects of rating scales and multiple choice questions. Users rank order a limited set of choices according to their preferences. There are also times when it is important to have users express what they believe is important about a product. For instance, open ended questions have little experimenter imposed structure and therefore allow users more freedom to offer information about what they feel is relevant about a product. On the other hand, fill-in-the-blank questions can be used to elicit specific details, but still allow users to answer in their own words. There are many issues that need to be considered when designing a questionnaire. Unfortunately, a more comprehensive treatment of survey construction is beyond the scope of this chapter (See Hayes (1992) and Meister (1985) for additional information).

[1]A variant on this method,co-discovery, is presented in Chapter 9, section 4.2. Co-discovery uses two users, rather than a single user, who are encouraged to interact while using the product. The idea is that the two subjects must converse in order to work together, and the content of their interaction can provide important clues about why certain features of the products are difficult to use. Co-discovery has been successfully used by Digital Equipment Corporation and Philips Electronics.

A well designed, comprehensive checklist can be invaluable in helping to ensure that important aspects of usability are not overlooked in a test. Ravden and Johnson (1989) developed a checklist for evaluating human-computer interfaces, which addresses 9 aspects of usability: visual clarity, consistency, informative feedback, explicitness, appropriate functionality, flexibility and control, error prevention and control, user guidance and support. The last section of the checklist addresses more general system usability issues. The visual clarity portion of the checklist is shown in Figure 4-8. Specific questions about the system's appearance are listed on the left, followed by a 4-item rating scale and a comments section.

	Always	Most of the time	Some of the time	Never	Comments
1. Is each screen clearly identified with an informative title or description?					
2. Is important information highlighted on the screen? (e.g. cursor position, instructions, errors)					
3. When the user enters information on the screen, is it clear: (a) where the information should be entered?					
(b) in what format it should be entered?					
4. Where the user overtypes information on the screen, does the system clear the previous information, so that it does not get confused with the updated input?					
5. Does information appear to be organized logically on the screen? (e.g. menus organized by probable sequence of selection, or alphabetically)					
6. Are different types of information clearly separated from each other on the screen? (e.g. instructions, control options, data displays)					
7. Where a large amount of information is displayed on one screen, is it clearly separated into sections on the screen?					
8. Are columns of information clearly aligned on the screen? (e.g. columns of alphanumerics left-justified, columns of integers right-justified)					
9. Are bright or light colours displayed on a dark background, and vice versa?					
10. Does the use of colour help to make the displays clear?					
11. Where colour is used, will all aspects of the display be easy to see if used on a monochrome or low resolution screen, or if the user is colour-blind?					
12. Is the information on the screen easy to see and read?					

Figure 4-8. Usability Checklist for Visual Clarity.
Adapted from Ravden and Johnson (1989).

Ravden and Johnson suggest that this checklist be used in conjunction with a benchmark task that represents as much of the functionality and breadth and depth of the system as possible. Users are asked to perform a benchmark task, completing the checklist as they progress through the activities. Afterward, the numbers of favorable and unfavorable responses are determined for each of the nine areas of usability and for the system as a whole. Response patterns can help pinpoint aspects of the interface that are problematic as well as those that are successful.

In addition to providing a great deal of information about the usability of a system, there can be other advantages to a checklist of this sort. Johnson, Clegg, and Ravden (1989) reported that the checklist they developed was successful both in eliciting detailed evaluations from users with different backgrounds and in distinguishing usability differences between separate interfaces. Moreover, designers who participated in a test session using the checklist felt that it had a high degree of face validity.

Despite these advantages, it is important to realize that the data produced by a checklist of this type are subjective and represent only the users' opinions of usability. Any recommendations about the usability of a system should be based upon both objective/performance data and subjective data. Thus, a checklist should not be thought of as an alternative to gathering performance data, but as a method to generate supplementary data. It would be unwise to invest the amount of effort recommended by Ravden and Johnson to develop a benchmark task, and then only consider the checklist data.

8.0 Assessing Costs and Benefits

Conducting a usability study has costs associated with it. These costs must be weighed against the potential benefits of the study to determine if the project merits an investment of resources. On the expense side, there are costs associated with the personnel involved in planning and executing the study and for any materials used in testing. If a prototype is to be tested, there will be costs associated with developing that as well. Test subjects may need to be compensated and a travel budget may also be required.

Some of the many potential benefits gained from usability testing include an increase in sales or an increase in employee productivity. The following example illustrates one way that costs and benefits might be assessed for a usability study.

The usability testing process can be thought of as occurring in 4 major phases. The first of these is the preparation phase and encompasses several activities such as selecting the attributes to be studied and planning and designing the test session and accompanying stimulus materials. The laboratory equipment (hardware and/or software) may also need to be reconfigured. In addition, the test participants must be recruited and scheduled. The second phase of the process is the data collection phase.

During this phase, time is spent preparing the lab and materials for each participant and conducting the test. The third phase of the process is the analysis phase which can be one of the more labor intensive and time consuming portions of the project. The data must be coded, reduced and analyzed. In the fourth phase of the process, the results of the test must be documented. Typically, a report is generated detailing the objectives of the project, the methodology, the results, and recommendations for action.

To estimate the cost side of the equation, assume a usability engineer is responsible for conducting a usability test. In this example, the engineer also has an assistant available to share the work load. The time requirements for the usability manager and the assistant during each phase of the project are shown in Table 4-4. As can be seen in the table, the usability manager and the assistant spend 51 and 57 hours on the project, respectively. The cost associated with their time is calculated by multiplying each of their hours by their salaries. The salary figures used in the calculations should represent loaded salaries (i.e., the base salary plus some percentage for benefits, health care, etc.). In this example, the usability manager earns a loaded salary of $56,000 ($40,000 base salary plus 40% loading). Likewise, the assistant earns $37,500 ($30,000 base salary with 25% loading). Based on these figures, the cost of the manager's and assistant's time is approximately $27/hour and $18/hour, respectively.

Table 4-4. Personnel Expenses for a Usability Test.

PHASE	PERSONNEL	HOURS	COST
Preparation	Usability Mgr.	23	$621
	Assistant	5	$90
Data Collection	Usability Mgr.	5	$135
	Assistant	25	$450
Analysis	Usability Mgr.	8	$216
	Assistant	22	$396
Report	Usability Mgr.	15	$405
	Assistant	5	$90
TOTAL			$2,403

The total cost of the usability test must also include the value of the time for the test subjects. This might be wages paid to participants directly or expenses charged from one department to another. In other instances, this cost might be measured as a loss in productivity resulting from employees spending time away from their jobs.

In this example, assume that ten subjects participated for two hours a piece. If the loaded salary for each participant is $35,000, then the hourly rate for each subject would be approximately $17.00. The total subject expense would therefore be $340. Finally, the cost of any materials or supplies (e.g., video tapes, diskettes, booklets, etc.) needed for the study should be included. In this example, these expenses amount to $85.00. These costs appear in Table 4-5.

Table 4-5. Subject and Materials Expenses for a Usability Test.

Subject Expenses	$340
Materials	$85
TOTAL	$425

The total cost of conducting the usability test outlined in this example would amount to $2,828. This might seem like a modest investment, but it is important to realize that this example reflects the costs of only one usability test. In reality, there may be several iterations of testing before the usability goals have been met. Thus, a similar tally of costs would need to be determined for each iteration of testing. Further, this example does not include the costs involved in the initial investment of equipment in the usability lab. The initial investment and any subsequent additions or upgrades to equipment and facilities must also be considered in the cost of product development.

The costs of usability testing must then be weighed against the potential benefits of testing. It is in this area that usability testing has the potential to become a valuable part of the product development process.

To illustrate how to assess potential benefits, return to Figure 4-1. Recall that in this example, 9 categories of problems accounted for 22 minutes of unproductive time. If the proposed modifications to the system were implemented, 82% of this unproductive time or a total of 18 minutes on average for each user would potentially be eliminated. Recall as well that the programmer estimated that 7 of these problems could be addressed in one day. If we assume that the programmer also earns a loaded salary of $56,000, the cost to fix the targeted problems would be approximately $216.

Suppose 600 people use this system. Applying the cost figures from the preceding example, assume also that the users of this system earn $17 per hour. If every person encountered each category of difficulty just once (a very conservative estimate), the cost in terms of unproductive time would be $5.10 per user, (i.e., ($17/60 min.) x 18 min. = $5.10). Therefore, if the deficiencies identified in the usability test were corrected, $5.1 x 600 or $3,060 of unproductive time would be eliminated. Recall that the total cost of the usability study was $2,828. Adding to the usability costs, the $216 expense of implementing the proposed modifications, the complete cost of modifying the system is $3,044. This figure falls $16 short of the expected savings associated with increased productivity.

Clearly, the usability effort pays for itself. Moreover, this is a rather conservative estimate of gains in productivity. In reality, glaring problems such as categories A and B would probably be encountered several times a day by each user of the system. Over the life of the system these seemingly small inconveniences could add up to thousands of dollars in lost productivity (Karat, 1992).

Obviously, the potential benefits of every usability test will not always outweigh the costs. Conducting a full scale usability test on a system that has only a dozen users may not be a wise use of resources. Also, it may not be wise to prepare a usability study to address only one or two attributes. In these instances, using a less expensive technique (e.g., a checklist) might be a reasonable compromise between conducting an expensive series of usability tests and no assessment at all.

Assessing the costs and benefits of usability tests could become an invaluable asset to the human factors practitioner. Because the procedure allows you to demonstrate the impact of human factors efforts on the "bottom line", you should include these estimates on all of you projects. Space limitations prohibit a more detailed discussion of cost/benefit methods, but the reader is referred to Mantei and Teorey (1988) and Powers, Adams, and Mills (1984) for additional information.

The preceding cost/benefit example is representative of the scope of testing and potential impact on design of many software development organizations. Karat (1990) indicated, that on two projects at IBM, the savings-to-cost ratios ranged from 2:1 to as much as 100:1 The key to success rests with accurate record keeping. Counts of the kinds and frequencies of problems encountered by users should be maintained both in the lab and in the field. Moreover, attention should be paid to how the user deals with problems encountered in the field. Do they create "band-aid" solutions? Do they engage in less efficient uses of the system to avoid cumbersome areas? All of these behaviors point to usability problems and a corresponding loss in productivity and wasted resources.

The example above showed how benefits could be assessed through reductions in inefficient behavior. Benefits such as these are more likely to be observed on products developed for internal use. However, estimates of productivity improvements that customers might anticipate in their <u>own</u> organizations could be a valuable marketing tool to bolster sales. Aside from productivity estimates, other methods may be needed to determine potential benefits derived from products delivered to external customers. For instance, iterative testing helps ensure that problems are identified earlier rather than later in the development cycle where the costs to address them are minimal (DePree, 1984). This in turn, means less rework and a greater probability of delivering products on schedule. (In fact, Karat (1992) indicates there are ways to measure the opportunity cost of failing to meet delivery deadlines.) Less rework reduces development costs which brings a less expensive product to market. Further, a thoroughly tested product may result in fewer calls for help or service thereby reducing customer support costs. Last, but certainly not least, the effort invested in testing will result in a higher quality product which is likely to increase the customer base. Thus, it is possible to assess the benefits of usability testing on products sold externally, however, you may have to look outside the laboratory to do so.

9.0 Contextual Research

The primary focus of this chapter is aimed at laboratory techniques of usability testing. However, it is important to understand that the usability testing process may also require data collection from outside the lab. Whiteside et al. (1988) make a strong case for understanding the social, organizational, and physical context in which a product will be used. For instance, a major determinant of usability may be whether the product is compatible with other tools or whether the product fits on the desk. Equally important, may be whether management approves and supports use of the product.

Another issue concerns the differences between laboratory and field research. The behaviors users exhibit in a laboratory setting may differ substantially from what they do back on the job. For example, individuals who struggle with a product in a test session are likely to give a different impression of usability if a friend shows them how to use the same product. Moreover, as Eason (1984) has suggested, users in a test session may produce unrealistic expectations about the usability of a product they wouldn't even touch outside the laboratory.

Consequently, the importance of field testing and contextual research should not be overlooked. Further, as noted above, research outside the lab may provide opportunities to assess the dollar value of usability testing on products for external users.

10.0 Concluding Remarks

Usability testing has begun to flourish. The number of laboratories in operation is growing steadily. In addition, the number of articles appearing in the professional literature has increased dramatically over the last ten years. Many of these articles describe new techniques and tools (Hackman and Biers, 1992; Prasse, 1990).

Other articles have been less enthusiastic about the procedure. Specifically, some authors have expressed concerns about potential subject and procedural biases (Cordes 1992; Sweetland, 1988), while others have questioned the reliability and validity of the data (Holleran, 1991). Issues such as these merit consideration. Usability testing is a relatively new procedure, and although it shows much promise, it should continue to be scrutinized. It is also important to remember that usability testing is only one of many methods available to designers, engineers, and human factors practitioners to improve the quality of their products. It may not be appropriate in every situation, nor should it be viewed as a substitute for scientific research.

Perhaps, the most important contribution this testing procedure offers is the ability to take an abstract concept like "usability" and make it more tangible. Designers can define and measure important characteristics of usability and evaluate the effects of their decisions with greater precision. Moreover, it provides a way to demonstrate how human factors efforts can reduce costs and improve sales. For that reason alone, usability testing may prove to be the most valuable tool in the human factors tool kit.

11.0 Biography

Dr. Mark W. Scerbo began his research career at Bell Laboratories in 1980 where he studied human-computer interaction. He received a Ph.D. from the University of Cincinnati in 1987 in the area of experimental psychology. Upon graduating, he managed a human factors research laboratory at AT&T for three years. In 1990, he joined the faculty at Old Dominion University where he currently studies issues in human information processing and teaches courses in perception and human factors.

REFERENCES

Bennett, J.L. (1984). Managing to meet usability requirements: Establishing and meeting software development goals. In J. Bennett, D. Case, J. Sadelin, & M. Smith (Eds.) *Visual Display Terminals: Usability Issues and Health Concerns.* (pp. 161-184). Englewood Cliffs, NJ: Prentice-Hall.

Boehm, B.W., Gray, T.E., & Seewaldt, T. (1984). Prototyping versus specifying: A multiproject experiment. *IEEE Transactions on Software Engineering,*, 10, 290-302.

Carroll, J.M., & Mack, R.L. (1984). Learning to use a word processor: By doing, by thinking, and by knowing. In J.C. Thomas & M.L. Schneider, (Eds.) *Human Factors in Computer Systems.* Horwood: Ablex Publishing Co.

Chapanis, A. (1988). Some generalizations about generalization. *Human Factors,* 30, 253-267.

Cohen, J. (1988). *Statistical Power Analysis for the Behavioral Sciences* (2nd ed.). Hillsdale, NJ: Lawrence Erlbaum.

Cordes, R.E. (1992). Bias in usability studies: Is this stuff science? *Test & Evaluation Newsletter*, 7.2, 4-7.

Deming, W.E. (1986). *Out of the crisis.* Milwaukee, WI: ASQC Quality Press.

DePree, R.W. (1984). The long and short of schedules. *Datamation*, Jun. 15, 131-134.

Eason, K.D. (1984). Towards the experimental study of usability. *Behaviour and Information Technology*, 3, 133-143.

Ericsson, K.A., & Simon, H.A. (1980). Verbal reports as data. *Psychological Review*, 87, 215-251.

Flemming, T.E., Morrissey, S.J., & Kinghorn, R.A. (1992). Subjects in human factors: Who should they be? *Proceedings of the Human Factors Society 36th Annual Meeting* (pp. 1241-1243). Santa Monica, CA: Human Factors Society.

Good, M., Spine, T.M., Whiteside, J., & George, P. (1986). User-derived impact analysis as a tool for usability engineering. *CHI'86 Proceedings* (pp. 241-246). New York: ACM.

Gould, J.D. (1988). How to design usable systems. In M. Helander (Ed.) *Handbook of Human-Computer Interaction* (pp. 757-789). Amsterdam: Elsevier (North Holland).

Gould, J.D., Boies, S.J., Levy, S., Richards, J.T., & Schoonard, J. (1987). The 1984 olympic message system: A test of behavioral principles of system design. *Communications of the ACM*, 30, 758-769.

Gould, J.D., & Lewis, C. (1983). Designing for usability: Key principles and what designers think. *CHI'83 Proceedings,* (pp. 50-53). New York: ACM.

Grimes, J., Ehrlich, K., & Vaske, J. (1986). User interface design: Are human factors principles used? *SIGCHI Bulletin*, 17, 22-26.

Grudin, J. (1989). The case against user interface consistency. *Communications of the ACM*, 32, 1164-1173.

Hackman, G.S., & Biers, D.W. (1992). Team usability testing: Are two heads better than one? *Proceedings of the Human Factors Society 36th Annual Meeting* (pp. 1205-1209). Santa Monica, CA: Human Factors Society.

Hayes, B.I. (1992). *Measuring Customer Satisfaction: Development and Use of Questionnaires*. Milwaukee, WI: ASQC Quality Press.

Hewett, T.T., & Meadow, C.T. (1986). On designing for usability: An application of four key principles. *CHI'86 Proceedings,* (pp. 247-252). New York: ACM.

Holleran, P.A. (1991). A methodological note on pitfalls in usability testing. *Behaviour & Information Technology*, 10, 345-357.

Johnson, G.I., Clegg, C.W., & Ravden, S.J. (1989). Towards a practical method of user interface evaluation. *Applied Ergonomics*, 20.4, 255-260.

Kantowitz, B.H. (1992). Selecting measures for human factors research. *Human Factors*, 34,387-398.

Karat, C. (1990). Cost-benefit analysis of usability engineering techniques. *Proceedings of the Human Factors Society 34th Annual Meeting* (pp. 839-843). Santa Monica, CA: Human Factors Society.

Karat, C. (1992). Cost-justifying human factors support on software development projects. *Human Factors Society Bulletin*, 35, (11), 1-4.

Keppel, G. (1982). *Design & Analysis: A Researcher's Handbook* (2nd ed.). Englewood Cliffs, NJ: Prentice-Hall.

Klein, G.A., & Brezovic, C.P. (1986). Design engineers and the design process: Decision strategies and human factors literature. *Proceedings of the Human Factors Society 30th Annual Meeting* (pp. 771-775). Santa Monica, CA: Human Factors Society.

Laws, J.V., & Barber, P.J. (1989). Video analysis in cognitive ergonomics: A methodological perspective. *Ergonomics*, 32, 1303-1318.

Mantei, M.M., & Teorey, T.J. (1988). Cost/benefit analysis for incorporating human factors in the software lifecycle. *Computing Practices*, 31, 428-439.

Meister, D. (1985). *Behavioral Analysis and Measurement Methods.* New York: John Wiley & Sons.

Neal A.S., & Simons, R.M. (1984). Playback: A method for evaluating the usability of software and its documentation. *IBM Systems Journal,* 23, 82-96.

Nickerson, R.S. (1992). *Looking Ahead: Human Factors Challenges in a Changing World.* Hillsdale, NJ: Lawrence Erlbaum Associates, Inc.

Peters, T.J., & Austin, N.K. (1985). *A Passion for Excellence.* New York: Warner Books.

Philips, B.H., & Dumas, J.S. (1990). Usability testing: Identifying functional requirements for data logging software. *Proceedings of the Human Factors Society 34th Annual Meeting* (pp. 295-299). Santa Monica, CA: Human Factors Society.

Powers, M.J., Adams, D.R., & Mills, H.D. (1984). *Computer Information Systems Development: Analysis and Design.* Cincinnati: South-Western Publishing Co.

Prasse, M.J. (1990). The video analysis method: An integrated approach to usability assessment. *Proceedings of the Human Factors Society 34th Annual Meeting* (pp. 400-404). Santa Monica, CA: Human Factors Society.

Ravden, S.J., & Johnson, G.I. (1989). *Evaluating Usability of Human-Computer Interfaces: A Practical Method.* Chichester: Ellis Horwood.

Riche, M.F. (1989). Psychographics for the 1990s. *American Demographics*, 7, 24-31, 53-54.

Scerbo, M.W. (1991) Usability engineering approach to software quality. *ASQC Annual Quality Congress Transactions*, (pp. 726- 733). Milwaukee, WI: ASQC Quality Press.

Scerbo, M.W., & Fisk, A.D. (1990). Understanding strategic usage of 'on-the-job' reference aids. *Applied Ergonomics*, 21.1, 25-32.

Schrier, J.R. (1992). Reducing stress associated with participating in a usability test. *Proceedings of the Human Factors Society 36th Annual Meeting* (pp. 1210-1214). Santa Monica, CA: Human Factors Society.

Smith, L.L. (1987). Whyfore human factors? *Human Factors Society Bulletin*, 30(2), 6-7.

Sweetland, J.H. (1988). Beta tests and end-user surveys: Are they valid? *Database*, 11.1, 27-32.

Virzi, R.A. (1992). Refining the test phase of usability evaluation: How many subjects is enough? *Human Factors*, 34, 457-468.

Weimer, J., & Banks, W. (1992). *Effective Computer Display Design*. Englewood Cliffs, NJ: Prentice-Hall.

Wells, W.D. (1974). Life style and psychographics: Definitions, uses, and problems. In W.D. Wells (Ed.) *Lifestyle and Psychographics*. Chicago: American Marketing Assn.

Whiteside, J., Bennett, J., & Holtzblatt, K. (1988). Usability engineering: Our experience and evolution. In M. Helander (Ed.) *Handbook of Human-Computer Interaction* (pp. 791-817). Amsterdam: Elsevier (North Holland).

Wixon, D., & Whiteside, J. (1985). Engineering for usability: Lessons from the user derived interface. *CHI'85 Proceedings,* (pp. 144-147). New York: ACM.

Wright, P.C., & Monk, A.F. (1991). A cost-effective evaluation method for use by designers. *International Journal of Man-Machine Studies*, 35, 891-912.

Appendix 4-1
Sample User Profile

User Identification Number: 167-54-3437
System or Subsystem: Remote Sales System
Interviewer: Jon Weimer, Ph.D.

Date: 1/30/92
Job: Field Ordering

Physical Characteristics:

Age: 41-50 — Gender: Female — Color Blindness: No

Visual Acuity: 20/20 Corrected (Bifocals) — Hearing: Normal

Physically Challenged: No

Education:

Reading Level: 9th to 12th grade — Education: College Graduate

Mathematical Level: Algebra — Native Language: Spanish

Work-related Experience:

Job Category: Sales (Pharmaceutical Sales) — Typing Skill: "Hunt & Peck"

Experience With Targeted Task/Job: Expert (in sales)

Computer Experience:

General Computer Experience: Novice — Years Using Computers: 0-1

Computer Literacy: Low

Specific Computer Activities: Data Entry & Manipulation

Applications Used: Spreadsheet

Operating Systems Used: GUI Operating System (e.g. Macintosh, Windows)

Hardware Used: Personal Computers

Sample User Profile (Page 2)

User Identification Number: 167-54-3437 Date: 1/30/92
System or Subsystem: Remote Sales System Job: Field Ordering
Interviewer: Jon Weimer, Ph.D.

Job Characteristics:

Target Job Category: Sales Typing Skill Required: None

Computer Experience Required by Job/Task: Expert

Computer Literacy Required by Task/Job: Intermediate

Specific Job/Task Activities: On-line Order Placement, Inventory Monitoring

Type of Application: On-line, Field Ordering System

Type of Operating Systems Used: Graphical User Interface (GUI)

Frequency of Computer Use Required to Perform Task/Job: High

Turnover Rate on Job/Task: High

Job/Task Structure: High (Ordering task is rigidly defined)

Job/Task Importance: High

Type of Job/Task Training Provided: Manual only

Design Recommendations:

A remote, notebook pc-based system, with a fax/modem and a GUI based operating system. The language employed in the system should be Spanish, and the system should include a GUI shell that will enable the user to maintain the GUI interface while logged onto the mainframe via a modem connection. Training should be required to increase the literacy of the user, while the system should concomitantly be redesigned to require less literacy on the part of future users.

Appendix 4-2

Blank User Profile Worksheet[2] [3]

User Identification Number: ____________________ Date: ________
System or Subsystem: ____________________ Job: ________
Interviewer: ____________________

Physical Characteristics: (Check all that apply)

Age:
- ❑ 18-30
- ❑ 31-40
- ❑ 41-50
- ❑ > 50

Gender:
- ❑ Male
- ❑ Female

Color Blindness:
- ❑ No
- ❑ Protanope (Red Insensitive)
- ❑ Deuteranope (Green Insensitive)

Visual Acuity:
- ❑ 20/20
- ❑ 20/20 Corrected
  - ❑ Monofocals
  - ❑ Bifocals
  - ❑ Other ________________
- ❑ Legally Blind

Hearing:
- ❑ Normal
- ❑ Impaired ________________
- ❑ Corrected ________________

Physically Challenged:
- ❑ No
- ❑ Yes ________________________________

Education: (Check all that apply)

Reading Level:
- ❑ Less that 5th grade
- ❑ 5th to 9th grade
- ❑ 9th to 12th grade
- ❑ Collegiate

Education:
- ❑ Didn't graduate high school
- ❑ High School Graduate
- ❑ Technical Degree
- ❑ College Graduate

Mathematical Level:
- ❑ Arithmetic
- ❑ Geometry/Trigonometry
- ❑ Algebra
- ❑ Calculus

Native Language:
- ❑ English
- ❑ Spanish
- ❑ Japanese
- ❑ Other ________________

---

[2]This blank worksheet may be reproduced for your personal use in the practice of your craft, your research, or for classroom purposes. It may not be reproduced for any reasons other than those listed above.

[3]When referencing Appendices 4-1 and 4-2, please reference Weimer and Banks (1992). For additional information on each of the categories on the worksheet, see pages 42-49 of Weimer and Banks (1992).

User Profile Worksheet (Page 2)

User Identification Number: ____________________ Date: ________
System or Subsystem: ____________________ Job: ________
Interviewer: ____________________

Work-related Experience: (Check all that apply)

Job Category:

- ❑ Skilled Laborer
- ❑ Clerical
- ❑ Sales
- ❑ Professional/Technical
- ❑ Manager
- ❑ Executive

Typing Skill:

- ❑ None
- ❑ "Hunt and Peck" (< 40 wpm)
- ❑ Average Touch Typist (40-54 wpm)
- ❑ Good Touch Typist (55-89 wpm)
- ❑ Skilled Touch Typist (90-134 wpm)
- ❑ Expert Touch Typist (>135 wpm)

Experience With Targeted Task/Job:

- ❑ None
- ❑ Novice (requires supervised help to complete)
- ❑ Intermediate (occasionally requires help on more difficult parts)
- ❑ Expert (self-reliant, resource for others)

Computer Experience: (Check all that apply)

General Computer Experience:

- ❑ None
- ❑ Novice (requires supervised help)
- ❑ Intermediate (occasionally requires help)
- ❑ Expert (self-reliant, resource for others)

Years Using Computers:

- ❑ 0-1
- ❑ 1-3
- ❑ 3-5
- ❑ > 5

Computer Literacy:

- ❑ None (never used a computer and has no computer knowledge)
- ❑ Low (little or no knowledge of jargon, low level activities only, data entry)
- ❑ Intermediate (some knowledge of jargon & hardware, moderate activities such as word-processing and basic software installation)
- ❑ Advanced (proficiency with jargon, adept at learning new software and hardware, can perform most software and hardware installation tasks, could be a resource for others.

User Profile Worksheet (Page 3)

User Identification Number: ____________________ Date:________
System or Subsystem: ____________________ Job: ________
Interviewer: ____________________

Computer Experience: (Continued)

Specific Computer Activities:

❑ Data Entry ❑ Data Manipulation ❑ System Monitoring
❑ Programming ❑ Word-processing ❑ Other ______________

Applications Used:

❑ Graphics System ❑ Databases ❑ CAD/CAM
❑ Spreadsheet ❑ Word-processing ❑ Programming Language
❑ Other ____________________

Operating Systems Used:

❑ Command Language Operating System (e.g., DOS, UNIX, VM/CMS)
❑ Natural Language Operating System (e.g., SQL)
❑ GUI Operating System (e.g., Macintosh, Windows)

Hardware Used:

❑ Personal Computers ❑ Workstations ❑ Minicomputers
❑ Mainframes

Job Characteristics: (Check all that apply)

Target Job Category:	Typing Skill Required By Task/Job:
❑ Skilled Laborer	❑ None
❑ Clerical	❑ "Hunt and Peck" (< 40 wpm)
❑ Sales	❑ Average Touch Typist (40-54 wpm)
❑ Professional/Technical	❑ Good Touch Typist (55-89 wpm)
❑ Manager	❑ Skilled Touch Typist (90-134 wpm)
❑ Executive	❑ Expert Touch Typist (>135 wpm)

User Profile Worksheet (Page 4)

User Identification Number: ____________________ Date: ________
System or Subsystem: ____________________ Job: ________
Interviewer: ____________________

Job Characteristics: (Check all that apply)

Computer Experience Required by Job/Task:

- ❑ None
- ❑ Novice (requires supervised help)
- ❑ Intermediate (occasionally requires help)
- ❑ Expert (self-reliant, resource for others)

Computer Literacy Required by Task/Job:

- ❑ None (never used a computer and has no computer knowledge)
- ❑ Low (little or no knowledge of jargon, low level activities only, data entry)
- ❑ Intermediate (some knowledge of jargon and hardware components, moderate activities such as word-processing and basic software installation)
- ❑ Advanced (proficiency with jargon, adept at learning new software and hardware, can perform most installation tasks, can be a resource for others.

Specific Job/Task Activities:

❑ Data Entry ❑ Data Manipulation ❑ System Monitoring
❑ Programming ❑ Word-processing ❑ Other ____________

Type of Application:

❑ Graphics ❑ Databases ❑ CAD/CAM
❑ Spreadsheet ❑ Word-processing ❑ Programming Language
❑ Other ______________________________

Type of Operating Systems Used:

- ❑ Command Language Operating System (e.g., DOS, UNIX, VM/CMS)
- ❑ Natural Language Operating System (e.g., SQL)
- ❑ GUI Operating System (e.g., Macintosh, Windows)

Frequency of Computer Use Required to Perform Task/Job:

- ❑ None
- ❑ Low (Computer occasionally needed for infrequent tasks)
- ❑ Moderate (Computer used for infrequent to moderately frequent tasks)
- ❑ High (Computer required to perform the entire job)

User Profile Worksheet (Page 5)

User Identification Number: ____________________ Date:________
System or Subsystem: ____________________ Job: ________
Interviewer: ____________________

Job Characteristics: (Check all that apply)

Turnover Rate on Job/Task:

- ❑ None
- ❑ Low (< 10% within the last year)
- ❑ Medium (10%-20% within the last year)
- ❑ High (> 20% within the last year)

Job/Task Structure:

- ❑ None (Worker-defined structure)
- ❑ Low (Job is basically unstructured with a few structured component tasks)
- ❑ Moderate (Part of the job is structured and part is unstructured)
- ❑ High (Entire job is rigidly defined, e.g., by operating procedures)

Job/Task Importance:

- ❑ Low (Optional, small unrequired component of overall job productivity)
- ❑ Moderate (Required as part of overall job productivity)
- ❑ High (Failure to perform task results in financial loss or loss of life, e.g., monitoring a nuclear reactor, pilot monitoring altitude, etc.)

Type of Job/Task Training Provided:

- ❑ None (Optional, small un-required component of overall job productivity)
- ❑ Manual only
- ❑ Elective Formal (i.e., classroom lecture)
- ❑ Mandatory Formal
- ❑ Manual-based Tutorial
- ❑ Computer-based Tutorial
- ❑ Interactive-Video Tutorial

Appendix 4-3
Selecting an Eye Tracker That's Right For You

Some systems use electro-oculography or the application of an instrumented contact to the user's cornea (for more information, see Young & Sheena, 1975), some use head mounted optics, while others use optics attached to the room rather than the user. The most commonly used methods for measuring eye movement are listed in Table 4-6.

Table 4-6. Eye Tracking Methods

Method	Application	Characteristics	Referent
Electro-oculography (EOG)	Occular dynamics	High bandwidth Eyes can be closed Inexpensive Drift problems Obtrusive Very poor position accuracy	Head
Limbus tracking	Occular dynamics Point of gaze Scan path measuring	High bandwidth Inexpensive Poor vertical accuracy Obtrusive Head gear slip errors	Headgear (most common implement.)
Corneal reflex	Occular dynamics Point of gaze Scan path measuring	High bandwidth (If not video based) Very large head gear slip errors	Headgear (most common implement.)
Pupil-to-corneal reflex vector	Point of gaze Scan path measuring	Low bandwidth Unobtrusive Accurate Minimal head gear slip errors	Headgear or room-based optics
Double Purkinjie image	Occular dynamics flicks and drifts Point of gaze Image stabilization on retina	Very high accuracy High bandwidth Very obtrusive Complex to operate	Room
Contact lens	Occular dynamics Minute eye movement (including flicks, drifts, and tremors)	Best available High bandwidth Invasive Obtrusive Uncomfortable Limited range	Head

Issues and Questions to Consider.

The cost of eye trackers make them a non-trivial investment, while the diversity of available technologies makes selecting one complex. To make your decision easier, Table 4-7 lists some of the more important questions you need to answer before deciding if eye tracking is right for you, while Table 4-8 describes the level of functioning needed for certain tasks.

Table 4-7. Questions to Ask When Considering Eye Tracking

1. Is determination of point-of-gaze on a scene sufficient, or do you require the measurement of eye motion dynamics (e.g., nystagmus, saccadic velocity, etc.)?
2. Over what range (field of view) do you want to measure the user's eye motion? With respect to a screen, room, head, or outdoors (e.g., in a car, See Chapter 7)?
3. With what accuracy must the point-of-gaze on the scene or eye position be measured with respect to head position?
4. Is it acceptable to restrict the movement of the user's head? To what extent? (i.e., chin rest, bite bar, high backed chair?).
5. Is free head motion required? If so, how much? How important is it that the system be unobtrusive?
6. What form of data do you require? A videotape of the user's point-of-gaze only? A digital record for later analysis?
7. What level of performance do you require (See Figure 4-5).

(Adapted From ASL, 1990)

Table 4-8. Eye Tracker Performance Requirements for Certain Tasks

Task Category	Performance Requirements
Measure point of regard or scan path for off-line analysis	Accuracy = 1° visual angle Sample rate = 60 Hz
Real time control using point of regard (selection of switches, control of display, etc.)	Transport delay ≤ 50 msec Sample rate = 60 Hz Accuracy = 1° visual angle
Study saccadic velocity profiles, nystagmus	Sample rate ≥ 240 Hz Linearity ≤ 5% Resolution = 0.25°
Study flicks, drifts	Sample rate ≥ 240 Hz Linearity ≤ 5% Resolution = 10 arc minutes
Measure tremor	Sample rate ≥ 1000 Hz Linearity ≤ 5% Resolution = 1 arc second
Stabilize image on retina	Accuracy = 2 arc minutes Sample rate ≥ 240 Hz Transport Delay ≤ 10 msec

(Adapted From ASL, 1990)

Chapter 5
Aerospace Techniques

Christopher D. Wickens
University of Illinois, Aviation Research Lab

1.0 Introduction

The array of research techniques in aerospace psychology is as broad as the set of tasks and environmental conditions that confront the pilot or air traffic controller. In brief, as shown in Figure 5-1, the pilot can be thought of as an individual who (a) is part of a perceptual-motor loop designed to keep the plane aloft and move it through the air from point to point (flight control), (b) must follow a series of discrete procedures involving perceptual, cognitive and motor activity to meet goals of safety, (c) makes a series of discrete judgments and decisions whose outcomes represent a balance of risk minimization and efficiency, (d) must communicate and coordinate with others either in the air or on the ground, a coordination that is often described as "cockpit resource management." There are two general "states" of pilot experience that pervade the task domains described above and are of great relevance to aerospace research: The workload experienced by the pilot and his/her situation awareness of their current surrounding.

Furthermore, the characteristics of pilot performance in these activities can be influenced by four generic factors: (a) the skills learned by the pilot, (b) the abilities possessed by the pilot, (c) the level of stress in the pilot's environment, and (d) the degree of automation of the equipment with which the pilot works. Finally, the collection of issues relevant to research methodology must consider the four types of <u>remediation</u> that are generally available to address human factors problems and limitations in the aerospace system: equipment design, task design, training, and selection.

Together, all of these dimensions of the aerospace system provide a complex framework for discussing research methodology issues. In the following pages, I first describe the major domains of aerospace psychology research, considering the four meta-tasks of flight control, procedures, judgment and resource management, and the two experiences of workload and situation awareness. Within each of these six areas, I consider some key research issues. I then consider the influences of training, ability, stress, and automation. Finally, I conclude with a lengthy discussion of the costs and benefits of the different research techniques as applied to the areas listed. While my emphasis will be on the pilot, I also shall consider the air traffic controller as appropriate.

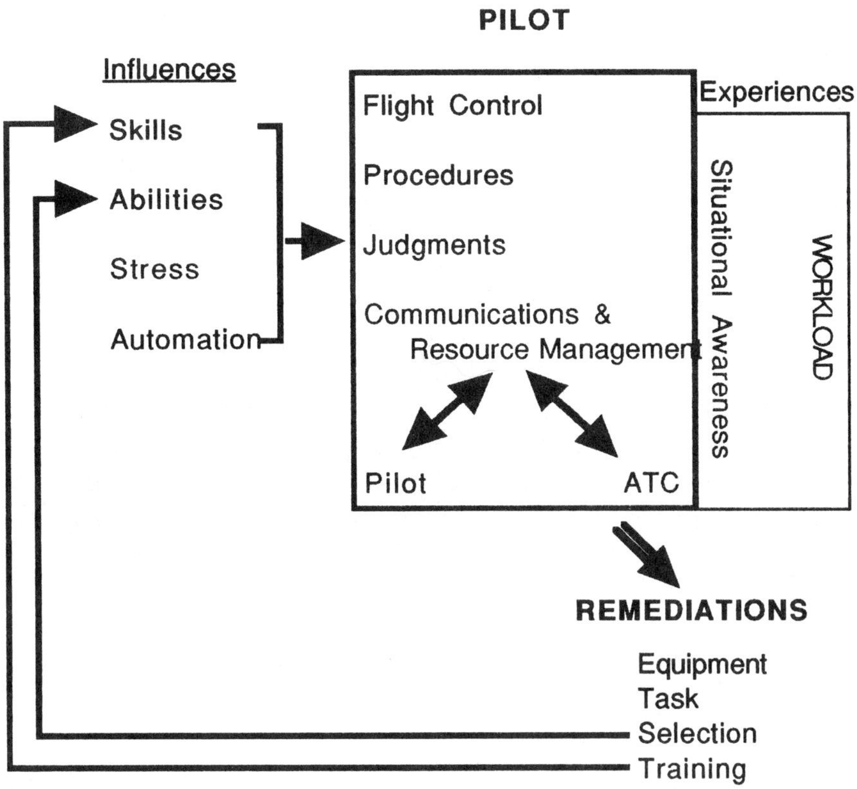

Figure 5-1. The Pilot as a System Component

2.0 Research Domains

2.1 Flight Control

Since the beginning of flight in 1903 there has been one invariant task confronting the pilot. The pilot must control and keep airborne a dynamic, closed-loop, complex, multidimensional system that may be unstable (helicopters) or sluggish (the jumbo jet). Control may depend upon a variety of changing information sources (flight instruments and the visual world), and may depend upon satisfying a variety of sometimes conflicting goals (e.g., minimize flight path deviation vs. minimize control activity). Two generic methodological approaches have been taken towards research in this domain. One has been the study of traditional tracking tasks in which emphasis has been placed on the task variables that contribute to error off of the flight path (Poulton, 1974; Kelley, 1968; Wickens, 1992a). The other has been from the perspective of control systems engineering, because of the closed-loop dynamics of the aircraft. Here the effort has been jointly to develop models of the pilot-vehicle as a closed loop system, and to quantify aspects of pilot performance that are more complex than error but equally critical, such as closed-loop instability (pilot-induced oscillations) or performance optimization (McRuer & Jex, 1967; McRuer, 1980; Baron, 1988; Wickens, 1986; Jex & Clement, 1979). Much of the early research in this domain was carried out at the Flight Dynamics Laboratory of Wright-Patterson Air Force Base and a rich source of research papers may be found in the 20 volumes of the NASA sponsored Annual Conference on Manual Control.[1]

The two approaches are by no means mutually exclusive, but are distinguished in part by the added technical language and training required by control theory that may thwart a full understanding by many who would otherwise wish to apply these concepts. The research that has been carried out from both perspectives has been employed to address three generic areas. The first of these concern the issues of how to design better displays to support flight control, including the development of flight path predictors (Kelley, 1960; Jensen, 1981; Grunwald, 1984; Wickens, Haskell, & Harte, 1989), integrated 3D displays (Barfield, Rosenberg, Han, & Furness, 1992; Haskell & Wickens, 1993; Ellis, McGreevy, & Hitchcock, 1987; Nataupsky & Crittendon, 1988), and electronic maps (Aretz, 1991; Kuchar & Hansman, 1993; Harwood & Wickens, 1991). One important research trend in this area has been the focus on incorporating appropriate ecological cues into the display (Owen, 1990; Weinstein & Wickens, 1992) by understanding how we naturally judge our position and orientation on the ground and in the air (Gibson, 1979). Note: Much of the research on aviation displays is supported by the broad line of research on the pilot's visual capabilities and limitations, (O'Hare & Roscoe, 1990).

Second, issues of manual control are highly relevant to performance measurement. Some of those issues are:

1. How do you determine when a student pilot is ready to move from a flight simulator to the aircraft?
2. How is flying performance affected by alcohol or drugs?
3. How does the introduction of a particular aspect of aircraft technology influences a pilot's flying performance?
4. How might an on-line intelligent system might monitor a pilot's workload (Eggemeier, Biers, Wickens, Andre, Vreuls, Billman, & Schueren, (1990)?

However, the underlying question is: How can we distinguish "good" from "bad" levels of flying performance (or normal vs. degraded levels)? Judicious application of control theory can augment the large amount of "raw" information gathered from flight simulation. Which measures should be chosen to discriminate high vs. low levels of stress, fatigue, expertise or workload remains a critical research question (Kelly, 1988; Gawron, Schiflett, Smiller, Slater, & Ball, 1990; Vreuls & Obermayer, 1985; McDaniel & Rankin, 1991)?

Finally, research on flight performance is directly relevant to issues of automation. Indeed, one of the major goals of automation is to relieve the

[1]Most of these proceedings have been published as technical manuals by the NASA Ames Research Center, Moffett Field, CA.

pilot of many of the high frequency, continuous demands of "inner loop" flight control, and allow instead, the focus of the pilot's attention to remain on the more cognitive issues of navigational planning. The models and measures of performance when the pilot is fully "in the loop" of unautomated aircraft provide critical baselines that can be compared with the flight performance of the more automated aircraft (Curry, Kleinman, & Hoffman, 1977; Baron & Levison, 1977) and the workload and situation awareness of the pilot.

2.2 Procedures

Many of the activities that the pilot must perform depend much less on monitoring the continuous changes in visual cues and controlling the continuous parameters of flight, than on remembering to perform discrete procedures correctly at appropriate times. These include activities like turning on (or off) autopilots, switching fuel tanks, calling air traffic control, retrieving flight information, or programming on-board computers. Research in this area has been approached from two somewhat different viewpoints. One has focused directly on the pilot-vehicle interface, considering the traditional issues of "knobs and dials" psychology (compatibility, control layout; O'Hare & Roscoe, 1990), as well as the issues associated with the human factors of emerging technology (e.g., voice control, touch panels).

The second view has focused, at a more cognitive level, on the pilot's "mental model" of the whole flight task. Hence, this domain makes close contact with many emerging issues in cognitive psychology. For example:

1. How are tasks managed and monitored (Adams, Tenny, & Pew, 1991; Funk, 1991)?
2. How is information managed in an increasingly electronic domain (Rogers, 1991; Ricks, Jonsson, & Rogers, 1994)?
3. What causes the pilot to forget to perform key operations (Nagel, 1988; Edwards, 1990)?
4. How should these factors guide the structure of electronic data bases (Roske-Hofstrand & Paap, 1986; Ricks, Jonsson, & Rogers, 1994; Seidler & Wickens, 1992)?.
5. How should the pilot's overall mental model of the task demands and the airspace guide the creation of "human-centered automation" (Billings, 1991)?

2.3 Pilot Judgment and Decision Making

Pilot judgment has become a major research area in aviation psychology. Diehl (1991a) has estimated that over 50% of accident-related human errors in military and civil aviation, from 1987-89, were due to faulty decision making in the cockpit. However, the introduction of progressively greater levels of automation will in no way alleviate the pilot's responsibilities for good decision and judgment. In fact, a critical aspect of pilot judgment, whether or not to follow the advice of automated devices, will become even more prevalent. On the one hand, the research questions are straight forward. Why do pilots sometimes make poor decisions (Orasanu, 1993), and how can training and systems be designed to improve this (Diehl, 1991b)? On the other hand, the research methodologies in this area have been far more difficult to apply. Despite the plethora of evidence for poor judgment from accident and incident reports (see Section 3.4 & 3.5), it is often difficult in hindsight to determine what causal factors were specifically responsible for the poor judgment. Furthermore, it is sometimes even difficult to determine if the judgment really was a bad one in foresight. Often we make the best judgment with the knowledge at hand--but the probabilistic nature of the world may conspire to produce an unfortunate outcome, given the inherent risky nature of flying.

In general, the research themes addressing pilot judgment have focused on three areas: (1) trying to "model" and describe the characteristics of pilot judgment (O'Hare, 1992; Orasanu, 1993; Wickens & Flach, 1988) and determining the extent to which there may be differences between novices and experts (Wickens, Stokes, Barnett, & Hyman, 1993; Klein, 1993; McKinney, 1993);[2] (2) assessing the ways in which the technology of either information display (Jonsson, 1991; Adelman, Cohen, Bresnick, Chinnis, Jr., & Laskey, 1993) or "intelligent" expert systems can improve and support pilot judgment (McNeese, 1986; Lizza & Friedlander, 1988); and (3) developing means of training good pilot judgment (Prince, Hartel, & Salas, 1993; Trollip & Jensen, 1991) and establishing the successfulness of such techniques (Diehl, 1991a).

2.4 Crew Interactions and Cockpit Resource Management

The pilot is a member of a team, often consisting of other members of the flight deck and always consisting of one or more air traffic controllers. This team membership is sometimes augmented to include an automated device or two. How well this team works together depends critically on the flow of information between the members. However, this flow is far from perfect. For example, a recent survey has revealed that over half of all pilot errors result from failures of information transfer (Nagel, 1988). Hence, one important focus of aerospace psychology research addresses the cause of such errors, and communications media that can prevent or reduce errors of communication. One major thrust here has been a focus on the digital channels of communication that will become available between pilot and controller in the new "data link" system (Kerns, 1991). The strength of the data link system is derived from the replacement (or augmentation) of traditional voice channels, by a new keyboard system that resolves communications ambiguity. However, the data link's interface also contains potential weaknesses that must be addressed by further research.

---

[2] An important issue here is the extent to which the quality of pilot judgment depends only partially, rather than primarily, upon domain knowledge of flying, and therefore is or is not, respectively, affected by the sorts of biases and heuristics influencing decision making in other areas (Wickens & Flach, 1988).

Second, as a result of accident analysis in the 1960's, and seminal papers by Ruffell-Smith (1979), Foushee (1984), and Kanki, Folk, and Irwin (1991), the aviation research community began to realize the critical role of social psychological factors (e.g., flight crew personality, leadership, and communication style). These studies suggested that strict militaristic top-down command structure was not ideal (Foushee & Helmreich, 1988). Cockpit Resource Management (CRM), how a crew manages its "resources," is an outgrowth of the application of social psychology to the cockpit environment (Wiener, Kanki, & Helmreich, 1993). In practice, the area has primarily focused on the management of human resources (e.g., delegating responsibilities, insuring adequate communications), but the concept applies to computer (i.e., automation) resources as well. A major focus of recent research in this area has been the evaluation of the success of CRM training programs (Alkov & Gaynor, 1991; Helmreich & Wilhelm, 1991).

2.5 States Experienced in Pilot Performance

The research domains in aerospace psychology outlined by the four areas described above must be augmented by research in a set of five other relevant domains. Two of these may be best described as states that are experienced by the pilot. The other three may be considered as influences on the pilot.

2.5.1 The workload experience. Since the 1970's there has been an extensive and productive program of research on pilot workload (Wierwille, 1979; Moray, 1979; O'Donnell & Eggemeier, 1986; Roscoe, 1987; Wierwille & Eggemeier, 1993; Hart & Wickens, 1990). Workload may be conceptualized as a state that the pilot experiences, when meeting the demands of tasks imposed by the system, given the limited mental resources that he or she has available. If workload is too low, then boredom or complacency sets in and critical monitoring functions may be degraded (Parasuraman et al., 1993). Such condition may result from excessive automation. If, on the other hand, workload is excessive, then at least three things can happen to performance:

1. Performance in high workload tasks may degrade (e.g., flight path error will increase if the system dynamics are difficult to control or if there is heavy turbulence).

2. The operator may "shed" tasks (e.g., fail to monitor altitude)

3. The operator may shift strategies to perform these tasks differently (Adams, Tenny, & Pew, 1991) (e.g., the air traffic controller may cease providing separate guidance to individual aircraft and deal with "clusters" of aircraft instead (Sperandio, 1978)).

The obvious importance of knowing when these kinds of changes may occur, has driven workload researchers to follow two parallel lines of investigation:

1. Identifying and quantitatively modeling what task, environmental, or personal (i.e., training) variables (and what level of those variables) will drive the operator's workload above a hypothetical "red line" at which these changes begin to happen, or will drop the operator below the baseline of low workload at which complacency and boredom may set in (Huey & Wickens, 1993).
2. Determining the ideal techniques for measuring operator workload (O'Donnell & Eggemeier, 1986; Wierwille & Eggemeier, 1993; Roscoe, 1987), and establishing the relative costs and benefits of measures based upon performance (Roscoe, 1987), physiology (Metalis, 1991; Sirevaag, Kramer, Wickens, Reisweber, Strayer, & Grenell, 1993), or operator opinion (Corwin, 1992; Hart & Wickens, 1990).

2.5.2 The situation awareness experience. Recent research interest in the concept of situation awareness has followed a trend very similar to the research interest in workload. Indeed there are many parallels between these two domains (Wickens, 1992b; Sarter & Woods, 1991; Endsley, 1993). Like workload, situation awareness may be considered an experienced state that cannot be directly measured (or at least there is no consensus on how to do so), but which has a direct impact on performance. As with workload, there have been several definitions of situation awareness offered. Loosely, the concept refers to the operator's awareness of the transient changes in the state of the aircraft systems, location, and environment, such that he or she will be able to react appropriately if unexpected circumstances require a quick response to those states. The concept has relevance both to training -- the objective of training operators how to acquire and maintain good situation awareness -- and to system design: How can display design and other task factors support a high level of situation awareness?

As with workload, situation awareness has also stimulated major research thrusts regarding the appropriate way to assess the state (e.g., performance, subjective ratings; recall Sarter & Woods, 1991). Interestingly, situation awareness and workload are sometimes related to each other, in a reciprocal fashion, through the "fulcrum" of automation. That is, automation, which is often designed to reduce workload by requiring the operator to do less, may degrade situation awareness by pulling the operator out of the loop, thereby curtailing an engagement in which the necessary cognitive activity had previously <u>forced</u> the operator to remain current with system states. Whether in the management of aircraft systems and flight paths for the pilot (Billings, 1991), or in offering assistance to the air traffic controller in scheduling a conflict resolution, a major challenge of research on human-centered automation is to establish ways of reducing workload to appropriate levels, without destroying situation awareness.

2.6 Influences on Operator Performance

2.6.1 Training influences. In contrast to workload and situation awareness, which may best be described as states that are experienced and have performance consequences, training is clearly a manipulation or influence (an independent variable) that can be imposed upon the pilot (or controller), to bring about learning, or the acquisition of the skills necessary to fly[3]. Research in pilot training has had a long history (Ritchie & Michael, 1955; Telfer & Biggs, 1988) and the heaviest focus of this research has been on training the perceptual motor skills necessary to continuously maneuver the craft through the airspace, and bring it to a touchdown at landing (Lintern, 1991; Lintern & McMillan, 1993). More recent in its implementation have been the efforts to train procedures (Cordell, 1991), judgment and resource management skills (Alkov & Gaynor, 1991; Diehl, 1991a; Orasanu, 1993; O'Hare, 1992; O'Hare & Roscoe, 1990), as well as the use of low cost trainers to teach generic skills of attention control (Gopher, Weil, & Bareket, 1992).

Inherent in nearly all facets of training research is the transfer of training paradigm, in which the effectiveness of a given training strategy (e.g., the computer or flight simulator) is evaluated by comparing how well students trained by that strategy transfer to a more realistic or expensive environment (e.g., the aircraft itself). A host of important issues associated with the appropriate measure of transfer effectiveness, and the role of training device costs, have been addressed by Roscoe and his colleagues (O'Hare & Roscoe, 1990; Roscoe, 1980).

A somewhat different approach to training has involved efforts to model or describe the differences between novice and expert performances in skills such as flight control (Crosby & Parkinson, 1979), pilot judgment (Wickens et al., 1993), or air traffic control (Redding, Cannon, & Seamster, 1992). Given the ability to characterize the features that discriminate the two groups, training efforts can then be focused on altering, in the novice, the specific features that differ from the expert. However, the success of this approach remains to be validated.

2.6.2 Ability influences. Pilots show large individual differences in their skills, but the issue of why these differences emerge remains far from clear. How much do individual differences relate to differences in the level or efficiency of training rather than differences in fundamental perceptual, motor or cognitive abilities? To the extent that the latter influences are substantial, then it should be feasible to predict who will have better flight proficiency on the basis of relatively generic tests. If such prediction is successful, and can be used to better screen admission to a flight training program, then such tests should have the potential to greatly reduce the extensive costs of training pilots or controllers who later will drop from the

[3]For more information on researching training effectiveness, see Chapter 14.

training program--or to avoid the dangers of pilots who do not drop, but possess inadequate skills to fly. The research issues in this area have naturally, focused on the predictive validity to a flight environment of various context-free tests or tests whose administration does not heavily depend upon flight experience (e.g., Carretta, 1989, 1991, 1992; Delaney, 1992). In these research efforts a number of tests are typically administered to students who possess little or no flight experience, and then correlations are obtained between performance on those tests and later assessments of flight proficiency. Such criterion assessments range from the more specific (e.g., flight path error on simulators), to the more global (e.g., class rank at graduation or number of hours until solo flight). Considerable research interest has been focused on the relative merits of paper and pencil tests vs. computer-based testing (Delaney, 1992; Carretta, 1989). A recurrent finding in such studies is that the longer the delay between testing and criterion assessment, the lower is the predictive validity, raising a second fundamental research issue: Are the subject's abilities themselves changed by their flight experience or does the nature of the abilities underlying flight change as experience is gained (Alvares & Hulin, 1972; Hanisch & Hulin, 1992).

2.6.3 Influences of automation. A final general theme of aerospace research concerns the influences of varying kinds and levels of automation on performance of the pilot-controller-aircraft system. In the aircraft, levels of automation have ranged from simple autopilots (Ephrath & Young, 1981) to checklist procedures (Degani & Wiener, 1993) to complex flight planners (Layton, Smith, & McCoy, in press) and decision aids (McNeese, 1986). Some research continues to focus on the issue of "which is best: pilot or computer" (the so-called "John Henry" question), particularly regarding complex intelligent processes (e.g., ATC conflict resolution, pilot decision aiding). However, three further issues seem to have received greater recent attention because of their relevance to the issue of "human-centered automation."

The first issue relates to situation awareness as discussed above, and addresses the concern that excessive automation can pull the operator so far "out of the loop" that he or she loses a sense of the current state of the system; a necessary awareness if appropriate human intervention is suddenly required. A corollary is the concern over the long term loss of skill that may result from the pilot or controller being taken "out of the loop" (Hughes, 1989; Stix, 1991; Wiener, 1985, 1989). At issue is how to retain some operator involvement "in the loop" without defeating the very purposes for which the automation was typically intended; namely, to reduce the workload demands on the human operator.

The second issue concerns the optimum level of automation. Automation is designed to reduce workload. However, too much automation lowers workload <u>below</u> its optional set point, so that boredom may set in. Hence, how can automation be <u>adaptively</u> or flexibly implemented so that it assumes responsibility for tasks when workload becomes excessive, but turns those tasks back to the operator when demands are reduced, thereby preserving the operator's participation in the loop? This is the issue of "adaptive automation" (Rouse, 1988; Parasuraman et al. 1993), and raises many important research questions involving the closed-loop interactions between humans and machines (Wickens, 1992a; Hancock & Chignell, 1989).

The third emerging issue concerns that of "trust" and is inherent in the fact that few automated devices can function with 100% perfection. (Neither can humans after all!). Trust in the automation's reliability should therefore be calibrated to the actual level of system reliability, but often it is not. Operators may become complacent (too trustful) if automation is too successful (and therefore fail to detect its failures; Parasuraman et al., 1993), or they may become overly critical and distrustful of slightly fallible automation, which may be performing tasks at, or exceeding, the level that would be characteristic of their own manual performance (Lee & Moray; 1992; Liu, Fuld, & Wickens, in press, 1993).

3.0 Research Methods

Transcending all the nine domains described in the previous pages (four meta tasks, two states, three influences), are a host of alternative methods that may be brought to bear in addressing the relevant issues. This section outlines both the methods and the dependent variables that are typically employed in aerospace human factors, and concludes by addressing an important statistical issue in applied research.

3.1 The Experimental Method

3.1.1 The experimental environment. The environment in which experiments have been carried out has ranged from the basic laboratory computer, to the flight simulator, to the aircraft itself. The benefits of the lab computer are, of course, the wider availability of subjects (no flight experience is often required for laboratory experiments), the cheaper cost of most research, and the greater degree of control that can be exerted on the subjects' strategies and behavior. Furthermore, because of their greater numbers, it is generally easier to get nonflying participants to engage in laboratory research than the skilled pilots who are typically required for simulator and aircraft research. Hence, you must consider the tradeoff between the greater statistical power usually available in laboratory research, and the greater face validity of simulator or in-flight research.

Because such tradeoffs exist, it seems apparent that no single environment is "right." Basic laboratory research with nonpilots can be highly informative on such perceptual-motor issues as control layout, sensory processing, display design and so forth, as long as the experimental tasks don't require excessive levels of domain knowledge, and the experimenter remains keenly aware of the potential limits of generalization to the aircraft environment. Furthermore, there may be certain issues, such as the examination of radically redesigned instrumentation concepts, in which past flight experience may be a hindrance to making an objective comparison. Clearly an optimal experimental research strategy is to try to address the same issues at all three levels of realism, capitalizing on the strengths of each and identifying the consistency of findings across all three to draw the firmest underlying conclusions. Such, for example, describes the pragmatic research efforts to develop predictive flight displays (Kelley, 1960; Jensen, 1981; Wickens, Haskell, & Harte, 1989; Grunwald, 1984), or to understand strategic task management (Funk, 1991; Madhavan & Funk, 1993; Chou & Funk, 1993).

If you are a laboratory researcher, who does not have access to full flight simulation capabilities, an important issue is the choice of what lower fidelity simulation should be used. To some extent this choice depends upon the domain of research being investigated. If one is examining procedural or judgment issues, (i.e., tasks that are not directly integrated with the control of the aircraft), then it often becomes important to simulate the information processing (i.e., perceptual, cognitive and motor) demands of flying, even if one does not try to accurately model the flight dynamics themselves. This can often be done with a straightforward two axis tracking task, that has the appropriate first order lags incorporated, and an input that demands corrective action, but is not of excessively high, and unrealistic bandwidth (Wickens, 1992a). On the other hand, these demands can often be more accurately simulated by the available technology of low cost, PC-based flight simulators, such as the MS Flight Simulator manufactured by Microsoft Corporation, or the ELITE.[4] While these commercial products have some advantage over tracking tasks in terms of their fidelity, their use is sometimes hampered by the fact that the software within the system is proprietary, and cannot be modified in ways that meet certain experimental demands (e.g., increasing the workload demands of flying in certain experimentally controlled ways).

For research within the flight control domain, addressing such issues as display design, or flight handling qualities, the issue becomes more tricky. Simple tracking tasks no longer adequately mimic the qualitative demands of the flying task in a way that allows reliable assessment of the impact of experimental manipulations. At the same time, the experimental need to modify and manipulate characteristics of the flight control loop generally precludes the use of commercially available simulator software. Hence the solution is usually to invest considerable time to develop a low level, "customized" simulator package, using more advanced computer graphics, and some knowledge of the nature of flight dynamics.

---

[4]The Microsoft simulator is a PC-based simulator for a visual environment (i.e., it provides a graphics view of the world beyond the cockpit. It is manufactured by Microsoft Corporation, Bothell, WA (800/227-4679) and markets for approximately $60. The ELITE simulator is designed for instrument flight, presenting no outside scene. It is marketed by Azure Soft in San Jose, CA (408/947-1121), and markets for around $600.

3.1.2 The experimental design. Much aerospace psychology research has employed the "traditional" factorial designs, and accompanying analyses of variance[5], so familiar to the experimental psychologist (Keppel, 1988). However, it is often critical in aerospace research, to extend the generalities of conclusions drawn from research across a wide range of operational conditions (e.g., different workload levels, flight phases). Furthermore, the design parameters of the systems under evaluation are themselves numerous. Thus, the employment of "traditional" factorial designs are at times unwieldy at best and often of "cells" with a linear increase in the number of factors or factor levels to be considered. Alternative approaches based on response surface methodology (Simon & Roscoe, 1984), have been effectively employed to determine the sensitivity of performance, to many dimensions of system variables simultaneously. While such approaches cannot easily reveal interactions between variables, they offer a very efficient way of assessing which variables exert the greatest influence on performance.

3.1.3 Dependent variables. Aviation psychology research has of course depended in part upon the traditional experimental variables of response time (RT) and accuracy for discrete tasks (e.g., identifying an airborne target), and flight path deviations (error) for continuous ones. An important methodological issue concerns the differences between response time and accuracy. Psychologists working in the controlled laboratory sometimes emphasize significant RT effects of a magnitude (10-100 msec) so small that it has little operational relevance, and the effects may "evaporate" or be swamped by other sources of variance, once the tight controls of the laboratory are released, and the phenomenon in question is examined in the simulator or the aircraft. Furthermore, it is not always easy to convince the operational community of the importance of, say, a hundred millisecond delay in getting something done in the cockpit. However, arguments based upon error rate (e.g., the prediction of higher error rate with one system than another) generally have considerably greater credibility with the operational community. In this regard it is important to bear in mind the explicit tie that can be made between response time and errors: System designs that lead to slower rates of information processing often be inclined to be more error prone (Pachella, 1974; Wickens, 1992a).

Subjective opinion data have also remained a popular dependent variable in aviation psychology. Scores of studies have evaluated such opinions in the areas of workload, as noted above, where they have often played a key role in design decisions (Corwin, 1992; Ruggiero & Fadden, 1987), and opinion ratings are beginning to show up to assess such concepts as situation awareness (Selcon, Taylor, & Koritsas, 1991) or automation complacency (Singh, Molloy, & Parasuraman, in press). Easy and cheap as opinion ratings are to collect, caution must be exercised in relying too much on their message, because of the dangers that they may "dissociate" from

[5]For more information on ANOVA and response surface designs, see Chapter 3.

performance (Yeh & Wickens, 1988). For example, subjective ratings may suggest that one design is superior, when in fact, a different design offers the better performance (Bailey, 1993). Subjective opinion scales may fail to reveal aspects of performance carried out automatically, they may be biased against novel systems in favor of more familiar ones, and if the opinion scales are designed in such a way that ratings on one end of the scale suggest inadequacies of pilot performance, the tendencies of pilots to bias their ratings away from that end are apparent.

One recent application of subjective opinion methodology has been to the understanding of mental models of complex systems, through multidimensional scaling (Derrick, 1988). Here operators rate the subjective similarity between entities under consideration, and from such data it is possible to understand how these entities are associated in the operator's "mental model" of the system (e.g., fighter pilot combat systems, Roske-Hofstrand & Paap, 1986; air traffic control systems, Weitzman, 1993). Such techniques provide useful guidelines for structuring user-friendly computer systems by which the pilot or controller may interface with these entities.

Physiological measures of stress and arousal have also been mentioned briefly in the context of workload. While there has been much written about their value in assessing the intensive aspects of these experiences (e.g., Wierwille & Eggemeier, 1993; O'Donnell & Eggemeier, 1986), equally valuable information may be provided by their ability to reveal the qualitative strategies of performance. Particularly useful measures here include eye movement and scanning measures, which can reveal the pattern of information access and utilization (Harris & Christhilf, 1980; Hameluck, 1991; Sirevaag et al.; 1993; Ellis & Stark, 1986) and potential strategic differences between novices and experts (Harris & Spady, 1985). Event related brain potentials (Kramer, Sirevaag, & Braune, 1987) also offer a methodology for mapping the allocation of human attention across information sources which eye movements may fail to discriminate (e.g., between the auditory and visual channel, between two foveal sources, or between foveal and peripheral vision).

A final dependent variable is one that describes the qualitative patterning of responses across tasks. What characteristics for example describe the shift of performance from one task to another, or unexpectedly long episodes of performance on one task, at the exclusion of others (Raby & Wickens, 1990). Discrete time series analyses (Sanderson, Scott, Johnston, Mainzer, Watanabe, & James, in press) and Markov analyses (T. Wickens, 1982) can provide useful ways of quantifying these qualitative characteristics of performance in the multitask environment typical of the flight deck.

3.2 Protocol Analysis[6]

Experimental approaches have as their goal the manipulation of conditions and the observation of effects, usually characterized by quantitative results. In contrast, protocol analysis typically involves the more qualitative analysis of streams of verbal (and sometimes nonverbal) behavior in an effort to gain insight into the processing and reasoning of the operator, whether pilot or controller (Kanki, Lozito, & Foushee, 1989; Sanderson, McNeese & Zaff, in press). Sometimes the natural discourse of the operator may be augmented by requests to verbalize what are otherwise internal cognitive processes.

3.3 Surveys

Recently surveys of the user community have provided valuable information regarding user satisfaction with certain products (e.g., aircraft automation) and with potential causes of dissatisfaction (Hughes, 1989; Wiener, 1989; James, McClumpha, Green, Wilson, & Belyavin, 1991). The advantage of such techniques is obvious in terms of the ability to sample large proportions of the population remotely. The disadvantages are inherent both in the biases that may influence the results, when those who respond are not fully representative of the population, and in the fact that user attitudes do not fully reflect system capabilities (e.g., there may be initial user resistance to "new technology" and therefore negative attitudes toward that technology). Still, the value of surveys in aerospace research has been very nicely demonstrated by the seminal study of glass cockpit technology carried out by Wiener (1989; Hughes, 1989). Here documented was both the overall satisfaction with the new technology and the identification of some specific concerns regarding the technology (e.g., reprogramming the interface, the concerns about the long term skill degradation). Knowledge of these concerns has provided a useful impetus for further improvement of the technology.

3.4 Incident Analysis

Surveys can identify potential problems with particular aspects of a system. When actual problems develop in actual operation, creating an incident, the latter may be documented by formal incident analysis procedures. The most familiar of these procedures to the aerospace community is the Aviation Safety Reporting Systems (ASRS) data base, coordinated by NASA (Nagel, 1988; Rosenthal & Reynard, 1991), which documents vast numbers of incidents reported by both pilots and controllers, and attempts, through actuarial data and follow-up interviews, to establish causal factors involved.[7]

---

[6]See Chapter 4, Section 7.4 for more information on verbal /think aloud protocols.

[4]Reports and information about services at ASRS may be obtained by writing to: The Office of the NASA Aviation Safety Reporting System, P.O. Box 189, Moffett Field, CA 94035-0189.

The ASRS is an extremely rich source of information and has been used to formally document specific problems in such areas as air traffic control communications (Nagel, 1988), visual clearance for approach (Monan, 1983), checklist operations (Degani & Wiener, 1993), geographical disorientation (Williams, Tham, & Wickens, 1993) and task management (Madhavan & Funk, 1993). Such documentation has been obtained as a result of follow-up analyses on collected incidents. Three major limitations of the current system as a research methodology may be identified however (Wickens & McCloy, 1993). First, in spite of the extreme care taken to guarantee anonymity of reporting, and immunity of the reporting pilot or controller from legal action, there are still biases in the class of pilots who will be likely to file a report (or in the classes of incidents that will or will not be likely to be reported). For example, commercial pilots, who have more to gain by the grant of immunity (because they have more to lose if the error is not self-reported, but noted by others), will be more likely to report, than will general aviation pilots. Incidents will be more likely to be reported if they occur in an environment in which the reporter believes that other pilots or controllers might also have noticed the incident.

A second limitation inherent in the ASRS system is that the language in which events are described (by the pilot or controller) is not necessarily the same language that psychologists needs to define causal relationships (e.g., "working memory overload," "task shedding"). Skilled ASRS personnel who do follow-up interviews, coupled with the appropriate key wording of incidents, address this problem to some extent. However, it is still not yet resolved in a fully satisfactory fashion and the solution to the problem may always be limited by a pilot's inability to appreciate and verbalize with precise accuracy the psychological causal factors in an incident.

The final limitation of the technique simply relates to the overwhelming volume of data. ASRS accumulates incidents at a rate of 30,000/year and there is simply no way that the staff is able to conduct the follow-up interviews on all (or even a majority) of these records in such a manner as to be able to provide an appropriate psychological description. Furthermore, fully user-friendly means of "exploring" the data base have not yet been developed. As such, it remains a data base that will, in the near future, probably be under-utilized relative to the wealth of potential information it contains.

3.5 Accident Reports

Where surveys identify problem areas, incident reports identify specific instances of problems and accidents typically reveal the confluence of a host of problems. Accidents (often referred to as mishaps) result when multiple defenses of the system break down (Reason, 1990). Accident prevention is, of course, a major -- if not <u>the</u> major -- objective of aerospace research. Hence in theory, accident or mishap analysis (Diehl, 1991b) can provide the most direct data point for understanding the cause of a breakdown in pilot or controller performance. Indeed accident analysis has been very illuminating in indicating system induced human factors problems related to memory failures (the Northwest Airlines Detroit crash in 1989), training and decision errors (the 1987 Air Florida crash at Washington National Airport), attentional tunneling (the Eastern Airlines Everglades crash in 1972) and a host of other performance limitations.[8] In spite of their potency value as <u>illustrations</u> of system-induced human frailties, accidents (and the consequent detailed accident analysis, Diehl, 1991a) have only limited usefulness as tools for understanding causal factors in aerospace human factors.

First, their frequency is extremely low compared to incidents and it is well known that valid statistical inferences are very difficult to draw on the basis of small sample sizes. As Diehl has noted, accidents are the mere "tip of the iceberg" whose identity is better revealed by studying the larger mass of incidents and hazards "under the water."

Second, as Reason (1990) has noted, accidents generally result from the coincidental breakdown of multiple elements, within a complex system. Many of these elements, such as inadequate training and maintenance, or poor attitudes toward safety, exist as initial conditions long before the critical "triggering event" occurs (e.g., the garbled communication or inappropriate action taken by the pilot or controller). Hence, it may be very difficult to go back after the fact and determine the critical causal events that were responsible for the accident, among the set of plausible candidates.

3.6 Modeling

The final research methodology is based on human performance modeling (Elkind, Card, Hochberg, & Huey, 1990; McMillan, Beevis, Salas, Strub, Sutton, & Van Breda, 1989). We often think of mathematical or computational models of human performance as an analysis technique (can I create a model to fit the data?). However, to the extent that models are <u>validated</u> with human performance data, they may equally well provide a research methodology for investigating pilot or controller performance. For example, the stability of flight dynamics of new generation of aircraft with the pilot "in the loop" can be evaluated in advance of expensive flight or simulator tests, by coupling mathematical equations of the flight dynamics, with control theory models of the human pilot (McRuer, 1980; Baron & Levison, 1977; Baron, 1988). The impact of automation on flight performance can be predicted from models of pilot performance with and without the automated element present (Curry et al., 1977), and the potential impact of system design changes can be predicted from computational or simulation models of workload or multiple task performance (Sarno & Wickens, in

---

[8]The National Transportation and Safety Board prepares accident report documents that can be purchased from the National Technical Information Service. However, more specific information regarding accidents, classes of accidents, or the identity of NTSB reports can be obtained by writing the NTSB Public Inquiries Branch, Office of Research and Engineering, NTSB, 490 L'enfent Plaza E, SW, Washington, D.C. 20594.

press). It is important to note however that such models are clearly only as useful and valid as the reliability and validity of the data that were used to validate them.

3.7 Literature Reviews.

Because of the diversity of areas that define the content of aerospace psychology research, it is difficult for any one research organization to fully master all the content of all domains, and the approaches characterized by all methodologies. Yet because of the interactive nature of the various influences on pilot performance, it becomes critically important that the effective researcher have an understanding of the diversity of research approaches and results, and hence, the vital importance of knowing the literature. There are indeed several important sources with which the researcher should be familiar. Three journals are particularly important: *Aviation, Space and Environmental Medicine*, the *International Journal of Aviation Psychology*, and the *Journal of Aviation / Aerospace Education and Research*. In addition, there are a series of less research-oriented magazines and journals, such as *Aviation Week and Space Technology*, *Airline Pilot*, and *Flight Safety*,

Several conferences also present relevant information. Most important here is the Bi-Annual Ohio State University *International Symposium on Aviation Psychology*, whose published proceedings provide a wealth of valuable information. The *Human Factors and Ergonomics Society Proceedings* also publishes several papers each year on aerospace psychology issues. Finally, there now exists a reasonable set of good textbooks in the area including O'Hare and Roscoe (1990), Hawkins (1993), Wiener and Nagel (1988), Edwards (1990), Trollip and Jensen (1991), Jensen (1989), and a book specializing on CRM by Wiener, Kanki, and Helmreich (1993).

3.8 Research Methodologies in Consort

Each methodology has its strengths and weaknesses, and the ideal solution to understanding causal factors in aerospace psychology (and remediating pilot-vehicle system deficiencies) will come from combining methodologies to focus on a given issue. Such a combination might allow accident analysis to identify the existence of a potential problem. Incident analysis and survey methods can then be used to reveal the problem's magnitude, prevalence, and suggested causes. Laboratory research can then be used to validate causal hypotheses suggested by incident analyses and to evaluate the efficacy of proposed remediating solutions (Figure 5-2). Long term statistical trends can then serve to provide a final validation of how successful the proposed solutions were on reducing accident rates (Diehl, 1991a; Alkov & Gaynor, 1991).

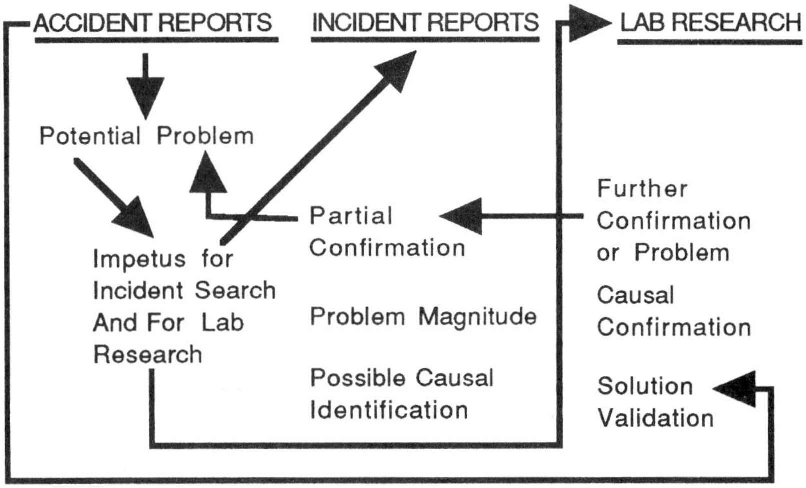

Figure 5-2. Methodologies Used in Consort

One example of this integration of methodologies is the approach taken to understanding breakdowns in cockpit task management, which has connected accident analysis (Funk, 1991) with ASRS reports (Madhavan & Funk, 1993; Williams et al., 1993) with simulator laboratory studies (Raby, Wickens, & Marsh, 1990; Chou & Funk, 1993; Laudeman & Palmer, 1993). Another example has been the concerted efforts to understand the automation-induced phenomenon of complacency and the resulting failure to intervene in a timely fashion when automation fails. This approach has tied accident analysis (the China Airlines incident, the Eastern Airlines Everglades crash, or the recent Airbus A320 crash) with incident analysis of performance in highly automated aircraft (Degani, Chappell, & Hayes, 1991), with extensive survey data (Wiener, 1989; Hughes, 1989; James et al., 1991) with experimental research in the environment of both the laboratory (Wickens & Kessel, 1981) and the flight simulator (Ephrath & Young, 1981; Wickens, Marsh, Raby, Straus, Cooper, Hulin, & Switzer, 1989).

4.0 Statistical Inference

Aerospace research, addressing any domain, and using whatever methodology, is ultimately intended to draw some inference about how the population of pilots or controllers behaves. Typically (and ideally) the researcher will rely upon some form of inferential statistics to establish his or her confidence that the conclusions drawn are "real," and will therefore generalize beyond the research environment. Classically, researchers (particularly those from the experimental laboratory tradition) have used a .05 criterion to assess the "confidence" in their results. A value equal to or less than .05 indicates the researcher's confidence that the observed effect was "real" (i.e., exists in the population of pilots) and could not have been due to chance or spurious factors. That is, there is less than one chance out of 20 that this kind of error in inference could happen. There is an implicit assumption that the 1 in 20 error--known as a "Type I" error--is a "bad thing" that shouldn't happen, and hence, results that have a higher probability of creating this error (e.g., 1 in 10) are typically reported as "not significant."

But a .05 significance level says nothing about the "power" of the test[9] (Cohen, 1977) to avoid the other kind of error (Type II): This is an error in which the researcher concludes that there is no effect in the real world of aviation, when in fact there really is, but the experiment doesn't reveal it. Thus, the .05 significance level does not consider the cost of making such a Type II error. However, the probability of these Type II errors is often high when the .05 criterion is used to avoid Type I errors, when the sample size of subjects is low (which may often be the case when highly skilled pilots are using expensive, hard to schedule simulators) and when the variance is high (which is often the case when data are collected in a complex "realistic" environment in which, by necessity, many controls on unwanted sources of variance must be lifted).

Are these circumstances of a high Type II error with a low Type I error acceptable? The answer to this question clearly depends on the relative <u>costs</u> of Type I and Type II errors, yet most aerospace research does not take these costs into account when deciding whether or not to call a given effect "significant." But let's consider two examples, one hypothesized and the other real, which reveal the importance of consideration of these costs. First, suppose a new technology or training methodology is evaluated that produces substantially safer flight conditions (for example, it reduces landing error by 20 feet, allows a 2 second faster response to emergencies or reduces procedural errors by 5%). However, the statistical test shows "no significant difference" ($p > .05$); this lack of significance could be attributable to the use of only 6-8 subjects, or high variance in the data. If the implicit recommendations of the statistical evaluation are then accepted (and the new technology is not implemented), but the power is low (e.g., a 40% chance of Type II error), then this would mean that there is a 40% chance that a real safety improvement is rejected. Is this desirable? Probably not.

As a second example, a similar analysis carried out by Harris (1991) was concerned about the power of statistical tests used to validate the inference that the fleet of two crew aircraft (pilot, copilot) was as safe as the earlier three crew aircraft cockpit (pilot, copilot, flight engineer). Earlier tests to validate this assertion had examined the statistical significance of the difference in accident rate between the two types of aircraft, and found there to be "no significant difference" despite the higher rate in the two crew

---

[9]It also says nothing of the size of the significant effect. Effect size can be easily computed with the following formula:

$$\hat{\omega}^2 = \frac{SS_{treatment} - \left(df_{error}\right)\left(MS_{error}\right)}{SS_{treatment} - MS_{error}}$$

For more information on the calculation and use of effect size, See Weimer and Hart (1989).

fleet. Harris then attempted to estimate the power of the statistical test and discovered it to be low enough that there was a 40% chance of a Type II error (i.e., that the difference really did exist, but was undetected). Harris asks whether this is the kind of error that should occur. Is it wise to commit an error that increases the possibility that an unsafe condition will go unidentified?

What then is the solution to Type II errors? Conventional solutions are to increase statistical power by running lots of subjects, and to control unwanted variables to keep the variance down. This is always a wise course of action, particularly when the experimental environment is complex. Between-subject designs and the use of analyses of covariance can also be useful in this regard. But it is also acceptable to consider lower levels of significance (e.g., $p = .10$), if the costs of Type II errors are high. There are, furthermore, even times when a formally adopted .10 criterion for significance will give the researcher greater confidence than 90% that the results are "real" and not due to chance. These are the circumstances when the researcher has prior reason to believe that the effect will be shown in the direction obtained (e.g., because of prior research; Hayes, 1968). (Such a "Bayesian" perspective on statistics of course requires the investigator to take the opposite approach and be less likely to accept as significant those findings that are surprising or contrary to prior expectations.)

In conclusion, there are no hard and fast answers to the issues of power in statistical inference. There is no clearly "right" or "wrong" approach. What is important however is for the investigator in aerospace psychology to have a good intuitive feel for the meaning of a p value (.05 significance), the existence of Type II errors, and the consequences to air safety that can result when decisions are taken on the basis of Type I errors without considering their Type II counterpart.

5.0 Summary

Aerospace human factors research is complex and diverse. The nine major research domains, when crossed with the seven research techniques, create a sizable matrix. Furthermore, the complexity of this matrix is amplified when the interconnectedness of the different domains is considered. For example, poor pilot decision making can lead pilots to conditions of high workload, poor situation awareness, and difficult flight control demands; poor resource management can create circumstances in which pilots are forced to use unfamiliar procedures under stress; automation changes in interface design can have direct effects on communications and resource management; and so on. This combination of complexity and diversity makes critical the need for the researcher to understand the breadth of the field through reading of the literature, and it is hoped that this chapter assists in providing that diversity.

As a final note, it is important to remain optimistic about the contributions that aerospace psychology research is making to air safety. On the one hand, accident statistics clearly point to the general trend toward safer flying over the last few decades. On the other hand, while human factors deficiencies still remain as the primary cause of serious accidents, it is also the case that information derived from human factors research is being increasingly accepted, valued and used, within the regulatory agencies, the accident investigation teams, and the aircraft manufacturers themselves. It is our hope that the current chapter will facilitate this information transfer.

6.0 Biography

Christopher D. Wickens is *currently* a professor of experimental psychology, head of the Aviation Research laboratory, and associate director of the Institute of Aviation at the University of Illinois at Urbana-Champaign. He received his A.B. degree from Harvard University in 1967 and his Ph.D. from the University of Michigan in 1974. He also served as a commissioned officer in the U .S. Navy from 1969 to 1972. He is currently involved in research at the Aviation Research Laboratory and Engineering Psychology Research Laboratory concerning principles of human attention, perception and cognition, and their relation to display processing, multitask performance, and navigation in complex systems. Dr. Wickens is a member and Fellow of the Human Factors Society, received the Society's Jerome H. Ely Award in 1981 for the best article in *Human Factors*, and the Paul M. Pitts Award in 1985 for outstanding contributions to the education and training of human factors specialists. In 1993 he received the Franklin Taylor Award from Division 21 of the American Psychological Association. He served as a Distinguished Visiting Professor at the Department of Behavioral Sciences and Leadership, U.S. Air Force Academy in 1983-84 and 1991-1992. He also served on the National Research Council Committee on Human Factors, and authored a college textbook titled *Engineering Psychology and Human Performance* (1992, 2nd ed.), co-authored a second college textbook titled, *Psychology*, and co-authored books titled, *Display Technology* and *Workload Transition*.

REFERENCES

Adams, M.J., Tenny, Y.J., & Pew, R.W. (1991). *Strategic Workload and the Cognitive Management of Advanced Multi-task Systems* (SOAR CSERIAC 91-6). Crew System Ergonomics Information Analysis Center, Wright-Patterson AFB, Dayton, OH.

Adelman, L., Cohen, M.S., Bresnick, T.A., Chinnis, J.O., Jr., & Laskey, K.B. (1993). Real-time expert system interfaces, cognitive processes, and task performance: An empirical assessment. *Human Factors,* 35(2), 243-262.

Alkov, R.A., & Gaynor, J.A. (1991). Attitude changes in Navy/Marine flight instructors following an aircrew coordination training course. *The International Journal of Aviation Psychology*, 1(3), 245-254.

Alvares, K.M., & Hulin, C.L. (1972). Two explanations of temporal changes in ability-skill relationships: A literature review and a theoretical analysis. *Human Factors*, 14, 295-308.

Aretz, A.J. (1991). The design of electronic map displays. *Human Factors*, 33(1), 85-101.

Bailey, R.W. (1993). Performance versus preference. *Proceedings of the 37th Annual Meeting of the Human Factors and Ergonomics Society* (Vol. 1, pp. 282-286). Santa Monica, CA: Human Factors and Ergonomics Society.

Barfield, W., Rosenberg, C., Han, S-H, & Furness, T. (1992). *A God's Eye (Exocentric) vs. Pilot's Eye (Egocentric) Frame-of-Reference for Enhanced Situational Awareness.* Interactive Computer Graphics and Human Factors Laboratory, Industrial Engineering, University of Washington.

Baron, S. (1988). Pilot control. In E. Wiener & D. Nagel (Eds.), *Human Factors in Aviation*. San Diego: Academic Press.

Baron, S., & Levison, W.H. (1977). Display analysis with the optimal control model of the human operator. *Human Factors,* 19, 437-457.

Billings, C.E. (1991). Toward a human-centered aircraft automation philosophy. *International Journal of Aviation Psychology*, 1(4), 261-270.

Carretta, T.R. (1989). USAF pilot selection and classification systems. *Aviation Space & Environmental Medicine*, 60, 46-49.

Carretta, T.R. (1991). Short-term reset reliability of an experimental U.S. Air Force pilot candidate selection test battery. *The International Journal of Aviation Psychology*, 2(3), 161-174.

Carretta, T.R. (1992). Understanding the relations between selection factors and pilot training performance: Does the criterion make a difference? *The International Journal of Aviation Psychology*, 2(2), 95-106.

Chou, C.-D., & Funk, K. (1993). Cockpit task management errors in a simulated flight mission. In R.S. Jensen & D. Neumeister (Eds.), *Proceedings of the 7th International Symposium on Aviation Psychology* (pp. 965-969). Columbus, OH: Dept. of Aviation, Ohio State University.

Cohen, J. (1977). *Statistical Power Analysis for the Behavioral Sciences* (Rev. ed.). New York: Academic Press.

Cordell, T.J. (1991). Computer-based procedural training. In R.S. Jensen (Ed.), *Proceedings of the 6th International Symposium on Aviation Psychology* (pp. 904-909). Columbus, OH: Dept. of Aviation, Ohio State University.

Corwin, W. H. (1992). In-flight and postflight assessment of pilot workload in commercial transport aircraft using the subjective workload assessment technique. *The International Journal of Aviation Psychology*, 2(2), 77-94.

Crosby, J.V., & Parkinson, S.R. (1979). A dual task investigation of pilots skill level. *Ergonomics*, 22, 1301-1313.

Curry, R.E., Kleinman, D.L., & Hoffman, W.C. (1977). A design procedure for control/display systems. *Human Factors*, 19, 421-436.

Degani, A., Chappell, S. L., & Hayes, M.S. (1991). Who and what saved the day? A comparison of traditional and glass cockpits. In R.S. Jensen (Ed.), *Proceedings of the 6th International Symposium on Aviation Psychology* (pp. 227-234). Columbus, OH: Dept. of Aviation, Ohio State University.

Degani, A., & Wiener, E.L. (1993). Cockpit checklists: Concepts, design, and use. *Human Factors*, 35(2), 345-360.

Delaney, H.D. (1992). Dichotic listening and psychomotor task performance as predictors of Naval primary flight-training criteria. *The International Journal of Aviation Psychology*, 2(2), 107-120.

Derrick, W. L. (1988). Dimensions of operator workload. *Human Factors*, 30(1), 95-110.

Diehl, A.E. (1991a). The effectiveness of training programs for preventing aircrew error. In R.S. Jensen (Ed.), *Proceedings of the 6th International Symposium on Aviation Psychology* (pp. 640-655). Columbus, OH: Dept. of Aviation, Ohio State University.

Diehl, A. (1991b). Human performance and systems safety considerations in aviation mishaps. *The International Journal of Aviation Psychology*, 1(2), 97-106.

Edwards, D.C. (1990). *Pilot - Mental and Physical Performance*. Ames, IA: Iowa State University Press.

Eggemeier, F.T., Biers, D.W., Wickens, C.D., Andre, A.D., Vreuls, D., Billman, E.R., & Schueren, J. (1990). *Performance Assessment and Workload Evaluation System: Analysis of Candidate Measures*. Final Technical Report (HSD-TR-90-023). Human Systems Division, Air Force Systems Command, Brooks Air Force Base, TX.

Elkind, J.I., Card, S.K., Hochberg, J., & Huey, B.M. (Eds.). (1990). *Human Performance Models for Computer-aided Engineering*. San Diego, CA: Academic Press.

Ellis, S.R., McGreevy, M.W., & Hitchcock, R.J. (1987). Perspective traffic display format and airline pilot traffic avoidance. *Human Factors, 29*, 371-382.

Ellis, S.R., & Stark, L. (1986). Statistical dependency in visual scanning. *Human Factors*, 28, 421-438.

Endsley, R. (1993). Situation awareness and workload: Flipsides of the same coin. In R.S. Jensen & D. Neumeister (Eds.), *Proceedings of the 7th International Symposium on Aviation Psychology* (pp. 906-911). Columbus, OH: Dept. of Aviation, Ohio State University.

Ephrath, A.R., & Young, L.R. (1981). Monitoring vs. man-in-the-loop detection of aircraft control failures. In J. Rasmussen & W.B. Rouse (Eds.), *Human Detection and Diagnosis of System Failures*. New York: Plenum Press.

Foushee, H.C. (1984). Dyads and triads at 35,000 feet: Factors affecting group process and aircrew performance. *American Psychology* , 39, 885-893.

Foushee, H.C., & Helmreich, R.L. (1988). Group interaction and flightcrew performance. In E. Wiener & D. Nagel (Eds.), *Human Factors in Aviation*. San Diego, CA: Academic Press.

Funk, K. (1991). Cockpit task management: Preliminary definitions, normative theory, error taxonomy, and design recommendations. *The International Journal of Aviation Psychology*, 1(4), 271-286.

Gawron, V.J., Schiflett, S.G., Miller, J.C., Slater, T., & Ball, J.F. (1990). Effects of pyridostigmine bromide on in-flight aircrew performance. *Human Factors*, 32, 79-94.

Gibson, J.J. (1979). *The Ecological Approach to Visual Perception*. Boston: Houghton-Mifflin.

Gopher, D., Weil, M., & Bareket, T. (1992). The transfer of skill from a computer game trainer in actual flight. *Proceedings of the 36th Annual Meeting of the Human Factors Society* (pp. 1285-1290). Santa Monica, CA: Human Factors Society.

Grunwald, A.J. (1984). Tunnel display for four-dimensional fixed-wing aircraft approaches. *Journal of Guidance, Control, and Dynamics*, 7(3), 369-377.

Hameluck, D. (1991). Relationship between mental models and scanning behavior during instrument approaches. In J.S. Jensen (Ed.), *Proceedings of the 6th International Symposium on Aviation Psychology* (pp. 939-944). Columbus, OH: Dept. of Aviation, Ohio State University.

Hancock, P.A., & Chignell, M.H. (Eds). (1989). *Intelligent Interfaces: Theory, Research, and Design*. Elsevier Science Publishers B.V. (North Holland).

Hanisch, K.A., & Hulin, C.L. (1992). *What Changes Occur During Complex Skill Acquisition?* (Final Technical Report). Armstrong Laboratory, Manpower and Personnel Research Division, Brooks AFB, TX.

Harris, D. (1991). The importance of the Type II error in aviation safety research. In E. Farmer (Ed.), *Stress and Error in Aviation* (pp. 151-157). Brookfield, VT: Avebury Technical.

Harris, R.L., & Christhilf, D.M. (1980). What do pilots see in displays? In G. Corrick, E. Hazeltine, & R. Durst (Eds.), *Proceedings of the 24th Annual Meeting of the Human Factors Society*. Santa Monica, CA: Human Factors Society.

Harris, R.L., & Spady, A.A. (1985). Visual scanning behavior. *Proceedings of the NAECON National Aerospace and Electronics Conference*. Dayton, OH.

Harwood, K., & Wickens, C.D. (1991). Frames of reference for helicopter electronic maps: The relevance of spatial cognition and componential analysis. *International Journal of Aviation Psychology*, 1, 5-23

Hart, S.G., & Wickens, C.D. (1990). Workload assessment and prediction. In H.R. Booher (Ed.), *MANPRINT: An Approach to Systems Integration* (pp. 257-296). New York: Van Nostrand Reinhold.

Haskell, I.D., and Wickens, C.D. (1993). Two- and three-dimensional displays for aviation: A theoretical and empirical comparison. *International Journal of Aviation Psychology*, 3(2), 87-109.

Hawkins, F.H. (1993). *Human Factors in Flight* (2nd ed.). Brookfield, VT: Ashgate Pub. Co.

Hayes, W. L. (1968). *Statistics for Psychologists*. New York: Holt, Reinhart, & Winston.

Helmreich, R.L., & Wilhelm, J.A. (1991). Outcomes of crew resource management training. *The International Journal of Aviation Psychology*, 1(4), 287-300.

Huey, M.B., & Wickens, C.D. (Eds.). (1993). *Workload Transition: Implications for Individual and Team Performance*. Washington, D.C.: National Academy Press.

Hughes, D. (1989 August). Glass cockpit study reveals human factors problems. *Aviation Week & Space Technology*, 32-35.

James, M., McClumpha, A., Green, R., Wilson, P., & Belyavin, A. (1991). Pilot attitudes to flight deck automation. *Proceedings of the 33rd Annual Meeting of the Human Factors Society* (pp. 107-111). Santa Monica, CA: Human Factors Society.

Jensen, R.S. (1981). Prediction and quickening in perspective displays for curved landing approaches. *Human Factors*, 23, 333-364.

Jensen, R.S. (Ed.). (1989). *Aviation Psychology*. Brookfield, VT: Gower. **not in text**

Jex, H.R. & Clement, W.F. (1979). Defining and measuring perceptual-motor workload in manual control tasks. In N. Moray (Ed.), *Mental Workload: Its Theory and Measurement* (pp. 125-177). New York: Plenum Press.

Jonsson, J.E. (1991). The role of behavioral decision theory for cockpit information management. In R.S. Jensen (Ed.), *Proceedings of the 6th International Symposium on Aviation Psychology*, 1 (pp. 72-77). Columbus, OH: Dept. of Aviation, Ohio State University.

Kanki, B.G., Lozito, S., & Foushee, H.C. (1989). Communication indices of crew coordination. *Aviation, Space, & Environmental Medicine*, 60, 56-60.

Kanki, B.G., Folk, V.G., & Irwin, C.M. (1991). Communication variations and aircrew performance. *The International Journal of Aviation Psychology*, 1(2), 149-162.

Kelly, M.J. (1988). Performance measurement during simulated air-to-air combat. *Human Factors*, 30 495-506.

Kelley, C.R. (1960). *Developing and Testing the Effectiveness of the Predictor Instrument* (TR-252-60-1). Office of Naval Research.

Kelley, C.R. (1968). *Manual and Automatic Control*. New York: Wiley.

Keppel, G. (Ed.). (1988). *Design and Analysis: A Researcher's Handbook* (2nd ed.). Englewood Cliffs, NJ: Prentice-Hall, Inc.

Kerns, K. (1991). Data-link communication between controllers and pilots: A review and synthesis of the simulation literature. *The International Journal of Aviation Psychology*, 1(3), 181-204.

Klein, G.A. (1993). A recognition-primed decision (RPD) model of rapid decision making. In G. Klein, J. Orasanu, R. Calderwood, & C. Zsambok (Eds.), *Decision Making in Action: Models and Methods*. Norwood, NJ: Ablex.

Kramer, A.F., Sirevaag, E. and Braune, R. (1987). A psychophysiological assessment of operator workload during simulated flight missions. *Human Factors*, 29, 145-160.

Kuchar, J.K., & Hansman, R.J., Jr. (1993). An exploratory study of plan-view terrain displays for air carrier operations. *International Journal of Aviation Psychology*, 3(1), 39-54.

Laudeman, I.V., & Palmer, E.A. (1993). Measurement of taskload in the analysis of aircrew performance. In R.S. Jensen & D. Neumeister (Eds.), *Proceedings of the 7th International Symposium on Aviation Psychology* (pp. 854-858). Columbus, OH: Dept. of Aviation, Ohio State University.

Layton, C., Smith, P.J., McCoy, E. (in press). Design of a cooperative problem-solving system for enroute flight planning: An empirical evaluation. *Human Factors*.

Lee, J.D., & Moray, N. (1992). Trust, control strategies and allocation of function in human-machine systems. *Ergonomics*, 35(10), 1243-1270.

Lintern, G. (1991). An informational perspective on skill transfer in human-machine systems. *Human Factors*, 33(3), 251-266.

Lintern, G., & McMillan, G. (1993). Transfer for flight simulation. In R. Telfer (Ed.), *Aviation Training and Instruction* (pp. 13-162). Aldershot, United Kingdom: Ashgate.

Liu, Y., Fuld, R., & Wickens, C.D. (in press, 1993). Monitoring behavior in manual and automated scheduling systems. *International Journal of Man-Machine Studies*, 39.

Lizza, C., & Friedlander, C. (1988). Pilot's associate: A forum for the integration of knowledge-based systems and avionics. *Proceedings of the IEEE National Aerospace and Electronics Conference* (NAECON), Dayton, OH.

Madhavan, D., & Funk, K. (1993). Cockpit task management errors in critical in-flight incidents. In R.S. Jensen & D. Neumeister (Eds.), *Proceedings of the 7th International Symposium on Aviation Psychology* (pp. 970-974). Columbus, OH: Dept. of Aviation, Ohio State University.

McDaniel, W.C., & Rankin, W.C. (1991). Determining flight task proficiency of students: A mathematical decision aid. *Human Factors*, 33(3), 293-308

McKinney, E.G. (1993). Flight leads and crisis decision making. *Aviation, Space, & Environmental Medicine*, 64(5), 359-362.

McMillan, G., Beevis, D., Salas, E., Strub, M.H., Sutton, R., & Van Breda, L. (Eds.) (1989). *Applications of Human Performance Models to System Design*. New York: Plenum Press.

McNeese, M.D. (1986). Humane intelligence: A human factors perspective for developing intelligent cockpits. *IEEE Aerospace and Electronics Magazine*, 1(7), 6-12.

McRuer, D. (1980). Human dynamics in man-machine systems. *Automatica*, 16, 237-253.

McRuer, D.T., & Jex, H.R. (1967). A review of quasi-linear pilot models. *IEEE Transactions on Human Factors in Electronics*, 8, 231

Metalis, S.A. (1991). Heart period as a useful index of pilot workload in commercial transport aircraft. *International Journal of Aviation Psychology,* 1(2), 107-116.

Monan, W.P., Cpt. (1983). *Cleared for the Visual Approach: Human Factor Problem Sin Air Carrier Operations* (NASA Contract Report 166573). Moffett Field, CA: NASA Ames Res. Ctr.

Moray, N. (Ed.). (1979). *Mental Workload: Its Theory and Measurement.* New York: Plenum Press.

Nagel, D.C. (1988). Human error in aviation operations. In E.C. Wiener & D.C. Nagel (Eds.), *Human Factors in Aviation*. San Diego, CA: Academic Press.

Nataupsky, M., & Crittendon, L. (1988). Stereo 3-D and non-stereo presentations of a computer-generated pictorial primary flight display with pathway augmentation. *Proceedings of the AIAA/IEEE 8th Digital Avionics Systems Conference*. San Jose.

O'Donnell, R.D., & Eggemeier, F.T. (1986). Workload assessment methodology. In K.R. Boff, L. Kaufman, & J. Thomas (Eds.), *Handbook of Perception and Human Performance: Volume II. Cognitive Processes and Performance* (pp. 42/1-42/49). New York: Wiley.

O'Hare, D. (1992). The "artful" decision maker: A framework model for aeronautical decision making. *The International Journal of Aviation Psychology*, 2(3), 175-192.

O'Hare, D., & Roscoe, S.N. (1990). *Flightdeck Performance: The Human Factor*. Ames, IA: Iowa State University Press.

Orasanu, J.M. (1993). Decision making in the cockpit. In E.L. Wiener, B.G. Kanki, & R.L. Helmreich (Eds). *Cockpit Resource Management* (pp. 137-172). San Diego: Academic Press.

Owen, D.H. (1990). Perception and control of changes in self-motion: A functional approach to the study of information and skill. In R. Warren & A. H. Wertheim (Eds.), *Perception and Control of Self-motion* (pp. 289-326). Hillsdale, NJ: Lawrence Erlbaum Associates.

Pachella, R. (1974). The use of reaction time measures in information processing research. In B.H. Kantowitz (Ed.), *Human Information Processing*. Hillsdale, NJ: Erlbaum.

Parasuraman, J., Molloy, R., & Singh, I.L. (1993). Performance consequences of automation-induced "complacency". *International Journal of Aviation Psychology*, 3(1), 1-24.

Poulton, E.C. (1974). *Tracking Skills and Manual Control*. New York: Academic Press.

Prince, C., Hartel, C., & Salas, E. (1993). Aeronautical decision making and consistency of crew behaviors: Implications for training. In R.S. Jensen & D. Neumeister (Eds.), *Proceedings of the 7th International Symposium on Aviation Psychology* (pp. 248-251). Columbus, OH: Dept. of Aviation, Ohio State University.

Raby, M., & Wickens, C.D. (1990). Planning and scheduling in flight workload management. *Proceedings of the 34th Annual Meeting of the Human Factors Society*. Santa Monica, CA: Human Factors Society.

Raby, M., Wickens, C.D., & Marsh, R. (1990). *Investigation of Factors Comprising a Model of Pilot Decision Making: Part 1. Cognitive Biases in Workload Management Strategy*. University of Illinois Institute of Aviation Final Technical Report (ARL-90-7/SCEEE-90-1). Aviation Research Lab.: Savoy, IL.

Reason, J. (1990) *Human Error*. Cambridge: Cambridge University Press.

Redding, R.E., Cannon, J.R., & Seamster, T. L. (1992). Expertise in air traffic control (ATC): What is it, and how can we train for it? *Proceedings of the 36th Annual Meeting of the Human Factors Society* (pp. 1326-1330). Santa Monica, CA: Human Factors Society.

Ricks, W.R., Jonsson, J.E., & Rogers, W.H. (1994). Cognitive representations of flight deck information attributes. *International Journal of Aviation Psychology*, 4, 1-28.

Ritchie, M.L., & Michael, A.L. (1955). Transfer between instrument and contact flight. *Journal of Applied Psychology*, 39, 145-149.

Rogers, W. (1991). Information management: Assessing the demand for information. In R.S. Jensen (Ed.), *Proceedings of the 6th International Symposium on Aviation Psychology* (pp. 66-71). Columbus, OH: Dept. of Aviation, Ohio State University.

Rosenthal, L.J., & Reynard, W. (Fall, 1991). Learning from incidents to avert accidents. *Aviation Safety Journal*, 7-10.

Roske-Hofstrand, R.J., & Paap, K. R. (1986). Cognitive networks as a guide to menu organization: An application in the automated cockpit. *Ergonomics*, 29, 1301-1311.

Roscoe, S.N. (1980). *Aviation Psychology*. Ames, IA: Iowa State University Press.

Roscoe, A. H. (1987). In-flight assessment of workload using pilot ratings and heart rate. In A.H. Roscoe (Ed.), *The Practical Assessment of Pilot Workload* (AGARDograph 282), (pp. 78-82). Neuilly Sur Seine, France, North Atlantic Treaty Organization, Advisory Group for Aerospace Research and Development.

Rouse, W.B. (1988). Adaptive aiding for human/computer control. *Human Factors*, 30, 431-443.

Ruffell-Smith, H.P. (1979). *A Simulator Study of the Interaction of Pilot Workload with Errors, Vigilance, and Decisions* (NASA TM 78482). Moffett Field, CA: NASA Ames Res. Ctr.

Ruggiero, F., & Fadden, D.M. (1987). Pilot subjective evaluation of workload during a flight test certification programme. In A.H. Roscoe (Ed.), *The Practical Assessment of Pilot Workload* (AGARDograph 282), (pp. 32-66). Neuilly Sur Seine, France, North Atlantic Treaty Organization, Advisory Group for Aerospace Research and Development.

Sanderson, P.M., McNeese, M., & Zaff, B. (in press). Knowledge elicitation and observation in engineering psychology: MacSHAPA and COGENT. *Behavior Research Methods, Instruments, and Computers*.

Sanderson, P.M., Scott, J.J.P., Johnston, T., Mainzer, J., Watanabe, L.M., & James, J.M. (in press). MacSHAPA and the enterprise of exploratory sequential data analysis (ESDA). *International Journal of Man-Machine Studies*.

Sarno, K.J., & Wickens, C.D. (in press). The role of multiple resources in predicting time-sharing efficiency: An evaluation of three workload models in a multiple task setting. *International Journal of Aviation Psychology*.

Sarter, N.B., & Woods, D.D. (1991). Situation awareness: A critical but ill-defined phenomenon. *The International Journal of Aviation Psychology*, 1(1), 45-58.

Seidler, K.S., & Wickens, C.D. (1992). Distance and organization in multifunction displays. *Human Factors*, 34, 555-569.

Selcon, S.J., Taylor, R.M., & Koritsas, E. (1991). Workload or situational awareness? TLX vs. SART for aerospace systems design evaluation. *Proceedings of the 35th Annual Meeting of the Human Factors Society* (pp. 62-66). Santa Monica, CA: Human Factors Society.

Simon, C.W., & Roscoe, S.N. (1984). Application of a multifactor approach to transfer of training research. *Human Factors*, 26(5), 591-612.

Singh, I.L., Molloy, R., & Parasuraman, R. (in press). Automation-induced "complacency": Development of the complacency potential rating scale. *The International Journal of Aviation Psychology*.

Sirevaag, E., Kramer, A., Wickens, C., Reisweber, M., Strayer, D. & Grenell, J. (1993). Assessment of pilot performance and workload in rotary wing helicopters. *Ergonomics*, 9, 1121-1140.

Sperandio, J.C. (1978). The regulation of working methods as a function of workload among air traffic controllers. *Ergonomics*, 21, 193-202.

Stix, G. (1991). Along for the ride? *Scientific American*, 265, 95-106.

Telfer, A., & Biggs, J. (1988). *The Psychology of Flight Training*. Ames Iowa: Iowa State University Press.

Trollip, S.R., & Jensen, R.S. (1991). Human Factors for General Aviation. Englewood, CO: Jeppesen Sanderson.

Vreuls, D., & Obermayer, R.W. (1985). Human-system performance measurements in training simulators. *Human Factors*, 27, 241-250.

Weimer, J., & Hart, A. (1989). Dollars and sense: Using effect size estimates to make design decisions. *Proceedings of the Human Factors Society's 33rd Annual Meeting*. (pp. 602-605). Santa Monica, CA: Human Factors and Ergonomics Society.

Weinstein, L.F., & Wickens, C.D. (1992). Use of nontraditional flight displays for the reduction of central visual overload in the cockpit. *International Journal of Aviation Psychology*, 2, 121-142.

Weitzman, D.O. (1993). Identifying information requirements for air traffic control problem solving. *Proceedings of the 37th Annual Meeting of the Human Factors and Ergonomics Society* (pp. 103-107). Santa Monica, CA: Human Factors and Ergonomics Society.

Wickens, T.D. (1982). *Models for Behavior: Stochastic Processes in Psychology*. San Francisco: Freeman.

Wickens, C.D. (1986). The effects of control dynamics on performance. In K. Boff, L. Kaufman, & J. Thomas (Eds.), *Handbook of Perception and Performance* Vol. II (pp. 39-1/39-60). New York: Wiley & Sons.

Wickens, C.D. (1992a). *Engineering Psychology and Human Performance* (2nd ed.). New York: Harper Collins.

Wickens, C.D. (1992b). Workload and situation awareness: An analogy of history and implications. *Insight*, 14(4), 1-3 (HFS Visual Performance Technical Group).

Wickens, C.D., & Flach, J. (1988). Human information processing. In E. Wiener & D. Nagel (Eds.), *Human Factors in Aviation* (pp. 111-155). San Diego: Academic Press.

Wickens, C.D., Haskell, I., & Harte, K. (1989). Ergonomic design for perspective flight-path displays. *IEEE Control Systems Magazine*, 9(4), 3-8. New York: IEEE.

Wickens, C.D., & Kessel, C., (1981) Failure detection in dynamic systems. In J. Rasmussen & W. Rouse (Eds.), *Human Detection and Diagnosis of System Failures*. New York: Plenum Press.

Wickens, C.D., Marsh, R., Raby, M., Straus, S., Cooper, R., Hulin, C.L., & Switzer, F. (1989). Aircrew performance as a function of automation and crew composition: A simulator study. *Proceedings of the 33rd Annual Meeting of the Human Factors Society*. Santa Monica, CA: Human Factors Society.

Wickens, C.D., & McCloy, T. (1993). ASRS and aviation psychology. In R.S. Jensen & D. Neumeister (Eds.), *Proceedings of the 7th International Symposium on Aviation Psychology* (pp. 1028-1030). Columbus, OH: Department of Aviation, Ohio State University.

Wickens, C.D., Stokes, A., Barnett, B., & Hyman, F. (1993). The effects of stress on pilot judgment in a MIDIS simulator. In O. Svenson & J. Maule (Eds.), *Time Pressure and Stress in Human Judgment and Decision Making* (pp. 271-293). New York: Plenum Press.

Wiener, E. L. (1985). Beyond the sterile cockpit. *Human Factors*, 27(6), 75-90.

Wiener, E. L. (1989). *Human Factors of Advanced Technology "Glass Cockpit" Transport Aircraft* (NASA Contractor Report 177528). Moffett Field, CA: NASA Ames Res. Ctr.

Wiener, E.L., Kanki, B.G., & Helmreich, R. L. (Eds.), (1993). *Cockpit Resource Management*. San Diego: Academic Press.

Wiener, E., & Nagel, D. (Eds.). (1988). *Human Factors in Aviation*. San Diego: Academic Press.

Wierwille, W.W. (1979). Physiological measures of aircrew mental workload. *Human Factors*, 21, 575-593.

Wierwille, W.W., & Eggemeier, F.T. (1993). Recommendations for mental workload measurement in a test and evaluation environment. *Human Factors*, 35(2), 263-282.

Williams, H.P., Tham, M., & Wickens, C.D. (1993). Workload management and geographic disorientation in aviation incidents: A review of the ASRS data base. In R.S. Jensen & D. Neumeister (Eds.), *Proceedings of the 7th International Symposium on Aviation Psychology* (pp. 960-964). Columbus, OH: Department of Aviation, Ohio State University.

Yeh, Y.Y., & Wickens, C.D. (1988). Dissociation of performance and subjective measures of workload. *Human Factors*, 30, 111-120.

Chapter 6
Aging Techniques

Lila Laux
U.S. West Technologies

1.0 Introduction

Why does a book entitled *Research Techniques in Human Engineering* need a chapter on aging? Aging effects are both pervasive and complex. Both the mean age and age distribution of the population are undergoing rapid and significant change worldwide (Johnston & Packer, 1987; Serow, Sly & Wrigley, 1990). In 1900, only one in 25 persons was over 65; today the ratio is between one in six and one in five (Small, 1987)! The average age of the population is increasing, as well, and the number of people aged 20-29 will actually decrease as we reach the twenty-first century (Johnston & Packer, 1987). At the same time, the population of people 85 and older is growing faster than any other segment of the population.

With increasing age there are changes in functional abilities. Thus, it has become increasingly important for human factors researchers to assess how age affects the way people interact with environments and devices such as those found in homes, workplaces, vehicles, medication packaging and medical equipment, recreational facilities, etc. The aging process affects essentially all of the person characteristics which have typically been the focus of human factors research:

1. performance characteristics, especially those related to sensation, anthropometry, biomechanics, and kinematics;
2. intellectual characteristics, including perception, cognition, decision making, and memory;
3. personality and attitudinal characteristics, including interests, fears, and beliefs; and
4. experience, including education, training, and hands-on practice.

Some trait differences associated with age are due to sensory and physiological changes (e.g. vision, size, strength), while others (e.g., willingness to use automated teller machines or experience with computers) are due to age cohort[1] differences.

But age-related changes are not universal and they are not uniform. Age affects some aspects of performance more than others, and people experience age-related changes in functioning at different rates. This means

[1] An age cohort is a group of people whose development took place within the same time period.

that functional age and chronological age, while strongly correlated, are not synonymous. It also means that members of older populations differ more from each other on many attributes than their younger counterparts.

Successive age cohorts may differ from each other in important and unpredictable ways. The average 70 year old of today is very different from the 70 year old of the Victorian era (e.g. he or she is certainly taller and more educated), and the 20 year old of today will probably differ at 70 from today's 70 year old. But, we cannot assume that it is generally true that the older person of the future will differ on all dimensions from today's older person.

Because of innovative technology and health enhancements, the average 70 year old of 2050 will probably be functioning much more adequately in their environment than is today's average 70 year old. But in spite of these changes, age-related changes will still occur which will negatively affect the ability to function. The goal of human factors research on aging is to identify where changes in design can reduce the negative impact of those functional losses, irrespective of the age at which they occur.

2.0 Who Are Older People?

One of the problems, which always arises when decisions are being made about including older subjects in human factors research, is defining "older." There is no accepted standard definition of older. In the Age Discrimination Acts of 1967 and 1978, older workers were defined as workers over 39, but national employment statistics define older as 45 or over (Smith, 1990). A glance through the special issue on aging of *Human Factors* (Vol. 32, No. 5, 1990) revealed that older was variously defined as 55 or over (Czaja, 1990), 61 or older (Kline, Ghali, Kline & Brown, 1990), 65 or older (Kelly & Kroemer, 1990; Lawton, 1990), or 70 or older (Kosnik, Sekuler, & Kline, 1990). And in a recent volume of *Experimental Aging Research*, in one study *older* pilots were as young as 31 (Morrow, Yesavage, Leirer, & Tinklinberg, 1993). So if aging is defined by legislators or by what human factors researchers have chosen in the past, the lower limit which defines an "older" subject may be as low as 31, or as high as 70.

So, how does a researcher choose the age of subjects when researching "older" populations? The answer is: It depends. It depends on what task(s) interest the researcher and whether there is evidence that age affects performance on some aspect of the task; it also depends on what information is available to suggest an age at which performance may be affected.

3.0 Research Issues

There are basically three types of questions about aging which human factors researchers want to answer:

1. What are the basic anthropomorphic, sensory, attitudinal, etc. characteristics of older individuals, and do they differ significantly from younger individuals?

2. How do age-related changes in these dimensions affect older people's ability to interact safely and efficiently with their environment and the devices in their environment?

3. What design characteristics support safe and effective functioning in older people?

As examples of studies performed to answer the first question, many articles report findings on the anthropometry of the elderly (e.g. Annis, Case, Clauser, & Bradtmiller, 1991; Kelly & Kroemer, 1990), on vision in the elderly (e.g. Kline & Schieber, 1982; Pitts, 1982), and on attention in the elderly (e.g. McDowd, 1986). The goal of such studies is to establish the characteristics of older people so that decisions about design parameters for the devices and environments used by older people can be made. For instance, knowing the visual capabilities of older people allows designers to determine how large the letters on signs need to be if older pedestrians and drivers must read them; likewiase, it tells city engineers how much lighting is needed in subway stations for older passengers to reliably detect level changes such as steps and ramps.

Studies falling into the second and third categories examine how age-related changes in functional abilities, experience, or attitudes affect the way older persons perform specific tasks. That information in turn can be used to determine the design parameters support the best functioning. For example:

1. Halpern (1984) evaluated the effect of age-related slowing on the speed with which drivers responded to traffic signs.

2. Hill, Crook, Zadek, Sheikh, & Yesavage (1989) investigated the effect of age-related memory changes on older people's ability to recall of information from news broadcasts.

3. Bordett, Koppa, & Congleton (1988) assessed the ability of older women to turn faucet handles.

3.1 Which Characteristics of Older People Are of Interest to Human Factors Researchers?

Human factors researchers are interested in knowing whether and how older people's functioning differs from younger people's. For example, we know that aging is associated with hearing loss, loss of static visual acuity, and arthritis: About 25% of Americans over 65 are visually impaired (Small, 1987) and 800,000 of them are legally blind or severely visually impaired (Haber, 1990). Thirty percent of people over 65 have hearing impairments; and, 50% have arthritis (Brody & Persky, 1990).

Medical technology is developing interventions capable of ameliorating the functional effects of some morbid conditions such as cataract (lens implants) and arthritis (joint replacements). More of these types of interventions can certainly be expected (cochlear implants are already being tried out to improve hearing in the profoundly deaf)[2].

Changes in workplace practices and workstation design will surely reduce the incidence or severity of conditions such as noise-induced hearing loss and arthritis. But given today's knowledge base, it is not likely that we will see technological advances which will prevent or obviate all effects of age-related morbidity soon enough to allow us to decide that we will not need to accommodate age-related functional losses for the current middle-aged and elderly population.

Thus, although improved education, nutrition, and health practices have resulted in a generally healthier and more educated populace, older persons still experience a number of age-related functional losses due to age-related morbidity[3]; and, because more people are living into their eighties and nineties, there is likely to be *more* significant morbidity in the older population of the future than there is today. It is obvious that to the extent that older people have reduced strength and sensory sensitivity, we need to design systems to accommodate these changes.

Increasing age is associated with changes in a) functional ability, and, b) traits that can substantially influence functioning, such as knowledge, experience, and beliefs. Functional categories include sensory, psychomotor, physical, and cognitive functioning. Traits which can influence functioning include motivation, attitudes/beliefs, and experience. Being aware of how age affects each of these areas will guide you in clarifying your research question and selecting subjects for your research.

3.2 Age-Related Changes in Sensory Functioning.

Although all sensory systems lose sensitivity with age, not every sensory loss begins at the same time or progresses at the same rate. Thus, while sensory performance is negatively correlated with age, most older people do not experience handicapping sensory loss in every system. In many elderly, loss in one system is compensated for by increased reliance on other systems; so unless you screen your subjects carefully, you may enroll an older subject who has significant loss of hearing, vision, etc., without being aware of it. This section is intended to inform you about the kinds of sensory changes which older subjects are likely to experience and to alert you to the ways in which these changes might affect your research..

3.2.1 Vision. By about age forty, visual functioning begins to change significantly enough to affect performance on everyday tasks. Near visual acuity begins to deteriorate at about this time and the deterioration

---

[2]Over 7,000 people worldwide have Cochlear implants (Branwyn, 1993). For more information on cochlear implnats, consult the chapter by Terry Hambrecht in the 1979 *Annual Review of Biophysics and Bioengineering*.

[3]Morbidity, as it is used here, refers to the onset of age-related diseases such as cataracts.

accelerates through the 40s and 50s, resulting in presbyopia, or age-related far-sightedness. Ninety percent of older people need glasses and up to 20% of people over 80 cannot read a newspaper, even with their glasses (Brody & Persky, 1990). About eight in 100 people over 75 have diabetes and half of them have diabetic retinopathy, which, like cataract, macular degeneration, and glaucoma (other common morbid conditions in people over 75) causes visual impairment and sometimes blindness. Each of these conditions has a rate of around five percent in people at age 65 and the incidence of these conditions increases with increasing age until as many as 20 in 100 experience each of these conditions after age 85 (Brody & Persky, 1990).

Similarly, age is associated with loss in almost every other area of visual functioning. With increasing age there is a shrinking of the peripheral field, a diminution of the ability accurately to judge how far away something is, the speed with which objects are approaching them, and a reduced ability to discriminate colors, especially in the blue-green range. Dynamic visual acuity (the ability to resolve and identify moving stimuli) also declines, and the ability to see in low light and in the presence of glare becomes progressively poorer. These functional changes in vision threaten older people's safety and substantially impair their ability to perform many everyday tasks such as driving, walking in public facilities, and reading medicine labels.

Since much of the information that influences our behavior comes to us through the visual system, one of the first things to be considered when designing an experiment with older people is how their visual functioning will influence performance on the task you are interested in studying. If you interested in answering questions involving some aspect of visual functioning (e.g., you want to know how large newsprint needs to be to accommodate most people over 80, or whether increasing the print/paper contrast or changing the font style will influence newspaper readability for that population), then you will want to oversample subjects from that part of the over-80 population whose visual functioning is below the mean[4]. If you want to know how large to make a traffic sign so that most drivers over 65 can see and recognize it at a safe distance, than you must include an adequate number of drivers who represent the poorest visual functioning permitted for licensed drivers.

While the questions you want to answer may not be directly related to visual acuity, you still may need to assess visual functioning. For example, if you are interested in determining whether older people comprehend written instructions differently than younger people, then you need to have a measure of visual functioning. This will insure that any differences you might find in comprehension are not related more to differences in visual functioning than differences in cognitive functioning. When studying comprehension you are not interested in visual functioning *per se*, but the

[4] Any time you are dealing with extreme scorers, there is a danger of regression toward the mean. See Chapter 2, sections 5.1.4 and 5.2.2. for a more in-depth discussion of this threat to experimental validity.

only way to be sure that differences in performance on the comprehension test are not at least partly due to differences in visual functioning is to determine whether differences in vision predict differences in comprehension. Certainly, if your reading task is timed, then differences in visual functioning may directly affect reading rates and, thus, comprehension scores.

When visual functioning is not a variable of interest in your study, you can also control for differences by pretesting subjects and making adjustments in the stimuli, such as increasing print size or contrast, so that visual processing demands are reduced for people with age-related visual loss. Depending on the task the subjects will perform, pretesting[5] may range from asking the participants whether they have difficulty on certain visual tasks (e.g. reading medicine labels or telephone books), through having them perform the traditional Snellen vision test, to assessing essentially all aspects of visual performance using a device such as a Titmus Vision Tester (Titmus Optical, 1986) which assesses day and night visual acuity, color sensitivity, peripheral field, etc.

If your older population can't see the stimulus clearly (it is "degraded" for them), their response to that stimulus will be different than that of younger subjects. A study which shows that older people do not learn the *meaning* of icons on computer screens as well as younger people may be hopelessly flawed if the older people were simply unable to discriminate among the icons because of their small size and/or degree of detail.

Whatever you are interested in knowing about older people, if visual functioning is required to carry out the task then you must familiarize yourself with the literature on aging and vision. There are a number of excellent general texts on vision and aging (e.g. Birren & Schaie, 1985; Sekuler, Kline & Dismukes, 1982), and you will find numerous articles on age-related changes in specific aspects of visual functioning in journals such as *Human Factors*, *The Journal of Experimental Aging Research*, and *The Journals of Gerontology*.

3.2.2 Hearing. Age-related hearing loss (presbycusis) is a common problem among older people. More men experience age-related hearing impairment than women of the same age, but hearing loss of some type affects more than half of all older people (Gulya, 1990).

Typically, older people experience their first hearing problems for sounds of higher frequencies. This affects their ability to hear many sounds which are commonly used as warning or alerting devices such as whistles, sirens, beepers, and horns. As people get older, hearing loss also occurs for the higher frequencies of speech, making it difficult for them to

[5]You must be cautious of a treatment by pretest interaction in situations where pretests are used. For example, pretesting the subjects on their current level of functioning may result in their refusal to participate or their withdrawl, because they don't want to admit the diminishing of their ability to perform (See Section 3.6 of this chapter). It may also sensitize them to the dependent measure or to the experimental situation, resulting in a Hawthorne effect. See Chapter 2, section 5.2.1 or a more in-depth discussion of pretest by threatment threats to validity and section 5.2.3 for a discussion of the Hawthorne effect..

understanding speech, especially that of women and children (whose voices are higher pitched). They also begin to have difficulty understanding speech against noisy backgrounds such as in assembly plants or restaurants.

When research involves older subjects, attention must be paid to insure that nothing in the design of the experiment (for instance, tape recorded instructions, high frequency signals, or computer generated speech) affects the older subject's performance in ways not intended or anticipated. You must also insure that losses in hearing ability (which are not always obvious in verbal interactions with the older person) do not indirectly affect performance on the independent variable or become a confounding variable in interpreting your findings. For instance, if your signal to begin a timed task is a high pitched tone, response times may be affected because older subjects are uncertain whether they heard the tone.

Although a thorough assessment of hearing probably involves the services of an auditory specialist, hearing and speech comprehension can be tested by asking subjects to repeat whispered passages or to repeat phrases spoken in a normal speaking voice when the subject cannot see the speaker's face. Since older people lose sensitivity at higher frequencies first, try to use stimuli in middle or lower frequency ranges. Also, older people have more difficulty than younger people understanding computer generated speech; for tasks which require responding to computer generated speech, or to other sound generating devices, test the subjects for sensitivity and comprehension before beginning to collect data. Be sure to pilot test any tasks which have auditory components on older subjects before beginning data collection in.

Auditory sensitivity can be determined by asking subjects to press a button or raise a finger when they hear a specific sound. Comprehension can be assessed by asking questions regarding the auditory message. If comprehension must occur against a background of noise, be sure to evaluate whether the subjects can discriminate the signal from the noise. If subjects wear hearing aids, make sure that the batteries are working and that the device is properly adjusted.

3.2.3 The skin senses: pain, pressure, temperature, touch. Each of these sensations occurs in the skin and underlying tissue. Like vision and hearing, sensitivity in all sensory systems decreases with age (Kenshalo, 1979; Montagna, 1965). Consequently, older people are less sensitive to temperature changes and extremes, skin pressure, etc. They are also less likely to experience pain appropriately. Thus, when conducting research with older subjects, it is important to remember that they may experience environmental characteristics, such as temperature and cutaneous pressure, differently than younger subjects. These factors are important in the design and evaluation of living and working spaces, clothing, and assistive and accommodative devices for older people.

The ability to discriminate shapes and textures by touch also diminishes with advanced age. This may be very important if your task involves any manual manipulation of objects or devices, or requires that people discriminate between objects based on shape or feel. If your task requires subjects to identify -- or discriminate between -- controls by touch, adequate pretesting should be done to determine whether they can perform the task.

3.2.4 Olfaction and taste. As with all other sensory systems, there is a decline in the sensitivity of the senses of smell and taste (Corso, 1981). For example, this loss of sensitivity handicaps the older person in detecting noxious gases (including smoke) and spoiled food, and in discriminating between oral medications. These losses may underlie, at least in part, the increased incidence of medication poisonings which older people experience.

3.2.5 Balance. Dizziness or disequilibrium is reported by up to 90% of outpatients in geriatric clinics (Gulya, 1990). Postural instability, which includes loss of righting reflexes and increased body sway, also increases with age (Kay & Tideiksaar, 1990). Tasks which require older people to stand, walk, or climb stairs and ramps put them at increased risk of falls. There are several brief performance instruments for assessing balance and gait in older people (Tinetti, 1986; Wilson & Nadol, 1983). If your task includes any of the activities listed above, it would be wise to screen older subjects for balance and gait problems..

3.3 Age-Related Changes in Psychomotor Functioning.

3.3.1 Response time. As people age, essentially all behaviors slow (Small, 1987). This includes response time to both simple and complex stimuli. Older subjects are slower at processing stimuli, selecting responses, and initiating and carrying out those responses than their younger counterparts. The more complex the task, the slower the performance of older subjects relative to younger ones (Laux & Lane, 1985).

Why response times increase with age is still not fully understood. Part of the slowing results from slower nerve conductance. Another part is attributable to the degradation of the stimulus which accompanies the aging of the sensory systems. Still another component of the slowing is due to musculoskeletal changes such as those associated with osteoarthritis and loss of strength. The issue is complex, and whether you need to consider behavioral slowing when you design your study depends upon the behaviors you are assessing and how you measure them.

A good rule of thumb, however, would be that any time your study involves timed responses, you should remember that response time will be affected by age-related psychomotor slowing and take steps to deal with that slowing statistically. For instance, in a study to determine why there is an age-related decline in performance on substitution tests, writing speed was assessed and the effects of writing speed were controlled statistically (by partialling writing speed out of response times)[6], so that it could be determined whether older subjects also performed other components of the task (encoding, searching, matching, etc.) more slowly than younger subjects.

The results indicated that differences in writing speed *were* an important predictor of differences in test scores and that older people were slower at writing than younger people (not very surprising or important information). But older people were also slower on all of the cognitive components of the task, as well. Likewise, differences in performance on other components of the task predicted test scores in the older population but not in the younger population (Laux & Lane, 1985).

If we had not controlled for differences in writing speed, it would have been difficult to conclude with any confidence that older people perform more poorly on this type of test than young adults because it takes them much longer to search an array and match a figure, especially when components of the array are unfamiliar.

3.3.2 Tracking. Some experimental and real-world tasks require subjects to track targets with pointers, trackballs, joysticks, steering wheels, etc. Older subjects tend to make significantly more deviation, or tracking, errors, on these tasks than younger ones, because the tracking task makes greater attentional demands on them (Mayer & Laux, 1991). If you are trying to decide whether or not older people will have problems using devices that require tracking, your question and the procedure you will use to get the answer are relatively straightforward. But, unless you are interested in knowing how age-related changes in tracking performance affect interactions with specific devices or tasks, be very careful about incorporating a tracking task into your research.

3.4 Age-Related Changes in Anthropometry and Physical Functioning.

3.4.1 Anthropometry. Stature and weight decline gradually with age from about age sixty, with weight loss accelerating after age eighty (Annis et al, 1991). These changes have been found in both longitudinal and cross-sectional studies and are independent of secular[7] or cohort effects. Changes in stature and weight are correlated with changes in most other dimensions such as sitting height, seat breadth, and calf circumference (Kelly & Kroemer, 1990).

To the extent that size on any dimension could affect performance on your research task, age-related differences in anthropometry should be considered in the design of your study. In designing experimental apparatus,

---

[6] LISREL (Linear Structural Relations) is another powerful analytic procedure which allows researchers to tease apart the various components of age-related differences in performance (Joereskog & Soerbom, 1989; Joereskog & Soerbom, 1993; Long, 1983).

[7] A secular effect is a long term population trend For example, average weight in a population tends to fluctuate over long periods of time as function of changes in nutrition, health care, advances in medicine, widespread changes in eating habits, etc.

you need to be aware of age-related changes in anthropometry to avoid inadvertently handicaping older people. Limited anthropometric data on older people can be found in the Health and Nutrition Survey I (Engel, Murphy, Maurer & Collins, 1978); Annis *et al* (1991) cite numerous studies which have assessed various anthropometric dimensions in older populations.

3.4.2 Strength and flexibility. Three factors play a role in the significant loss of strength and flexibility associated with increasing age: loss of muscle mass, loss of conditioning, and the increased incidence of osteoarthritis. Osteoarthritis is present in at least one third of adults by the time they are 40, and it is the leading cause of disability in people over 65 (Ettinger, 1990). Loss of strength directly affects the older person's ability to perform any manual or physical task, from gross motor tasks such as climbing stairs or lifting grocery sacks, to fine motor tasks such as pressing levers or opening pill containers. This can have an unwelcome effect on your research if you don't think about it in advance; for instance, if you are studying different medicine label designs to assess which leads to the best patient compliance, and you find that patients are not very compliant no matter what label they have, it might be because they couldn't get the pill containers open.

In designing and evaluating any device, environment, or interface for use by older people, it is always important to consider whether they will be physically able to use the device. It doesn't matter what kind of door opening device you design (e.g. knob or lever) if the older person doesn't have the strength to operate it. Although there are a number of handbooks which have some data on grip strength, lift strength, finger press strength, etc., these data tend to be sparse for older populations, especially for the old-old[8] (Annis *et al*, 1991; Denno *et al*, 1992).

3.5 Age-Related Changes in Cognitive and Intellectual Functioning.

Cognitive functioning includes perceiving, learning, remembering, thinking, reasoning, and decision making. Intelligence is defined as the potential to learn, and is assessed by tests such as the Wechsler Adult Intelligence Scale (WAIS) and the California Test of Mental Maturity. Numerous studies employing measures of cognitive skills and intelligence have found that increasing age is generally associated with a decline in these abilities. Typically, these declines begin in the fifth or sixth decade of life and the rate of decline increases as age increases. Cross sectional studies indicate that the magnitude of these losses is greater than do longitudinal studies; in both types of studies there are always subjects in older cohorts who outperform some subjects in younger cohorts (Laux & Brelsford, 1990; Laux & Lane, 1985).

---

[8]One way of stratifying the older population is by classifying subjects into age categories such as young-old (65-74), old (75-84), and old-old (84+)

To the extent that performance on the task you want to study requires memory, thinking, decision-making, etc., it is important to carefully define your older population since factors such as health, education, and experience also influence how older people function on many cognitive tasks. Some important dimensions of cognitive functioning that are affected by age are briefly discussed below. For more detail, consult texts such as *Aging and Cognitive Processes* (Craik & Trehub, 1982) and *The Handbook of the Psychology of Aging* (Birren & Schaie, 1985).

3.5.1 Memory and learning. Memory begins to show significant age-related changes at about age sixty. By age eighty, recall of information in short term memory, and recall time for material in long term memory, show age-related decrements. But studies have also shown that the size of age-related memory deficits can be influenced by the methods employed to assess memory. For instance, older subjects show larger memory decrements in recall than in recognition tests, and they are able to remember experienced events, in the distant past, as well as younger subjects (Fozard, 1980.)

Even if your task does not directly require the recognition or recall of information, if your subjects will include people over 80, it is probably wise to screen them for cognitive functioning, including memory. This will allow you to determine if any age-related performance decrements you find are due to differences in the variables, or to subjects simply not remembering the instructions. There are many tests of memory functioning, some which assess short term memory, such as the Digit Span subtest of the WAIS, and others which assess general memory functioning (Wechsler, 1945). Kane and Kane (1986) provide a number of methods for assessing memory in the old-old and frail elderly. It is always useful, no matter the age of your subjects, to insure that participants understand and remember instructions by monitoring their performance on a few practice items before beginning to collect data.

3.5.2 Attention. Attention is conceptualized as a limited resource which allows us to process information in the environment. Attention is typically thought of as a resource which can be distributed in several ways:

1. *selective attention*, where the person must attend to one source of information although other sources of information may be competing for the resource, and
2. *divided or distributed attention*, in which the person distributes attentional resources among two or more sources of information (Wickens, 1992).

Examples of selective attention in the real world are detecting a phone ring against a background of music, or detecting the color of a specific traffic signal against a background of multiple traffic signals and signs. Examples of distributed attention include driving and tuning the car radio at the same time, or following a recipe while monitoring children's play.

Typically, older people show decrements in performing laboratory tasks intended to assess both selective and distributed attention. Older people are less efficient at attending to a single stimulus against a "busy" background, and they are less efficient at dividing attention among two or more stimuli. The concept of "mental workload" assumes that some tasks make greater demands on attentional resources than others. Thus, if performing a task requires that all attentional resources are allocated to perform one task (e.g. a detection task), no resources are left to attend to other information. Studies to date have suggested that older people have fewer attentional resources and are not as efficient at allocating them as younger people. Thus, tasks which younger people do not find taxing or effortful may exceed the attentional capacity of older people. Decreasing attentional resources may underlie the increase in accidents that older drivers experience beginning at about age 75: The older driver simply can no longer attend to tracking and navigating **and** still have resources left for monitoring other vehicles and environmental conditions.

The related topics of attention and mental workload are very important in answering many questions about performance in the elderly and how to design to accommodate their abilities. To get a more comprehensive description of the issues, read *Attention and Effort* (Kahneman, 1973) and *Mental Workload: Its Theory and Measurement* (Moray, 1982).

3.6 Age-related changes in motivation and attitudes/beliefs.

One problem that many researchers find when researching older populations is that many older people are unwilling to participate in studies, because they often feel threatened by the notion of someone assessing their performance on any task. In some instances there is an unwillingness to face the fact that their abilities and skills have diminished. In other instances, older people are simply reticent or afraid to engage in unfamiliar activities.

The first problem, resistance, is more of a threat to the validity of your research than reticence or anxiety. If you somehow cajole or coerce unwilling subjects to participate, their performance may not reflect their actual functional level[9]. But if you don't somehow recruit a representative sample, your findings may not be generalizable to the intended target population. Obtaining a representative sample of older subjects will require some creative advertising and recruiting techniques by you or your outside recruiter.

In one study of older drivers, we approached a church which had many older members and needed money for a new roof. We offered to donate $75.00 to the church for every church member in the desired age and sex

[9]By using coercion to gain the participation of subjects who would rather not participate, you are running the risk of a Hawthorne effect at the very least and possibly invalidity from epxerimental mortality (i.e., subjects withdrawing from an experiment leaving you with unequal numbers of subjects per observation). For more information on the Hawthorne effect and experimental mortality as threats to experimental validity, see Chapter 2, sections 5.2.2 and 5.1.5, respectively.

categories who participated in our study. We successfully recruited more than 100 older drivers (up to age 92) who demonstrated a wide range of cognitive, perceptual, and physical characteristics and who stayed with the project for the entire three months of data collection (Laux & Brelsford, 1990).

But, in another study, we attempted to recruit a representative sample of older persons who had renewed their driver license within the last five years by contacting people from the Texas drivers license registration list. This was not very successful: People were suspicious and reluctant to come to our laboratory or did not want to drive to unfamiliar locations. There is no simple solution to the problem of recruiting a representative sample of older subjects, and it can be a serious threat to the generalizability of your findings.

There are numerous ways to contact members of the older population: Area Centers on Aging, nutrition centers, AARP Chapters, nursing homes, adult day care facilities, advertisements in "senior" newspapers, geriatric assessment centers, church groups, YMCA groups, retirement communities, community health clinics, etc. Many cities have annual senior "fairs" where products of interest to older people are displayed, blood pressure and cholesterol are screened, presentations are made about Medicare, etc. These fairs attract large numbers of older people. The Census tract data indicate the age of residents by name and address which allows older people to be located by neighborhood. Driver license bureaus have files listing driver age and address. The possibilities are almost limitless. But finding older people does not guarantee that they will be willing to participate in your research.

In addition to the problem of resistance to participating, other factors such as frailty, lack of safe transportation, or a mobility difficulty such as wheelchair or walker use, may prevent or discourage older people from participating in your research. Subjects who are willing to participate may find the process too fatiguing to complete the study as scheduled, causing an unacceptable attrition rate[10], or they may become discouraged and fail to complete a multi-part project. These are all issues which must be resolved through careful recruitment, researcher flexibility, innovative support of participation, and thoughtful experimental design.

Often the frail or fearful older people who **do not** get included in the study population are the very people you are interested in knowing about and designing for. Not including them in a study population clearly limits the ability to answer the questions which will help accommodate them.

---

[10]Attrition of subjects is called mortatily and can be a threat to the validity of your study. This problem is particularly bad if you are comparing older subjects and younder subjects, and the older subjects are dropping out at a faster rate. For more information on mortality as a validity threat, see Chapter 2, section 5.1.5.

4.0 Research Design

Once you have a research question clearly defined[11], the next step is to define the study population. Since age cannot be directly manipulated in research (subjects cannot be randomly assigned to an age group), there are several alternative choices for designing a study: the older population can be sampled by age strata or cohort, which results in what is known as a cross-sectional design, or one cohort can be followed over an extended time period, which is called a longitudinal design.

4.1 Stratified Designs

4.1.1 Cross-sectional designs. In a cross-sectional design the study population is stratified by age in some reasonable way, and each stratum is randomly sampled. Some typical ways of stratifying the older population include stratifying by five year age periods or decades, or classifying subjects into age categories such as young-old (65-74), old (75-84), and old-old (84+).

4.1.2 Other ways of stratifying. Some other methods of stratifying are based on empirical data such as driving accident rates: Driving accident rates hold steady in the over-25 population until about age 55, when a gradual increase begins which turns up sharply after age 75. For this reason, studies of older drivers typically divide the older population into three groups: 40-55, 56-74, and 75 and older; however, pronounced changes in color vision are not reported until after about age 75. So if you are interested in determining whether age effects on color vision affect people's abilities to do some task, it might be more appropriate to look at color vision performance in only two strata: 60-74 and 74+. Once the strata have been defined, subjects should be randomly selected from each stratum. To determine how large your samples should be, consult a power table (i.e., how many subjects you need will depend on how strongly you think age affects the traits you are interested in assessing and how large the variance in the study population is)[12].

If you are interested in describing the older population in general, random sampling, which should result in a sample which reflects the age distribution of the older population, is generally preferred. But, as was discussed earlier, the members of the older population are a diverse lot and their diversity increases with each decade of age. This makes means and variances derived from the entire population of older people not very descriptive of any single cohort or stratum. It is generally more useful to describe each stratum or cohort and determine whether members of different strata differ from each other.

---

[11]See Chapter 2 for information on defining and developing a research problem.

[12]Power tables can be found on pages 549-552 of Keppel (1982). Keppel discusses the calculation of power on pages 69-77 and 204-206 of the same book. Those interested in a more in-depth discussion of power computation and the issues surrounding it are referred to Cohen (1988).

4.2 Longitudinal Designs

If you choose a longitudinal design, you will select subjects from a single cohort and assess their performance over time. The longitudinal design reduces the chances that functional differences between younger and older people are due to cohort (generational) differences rather than to effects of aging *per se*. But the longitudinal method is cumbersome, requires large numbers of subjects, and takes a long time (typically five or more years). Longitudinal designs are not often employed in human factors research for those reasons. If this type of design *is* chosen, it is important to anticipate subject attrition in older populations when deciding how many subjects to include in your study[13].

4.2.1 Pros and cons. A finding from a longitudinal study about the effects of aging might differ from a cross-sectional one involving people of the same ages because a cross-sectional study only includes survivors in each age cohort. In a cross-sectional study of older drivers, for instance, those older people who have ceased driving are not part of the study population. This means that if you want to extrapolate our findings to the next generation of older drivers, you don't have all the information you need, particularly if your goal is to design roadways and vehicles that allows people to continue to drive in spite of age-related functional changes.

For a more detailed discussion of the advantages and disadvantages of both longitudinal and cross sectional aging studies see *Methodological Issues in Aging Research* (Schaie, Campbell, Meredith & Rawlings, 1988). For a discussion of more sophisticated designs, such as cross-sequential design, which attempt to address the shortcomings of typical cross-sectional or longitudinal designs, see Schaie (1977).

Choosing between a cross-sectional design and a longitudinal one is an important decision for both theoretical and pragmatic reasons. It is usually simpler and quicker to use a cross-sectional design; but, as can be discovered from examining the large body of literature on the relationship between age and IQ scores, the two methods sometimes result in very different conclusions about the relationship between increasing age and performance (Matarrazzo, 1973).

What kind of design you should choose will depend, at least in part, on why you are asking the question. For much human factors research, the goal is to assess members of the current older population, in order to make decisions that can be implemented now. The cross-sectional design is most often chosen as the way to determine whether there are age-related differences in performance on the dependent variable(s) of interest. But the researcher must be aware that this design may not provide answers about how people who are currently young or middle-aged will perform when they reach their eighties or nineties.

---

[13]See the discussion of mortality as a threat to validity in Chapter 2, section 5.1.5.

For example, data collected on computer use and general attitudes toward technology in today's older population will probably not be useful in helping develop technology for the older user of 2050. Similarly, anthropometric data collected on today's 80 year olds may not be accurate for 80 year olds in 2050 because of secular trends (long term population trends) in height.

And, whereas knowing about the older user of today may help you to design roadway systems to accommodate the older driver into the next decade, ongoing changes in medical technology, automotive engineering, and roadway design, such as those already being considered for the Intelligent Vehicle Highway System, may render much of that information irrelevant by 2050. A longitudinal study on older drivers' decisions about giving up driving could certainly be more useful than a cross-sectional one in *understanding* the decisions older drivers make about driving and the driving patterns they adopt as they age.

There are data bases from large longitudinal studies that allow researchers to assess some effects of increasing age in a single cohort. From data like those collected in the Baltimore Study on Aging (Shock et al, 1984), the Duke University Longitudinal Studies (Busse & Maddox, 1983), or the Veteran's Administration Normative Aging Studies (Bell, Rose & Damon, 1966) we can track a large group of subjects over an extended period of time. This allows us to determine how age affected a single cohort. Unfortunately, when these data were collected, the researchers probably did not have your research questions in mind. Although examining such data bases can often reveal important information, such as how living arrangements change with age, these data can seldom be used to answer questions like: "What stair riser dimensions are safest for older people?" or "What colors should the display (numbers and background) of a blood glucose monitor be?" And **none** of these data bases includes a representative sample of older people.

4.3 Methods for Studying the Effects of Aging

The following methods are typically used when studying aging:

1. Observing older people in the world.
2. Assessing the characteristics of older people.
3. Surveying or questioning people about their experiences.
4. Using controlled experiments.

When collecting data by directly observing older people in the world, some examples of the questions that you might ask include:

1. What percentage of older divers wear seatbelts, and are some seatbelt types preferred by older drivers?
2. What percentage of older library users actually read large print books, and on what topics?

Researchers who assess the characteristics or traits of older people, typically ask questions such as:

1. How fast do older pedestrians walk when crossing an intersection?
2. How many older farm laborers can read English?

When human factors researchers survey or "test" older people to determine their behavior, knowledge, beliefs, and experiences, examples of the types of questions they want to answer are:

1. What percentage of older drivers know the meaning of "new" traffic signs?
2. What percentage of older people do not like using automated teller machines, and why?

In many of these studies the performance of older and younger individuals is compared. The goal of such studies is to identify significant and meaningful age-related differences with the goal of accommodating these differences.

The fourth type of study on aging involves controlled, laboratory experiments, in which only the variables of interest are allowed to vary. This research attempts to answer questions such as:

1. How do differences in the orientation of visual displays affect response time?
2. How do differences in the explicitness of descriptions of product hazards affect people's purchasing decisions?

In this type of study, comparisons of older and younger people's performance are typically drawn. This can result in a better understanding of how to design to support older users without penalizing younger users.

For example, in a study of displays such as those used on vehicle dashboards, older subjects were slower than younger subjects at reading some, but not all, types of indicators. By identifying display types which were quickly read by both older and younger drivers, and which did not penalize older subjects compared to younger subjects, it was possible to make suggestions for vehicle display types which would result in the best performance by both older and younger drivers (Mayer & Laux, 1991).

From these descriptions it is clear that there are many ways that human factors researchers attempt to answer questions about the traits and performance characteristics of older people and how to design to fit those characteristics. Since the principal reason for all human factors research is to "get good answers to practical questions" (Chapanis, 1959, p. 21), the most important steps in deciding what research design to use include clearly articulating a practical question and specifying how the independent and dependent variables will be measured in order to get "good" or usable information. (Refer to chapters 2 and 3 of this book for a review of developing a research problem and designing experiements).

5.0 Useful General References on Aging

One problem with doing human factors research on aging, is that relevant information about aging and older people is widely dispersed through many disciplines and their literatures. You will find useful and usable information in journals and texts from medicine, nursing, nutrition, optometry, psychology, education, engineering, sociology, biology, economics, safety, epidemiology, etc. The following short bibliography provides some general references on aging which most researchers find helpful in identifying the characteristics and changes typical of older populations. It is by no means exhaustive, but is intended to provide an entry point into the voluminous and widely dispersed literature on age-related change and functional ability.

Abrams, W. & Berkow, R. (Eds.) (1990). *The Merck Manual of Geriatrics.* Rahway, NJ: Merck & Co., Inc.

Abramson, M., & Lovas, P.M. (1988). *Aging and Sensory Cange: An Annotated Bibliography.* Washington, DC: The Gerontological Society of America.

Birren, J. & Schaie, W. (1985). *Handbook of the Psychology of Aging.* New York: Van Nostrand Reinhold Co.

Birren, James & Sloane, R.B. (1980). *Handbook of Mental Health and Aging.* Englewood Cliffs, NJ: Prentice-Hall, Inc.

Czaja, S.J. (Ed.) (1990). *Human Factors Needs for an Aging Population.* Washington, DC: National Academy Press

Czaja, S.J. (Ed.). (1990). Special Issue: Aging. *Human Factors*: 32(5), 505-619.

Department of Health & Human Services, Public Health Service (1987). *Health Statistics on Older persons United States 1986. Analytical and Epidemiological Studies Series 3. No. 25.* Hyattsville, MD: National Center for Health Statistics.

Finch, C. & Shanas, E. (Eds.) (1985). *Handbook of the Biology of Aging.* New York: Van Nostrand Reinhold Co.

Garg, A. (1991). Ergonomics and the older worker: An overview. *Experimental Aging Research*, 17(3), 143-155.

Kane, R., & Kane, R. (1986). *Assessing the Elderly: A Practical Guide to Measurement.* Lexington, MA: Lexington Books, D.C. Heath & Co.

Lavizzo-Mouray, R., Day, S., Diserens, D. & Grisso, J. (1989). *Practicing Prevention for the Elderly.* Philadelphia: Hanley & Belfus, Inc.

Serow, W., Sly, D., & Wrigley, J.M. (1990). *Population Aging in the United States.* New York, New York: Greenwood Press.

6.0 Biography

Lila Laux received her M.S. in Applied Psychology from the University of Southwest Louisiana and a Ph.D. in Industrial/Organizational Psychology from Rice University. From 1986 through 1993, she was on the faculty of the Department of Community Medicine at Baylor College of Medicine and also taught at Rice. She is currently a member of the technical staff at U.S. West Technologies. Readers with questions concerning this chapter are invited to E-mail Lila at LilaLaux@AOL.COM.

REFERENCES

Annis, J.F., Case, H.W., Clauser, C.E., & Bradtmiller, B. (1991). Anthropometry of an aging work force. *Experimental Aging Research*, 17(3), 177-188.

Bell, B., Rose, C.L., & Damon, A. (1966). The Normative Aging Study (NAS), the Veteran's Administration longitudinal study of healthy aging. *Gerontologist*, 6, 179-184.

Birren, J., & Schaie, W. (Eds.) (1985). *Handbook of the Psychology of Aging*. New York: Van Nostrand Reinhold Co.

Bordett, H.M., Koppa, R., & Congleton, J.J. (1988) Torque required from elderly females to operate faucet handles of various shapes. *Human Factors*, 30, 339-346.

Branwyn, G. (Sept/Oct, 1993) The desire to be wired. *Wired*, 1.4

Brody, J., & Persky, V.W. (1990). Epidemiology and demographics. In W. Abrams & R. Berkow (Eds.), *The Merck Manual of Geriatrics*. Rahway, NJ: Merck & Co., Inc.

Busse, E.W., & Maddox, G.L. (1983). *The Duke Longitudinal Sudies on Aging and the Aged*. Durham, NC: Duke University Press.

Chapanis, A. (1959). *Research Techniques in Human Engineering*. Baltimore: Johns Hopkins Press.

Cohen, J. (1988). *Statistical Power Analysis for the Behavioral Sciences* (2nd ed.). Hillsdale, NJ: Lawrence Erlbaum.

Corso, J.F. (1981). *Aging Sensory Systems and Perception*. New York: Praeger.

Craik, F.I.M., & Trehub, S.E. (1982). *Aging and Cognitive Processes*. New York: Plenum Press.

Czaja, Sara J. (Ed.) (1990). *Human Factors Needs for an Aging Population*. Washington, DC: National Academy Press.

Denno. S., Isle, B.A., Ju, G., Koch, C.G., Metz, S.V., Penner, R., Wang, L, & Ward, J. (1992). *Human Factors Design Guidelines for the Elderly and People with Disabilities*. Minneapolis, MN: Honeywell Inc.

Engel, A., Murphy, R.S., Maurer, K., & Collins, E. (1978). *Plan and Operations of the HANES I Augmentation Survey of Adults 25-74 Years,*

United States 1974-1975. DHEW Publication No. (PHS) 78-1314, Series 1, No. 14, Public Health Service, Hyattsville, MD:NCHS.

Ettinger, W. (1990). Joint and soft tissue disorders. In W. Abrams & R. Berkow (Eds.), *The Merck Manual of Geriatrics*. Rahway, NJ: Merck & Co., Inc.

Fozard, J.L. (1980). The time for remembering. In L.W. Poon (Ed.), *Aging in the 1980s*. Washington, DC: American Psychological Association.

Gulya, A.J. (1990). Ear disorders. In W. Abrams & R. Berkow (Eds.), *The Merck Manual of Geriatrics*. Rahway, NJ: Merck & Co., Inc.

Haber, P. (1990). Diagnostic and therapeutic technology. In W. Abrams & R. Berkow (Eds.), *The Merck Manual of Geriatrics*. Rahway, NJ: Merck & Co., Inc.

Halpern, D.F. (1984). Age differences in response time to verbal and symbolic traffic signs. *Experimental Aging Research*, 10, 201-204.

Hill, R.D., Crook, T.H., Zadek, A., Sheikh, J., and Yesavage, J. (1989). The effects of age on recall of information from a simulated television news broadcast. *Educational Gerontology*, 15, 607-613.

Joereskog, K.G. & Soerbom, D. (1989). *LISREL 7: A Guide to the Program and Applications, 2nd Ed*. Chicago, IL: SPSS Inc.

Joereskog, K.G. & Soerbom, D. (1993). *LISREL 8: Structural Equation Modeling with the SIMPLIS Command Language*. Chicago, IL: Scientific Software International.

Johnston, W., & Packer, A. (1987). *Workforce 2000: Work and workers for the twenty-first century*. Indianapolis, IN: Hudson Institute.

Kahneman, D. (1973). *Attention and Effort*. Englewood Cliffs, NJ: Prentice Hall.

Kane, R., & Kane, R. (1986). *Assessing the Elderly: A Practical Guide to Measurement*. Lexington, MA: Lexington Books, D.C. Heath & Co.

Kay, A., & Tideiksaar, R. (1990). Falls and gait disorders. In W. Abrams & R. Berkow (Eds.), *The Merck Manual of Geriatrics*. Rahway, NJ: Merck & Co., Inc.

Kelly, P.L., & Kroemer, K.H.E. (1990). Anthropometry of the elderly: Status and recommendations. *Human Factors*, 32(5), 571-596.

Kenshalo, D.R. (1979). Aging effects on cutaneous and kinesthetic sensibilities. In S.S. Han & D.H. Coon (Eds.), *Special Senses in Aging: A Current Biological Assessment*. Ann Arbor, MI: University of Michigan, Institute of Gerontology.

Keppel, G. (1982). *Design and Analysis: A Researcher's Handbook*. (2nd. Ed). Englewood Cliffs, NJ: Prentice-Hall.

Kline, T., Ghali, L., Kline, D., & Brown, S. (1990). Visibility distance of highway signs among young, middle-aged and older drivers: Icons are better than text. *Human Factors*, 32(5), 609-620.

Kline, D., & Schieber, F. (1982). Visual persistence and temporal resolution. In R. Sekuler, D. Kline & K. Dismukes (Eds.), *Aging and Human Visual Function*. New York: Alan R. Liss.

Kosnik, W., Sekuler, R., & Kline, D. (1990). Self-reported visual problems of older drivers. *Human Factors*, 32(5),597-608.

Laux, L., & Brelsford, J. (1990). *Age-Related Changes in Sensory, Cognitive, Psychomotor, and Physical Functioning and Driving Performance in Drivers Aged 40 to 92*. Washington, DC: AAA Foundation for Traffic Safety.

Laux, L., & Lane, D. (1985). Information processing components of substitution test performance. *Intelligence*, 9, 111-136.

Lawton, M. (1990). Aging and performance of home tasks. *Human Factors*, 32(5), 527-536.

Long, J.S. (1983). *Covariance Sructure Models. An Introduction to LISREL*. Newbury Park, CA: Sage Publications.

Mayer, D., & Laux, L. (1991). *Evaluating Vehicle Displays for Older Drivers*. Washington, DC: AAA Foundation for Traffic Safety.

Montagna, W. (Ed) (1965). *Aging (Advances in Biology of the Skin, Vol. 6)*. New York: Pergamon Press.

McDowd, J. M. (1986). The effects of age and extended practice on divided attention performance. *Journal of Gerontology*, 41, 764-769.

Moray, N. (1982). *Mental Workload: Its Theory and Measurement*. New York: Plenum Press.

Morrow, D., Yesavage, J., Leirer, V., & Tinklinberg, J. (1993). Influence of aging and practice on piloting tasks. *Experimental Aging Research*, 19(1), 53-70.

Pitts, D. (1982). The effects of aging on selected visual functions: Dark adaptation, visual acuity, stereopsis, and brightness contrast. In R. Sekuler, D. Kline & K. Dismukes (Eds.), *Aging and Human Visual Function*. New York: Alan R. Liss.

Schaie, K.W. (1977). Quasi-experimental designs in the psychology of aging. In J. E. Birren and K. W. Schaie (Eds.), *Handbook of the Psychology of Aging*. New York: Van Nostrand.

Schaie, K.W., Campbell, R. T., Meredith, W., & Rawlings, S. C. (1988). *Methodological Issues in Aging Research*. New York: Springer.

Sekuler, R., Kline, D., & Dismukes, K. (1982). *Aging and Human Visual Fnctioning*. New York: Alan R. Liss.

Serow, W., Sly, D., & Wrigley, J. (1990). *Population Aging in the United States*. New York: Greenwood Press.

Shock, N.W., Greulich, R.C., Andres, R., Arenberg, D., Costa, P.T., Lakatta, E.G., & Tobin, J.D. (1984). *Normal Human Aging: The Baltimore Longitudinal Sudy of Aging: Volumes 1 & 2* (NIH Publication 84-2450). Washington, DC: U. S. Government Printing Office.

Small, A. (1987). Design for older people. In Gavriel Salvendy (Ed), *Handbook of Human Factors*. New York: John Wiley & Sons.

Smith, D.B.D. (1990). Human factors and aging: An overview of research needs and application opportunities. *Human Factors*, 32(5), 509-526.

Tinetti, M. (1986). Performance-Oriented Assessment of Mobility Problems in Elderly Patients. *JAGS*, 34, 119-126.

Titmus Optical, Inc. (1986). *Titmus II-S Vision Tester Training Manual*. Petersburg, VA: Author.

Wechsler, D. (1945). A Standardized Memory Scale for Clinical Use. *Journal of Psychology*, 19:87-95.

Wickens, C. (1992). *Engineering Psychology and Human Performance*. New York: Harper Collins Publishers.

Wilson, W. & Nadol, J. (1983). *Quick Reference to Ear, Nose, and Throat Disorders*. New York: Lippincott Co.

Chapter 7
Automotive Techniques

Paul Green
University of Michigan Transportation Research Institute (UMTRI)

1.0 Perspective

This chapter reviews methods used to evaluate the safety and ease of use of driver-related aspects of passenger cars. However, these methods are directly applicable to trucks and buses, and to construction, agricultural, and military equipment as well. This chapter was written primarily for human factors engineering/ergonomics graduate students, with a secondary audience of human factors specialists interested in learning more about automotive applications and automotive engineers seeking to expand their knowledge of human factors. The chapter's emphasis is on design and evaluation, themes that will be predominant in future automotive HF research. Driver training and evaluation, highway design, and basic research are given less attention.

2.0 Introduction

Historically, automotive human factors research has strongly emphasized matters related to impact biomechanics (Lissner, Lebow, and Evans, 1960), lighting and signs (Hemion and Hull, 1973; Hemion, 1975; Bhise, Farber, Saunby, Troell, Watunas, and Bernstein, 1977; Olson, 1977; Sivak, Olson, and Pastalan, 1981), and driver accommodation -- especially field of view and reach (Meldrum, 1965; Hammond and Roe, 1972). Proposed federal safety regulations had an important influence on the topics examined in government-supported human factors research.

The emphasis of automotive human factors shifted markedly to design applications in the mid-1980s, due in part to the success of the Ford Taurus. Ford systematically examined customer-related, product characteristics, identifying competitive products that best implemented each characteristic. This benchmarking approach, which Ford called Best-In-Class (BIC) (Callahan, 1986a, b, c), had been used by the automotive industry for some time, but not always with the same rigor. Table 7-1 lists some of the 400 characteristics examined, which are primarily human factors considerations. Ford's strategy was to design products that were superior to competitors' (best-in-class) for an overwhelming number of individual characteristics, with the expectation that the resulting product would be superior overall. While not a human factors method, the BIC approach increased focus on the customer, and consequently, expanded the attention given to human factors.

Table 7-1. BIC Categories, Characteristics, and Examples

Feature Category	Feature Characteristics	Examples
Interior Controls	effort location feel	lowest tilt column release effort lowest turn signal switch effort best accelerator pedal feel
Instruments	readability accuracy	best nighttime switch illumination best speedometer accuracy
Underhood Accessibility	ease of checking ease of access	best underhood appearance best hood opening angle best oil filter accessibility
Comfort Convenience	comfort ease	best front seats for ingress and egress best rear armrest comfort best inside rear view mirror size best air conditioner, best radio sound
Exterior	usability	best latching of hood best side door outside key locking/manual
Windows Openings	access operation	best window handle accessibility best side door open angle best decklid-slam best fuel cap removal and installation
Interior	access	best seat track release handle best front seat comfort
Restraints	ease of adjustment	best vertical head-restraint adjustment
Signals	effort feel	lowest dimmer switch effort
Lighting	feel light level	best rear seat illumination
Climate Control	access performance	best heater performance best fresh air ventilation best climate control head access
Windshield Wipers/Washers	performance access	best washer coverage best wiper system noise best washer reservoir capacity
Powertrain	accessibility feel	best clutch pedal feel least transmission gear noise best transmission control (travel/feel),
Brakes	size/shape effort	best brake pedal (effort/feel) best brake pedal height
Steering	effort ease of adjustment	best steering wheel feel best steering column fit
Storage	capacity stowage	best shopping bag capacity best cassette tape stowage
Space Perceptions	roominess	best perceived driver leg room
Foot Comfort	comfort	best driver's left foot comfort
Miscellaneous	performance fit	best cruising range best turning diameter least jacking effort (turns/force)

Ford's efforts were motivated by the success of Japanese cars in the American market. Japanese companies employed a more sophisticated approach than BIC, called Quality Function Deployment (QFD). QFD involves identifying the customer attributes and their relative importance, measuring them against competitive products, setting attribute targets, and identifying the cost of achieving them (Hauser and Clausing, 1988; McElroy, 1987). (See also Green, Serafin, Williams, and Paelke, 1991; McCarthy and Tay, 1989.) This approach established a connection between traditional human factors considerations, such as switch travel forces, and the desirability of a product.

Table 7-2. Automotive Human Factors Evaluation Contexts

	Marketing and Preference	Ease of Use Learning Understanding Repair	Comfort Convenience	Safety	Driveability
Field Surveys and Evaluations	clinics focus groups mall licensing surveys	mall licensing office surveys			
General Lab Facilities		ingress/egress trunk/hood access mockup-control/ display location & efforts			
Special Lab Facilities			thermal-wind tunnel sound-anechoic chamber	impact tolerance crash sled	
Driving Simulators				collision avoidance	handling dynamics
Proving Grounds			ride quality	collision avoidance	handling dynamics
Research Cars on Public Roads		ease of use ease of learning understandability		new info systems	handling dynamics
Operational Field Tests				new info systems	

To satisfy customers and make vehicles safer to drive, human factors efforts have been conducted in a variety of contexts. A summary table, based on the literature (DRIVE Safety Task Force, 1991), appears in Table 7-2. Each of these evaluation contexts (field surveys, general and special laboratory facilities, simulators, proving grounds, research cars on the road, operational field tests) and associated methods will be examined in a separate section of this chapter. Issues addressed include:

- vehicle design aspects to be evaluated,
- the independent and dependent variables examined,
- the equipment and facilities required,
- the selection of participants in experiments, and
- advice and comments (primarily for students).

For each method at least one example experiment is described. Because a complete understanding of a method often requires experience or direct contract with the method, not merely reading about it, many examples are drawn from my own research and that of my colleagues at UMTRI.

3.0 Field Surveys and Evaluations

Evaluations in this category include clinics, focus groups, and conventional surveys. Evaluations are generally conducted off site. Materials required may be just pencil and paper to record responses, or may also include products to be presented to prospective customers (Sivak, Flannagan, Traube, Battle and Sato, 1993).

3.1 Clinics

Marketing research clinics provide insight into what customers desire in future products. There is virtually no published literature on this topic because of its proprietary nature. In a typical clinic, a manufacturer, working with a marketing firm, recruits 50 to 200 potential customers to compare a prototype future vehicle with 2 or 3 contemporary competitors. Because nationwide trends in fashion and products tend to appear first in California, clinics are often conducted in Los Angeles. Other target cities include Minneapolis and Columbus, because responses in those markets are typical of the United States as a whole. Evaluations are generally static and involve getting in and out of vehicles, though clinics may include an opportunity to drive the comparison vehicles. Participants make pairwise comparisons of products by either ranking or rating them on general qualities (interior room, overall appearance, etc.). Vehicles are carefully matched in color and feature content. If real products are not available, a videotaped explanation may be provided along with prices. Customer demographics are given considerable attention. Because of the effort required to rent facilities and analyze the data (as well as prepare vehicles and recruit participants), clinics typically cost in excess of $100,000 per study.

3.1.1 Advice and comments. Manufacturers are very sensitive as to who can see future products, and consequently, access must be restricted to essential personnel. This may include special card key access to the room where the products are stored or security guards posted by the entrance. Vehicles are delivered to the test area under cover. Personnel and subjects involved may be asked to sign confidentiality agreements. For students working on projects as university employees, the university attorneys should review the confidentiality agreement before it is signed.

Computer-aided interviewing in clinics using laptop computers and hand-held computers/personal digital assistants (e.g., Newton) should be considered, though their use can increase the initial project planning and set-up costs. However, these devices reduce data analysis time and problems from illegible handwriting, reducing total project cost and completion time.

3.2 Focus Groups[1]

In arranging focus groups, the goal is to have 10 potential users of a product or service in each group. Groups meet for one to two hours in a conference room. A discussion guide contains the sponsor's questions of interest (e.g., Have drivers had accidents while using advanced driver information systems? Which features do drivers want in cars of the future?). The group is led by a skilled moderator who uses the discussion guide to identify questions and topics to be considered. The discussions are always audiotaped, and many times are videotaped using a camera hidden behind a one-way mirror. Representatives of the sponsor may be present behind the mirror as well, and they may communicate with the moderator (by passing notes or via an earphone) to follow up on points made. Typically, observers make suggestions to the moderator between group sessions.

The moderator attempts to get the group to identify common opinions with regard to questions in a discussion guide (without interjecting his or her own opinion). Generally, the amount of voting is limited, though some organizations use hand-held response boxes to record votes or ratings in real time. In one organization, the output of the response boxes was a graph superimposed on the videotape.

The focus group report may be written by the moderator, who summarizes the responses to each of the questions in the discussion guide. In other situations, observers from the sponsor write the report. Because of their interactive quality, focus groups tap customer concerns that surveys might miss, and, consequently, provide input useful to guide product design.

As an example, Brand (1990) describes a study involving 45 drivers split into four groups, two groups in Los Angeles and two groups in the New York City area. (See also Green and Brand, 1992). Similar to clinics, participants were selected to match the target population, based on age, income, and other demographics. In Brand (1990), all participants drove cars with some advanced information system (cellular phones, touch screen computers, trip computers, etc.). Their median annual income was $50,000 to $75,000. They tended to drive more expensive cars (Corvette, Saab 9000, Lincoln Town Car), and were mostly white-collar workers (architect, dentist, engineer, etc.).

Participants in that study from Los Angeles were much more interested in advanced information systems than those in New York. While this study provided some insights into customer concerns with regard to advanced information systems, it was unable to provide specific design guidance because participants had no experience with systems such as those proposed to be used for navigation.

3.2.1 Advice and comments. Focus groups are not without their limitations. Drivers cannot offer valuable suggestions about the usefulness of technology they have not used, making the evaluation of new technology

---

[1]For more information on focus groups, see Chapter 9, section 3.1.

quite difficult. At the time the Brand (1990) research was conducted, commercial or experimental navigation systems (or even mockups) were not available, and hence comments about them were of limited utility.

Selecting subjects for focus groups (and clinics) requires much more effort and is much more expensive than obtaining subjects for traditional human factors research. Names of drivers satisfying particular market demographics can be obtained from vendors such as R.L. Polk. Fees for subjects are typically $25 to $50 per hour (in 1990), running as high as $150 to $200 for doctors and lawyers.

Moderator selection is also important. Because of group dynamics, moderating focus groups requires special skill and should be performed by someone with experience in conducting them. It is important that the moderator be fully briefed, so that they have intimate knowledge of the product being discussed and can follow up on user questions. In some situations, it may be difficult to provide that knowledge to the moderator, and it may be necessary to use a potentially more biased, but more knowledgeable, technical person (such as a human factors specialist). It is difficult for product champions to avoid biasing groups.

Because of the subjective nature of focus groups, accurate communication of what transpired during sessions (by the moderator or others) can be challenging. Reports summarizing the results of focus groups should contain verbatim quotes from participants, not just the opinions of the entire group or subgroups as interpreted by the moderator. For example, in responding to questions about radios, Green and Brand (1992) reported the following:

> **With my last car before this, I was in an accident where the radio was down low. By the time I looked up, I was kissing someone else's rear end. It was my fault.**

Had this been summarized, a report might have merely said "the radio contributed to an accident," and much of the impact of the customer's comment would have been lost.

To aid in report preparation, transcripts of each session are desired. Written reports should be supplemented by videotapes, including raw footage from each session. Selected outtakes can often be more informative than a written report.

Hence, the proper conduct of focus groups poses many challenges to the academic researcher, and therefore, conduct of them in university settings is uncommon. However, because of their importance in industry and benefit to product development, exposure to focus group methods as part of an academic experience is desired.

3.3 Mall/Licensing Office Surveys[2,3]

Surveys of drivers are a relatively inexpensive means of determining driver preferences for vehicle features and driver understanding of how to operate them. Typically, these studies are conducted in shopping malls (because of the steady stream of people) or in driver licensing offices (because of the appropriateness of the sample). Waiting in line in a licensing office is not unusual. With nothing else to do, attracting participants for experiments is not difficult. Other venues and sample combinations that have been used include paid subjects in laboratories (recruited via newspaper advertisements), volunteers poolside at a swim club (Green, 1979), factory tour participants (Frank, Koenig, and Lendhold, 1973), and undergraduate psychology students completing a course requirement. Human factors surveys can also be conducted over the phone, but there is nothing in the published literature describing the execution of such surveys for automotive products.

Mall/licensing office surveys generally involve rating or ranking various alternatives (such as warnings) or writing down what different alternatives mean. For example, Saunby, Farber, and DeMello (1988) had 505 drivers at a licensing office write in the names for 25 symbols. In the second part, symbols were matched with a list of 25 names for controls and displays. The results identified the percent correct for each symbol.

Survey-like methods can also be used to obtain ideas as to how information should be presented to drivers. Green (1979) presented drivers with the names of vehicle controls (e.g., radio volume, radio tuning, heater) and asked drivers to draw a picture (a symbol) to label each control. Using the ideas from those drawings, an illustrator was able to develop a variety of symbols for further testing. Variations of this approach have been used to develop graphic warnings for garage hoists (Eberhard and Green, 1989), road hazards (Hoekstra, Williams, and Green, 1993), and text messages for vehicle monitoring systems (Williams, Hoekstra, and Green, 1993).

3.3.1 Advice and comments. Because of their low cost, surveys are particularly attractive to those with minimal resources such as students. However, if the results of the survey are to be used by designers, the sample size should be large (at least 100 drivers) and include drivers of all ages. In some studies, gender and income demographics may be critical.

A common stumbling block for students in planning surveys is underestimation of the time required to obtain permission to distribute surveys at a driver licensing office. The materials submitted to the authorities should include a survey that has been pilot tested. Those authorities (generally in the department of motor vehicles in the state capitol) can be identified by contacting the manager of the local licensing

---

[2]For more information on the mall intercept technique, see Chapter 9, Case Studies #4, and #6.

[3]For more information in the use of the licensing office intercept technique, see chapter 6, section 3.6.

office. Expect that a series of long distance phone calls, phone messages, and referrals will be required until the appropriate contact person is identified. Approval is most likely when the survey has a clearly identifiable contribution to driving safety, does not interfere with office operations or service (e.g., takes no more than 10 minutes per person), and does not request privileged information (e.g., Have you ever been arrested for a traffic violation?).

The draw-a-picture approach, sometimes referred to as the population stereotype method in the literature, is a bit of a misnomer. It suggests that the frequency with which an image is offered is representative of something (for example, how understandable the graphic is). A limiting factor in this type of experiment is the artistic talent of the respondents. Hence, what participants draw is affected by what they can draw.

To obtain concepts users can relate to, participants in these experiments should have technical backgrounds similar to that of the user population. Engineers, when asked to draw a graphic to represent the transmission, draw gears (an internal view), while nonengineers draw shift levers (an external view). Similarly, engineers depict the brake as a brake drum and shoes, while nonengineers present images of brake pedals.

In carrying out symbol production experiments, it is important to give participants a full description of the function (not just its name), to restrict the area available for the drawing (by providing a box), and to constrain the detail provided (by requiring use of a fat tip marker). Simple images are generally the most legible.

4.0 General Laboratory Studies

A key element of every automotive research laboratory is a full size mockup (or buck) of a real vehicle. Mockups may be either bumper to bumper or firewall to back seat. The car companies produce mockups of wood and clay prior to production and these are often used in human factors evaluations. If the tires and steering system are kept intact, they should continue to be functional so the vehicle can be moved about the laboratory. If not, then the mockup should be mounted on a wheeled frame. In most cases, identifying logos are removed. If the mockup includes only the passenger compartment, identification of the make and model is difficult for participants.

4.1 Secondary Control Evaluation

Several experiments have examined driver preferences for control location, type, and method of operation (Green, and Goldstein, 1989; Green, Paelke, and Clack, 1989; Wierwille and McFarlane, 1991). In my research, a wide variety of drivers varying in age and gender sat in two versions of a mockup whose specific interior dimensions were identical to those of proposed future products. The interior of the mockup was covered with Velcro®·

Mounted on panels surrounding the driver were several hundred controls -- knobs, pushbuttons, rocker switches, slide switches, stalk controls, etc. obtained from production vehicles. (See Figure 7-1.) For surface-mounted controls, the backs had been covered with Velcro®. Drivers were asked to identify the specific switch they preferred for each function (wiper speed, hazard, etc.) and place it where they wanted it. The experimenter recorded the specific switch number, the class of switch, the zone in which it was mounted, and a vector code for the method of operation. Drivers then operated a driving simulator and were verbally cued to touch each control. Drivers were given the option of replacing or relocating switches they had difficulty operating, which occurred for 10 to 15 percent of the switches. From this research, preferred switch types, locations, and methods of operation were identified for most secondary controls for sedans and sports cars.

Figure 7-1. Test Configuration for Secondary Control Research

Because the assembly of an instrument panel from parts is analogous to the assembly of a toy character's face using parts for the nose, eyes, ears, and mouth, this approach has become known as the "Potato Head" method (Green, Paelke, and Boreczky, 1992). In variations of this method, magnetized elements have been used to design a car radio, and other work has been carried out to design speedometer and gauge clusters.

4.1.1 Advice and Comments. This method is conceptually simple and subjects find participation to be enjoyable. This approach allows users and designers to visualize and directly experience design alternatives. In doing so, it makes design conflicts (competition for the same space, movement incompatibilities between controls, etc.) readily apparent. However, the effort necessary to acquire and modify a vast selection of switches (or displays) is considerable. (In one case, two students worked part time for at least six months.) It may be possible, with a moderate level of effort, to simulate a wide variety of displays using the rapid prototyping tools described later in this chapter.

4.2 Response Time to Displays

Display evaluations often utilize mockups. For example, Boreczky, Green, Bos, and Kerst (1988) describe research in which the main cluster in the mockup was replaced with a rear projection screen. On half of the trials drivers were shown a slide of an arrow on a distant wall pointing left or right. In response, the driver pressed a left or right button. This task was intended to keep drivers focused at a distant point similar to actual driving. On other trials, a slide of an instrument cluster (Figure 7-2) was presented by a random-access slide projector on the in-vehicle screen. The driver read the digital speedometer and then pressed one of two buttons (to indicate not speeding or speeding). The dependent measures were response time and error rate; the independent variables were digit size, speedometer location, ambient illumination (to simulate dusk and night), digit contrast ratio and color. This method was used to develop an equation to predict the time to read a speedometer, but it could be used to assess the legibility of a wide variety of displays.

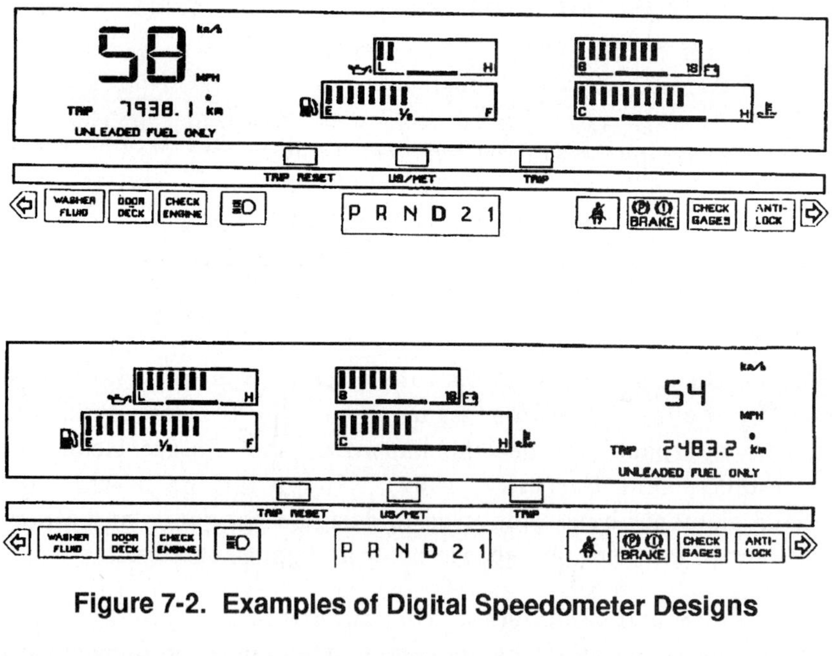

Figure 7-2. Examples of Digital Speedometer Designs

4.2.1 Advice and comments. The equipment required for this type of evaluation are found in most human experimental or cognitive psychology labs. The critical equipment are a random-access slide projector (> $1000) and computer interfaces for it. Software for controlling these types of experiments is regularly described in *Behavior Research Methods, Instruments, and Computers*.

Response time experiments examining instrument panel displays must contain an external task, one that causes subjects to accommodate as if they were looking at the road (optical infinity). When not present, interactions with display size and contrast can occur, resulting in misleading expectations of driver performance and recommendations concerning character size (Bos, Green, and Kerst, 1988).

4.3 Rear Lighting Design

Rear light experiments can be conducted in the laboratory using a vehicle buck or simple test fixtures. (See Projector, Cook, and Peterson, 1969 for a classic review of the literature on rear lighting research.) As an example, Sivak and his colleagues have examined response time to various brake light designs, considering issues such as the effect of automobile body color and lamp technology (e.g., LED, neon, fast incandescent) (Chandra, Sivak, Flannagan, Sato, and Traube, 1993; Sivak, Flannagan, Sato, Traube, and Aoki, 1993). In those experiments, subjects were given a central tracking task (following a moving target using a paddle controller) to simulate the attentional demands of steering. Flanking the tracking display were brake lamps. Ambient illumination levels and brake lamp luminance levels were carefully matched to real world conditions. When either of the brake lamps illuminated, subjects pressed a button. The dependent measure was response time, recorded by a computer.

In addition to this method, alternative rear lighting systems have been evaluated using a variety of other methods. (See Projector, Cook, and Peterson, 1969 for a classic review of the literature on rear lighting research.) A very creative method involves two test vehicles, one ahead of and one behind an unsuspecting motorist (Sivak, Post, and Olson, 1981). The lead test vehicle turns on its brake lights. The following test vehicle monitors the speed of the "trapped" motorist and when the trapped vehicle's brakes are applied (as indicated by the illumination of its brake lamps, visible from the rear).

4.3.1 Advice and comments. The most important items required for laboratory lighting experiments are a good illumination meter and a photometer capable of measuring luminance levels of small areas, as well as the CIE coordinates of a chromatic source. For wide area sources such a taillights, most photometers should be acceptable. For examining instrument panel displays, specialized photometers with less than one degree field of view are required.

4.4 Ingress/Egress, Trunk, and Underhood Access

Studies of the ease with which drivers get in and out of cars, and related topics are regularly conducted by the car companies. However, there is virtually no published literature on this topic (Loczi, 1993). In those proprietary studies, employees (sometimes selected to represent varying driver anthropometry) are asked to enter and exit mockups of future production vehicles. Tests are conducted indoors in well-illuminated laboratories, with subjects not wearing overcoats or jackets. Access to the vehicle is unobstructed. Entry and exit behavior is videotaped, with the primary interest being the number of contacts between the subject and the vehicle (other than with the seat), and the time required to complete the task. This type of data has been used to redesign door and body structures.

Interesting related research has been reported by Karwowski, Yates, and Pongpatana (1993) on access to the trunk of a car. The test fixture was the rear of a car mounted on a lift table. Below the trunk bottom was another lift table (so its vertical height could be adjusted). Adjustments could also be made to the trunk lip height and thickness. Subjects, varying in age, lifted laundry baskets, suitcases, and grocery bags from shopping carts into the trunk. After each lift sequence, one of the trunk dimensions was adjusted based on subject instructions to identify the worst case acceptable value for various trunk dimension combinations. Resulting from this research were plots of acceptable trunk dimension combinations.

4.4.1 Advice and comments. There are significant opportunities for quality research on this topic at low cost. Required are access to a wide range of vehicles, drivers varying in size and age, and a camcorder. For some types of experiments, mockups whose dimensions can readily be modified may be preferred. Particularly useful are blocks of Styrofoam® that can be attached to existing surfaces and cut into complex shapes using a bare hot wire.

4.5 Driver Anthropometry Studies[4]

Designers need descriptive statistics of driver body size, strength, and range of motion. Driver anthropometry affects what the driver can see, which controls they can comfortably reach, how comfortable the seat is, and other characteristics. A comprehensive overview of this topic appears in Roe's chapter in *Automotive Ergonomics* (Roe, 1993). The most commonly used set of instruments is found in a GPM anthropometric tool kit. Typically included are steel tape measures to determine circumferences, vernier calipers (generally 30 and 210 cm sizes) for measuring limb lengths, stature, and internal dimensions, a curved blade caliper for measuring external dimensions, and a goniometer for measuring joint angles. A bubble level may be used to assure measurement consistency. For examining driver

---

[4]See Chapter 11, sections 6.4, 7.2, and 8.3.

positioning, an H-point machine (to determine the location of the hip pivot point of a typical occupant in a car seat), and stereophotographic systems (to identify the three-dimensional location of anatomical landmarks by triangulation) are commonly employed. The H-point machine (Figure 7-3) is a special contoured mannequin that can be placed in a car seat, weighted so the downward pressure distribution resembles that of a seated occupant.

As an example of research on this topic, Schneider, Robbins, Pflug, and Snyder (1983) carried out a multi-year project to develop physical dimensions for dummies used in crash tests and other evaluations. This included the design of three-dimensional molds of various driver percentiles.

In the first phase, 177 drivers from four size-gender groups were selected based on height and weight (small female, mid-sized female, mid-sized male, large male). While considerable effort was made to recruit participants, there were major problems in recruiting small women and large men. Subjects sat in one of four vehicles while fully clothed. Photographs were taken from the side as well as a seat casting.

In the second phase, subject posture and anatomical landmarks for the same subjects were recorded using stereophotogrammetry in bucks duplicating package dimensions of vehicles from the first phase. Subjects wore only their underwear.

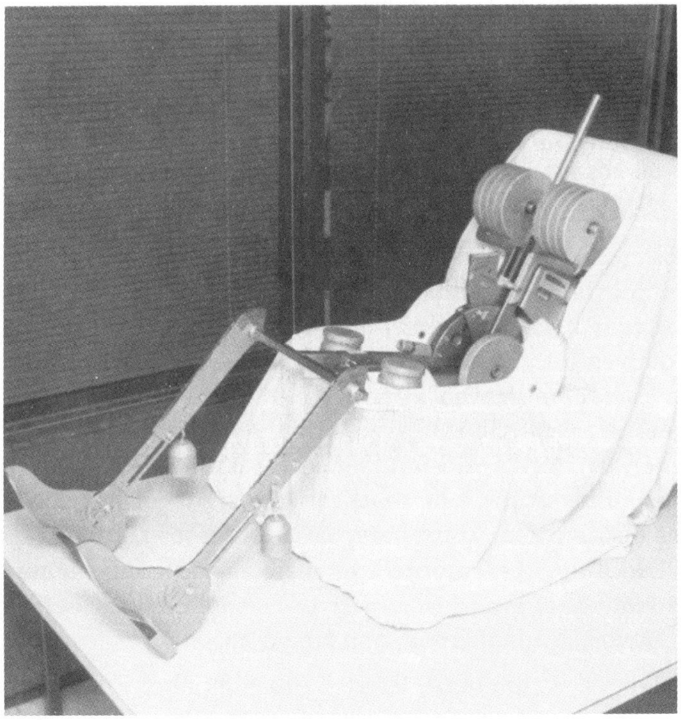

Figure 7-3. H-Point Machine

In the third phase, traditional standing and seated anthropometric measures were recorded. Measurements included 101 surface landmarks obtained by stereophotogrammetry (e.g., substernale, clavicle), 39 manually recorded standard seated measures (e.g., head breadth, radius length, foot length), and manually recorded surface contours (of the shoulder, knee, and thigh). From the data collected in all three phases, means and standard deviations of all measures were reported, as well as plots showing the various contours.

4.5.1 Advice and comments. The information designers need most is in-situ data, how drivers position themselves in vehicles, especially in trucks, buses, and construction, and farming equipment. Information on elderly driver anthropometry is also lacking. To collect that information, one needs an array of simultaneously actuated cameras (that is, a stereophotogrammetry system) and some method of identifying the location of anatomical landmarks (usually from markers placed on subjects). Careful placement and rigid mounting of the cameras is critical. If that equipment is not available, there are still opportunities for significant contributions concerning driver positioning. Basic anthropometric data can be collected using minimal equipment (a GPM anthropometric tool kit and a 35 mm camera mounted on a tripod).

4.6 Component Evaluation - Seat Comfort

QFD analyses have highlighted seat comfort as being important to drivers. In seat comfort, there is concern for both showroom comfort and long-term driving comfort. In the showroom, the emphasis is on a seat that feels soft and is easy to get in and out of. For long-term driving, good lumbar support and pressure distributions are key issues.

The most commonly used dependent measures in seating studies are ratings on bipolar scales (Habsburg and Middendorf, 1977). Pairs include spacious-constricted, soft-firm, cool-hot, deep-shallow, and others, as well as overall measures of comfort (comfortable-uncomfortable). The key independent variables are between seat differences. Typically the seats chosen represent a selection of production seats rather than varying in a methodical manner in their design (bench versus bucket, pan depth, cushion depth). To help understand why seats may be highly or poorly rated, data on seat pressure distribution (Hertzberg, 1972; Kamijo, Tsujimura, Obara, and Katsumata, 1982) may be recorded, as well as electromyograms (EMG)[5] to examine the activity of muscles subject to fatigue during seating (Sheridan, Meyer, Roy, Decker, Yanagishima, and Kishi, 1991).

As an example of this topic, Reed, Saito, Kakishima, Lee, and Schneider (1991) had eight male drivers participate in five test sessions. During the first session, each subject rated each of four production seats on 24 bipolar

[5] For more information on EMG, see Chapter 11, section 6.2.

scales. In the remaining sessions subjects operated a driving simulator for three hours, rating the body discomfort in four areas every 30 minutes. Also recorded was their posture (via the sonic emitters), EMG activity from various muscle groups, and seat pressure at 12 points. Finally, discomfort was assessed using cross-modality matching. Subjects adjusted a blood pressure cuff, a heat source on their left palm, and a vibrator on their left forearm to match the intensity of their discomfort. The cross modality provided better between-seat differentiation than revealed by the bipolar ratings. This was achieved at a cost of additional training time. The EMG data collected did not provide a clear view of postural muscle activity because of interference from muscle contractions associated with posture shifts. Finally, the results from the short term evaluations were different from those of the three-hour driving simulation.

4.6.1 Advice and comments. There are significant opportunities for students to conduct comparative evaluations of real seats using subjective methods. It is important, however, that such evaluations include a long exposure to each seat and that subjects be given tasks that simulate driving. Efforts that attempt to identify comfort mechanisms require specialized equipment and significant training in bioengineering.

4.7 Computer Testbeds-Rapid Prototyping[6] of Driver Interfaces

Recently, there have been concerted efforts to improve highway and other transportation systems by applying computer and communications technologies under the banner of Intelligent Vehicle-Highway Systems (IVHS). Some of the systems being considered include navigation, in-vehicle signing, and electronic yellow pages. These systems require driver interaction with either a visual or auditory interface that must be easy to use and not distracting to the driver. Safety and usability concerns can be examined by developing rapid prototypes of these interfaces and having drivers try to use them. An alternative approach, waiting until a working product is available, is unsatisfactory, since feedback occurs too late to have any significant impact on the product. Typical dependent measures include the time required to complete common tasks, the number of errors made, and comments about the ease of use. Independent measures typically concern interface design differences.

As an example of this approach, Paelke (1993) examined four different methods to enter destinations into a route guidance system using a small touch screen. Figure 7-4 shows the four SuperCard screens, most of which operated in a manner similar to products being developed. To enter a destination, drivers either scrolled through a list of destinations or entered it character by character. Character entry schemes included a standard (Qwerty) keyboard, a voice-mail-like phone pad design, and a design

---

[6]For more information on HyperCard, SuperCard, and MacroMind Director rapid prototyping, E-Mail Jon Weimer at: WEIMERJ@AOL..COM

requiring two keypresses to select each letter. Overall, the phone pad design had the shortest entry times. While the Qwerty design required only a single keypress to enter characters, their small size on the touch screen presented challenges to drivers over 60. Also noteworthy was the correlation of measured entry times with predictions from the Goals, Operations, Methods, and Selection rules (GOMS) model (Card, Moran, and Newell, 1983).

4.7.1 Advice and comments. Rapid prototyping is the most significant recent advance in human factors research methods. Currently, most rapid prototypes are developed in SuperCard, HyperCard, and MacroMind Director on Macintosh computers (Green, Boreczky, and Kim, 1990). For IBM-compatible computers, Toolbook is the application of choice, though it can be slow and does not support graphics as well as the Macintosh applications[7]. Within the defense industry, most prototyping is done on UNIX workstations using applications such as VAPS by Virtual Prototypes.

Currently, Macintosh computers are generally preferred for prototyping, with 68040 or higher processors being required for reasonable performance. Key considerations include hardware and software cost, ease of use and learning, transparent support for a variety of input devices (touch screens, trackballs, etc.), and support for a variety of output formats (various displays through RGB to NTSC converters, speech, etc.). Compactness and low power consumption are desired so computers used in laboratory experiments can be installed in test vehicles for between context comparisons.

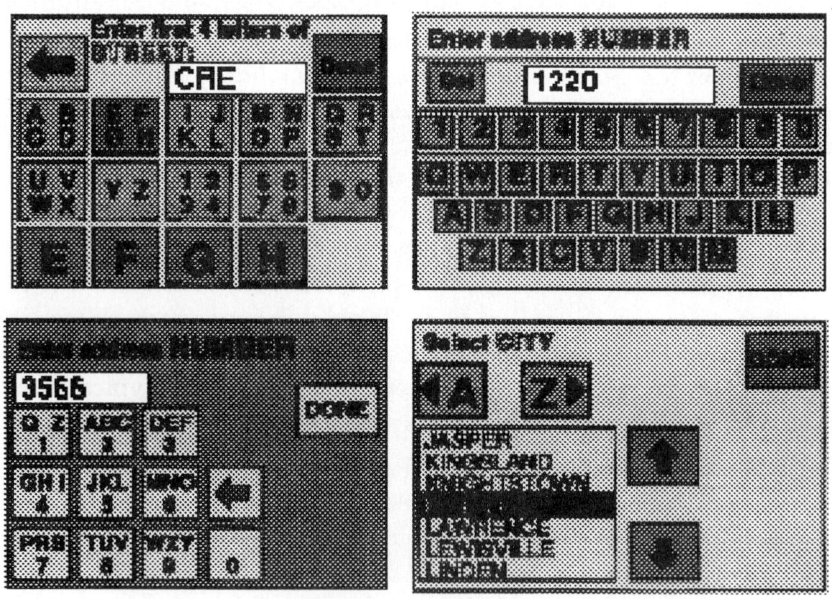

Figure 7-4. Prototype Destination Entry Screens

[7]Some industries are exploring the use of Microsoft Visual BASIC as a prototyping tool. However, you should realize that Visual BASIC is a programing language and not an authoring package, such as HyperCard or SuperCard. Thus, VB requires substantially more programming skill and development time than HuperCard or SuperCard. E-mail Jon Weimer for more information.

While clearly more rapid than developing real products (which can take many years), two months or more may be required for a HyperCard or SuperCard programmer to develop a simulation of a moderately complex interface from scratch.

5.0 Specialized Laboratory Studies

The studies described in this section require specialized facilities, some of which may be used both for automotive and nonautomotive research. Most automotive manufacturers have such facilities at their main research and development site. Facilities large enough for full size vehicles are not commonly found in universities.

5.1 Thermal Comfort

Tests of the adequacy of air conditioning systems are often conducted in climatic wind tunnels (Kawamoto, Hosokawa, Suto, and Nakajima, 1986; Rolle, Romitelli, and Savasta, 1992). In those evaluations, a static vehicle is placed in a tunnel facing a large fan. Air movement is necessary to assure proper operation of the cooling system. Special high-intensity lights simulate the heating effects of the sun. Steady state thermal comfort is generally assessed using mannequins, though human subjects may be used. Generally only the driver is considered. The dependent variables in these evaluations are surface skin temperature at numerous sites (as sensed by thermocouples or thermisters), air temperature, and relative humidity, and weighted combinations of these variables. The independent variables are solar load, air conditioner temperature setting, fan speed, and vent aim.

Experiments concerned with the adequate heating of the passenger compartment are usually conducted in a cold chamber without wind or solar load. These chambers are different than those used for high temperature studies. While the emphasis is on steady state conditions, the time to reach a comfortable level is receiving increased attention. Again, mannequins may be used to collect the same dependent measures, with the independent variables being external air temperature, heater setting, fan speed, and engine temperature at the start of the experiment.

5.1.1 Advice and comments. Experiments on thermal comfort can be conducted without resorting to expensive wind tunnels and cold chambers (found only in industry), relying instead on ambient conditions to provide the desired environment. However, this limits testing to particular times of the year and assumes the weather is cooperative and consistent. If thermocouples, A/D interfaces, and a personal computer are not available, data can be collected using thermometers to measure local temperatures, sling psychrometers to determine humidity (from the dry bulb and the associated saturated bulb temperature), and an anemometer to measure air speed. Local temperatures can also be determined from special liquid crystal displays (LCDs) that show a variety of temperatures, only one of which is legible at each particular temperature. If necessary, a globe thermometer to measure radiant heat can be made from a copper toilet tank float that has been spray painted black. Because of the equipment and facilities required, automotive thermal comfort studies are rarely conducted by students.

5.2 Vehicle Sound Measurement

Most engineering evaluations of interior sound levels are conducted with test vehicles mounted on a chassis dynamometer inside a sound-proof (anechoic) chamber, such as those owned by automotive manufacturers and acoustics laboratories. Evaluations to confirm computer models and laboratory data are conducted on the open road. Issues of interest include an overall impression of how quiet the vehicle sounds when it is driven, the presence of annoying sounds from wind noise and vehicle components (climate control fan, wiper noise, door closing), and the quality of the audio system. (Wind noise checks may also be conducted in a wind tunnel.)

As an example, Fujita, Nishiyama, and Hayakawa (1988) describe methods for evaluating the quality of an exhaust sound, an important characteristic of sports cars. Vehicles were placed in a semianechoic chamber, and recorded sounds were presented by a speaker mounted near the exhaust. Twenty male sound experts identified where each sound fell on several 7-point semantic differential scales (e.g., strong - weak, powerful - powerless, etc.). For each sound, spectral data were available. Their use of subjective ratings and objective sound measurements as the dependent measures is typical of sound quality evaluations.

5.2.1 Advice and comments. It may be possible to conduct noise evaluations using less sophisticated facilities, such as an enclosed mockup (or even a parked car) in a quiet area. Most enclosed areas, e.g., garages and other concrete structures, are not suitable for sound evaluations because they are reverberant. Sounds could be presented using open earphones (which tend to provide a higher quality sound than muff type headphones) or via an array of small speakers located in the vehicle interior and distributed to provide desired directionality. Placing speakers outside the vehicle may lead to problems with room acoustics. For sounds from components, the speaker should be in the same location as the component (e.g., in evaluating blower noise, the speaker should be under the dash).

Faithfully capturing and measuring automotive sounds requires high-fidelity equipment. This includes a spectrum analyzer to identify the presented sounds and a high quality tape drive or CD player to present them, along with an assortment of microphones, speakers, ear phones, and amplifiers. While the playback equipment can be found in a well-equipped dorm room, the recording equipment is less common.

5.3 Crash Tests

No topic has received more study in automotive human factors than impact biomechanics. In fact, an annual conference is devoted to this topic. (See the *Stapp Conference Proceedings*) Over 40,000 people are killed each year in the U.S. in motor vehicle crashes (National Safety Council, 1993) and several times that number receive significant injuries. Crash tests may involve whole vehicles, in which an instrumented vehicle is propelled into another vehicle or a barrier, or barriers that strike the test vehicle. Tests of this type examine responses of instrumented dummies to the impact.

Most impact tolerance tests use crash sleds, not whole vehicles. The major component is a carriage mounted on wheels or on rails (See Figure 7-5). The carriage holds seats, the occupant restraints including seat belts and air bag, the dummies, and possibly some interior components such as the instrument panel. Surrounding the impact area are specialized lighting and high speed cameras to record the impact. Numerous accelerometers are mounted on the crash dummies.

Figure 7-5. UMTRI Impact Test Facility

Independent variables of interest include the change in velocity (ΔV) associated with the crash; the model, percentile, and gender of the dummies; and the restraint type and design. Dependent variables include the maximum acceleration of the center of gravity of the head, the maximum average acceleration over short time period (3-4 ms.), various measures of chest acceleration, femur axial load, and specific injury indicators (e.g., the Head Injury Criterion (HIC): McIntosh, Kallieris, Mattern, and Miltner, 1993; Seyer, 1993). The HIC value is the maximum cumulative integration of the acceleration over a period not exceeding 36 milliseconds.

5.3.1 Advice and comments. Unless students are working at a university that has a crash sled and instrumented dummies, the specialized facilities required for these types of tests will be unavailable to them. Live animals and cadavers are rarely used for this research because of the difficulty in obtaining approval from human subjects and animal use review boards, and -- most importantly -- because their motion can be well simulated by instrumented dummies. Sled tests cost $1000 or more per impact when conducted as part of a series of tests, so significant funding is required for this type of research. Also, the risks associated with flying debris make stringent safety precautions and experienced supervision a necessity.

6.0 Driving Simulation[8]

Driving simulators are ideal for experiments that are too dangerous to be conduced in real vehicles, especially those related to collision avoidance. Also well suited for simulator evaluations are comparisons of alternative vehicle handling packages. (See Repa and Bertollini, 1991, for a detailed overview of potential applications.)

Most car companies and major transportation research organizations either have or are developing advanced driving simulators, some with motion bases (Guyard and Boulanger, 1992; Nordmark, Jansson, Lidstrom, and Palmkvist, 1985; Park, Greenberg, and Mousseau, 1992; Evans, 1992). The Mercedes-Benz simulator is the best known, high-fidelity driving simulator (Drosdol and Panik, 1985). Its moving platform supports full size vehicles. A surrounding dome serves as the projection surface. A wide variety of objects (signs, buildings, etc.) and traffic can be presented. Schill and Schmeider (1992) report that the simulator has been used for 60 experiments, involving approximately 1500 subjects. The major drawback of high-fidelity driving simulators is the cost of their development (often a million dollars or more) and their operation (as much as $2000 per hour).

As a result, lower cost alternatives (approximately $25,000 each) have been developed, such as the Systems Technology Incorporated (STI) driving simulator (Allen, Stein, and Aponso, 1990). The STI simulator (Figure 7-6)

---

[8] For more information on the use of simulation in human factors research, see Chapter 5 and Chapter 13, sections 2.3, and 4.0-4.6,

uses a 386 or 486 computer with a graphics coprocessor card to generate texture-free road scenes that include straight and curved roads, highway signs, a speedometer display, and secondary tasks. A separate video game sound card is also used. A powerful aspect of the simulator is the scenario definition language, which allows for sequences of traffic events to be specified. The modeling of vehicle dynamics is fairly sophisticated. Input to the simulator is by a steering wheel and foot controls. Output can either be presented on a video monitor or on a projection video display.

Figure 7-6. STI Driving Simulator
(Courtesy of Systems Technology Incorporated)

Another low-cost simulator, the UMTRI driving simulator, comes in two versions for Macintosh computers (Sweet and Green, 1993). The monochrome version shows only straight roads. The color version shows straight and curved roads, and intersections (Figure 7-7). The monochrome version is primarily used for studies of on-center vehicle handling. The color version has been used for experiments on driver workload, seat comfort, elderly drivers, and medical disabilities. It consists of a vehicle buck (with active foot controls and a steering wheel), a reflective wall to show road scenes, an LCD projection panel, an overhead projector, and several Macintosh computers. The main computer processes input from the vehicle controls and updates the screen. A second, networked Macintosh presents the vehicle sounds. Also, because of their simplicity, novice users, such as students, can learn to use them fairly quickly.

Figure 7-7. UMTRI Driving Simulator Road Scene

Dependent measures recorded by the UMTRI driving simulator include speed, lateral position, longitudinal position on each road segment, yaw angle, steering wheel angle, and throttle position for each screen update. Update rates of 30-60 Hz are planned for the near future. Performance measures derived from the raw data include the mean and standard deviation of speed and lane variance for each road link.

Independent measures vary with the topic being investigated. In medical studies measures might include the duration of the disability or the time since release from the hospital, the level of a treatment (e.g., a drug), and of course, the age and gender of the patient. Most medical experiments involve other indicators of disability, such as performance on a neuropsychiatric battery or in a driving test (Chatel, Bieliauskas, Green, Warner, and McSweeny, in press).

As an example of the application of driving simulation, Janssen and Nilsson (1990) compared seven collision avoidance warning systems with a control condition (no warning). While driving on a winding two-lane road, a lead vehicle driving at various speeds appeared 7 seconds ahead of the subject. The lead vehicle continued at a set speed and then left the road unless it was passed by the subject. Objects in the left lane interfered with passing. Warnings could be presented based on two time criteria three different ways: by a light, a buzzer, or a smart gas pedal (one whose resistance changes when a driver follows a vehicle ahead too closely). Dependent measures included the number of warnings per subject per run, the percentage of time the warning was on, and the distribution of headways. Questionnaire data were also collected. (e.g., How useful is the warning system? How much would you pay for it?) The results suggested that the smart gas pedal, combined with the time-to-collision criterion, provided the greatest benefits.

6.1 Advice and Comments

Unless you planning to spend a career conducting driving simulator experiments, and have a staff and funding to provide long term support, developing one's own driving simulator is not recommended. Developing even a simple simulator to show a single-lane-winding road, can take months (Green and Olson, 1989). More sophisticated simulators can take years. Simulator development includes not only development of the basic graphics and input/output routines, but specification of the simulated world, as well. The specification of each shrub, tree, building, and sign is very time consuming. Prior to using the simulator for product evaluation, some attempt should be made to verify that the simulation (and which features of it) capture the essential qualities of driving on the road.

As an alternative to a research driving simulator, some researchers have used driving games as a loading task. Except for computing the time to complete a course, games do not provide real time performance measures. Also, the competitive nature of games can make them more attention demanding but less threatening than normal highway driving. Consequently, people drive more recklessly than they would on the road.

In the future, virtual reality technology may be used to provide low-cost, high-fidelity driving simulation because it eliminates the need for a projection dome and expensive projection devices. However, much of the cost of the simulation is in developing the graphics software and specification files for the simulated world, costs that will not be reduced.

In addition to cost and fidelity concerns, the most significant problem in using a simulator is subject motion sickness. While the incidence varies from simulator to simulator, it is not unusual for 25% of the participants to withdraw, with rates being higher for older drivers, especially women.

Driving simulators provide a flexible, well-controlled environment for human factors research and can be extremely useful. However, many in the engineering community have been campaigning for high-fidelity (and very costly) driving simulators. Human factors research needs suggest that low cost simulators will often be more cost effective.

7.0 Proving Grounds Experiments

Proving grounds are a test environment unique to automotive research. Generally, they contain three types of facilities: high speed oval tracks for testing vehicle endurance and lane change maneuvers, skid pads for braking and emergency handling tests, and large paved areas for nonemergency maneuvers. Each major U.S. car manufacturer has an oval track in southeastern Michigan and a second track in Arizona for hot-weather testing. Many of the suppliers (e.g., Dana Corporation, Allied-Signal Corporation) have tracks, as well. Commercial race tracks are also a viable option (e.g., Michigan International Speedway). Except for the lane change experiments (currently focusing on the advantages of four-wheel steering), few human factors experiments are conducted on high speed ovals, primarily because of the risk to drivers in the event of a mishap. In the near future, many experiments related to automated highway concepts are likely to take place on test tracks.

To obtain access to a test track, a certificate of track safety procedures may be required. Engineers working for automotive companies have little difficulty in obtaining access to test tracks. For others, there is an hourly charge for track access ($100 per hour) and special insurance requirements.

In the past, when access to test tracks was not available to researchers, experiments were conducted on unopened sections of limited-access highways. Presently, opportunities for such are limited because of public pressure to open limited-access highways as soon as they are completed, potential interference with construction, and the general absence of expressway construction (at least in the U.S.).

Access to skid pads, used for braking and handling tests, can be more restricted than access to an oval because of the risk involved in performing maneuvers, with specific training in emergency maneuvers being a prerequisite. Standard practice is to wet the skid pad to make it slippery, which is done using either a sprinkler system or a water truck. Consequently, access to a skid pad often requires prior notice.

Access to other parts of the proving grounds (hill courses, Belgium block roads for ride quality checks, large paved areas, etc.) is generally unrestricted. As an alternative, some have used abandoned airport runways and tarmacs for tests (Zwahlen and Balasubramanian, 1974). These areas are used for general tests of ride quality, vehicle performance, and vehicle handling.

As an example, Green, Gillespie, Reifeis, Wei-Haas, and Ottens (1984) had 45 Ford employees drive a 1984 Ford Thunderbird and a Ford LTD through eight maneuvers. (See also Koide and Kawakami, 1988) In the Green, et al. research, test cars were fitted with an adjustable boost, power-steering system, and a digital display of steering wheel torque. Maneuvers included parallel parking, a low speed slalom, driving on a banked high-speed track (60 mph), driving in circles on a skid pad, and two routes through residential neighborhoods. Maneuvers were selected to cover the range of speeds and conditions encountered during ordinary driving. While driving each maneuver, the power-steering assist level was adjusted from one extreme to another (lightest to heaviest effort, then heaviest to lightest). At each level, drivers rated the steering effort on a five-point scale (too easy, a bit too easy, OK, a bit too hard, too hard). The research indicated the desired boost settings (specific to the vehicle tested) as a function of speed.

7.1 Advice and Comments

Experiments on high speed ovals and skid pads can expose subjects to particularly high levels of risk. Because of the need for a test track, such studies are unlikely to be conducted by students. However, considerable contributions can be made in exploring low speed handling, experiments that can be conducted in unused parking lots.

8.0 Experiments on Open Roads

8.1 Individual Cars With No or Minimal Instrumentation

For research of this type, dependent measures include subjective evaluations of workload, expert ratings of driving skill, identification of driver errors, and similar measures that can be obtained strictly by observation. In some studies a stopwatch or other device might be used to time the duration of events (such as the use of controls) or, when combined with a speedometer reading of speed, the distance between two points.

As an example of an experiment in this category, Sivak, Olson, and Pastalan (1981) had groups of three subjects in the front seat of a car (one driver and two passengers) drive past signs with the letter "E" on them. The evaluation was conducted on a straight, flat, dead end road. Subjects pushed buttons indicating if the E was facing left or right. When the sign was passed, the experimenter pushed a button to stop the distance counter. The distance counter, response lights for each subject, and the sign were videotaped for later analysis so the sight distance and errors could be determined for each subject. Independent measures included the driver age and sex, color of the sign background, color of the letter, and the material from which the letter was made. This experiment is typical of those used to examine the legibility of highway signs and sight distance. In other studies, sign content (symbolic vs. text messages, choice of particular words, etc.) has been examined.

Another class of related studies concerns the comparison of alternative headlight systems (Olson, 1978; Sivak and Flannagan, 1993). In these experiments sight distance was again the dependent measure, while the independent measures included target type (sign, pedestrian, etc.), target location, type of headlamp used, and beam selected (e.g., high vs. low). To simplify data collection, some studies of lighting systems have been conducted with static vehicles (but out of doors) (Flannagan, Sivak, Battle, Sato, and Traube, 1993).

8.1.1 Advice and comments. By definition, experiments in this category require minimal equipment, though for studies of night driving the headlamp voltage needs to be carefully regulated so lamp output level is consistent. For studies pertaining to signs and headlights, identifying a site where there is minimal traffic and other interference (e.g., private roads) is critical. If testing concerns one road segment, and is to be repeated on a daily basis, notifying the police of the testing should be considered.

8.2 Instrumented Cars

Clearly, the ultimate test of how well a product functions or what constitutes safe driving behavior must be examined on the road. For this purpose, a limited number of specialized vehicles have been developed. One of the first examples of such was the Driver Performance Measurement and Analysis System (DPMAS), an instrumented 1970 Chrysler Imperial. Vehicle modifications included an oversized, power inverter and two additional batteries for electrical power, a digital tape recorder, two audio recorders, a printer, and a 35 mm slide projector. The projector was mounted in the back of the car and aimed at the windshield. It was used for experiments on in-vehicle signing (Mast, Ballas, and Peters, 1976).

More contemporary vehicles include the Institute for Perception (TNO) Instrumented Car for Computer Assisted Driving (ICACAD) (Piersma, Burry, Verwey, and Van Winsum, 1993), the Virginia Polytechnic Institute instrumented car (Dingus, Antin, Hulse, and Wierwille, 1989), the TravTek camera car developed by General Motors (Fleischman, 1992), and UMTRI's Driver Interface Research Vehicle (DIRV) (Sweet and Green, 1993). A compact recording system is described by Allen, Hogue, Rosenthal, and Parseghian (1989). Data commonly recorded by these vehicles include speed, distance traveled between points to the nearest 0.01 miles, driver response times to the nearest 0.01 seconds, steering wheel and accelerator position to the nearest percent of full scale, the number of steering wheel and accelerator reversals, and the number of brake applications per second, as well as codes for events. In some vehicles, activation of specific controls can also be recorded.

The number of potential classes of measures and specific measures is considerable. (See Green, 1993a for an extensive listing.) Some of items of interest are described in the following sections.

8.2.1 Forward scene. Normally traffic is recorded by a fixed camera mounted between the driver and passenger, in the center of the vehicle, or in front of the inside rear view mirror. For those on a strict budget, a camcorder could be used, though color subminiature (thumb-sized or lipstick) cameras are recommended. These cameras are less likely to block the driver's vision and their small size makes them easier to ignore, though they cost several thousand dollars each.

8.2.2 General driver actions. Normally, a second camera is aimed at the driver to record head motions, eye fixation locations, and facial expressions. In the Virginia Tech vehicle, the camera was mounted on the hood under a special protective cover. UMTRI used a wide field of view subminiature camera mounted on the A-pillar. Others have concealed a camera inside a climate control vent, which provides a distorted image. To facilitate analysis, the output from this camera is mixed with the output from the forward scene camera and recorded on the same video track.

8.2.3 Audio. Driver comments and environmental sounds (auditory warnings, etc.) are essential to understand an event sequence. Locating the microphone and its cable to minimize interfering drivetrain noise is desired. One possibility is to use the microphone built into the A-pillar for a hands-free phone.

8.2.4 Driver eye movements[9]. To drive safely, drivers must look where they are going and must minimize the time looking elsewhere (for example, at in-vehicle displays). Of interest are the frequency and duration of driver eye fixations to various locations. (See Green, 1992 for a summary of the devices for recording driver eye fixations). On-the-head systems with a head tracker typically cost $50,000. Off-the-head systems typically cost $100,000. On-the-head systems can be uncomfortable to wear and can reduce the field of view, making them unsuitable for urban driving. Many systems can not record fixation data if drivers wear glasses or contacts, or in bright sunlight. For some systems, the problems with sunlight can be overcome by fitting the headgear with an infrared reflective visor and blinders.

8.2.5 Vehicle speed. In modern vehicles, the wheel pulse signal to the engine computer is used to determine vehicle speed to the nearest 0.1 mph (at 10 Hz), though speed can be obtained by videotaping the speedometer. Both excessive speed and speed variability are indicative of unsafe driving.

8.2.6. Vehicle lateral position in the lane. If drivers are not paying attention to their driving, they may weave excessively or drive erratically. Lateral position can be sensed by either a forward scene camera or by a separate camera aimed downward at the lane markings, which provides a more accurate measurement. Roof mounting is unsatisfactory as the

---

[9]For more information on eye movement tracking, see Chapter 4, section 7.3.

enclosure draws undue attention to the test vehicle. For the UMTRI instrumented car, the camera is hidden in the driver's outside mirror (Sweet and Green, 1993) and lateral position is computed by a machine vision algorithm in real time to the nearest 0.1 feet at 10 Hz. Lane position can also be determined manually from videotapes.

A clever alternative is to attach a dripping container of liquid dye to the bumper of a car so its path can be marked (Zwahlen and Balasubramanian, 1974). Since Zwahlen's test course was on an abandoned airport runway, he could return after each trial to measure droplet location in relation to pavement markings. Not everyone has access to an abandoned airport.

8.2.7 Other vehicle dynamic characteristics. Accelerometers can be used to obtain numerous measures of vehicle behavior such as longitudinal acceleration (indicative of rapid acceleration and hard braking), yaw angle (indicative of misalignment with the road) and yaw rate. Roll angle and pitch angle threshold may be used to identify sudden maneuvers. Except in studies of vehicle handling, these measures are not collected in most human factors studies involving instrumented cars as they tend to be insensitive to differences that occur in ordinary driving.

8.2.8 Steering wheel position. The driver's input to the vehicle appears to be more sensitive to attentional demands than output measures such as lateral position. Potential measures of interest include the standard deviation of steering wheel angle, the number of steering wheel reversals, the number of steering wheel movements, and the steering wheel action rate (the number of times the steering wheel velocity exceeds five degrees per second) (MacDonald and Hoffmann, 1980). Steering wheel position is generally sensed by a high precision multiturn potentiometer. An alternative is to place bands of high contrast tape around the steering wheel rim and videotape the wheel position using the camera recording the forward scene from the center of the vehicle.

8.2.9 Brake pedal position. The number of times the brake pedal was pressed and driver response time since a triggering event are of primary interest, not the brake pedal's absolute position. Brake position can be sensed by a string potentiometer attached to the pedal linkage or a pressure transducer.

8.2.10 Timing of external events. To record events, such as passing a landmark or a near collision, the experimenter presses a key on the keyboard of the data logging computer. The millisecond timing accuracy desired is handled by the recording computer. Timing should be synchronized with the videotape record so the data sets can be combined. Placing Society of Motion Picture and Television Engineers (SMPTE) time codes on videotapes can be useful.

8.2.11 Control of displays. The time associated with switch closures, the switches operated and the timing of associated display actions need to be recorded, generally to the nearest millisecond. This is accomplished by either a computer connected to the device being tested or, for devices being simulated in HyperCard, SuperCard, or Director, by the controlling program.

8.2.12 Time to line crossing (TLC) and time to collision (TTC). TLC is the time required at any given moment for any vehicle tire to come in contact with a lane edge marking if the steering wheel position remains unchanged (Godthelp, Milgram, and Blaauw, 1984). In some sense, it represents the size of the safety cocoon that surrounds the vehicle. Until recently, on-board equipment to determine this measure has been beyond the state of the art.

TTC is the time until a crash, if the driver maintains the current speed and steering wheel angle (Van Der Horst, and Godthelp, 1989). While the measure has been examined in the context of intersection behavior, it has not been examined for other contexts. Computing TTC requires radar data on all large surrounding objects (both stationary and fixed) and computation of their trajectories. This is a significant technical feat. It is only recently that the capability to determine this measurement has existed.

8.2.13 Physiological measures. Measures of interest include heart rate variability (Mouri, Yanai, Kishi, Sugasawa, and Furusho, 1993), galvanic skin response, and brain waves (electroencephalogram or EEG) (Yoshida, Tanaka, Isoda, and Kamiya, 1991). These have been used as indicators for stress, fatigue, and alertness.

8.2.14 Subjective measures of workload. Two measures of workload are given the most attention in the literature: the National Aeronautics and Space Administration (NASA) Task Loading Index or TLX (Hart and Staveland, 1988), and the Subjective Workload Assessment Technique (SWAT) (Lysaght, Hill, Dick, Plamondon, Linton, Wierwille, Zaklad, Bittner, and Wherry, 1989). In TLX workload is rated on six dimensions: mental demand, physical demand, temporal demand, performance, effort, and frustration. The scales for each range from very low to very high, except for performance (perfect to failure). The SWAT has three dimensions: time load, mental effort, and psychological stress. For each dimension there are three levels with short statements describing each level. The result is a workload score ranging from 0 to 100. The advantage of these methods is that they do not require instrumentation, only paper and pencil forms. Hicks and Wierwille (1979) show that subjective estimates of workload do vary with primary task difficulty. With specific regard to TLX, Noy (1989) found that only two of the scales (mental demand and physical demand) and, to a lesser degree, the weighted composite TLX rating, were significantly linked with driving task difficulty.

8.2.15 Occlusion time. The argument for occlusion data is that the more difficult the driving task, the more time the driver needs to spend looking at the road. In their classic occlusion experiment, Senders, Kristofferson, Levison, Dietrich and Ward (1967) had drivers wear a helmet with a translucent visor. Depending on the condition, pressing a button either allowed drivers a 0.5-second look at the road (by raising the visor) or short duration looks periodically, while driving at a safe speed. Participants drove on both a closed circuit race course and on an unopened section of an expressway. Look times varied with the difficulty of the road driven. Because of the risk to drivers, this technique is not used in open road studies but has been used in closed course experiments. Glasses with LCD lens to block the driver's view are now used for experiments of this type.

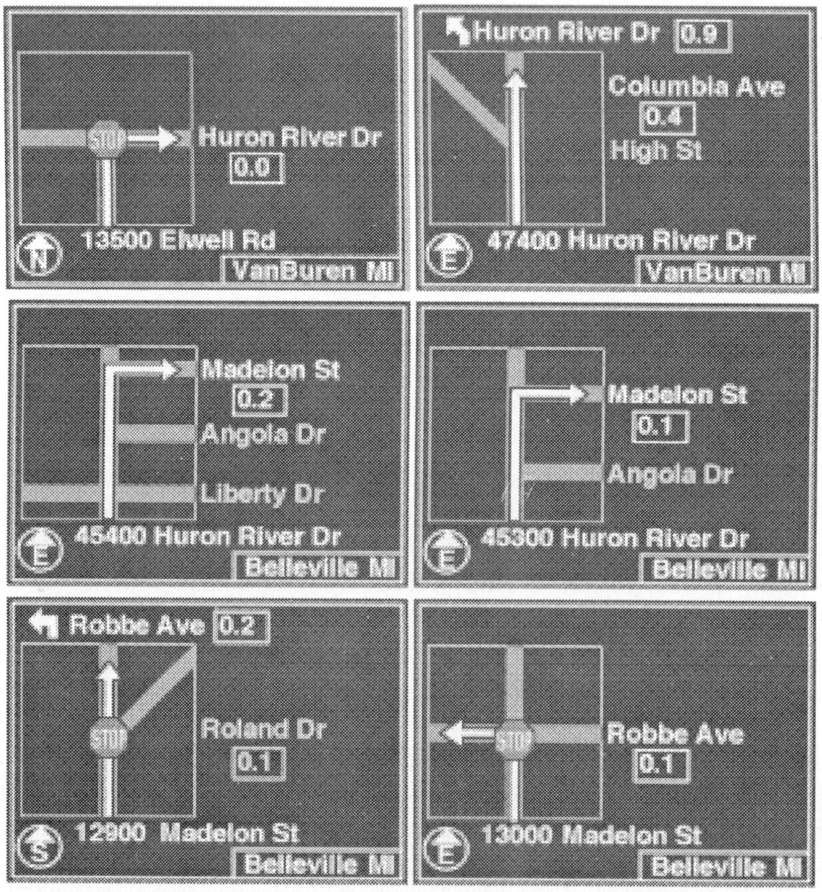

Figure 7-8. Sample Route Guidance Screens

8.2.16 Navigation measures. The number of turn errors, time to reach the destination, and distance traveled are measured. As an example of the use of an instrumented vehicle, Green, Williams, Hoekstra, George, and Wen (1993) describe two experiments. In the first, six pairs of drivers drove an instrumented car over a 19-turn, 35-minute route aided by an experimental route guidance system. The route guidance was provided on a head-up display (HUD), on the instrument panel (IP), or by voice, all controlled by a computer program written in SuperCard. Sample screen are shown in Figure 7-8. Drivers also used the other three information systems.

As part of the collaboration process, participants identified what they did and did not understand without prompting[10]. They also offered suggestions for improvements. Following is a hypothetical conversation to give the reader a sense of the data collected in this type of experiment.

subject 1: I wonder what this arrow means.

subject 2: I think it is the compass because it keeps pointing the same way whenever we turn.

subject 1: It would be clearer if north was shown by the letter N and the arrow was not as fat.

In this experiment, no major problems were encountered by drivers which prohibited further evaluation of the driver interface. The subjects-in-tandem method described above has broad applicability for a variety of questions having to do with driver understanding of new interface designs.

In the second experiment, 43 drivers followed the same route using the same route guidance system and other information systems. Drivers made very few turn errors, with the fewest for the HUD, followed by the IP and voice designs. There were very few differences among performance measures recorded (mean and standard deviation of steering wheel angle, throttle position, speed and lateral position) for the three route guidance interfaces. Eye glance durations and frequencies were also obtained, as well as ratings of safety and ease of use of the driver interfaces.

8.2.17 Advice and comments. There are a large number of driving performance measures that can be recorded, and the selection of the measures to be recorded requires careful thought. It is easy to be overwhelmed by data. As an example, the UMTRI instrumented car collects four megabytes of numeric data for each 30 minutes of driving as well as a video record of events. The forward scene, driver comments from the videotape (both positive and negative), vehicle speed, and lateral position are the most consistently useful dependent measures.

Data analysis also needs careful thought. Many of the measures (e.g., speed, lateral position, steering wheel angle, driver eye fixation) can be captured on videotape and reduced manually. This is tedious and boring, and is generally not recommended. It is not unusual for some measures to require 30 hours of reduction time for each hour of data collected, though some creativity can reduce that time. For example, if only eye fixation frequencies for selected locations are needed (and not durations), tapes can be

[10]This is also known as the Co-Discovery technique. This technique is sometimes more effective at generating subject comments than think aloud protocols, because discussing a problem with another person feels more "natural" and less self-conscious than describing your thought processes aloud. For more information on Co-discovery technique, see Chapter 9, section 4.2.

replayed at normal speed and coded using special software. (See Green, Williams, Hoekstra, George and Wen, 1993 for details.) Coding the data as it is collected (to indicate the beginning and end of key test segments) can also aid analysis.

Depending on the equipment provided, an instrumented car can cost a quarter of a million dollars or more to develop. In spite of its expense, on-the-road testing using an instrumented car is the method proposed for certifying the safety and ease of use of IVHS driver interfaces (Green, 1993b). It is not unusual for a major experiment to take a year for a staff to plan, execute, analyze, and write up, and to cost in excess of $100,000.

The general tendency has been to use large cars (or in TNO's case, a van) because of the space and power requirements of the equipment. The drawback of large cars is that they may not be typical of what most people drive, having very different handling characteristics. In the case of a van, the driver eye height and greater sight distance are much greater, but the field of view is decreased. Given the competing requirements for space and commonality with what people normally drive, a minivan may be a good compromise for future instrumented vehicles.

9.0 Operational Field Tests

Operational field tests are a relatively new approach for automotive human factors evaluations. While various field tests have been conducted in the past (for example, fleet evaluations of high-mounted stop lamps on taxis), those evaluations have not been of the magnitude that has occurred as the result of IVHS activities. Operational field tests generally cost millions of dollars and involve fleets of vehicles, traffic management centers, and considerable infrastructure.

The best known operational field test is TravTek, a cooperative effort of General Motors, the Federal Highway Administration, the Florida Department of Transportation, the City of Orlando, and others (Fleischman, 1991). The project included a fleet of 100 specially equipped cars, an information center operated by the American Automobile Association (AAA), a traffic management center to assemble and automatically distribute information on accidents and congestion to the test vehicles, and a variety of traffic sensors. The project examined both the usability of a particular set of driver interfaces, the value of traffic information, and the overall system effectiveness in reducing congestion and accidents. That evaluation included 10 experimental approaches, some of which emphasized safety and human factors, while in other cases, system performance was emphasized. The 10 included a field experiment with rental users, a field experiment with local users, a yoked driving experiment, the Orlando test network experiment, the camera car experiment, the questionnaire experiment, debriefing and interviews, traffic management center/traffic probe experiments, modeling exercises, and a global evaluation.

In the rental car experiment, AAA members rented special vehicles from Avis Rent-A-Car at the Orlando airport and drove them as they normally would. The vehicle used a global positioning system (GPS) and map-matching hardware to continuously track its location. The navigation computer also recorded every keypress made by drivers. The data were sorted by origin-destination pairs, and the differences between different versions of the interface were considered.

The field experiment with local users involved several groups of 10-25 drivers, the same vehicles, and the same data recording equipment. Participants had the vehicle for a longer period (sometimes a month) allowing for examination of novice-expert differences. The yoked drivers experiment involved groups of participants driving from the same origin to the same destination at approximately the same time (and therefore experiencing the same congestion). Between participants, the driver interface was varied. Data were accumulated to examine differences due to trip length, congestion, and day versus night. Dependent measures included travel time, mean speed, number of stops, time at zero speed, speed variance, and trip distance.

In the Orlando test network experiment, sets of origin-destination pairs were grouped into routes to be driven by participants. Interface combinations included paper maps, arrow-based turn displays, two types of moving maps, and voice guidance. Data were collected both during the day and at night. Dependent measures included trip time and various ratings.

The camera car experiment involved an instrumented car. Drivers used either a paper map, a moving map with a route overlay, a turn arrow display, or voice guidance to navigate. Eye glance data, speed variance, and lane variance were collected.

The questionnaire experiment involved rating the TravTek system on system reliability, display readability, accuracy of the traffic information, etc. This was not a separate experiment, but a common survey format used in all experiments. These data were supplemented by debriefing and interviews carried out in several experiments. The traffic management center and modeling evaluations were primarily concerned with non-human factors issues. The global evaluation was a synopsis of all of the evaluations.

From the research perspective, the most notable aspects of the TravTek evaluation are the wide variety of experimental approaches examined and the broad scope of each evaluation.

9.1 Advice and Comments

Operational field tests cost millions of dollars and require large teams of researchers from many organizations. The time from conception to completion is a minimum of six years and can take 10 years. While students can assist in these projects, they are unlikely to play a major role. Because operational field tests are a new approach, it is premature to assess their cost-benefit ratio.

10.0 Lessons from My Experience

10.1 Which Method is Best?

The most appropriate method depends upon the question of interest. Certainly many topics to be addressed (e.g., thermal comfort, sound) require special test facilities.

Where possible, multiple measures of driver performance and behavior are recommended. A conclusion is much stronger when multiple measures converge on the same finding. For example, if users required less time to read a particular display than alternatives, made fewer mistakes, and were willing to pay more for it, then it would be the desired display. Another possible occurrence is that a reader may not believe that a particular measure is appropriate, such as reading time in the example just given. In this example, two other measures would remain (errors, willingness to pay) from which a conclusion could be drawn. For further information on selecting measures, see Kantowitz (1992) and Muckler and Seven (1992).

10.2 Maintain an Automotive Context

For automotive designers to accept and apply human factors research, it is very important that the research context look and feel like a motor vehicle. Green (1984) describes an experiment in which drivers were shown slides of instrument clusters, identified malfunctions indicated by the displays, and stated how they would respond. The original plan was for seating drivers in a chair and showing slides on a screen at the proper viewing distance. The automotive sponsor insisted that a vehicle mockup be used, which they provided at considerable expense. While the mockup helped put subjects in the proper frame of mind, the impact of the context was not examined experimentally and its effect on the experiment's results is unknown. However, automotive managers visiting university facilities have been more accepting of results conducted using realistic mockups.

Mockups can sometimes be obtained from automotive design studios, but the most common source is junkyards. Vehicles that had been struck from the rear are the best choice. Purchasing a wrecked car with a complete interior, transporting it to the laboratory site, disassembling it so it can be moved inside piece by piece, and then reassembling it typically costs several thousand dollars. For mockups used as driving simulators, a hood is needed to help subjects "aim" the car.

10.3 Collect Data on the Road When Possible

Engineers are more likely to be convinced that the results from an on-the-road experiment are applicable to vehicle design than the results from a laboratory experiment. However, real world conditions contain many sources of variability that make it difficult to exert good experimental control. It is particularly difficult to simulate the effects of traffic, the stress of driving in the laboratory, and complex tasks in the laboratory. Simple perceptual and cognitive tasks such as those related to display legibility and understanding, are best conducted in the laboratory.

10.4 Test Drivers of All Ages

It is important that participants in experiments be licensed drivers of all ages, and in particular, to include drivers over 60 or 65 in the sample. Potential age interactions must be examined where findings from experiments are to be applied to the driving public as a whole. Even when interactions are unlikely, including older drivers in the sample adds to the experiment's validity, especially to reviewers without research backgrounds. Studies in which only students serve as subjects are generally not recommended. Retirement homes and activity centers are an excellent place to recruit elderly drivers. Elderly drivers can be very punctual (often early), willing to participate, and relatively easy to schedule. Chronologically-broad samples can also be obtained at local driver licensing offices.

In the driver interface research at UMTRI, where performance is an issue, the standard practice is to test two age groups, ages 30 years or less, and, ages over 65 (or sometimes 60). Within each age category there are an equal number of men and women. Budget and schedule permitting, a third middle-age group, the initial purchasers of new IVHS products, should be included IVHS-related studies.

For surveys or evaluations where the key piece of information is how participants vote for alternatives, 100 or more subjects may be required. For experiments involving repeated measures of driver performance (e.g., response time to displays, tests with instrumented cars or driving simulators), samples of 20 to 30 drivers are typical. For experiments to find major usability problems with new designs, 10 or fewer carefully chosen drivers can be acceptable. (See Virzi, 1992.)

10.5 Videotape Participant Interactions

While it is important to fully describe the methods used to collect data in detail, along with the results and supporting statistics in technical reports and journal articles, it is also important to get automotive engineers interested in the work. A short videotape showing participants interacting with the equipment, along with comments saying what was liked or disliked, or found easy or difficult to do, can be very effective in conveying information. In the UMTRI driver interface research, it is standard practice to videotape a complete test session for at least one participant, and, for some experiments, every participant is taped.

11.0 Closing Remarks

The recent trend has been to increase the realism of automotive human factors research by making greater use of driving simulators and instrumented cars, a trend that decreases opportunities for student contributions because of the cost of the research and difficulty of obtaining access to equipment. Countering those trends have been advances in the development of rapid prototyping tools, low-cost camcorders, and new subjective methods for evaluating driving. These methods, when used with driver samples varying in age, and applied with creativity, can lead to numerous opportunities for research contributions, especially by students.

12.0 Suggestions For Further Reading

If you are interested in:	Read:
A briefer treatment of this topic	Green (1993c)
A standard reference on human factors	Sanders. and McCormick (1993) or Chapanis (1959)
Basic information on the design of experiments involving people	Martin (1991)
A detailed treatment of automotive human factors research and design issues	Peacock and Karwowski (1993)

Most of the journals (e.g., *Human Factors*, *Public Roads*) and the SAE papers listed in the references section that follows should be available at local corporate or university libraries with substantial holdings in engineering or transportation. Most of the technical reports can be obtained from the National Technical Information Service in Springfield, Virginia for a fee. As an alternative, most of the materials listed can be obtained from the library at the University of Michigan Transportation Research Institute. Contact them (313-764-2171) for prices, method of payment, and delivery times.

13.0 Biography

Paul Green is an Associate Research Scientist in the Human Factors Division of The University of Michigan Transportation Research Institute (UMTRI) and an Adjunct Associate Professor of Industrial and Operations Engineering, and also of Mechanical Engineering and Applied Mechanics. He has worked at UMTRI since 1979. He has held academic appointments in the Departments of Psychology and Industrial Design.

Dr. Green has a B.S. in Mechanical Engineering and three degrees from The University of Michigan (M.S.E. - Industrial and Operations Engineering - 1974; M.A. - Psychology - 1979; joint Ph.D. - Industrial & Operations Engineering and Psychology - 1979).

Dr. Green has carried out automotive human factors research since he was an undergraduate student. Topics investigated include the legibility, understandability, and use of a wide variety of displays (navigation, speedometers, etc.), control design (driver preferences for switch type and location, etc.), the effectiveness of driver alertness devices, and other topics.

He has written the first set of guidelines for the design of IVHS driver interfaces and the first test protocol for evaluating their safety and ease of use. He leads the UMTRI driving simulator project and projects associated with its instrumented car.

Dr. Green is a member of the Safety and Human Factors Steering Committee of IVHS America and chairs it Research Subcommittee. He is a very active member of the Society of Automotive Engineers Controls and Displays Committee. In addition, Dr. Green is a member of the Human Factors and Ergonomics Society, a Fellow in the Ergonomics Society, and a member of several other professional organizations.

If you have questions or comments about this chapter, you can E-mail Dr. Green. His Internet address is: Paul_Green@um.cc.umich.edu

REFERENCES

Allen, R.W., Hogue, J.R., Rosenthal, T.J., & Parseghian, Z. (1989). Data acquisition and analysis system based on a lap-top computer. *Transportation Research Record*, No. 1213, 82-89.

Allen, R.W., Stein, A.C., & Aponso, B.A. (1990). *A Low Cost, Part Task Driving Simulator Based on Microcomputer Technology* (TRB Paper 890669). Washington, DC: Transportation Research Board.

Bhise, V.D., Farber, E.I., Saunby, C.S., Troell, G.M., Walunas, J.B., & Bernstein, A. (1977). *Modelling Vision with Hheadlights in a Systems Context* (SAE Paper 770238). Warrendale, PA: Society of Automotive Engineers.

Bos, T., Green, P., & Kerst, J. (1988). *How Should Instrument Panel Display Legibility be Tested?* (Technical Report UMTRI-88-35). Ann Arbor: The University of Michigan Transportation Research Institute. (NTIS No. PB 90 141375/AS)

Boreczky, J., Green, P., Bos, T., & Kerst, J. (1988). *Effects of Size, Location, Contrast, Illumination, and Color on the Legibility of Numeric Speedometers* (Technical Report UMTRI-88-36). Ann Arbor: The University of Michigan Transportation Research Institute. (NTIS No. PB 90 150533/AS)

Brand, J.E. (1990). *Attitudes Toward Advanced Automotive Display Systems: Feedback From Driver Focus Group Discussions* (Technical Report UMTRI-90-22). Ann Arbor: The University of Michigan Transportation Research Institute.

Callahan, J.M. (1986a, January). Ford finds 400 ways to say quality. *Automotive Engineering*, pp. 44-45.

Callahan, J.M. (1986b, February). Ford's Taurus best-in-class list: Part two. *Automotive Engineering*, pp. 97-98.

Callahan, J.M. (1986c, September). Ford's Taurus best-in-class list: Part III. *Automotive Engineering*, pp. 115-116.

Card, S.K., Moran, T.P., & Newell, A. (1983). *The Psychology of Human-Computer Interaction*. Hillsdale, NJ: Lawrence Erlbaum Associates.

Chandra, D., Sivak, M., Flannagan, M.J., Sato, T., & Traube, E.C. (1993). *Reaction Time to Body-color Brake Lamps* (SAE Paper 930725). Warrendale, PA: Society of Automotive Engineers.

Chapanis, A. (1959). *Research Techniques in Human Engineering*. Baltimore, MD: Johns Hopkins.

Chatel, D.C., Bieliauskas, L.A., Green, P., Warner, J., & McSweeny, A.J. (in press). Cognitive predictors of driving ability in the elderly. *The Clinical Neuropsychologist*.

Dingus, T.A., Antin, J.F., Hulse, M.C., & Wierwille, W.W. (1989). Attentional demand requirements of an automobile moving-map navigation system. *Transportation Research A,* 23A(4), 310-315.

DRIVE Safety Task Force (1991, June). *Guidelines on Traffic Safety, Man-Machine Interaction and System Safety*. Brussels, Belgium: Author.

Drosdol, J., & Panik, F. (1985). *The Daimler-Benz Driving Simulator: A Tool for Vehicle Development* (SAE Paper 850334). Warrendale, PA: Society of Automotive Engineers.

Eberhard, J., & Green, P. (1989). *The Development and Testing of Warnings for Automotive Lifts* (Technical Report UMTRI-89-26). Ann Arbor: The University of Michigan Transportation Research Institute.

Evans, D. (1992). Correlated database generation for driving simulators. *Proceedings of the IMAGE VI Conference of the IMAGE Society*, 353-361.

Flannagan, M.J., Sivak, M., Battle, D.S., Sato, T., and Traube, E.C. (1993). *Discomfort Glare From High-Intensity Discharge Headlmaps: Effects of Context and Esperience* (Technical Report UMTRI-93-10). Ann Arbor: The University of Michigan Transportation Research Institute.

Fleischman, R.N. (1991). Research and evaluation plans for the TravTek IVHS operational field test. *Proceedings of the Vehicle Navigation and Information Systems Conference (VNIS'91)* (SAE Publication SP-253), 827-837.

Frank, D., Koenig, N., & Lendhold, R. (1973). *Identification of Symbols for Motor Vehicle Controls* (SAE Paper 730611). Warrendale, PA: Society of Automotive Engineers.

Fujita, K., Nishiyama, T., & Hayakawa, Y. (1988). Research on sound quality evaluation methods for exhaust noise. *JSAE Review*, 9(2), 28-33.

Godthelp, H., Milgram, P., & Blaauw, G.J. (1984). The Development of a time-related measure to describe driving strategy. *Human Factors*, 26(3), 257-268.

Green, P. (1979). *Development of Pictographic Symbols for Vehicle Controls and Displays* (SAE Paper 790383). Warrendale, PA: Society of Automotive Engineers.

Green, P. (1992). *Review of Eye Fixation Recording Methods and Equipment* (Technical Report UMTRI-92-28, IVHS Technical Report 92-20). Ann Arbor: The University of Michigan Transportation Research Institute.

Green, P. (1993a). *Measures and Methods Used to Assess the Safety and Usability of Driver Information Systems* (Technical Report UMTRI 93-12). Ann Arbor: The University of Michigan Transportation Research Institute.

Green, P. (1993b). *Suggested Procedures and Acceptance Limits for Certifying the Safety and Ease of Use of Driver Information Systems* (Technical Report UMTRI-93-13). Ann Arbor: The University of Michigan Transportation Research Institute.

Green, P. (1993c). Tools and methods for developing easy to use driver information systems. In E.J. Haug (Ed.), *Concurrent Engineering Tools and Technologies for Mechanical System Design* (pp. 959-970). Berlin, Germany: Springer-Verlag.

Green, P., Boreczky, J., & Kim, S. (1990). *Applications of Rapid Prototyping to Control and Display Design* (SAE Paper 900470, Special Publication SP-809). Warrendale, PA: Society of Automotive Engineers.

Green, P., & Brand, J. (1992). *Future In-Car Information Systems: Input From Focus Groups* (SAE Paper 920614). Warrendale, PA: Society of Automotive Engineers.

Green, P., Gillespie, T., Reifeis, S., Wei-Haas, L., & Ottens, D. (1984). *Subjective Evaluation of Steering Effort Levels* (Technical Report UMTRI-84-39). Ann Arbor: The University of Michigan Transportation Research Institute. (NTIS No. PB 86 135019/AS)

Green, P., & Goldstein, S. (1989). *Further Analysis of Driver Preferences for Secondary Controls* (Technical Report UMTRI-89-4). Ann Arbor: The University of Michigan Transportation Research Institute. (NTIS No. PB 90 149782/AS)

Green, P., & Olson, A. (1989). *The Development and Use of the UMTRI Driving Simulator* (Technical Report UMTRI-89-25). Ann Arbor: The University of Michigan Transportation Research Institute. (NTIS No. PB 90 115940/AS)

Green, P., Paelke, G., & Clack, K. (1989). *Instrument Panel Controls in Sedans: What Drivers Prefer and Why* (Technical Report UMTRI-89-15). Ann Arbor: The University of Michigan Transportation Research Institute. (NTIS No. PB 90 184235/AS)

Green, P., Paelke, G., & Boreczky, J. (1992). The "Potato Head" method for identifying driver preferences for vehicle controls. *International Journal of Vehicle Design*, 13(4), 352-364.

Green, P., Serafin, C., Williams, M., & Paelke, G. (1991). What functions and features should be in driver information systems of the year 2000? (SAE Paper 912792). *Proceedings of the Vehicle Navigation and Information Systems Conference (VNIS'91)*, 483-498.

Green, P., Williams, M., Hoekstra, E., George, K., & Wen, C. (1993). *Initial On-the-Road Tests of Driver Information System Interfaces: Examination of Navigation, Traffic Information, IVSAWS, and Vehicle Monitoring* (Technical Report UMTRI-93-32). Ann Arbor: The University of Michigan Transportation Research Institute.

Guyard, I., & Boulanger, O. (1992). The driving simulator as a means to assist human engineering the design of car interiors. *Proceedings of the FISITA '92 Conference* (pp. 87-94). London, UK: Institute of Mechanical Engineers.

Habsburg, S., & Middendorf, L. (1977). *What Really Connects in Seating Comfort?-Studies of Correlates of Static Seat Comfort* (SAE Paper 770247). Warrendale, PA: Society of Automotive Engineers.

Hammond, D.C. & Roe, R. (1972). *SAE Controls Reach Study* (SAE paper 720199). Warrendale, PA: Society of Automotive Engineers.

Hart, S.G., & Staveland, L.E. (1988). Development of a NASA-TLX (Task Load Index): Results of empirical and theoretical research. In P.S. Hancock and N. Meshkati (Eds.), *Human Mental Workload* (pp. 139-183). Amsterdam, The Netherlands: Elsevier Science.

Hauser, J.R., & Clausing, D. (1988, May-June). The house of quality. *Harvard Business Review*, 63-73.

Hemion, R.H., & Hull, R.W. (1973). *Optimum Two-Lamp Headlighting Systems* (Technical Report DOT HS 800890). Washington, DC: National Highway Traffic Safety Administration.

Hemion, R.H. (1975). *Field Demonstration of Polarized Lighting* (Technical Report HS 801 511). Washington, DC: National Highway Traffic Safety Administration.

Hertzberg, H.T.E. (1972). *The Human Buttocks in Sitting: Pressures, Patterns, and Palliatives* (SAE Paper 720005). Warrendale, PA: Society of Automotive Engineers.

Hicks, T.G., & Wierwille, W.W. (1979). Comparison of five mental workload assessment procedures in a moving base driving simulation. *Human Factors*, 21(2), 129-144.

Hoekstra, E., Williams, M., & Green, P. (1993). *Development and Driver Understanding of Hazard Warning and Location Symbols for IVSAWS* (Technical Report UMTRI-93-16). Ann Arbor: The University of Michigan Transportation Research Institute.

Janssen, W., & Nilsson, L. (1990). *An Experimental Evaluation of In-Vehicle Collision Avoidance Systems* (Deliverable GIDS/MAN2). Haren, The Netherlands: University of Groningen, Traffic Research Centre.

Kamijo, K., Tsujimura, H., Obara, H., & Katsumata, M. (1982). *Evaluation of Seating Comfort* (SAE Paper 820761). Warrendale, PA: Society of Automotive Engineers.

Kantowitz, B. (1992). Selecting measures for human factors research. *Human Factors*, 34(4), 387-398.

Karwowski, W., Yates, J.W., & Pongpatana, N. (1993). Ergonomic guidelines for design of a passenger car trunk. In B. Peacock and W. Karwowski

(Eds.), *Automotive Ergonomics* (pp. 117-139). London, UK: Taylor and Francis.

Kawamoto, H., Hosokawa, Y., Suto., M., & Nakajima, K. (1986). *Comfort Evaluation of Heating and Air Conditioning Systems* (SAE Paper 860590). Warrendale, PA: Society of Automotive Engineers.

Koide, M., & Kawakami, S. (1988). Analysis of "steering feel" evaluation in vehicles with power steering. *JSAE Review*, 9(3), 36-42.

Lissner, H.R., Lebow, M., & Evans, F.G. (1960). Experimental studies on the relation between accceleration and intracranial pressure changes in man. *Surgery, Gynecology, and Obstretrics*, 111, 329-338.

Lysaght, R.J., Hill, S.G., Dick, A.O., Plamondon, B.D., Linton, P.M., Wierwille, W.W., Zaklad, A.L., Bittner, A.C., & Wherry, R.J. (1989). *Operator Workload: Comprehensive Review and Evaluation of Operator Workload Methodologies* (Technical Report 851). Alexandria, VA: U.S. Army Research Institute.

Leifer, J.C. (1976, September). Designing an instrumented driver response system. *Public Roads*, 40(2), 60-65.

Loczi, J. (1993). Ergonomic assessment of exiting automobiles. *Proceedings of the Human Factors and Ergonomics Society 37th Annual Meeting*, 401-405.

MacAdam, C.C., Green, P.A., & Reed, M.P. (1993, July-August). An overview of current UMTRI driving simulators. *UMTRI Research Review*, 24(1), 1-8.

MacDonald, W.A., & Hoffmann, E.R. (1980). Review of relationships between steering wheel reversal rate and driving task demand. *Human Factors*, 22(6), 733-740.

Martin, D.W. (1991). *Doing Psychology Experiments* (3rd ed.). Pacific Grove, CA: Brooks/Cole.

Mast, T.M., Ballas, J.A., & Peters, J.I. (1976, September). Instrumented vehicle research on highway information systems. *Public Roads*, 40(2), 53-59.

McCarthy, P. S., & Tay, R. (1989). Consumer valuation of new car attributes: An econometric analysis of the demand for domestic and Japanese/western European imports. *Transportation Research-A*, 23A(5), 367-375.

McElroy, J. (1987, June). For whom are we building cars? *Automotive Engineering*, 68-70.

McIntosh, A.S., Kallieris, D., Mattern, R., & Miltner, E. (1993). Head and neck injury resulting from low velocity direct impact (SAE Paper 933112). *Proceedings of the 37th Stapp Car Crash Conference* (SAE Publication P-269), 43-57.

Meldrum, J.F. (1965). *Automobile Driver Eye Position* (SAE paper 650464). Warrendale, PA: Society of Automotive Engineers.

Mouri, H., Yanai, T., Kishi, N., Sugasawa, F., & Furusho, H. (1993). An investigation of driver stress induced by vehicle handling characteristics (Paper 9306129). *Jidousha-Gijutsu* (Journal of the Society of Automotive Engineers of Japan), 10, 149-152.

Muckler, F.A., & Seven, S.A. (1992). Selecting performance measures: "Objective" versus "subjective" measurement. *Human Factors,* 34(4), 441-456.

National Safety Council. (1993). *Accident Facts (1993 ed.).* Chicago, IL: Author.

Nordmark, S., Jansson, H., Lidstrom, M., & Palmkvist, G. (1985). *A Moving Base Driving Simulator with Wide Angle Visual System.* Paper presented at the 64th Annual Meeting of the TRB, Washington, DC.

Noy, Y.I. (1989). Intelligent route guidance: Will the new horse be as good as the old? *Proceedings of the Vehicle Navigation and Information Systems Conference (VNIS'89)*, 49-55.

Olson, P.L. (1977). *The Relative Merits of Different Low Beam Headlighting Systems - A Review of the Literature* (Technical Report UM-HSRI-77-55). Ann Arbor: The University of Michigan, Highway Safety Research Institute.

Olson, P.L. (1978, January-February). Illumination vs. glare: The 'catch-22' of safe headlighting. *The HSRI Research Review*, 8(4), 1-16.

Paelke, G.M. (1993). A comparison of route guidance destination entry methods. *Proceedings of the Human Factors and Ergonomics Society 37th Annual Meeting*, 569-573.

Park, T., Greenberg, J., & Mousseau, R. (1992). Design and analysis of the Ford driving simulator. *Proceedings of the IMAGE VI Conference of the IMAGE Society*, 333-341.

Peacock, B., & Karwowski, W. (1993). *Automotive Ergonomics.* London, UK: Taylor and Francis.

Piersma, E.H., Burry, S., Verwey, W.B., & Van Winsum, W. (1993). GIDS Architecture. In J.A. Michon (Ed.), *Generic Intelligent Driver Support* (pp. 147-173). London, UK: Taylor and Francis.

Projector, T., Cook, K.G., & Peterson, L.O. (1969). *Analytic Assessment of Motor Vehicle Rear Signal Systems* (Final Report of contract F-11-6602). Washington, DC: National Highway Safety Bureau.

Reed, M.P., Saito, M., Kakishima, Y., Lee, N.S., & Schneider, L.W. (1991). *An Investigation of Driver Discomfort and Related Seat Design Factors in Extended-Duration Driving* (SAE Paper 910117). Warrendale, PA: Society of Automotive Engineers.

Repa, B.S., & Bertollini, G.P. (1991). Driving simulators and automotive engineering. *Proceedings of the Second Seminar in Transportation Ergonomics* (Publication TP 8855) (pp. 51-64). Montreal, Quebec, Canada: Transport Canada, Transportation Development Centre.

Roe, R.W. (1993). Occupant packaging. In B. Peacock & W. Karwowski (Eds.), *Automotive Ergonomics* (pp. 11-42). London, UK: Taylor and Francis.

Rolle, C.D., Romitelli, G.F., & Savasta, F. (1992). Real evaluation of thermal comfort in a car passenger compartment. *Proceedings of the FISITA '92 Conference*. London, UK: Institute of Mechanical Engineers.

Saunby, C.S, Farber, E.I., & DeMello, J. (1988). *Driver Understanding and Recognition of Automotive ISO Symbols* (SAE Paper 880056). Warrendale, PA: Society of Automotive Engineers.

Sanders, M.S., & McCormick, E. (1993). *Human Factors in Engineering and Design (7th ed.)*. New York, NY: McGraw-Hill.

Schill, V., & Schmieder, H. (1992). Car simulation - The challenge for a visual system. *Proceedings of the IMAGE VI Conference of the IMAGE Society*.

Schneider, L., Robbins, D., Pflug, M., & Snyder, R. (1983). *Development of Anthropometrically Based Design Specifications for an Advanced Adult anthropomorphic dummy family (volume 1)* (Report DOT HS 806715). Washington, DC: U.S. Department of Transportation, National Highway Traffic Safety Administration. (NTIS No. PB 86105046)

Senders, J.W., Kristofferson, A.B., Levison, W.H., Dietrich, C.W., & Ward, J.L. (1967). The attentional demand of automobile driving. *Highway Research Record*, No. 195, 15-32.

Seyer, K. (1993). Development of a new Australian design rules for frontal impact protection (SAE Paper 933117). *Proceedings of the 37th Stapp Car Crash Conference* (SAE Publication P-269), 105-120.

Sheridan, T.B., Meyer, J.E., Roy, S.H., Decker, K.S., Yanagishima, T., & Kishi, Y. (1991). *Physiological and Psychological Evaluations of Driver Fatigue During Long Term Driving* (SAE Paper 910116). Warrendale, PA: Society of Automotive Engineers.

Sivak, M., & Flannagan, M. (1993). Human factors considerations in the design of vehicle headlamps and signal lamps. In B. Peacock & W. Karwowski (Eds.), *Automotive Ergonomics* (pp. 185-204). London, UK: Taylor and Francis.

Sivak, M., Flannagan, M.J., Traube, E.C., Battle, D.S., & Sato, T. (1993). *In-Traffic Evaluations of High-Intensity Discharge Headlamsp: Overall Performance and Color Appearance of Objects* (Technical Report 93-10). Ann Arbor: The University of Michigan Transportation Research Institute.

Sivak, M., Flannagan, M.J., Sato, T., Traube, E.C., & Aoki, M. (1993). *Reaction Times to Neon, LED, and Fast Incandescent Brake Lamps* (Technical Report UMTRI-93-37). Ann Arbor: The University of Michigan Transportation Research Institute.

Sivak, M., Olson, P.L., & Pastalan, L.A. (1981). Effect of driver's age on nighttime legibility of highway signs. *Human Factors*, 23(1), 59-64.

Sivak, M., Post, D.V., & Olson, P.L. (1981). Driver responses to high-mounted brake lights in actual traffic. *Human Factors*, 23, 231-235.

Sweet, R.E., & Green, P. (1993, January-February). UMTRI's instrumented car. *UMTRI Research Review*, 1-11.

Van Der Horst, R., & Godthelp, H. (1989). Measuring road user behavior with an instrumented car and an outside-the-vehicle video observation technique. *Transportation Research Record*, No. 1213, 72-81.

Wierwille, W.W., & McFarlane, J. (1991). *Overview of a Study of Direction-of-Motion Stereotype Strengths for Automotive Controls* (SAE Paper 910115). Warrendale, PA: Society of Automotive Engineers.

Williams, M., Hoekstra, E., & Green. P. (1993). *Development and Evaluation of a Vehicle Monitor Driver Interface* (Technical Report UMTRI-93-22). Ann Arbor: The University of Michigan Transportation Research Institute.

Virzi, R.A. (1992). Refining the test phase of usability evaluation: How many subjects is enough? *Human Factors*, *34*(4), 457-468.

Yoshida, H., Tanaka, T., Isoda, K., & Kamiya, K. (1991). *Traction Control Technology for Improved Driving Safety* (Paper 91-S7-O-03). Paper presented at the 13th International Technical Conference on Experimental Safety Vehicles, Paris, France.

Zwahlen, H.T., & Balasubramanian, K.N. (1974). A theoretical and experimental investigation of automobile path deviations when driver steers with no visual input. *Transportation Research Record*, No. 520, 25-37.

Chapter 8
Communication Systems Techniques

Edmond W. Israelski
AT&T Bell Laboratories

1.0 Introduction

In the 90's there has been a increasing interest in enhancing the usability of communications products and services. The communications industry, in particular telecommunications, has been a major growth industry world-wide. The same electronics technology that changed the faces of the computer and the consumer electronic industries has also had a profound effect on the telecommunications industry. New technologies such as automatic speech recognition, digital video compression, high performance multimedia workstations and high-speed data transmission networks are challenging user interface designers to increase product functionality while preserving and enhancing usability.

After World War II, one of the first non-military applications of human factors was the design of new and enhanced telephones and telecommunication networks at AT&T Bell Labs. John E. Karlin, a student of S.S. Stevens, started the first human factor's group at AT&T Bell Labs in 1945 (Hanson,1983). Today, many telecommunications vendors have hired human factors specialists. In the 90's, the Total Quality Management (TQM) movement has given renewed interest to improving the quality and usability of telecommunications products and services. Customer needs are now being given primary attention and users are strongly demanding that their communications products and services be highly usable, as well as being functional. The promise of increased productivity and quality of life will not be realized by the new emerging technologies if usability engineering is not an integral part of the communications revolution.

This chapter will cover categories and descriptions of users for whom communications technologies and associated user interfaces are being designed; the design methodologies of telecommunications usability engineering; special usability issues that apply to telecommunications equipment; and specific usability problem areas for telecommunications.

2.0 Telecommunications Equipment and Service

Table 8-1 shows some of the underlying user interface technology categories, while Table 8-2 shows current telecommunication equipment and service categories for which there are significant user interface (UI) design considerations. You can see that the telecommunications industry includes a wide variety of product and service categories for which usability engineering principles can be effectively applied in the design of the user interface. Many more items will be added to this list in the coming years. Not all categories of equipment design have significant UI's design consideration (e.g. internal power systems for switches, microwave antenna systems, communication satellite panels, etc.). Eigen (1991) describes many of the UI design considerations specific to telecommunications services. Designers of services and equipment must be able to successfully merge their respective user interfaces so that the combined applications present a seamless interface to the user. Applications user interface design will continue to be a challenge for human factors engineers.

Table 8-1. Telecommunications User Interface Technologies.

Category	Technology	Type
Input	Speech	Digitizing Pad
	Buttons	Pen or Stylus
	Keyboard	Still Image
	Cordboard	Video Image
	Mouse	Eye-Gaze Movement
	Trackball	Touch Screens
	Joystick	Sip and Puff Device
	Data Glove	Membrane Switches
	Touch-Tone Signals	
	Scanned Paper	
Output	Audio Signals	Animated Images
	CRT's (Raster Images)	Paper (Graphics, Text)
	Plasma Displays	Transparencies
	LCD's	Photographic Slides
	LED's	Multimedia
	Fluorescent Displays	Vibrating Reeds
	Still Images	Audio Tones
	Full Motion Video	

The many categories of users interact with telecommunications products and services through a wide variety of technologies, all of which present human factors design challenges. User interfaces are not limited to the equipment or service itself. Designers must consider the extended user interface that includes on-line and paper documentation, as well as the various media used for product and service training and tutorials.

3.0 Categories of Users

There are many different types of users of telecommunications products and services. The following is a comprehensive -- but not exhaustive -- description of categories of users for some of the telecommunications products and services described in Table 8-2.

Table 8-2. Telecommunications Product and Service Categories with User Interface Design Considerations

Product/Service Category	Examples
Voice and Data Terminals	Voice Telephones (Corded) Cordless Telephones Modems Data Terminals Speakerphones Audio Display Voice Terminals Video Telephone Cellular Mobile Telephones Operator Consoles (Switchboards) Audio Teleconferencing Systems
Personal Workstations	Telemarketing Agent Workstations Network Manager Workstations Multimedia (PCs with Voice, Image, Video) Learning Stations (Multiple Displays)
Visual Products and Services	Teletext Services Network Video Switched Services Personal Video Telephones Pen Based Telephones Group Video Teleconferencing Systems Video on Demand Services Interactive TV Services Interactive Multimedia Services Still Image Telephones Facsimile Machines Facsimile Store and Forward Services Electronic Mail Systems Telex Terminals and Services Telegraph Services
Information Appliance Products (w/communications capabilities)	Personal Digital Assistants Personal Communicators Laptop/Palmtop computers with modems
Telecommunications Switches	Network Switches and Concentrators Telephone Central Office Switching Switches Private Branch Exchange (PBXs) Switches Key Telephone Systems Multimedia Video Multipoint Switches Multimedia Servers Automatic Call Distribution (ACD)

Table 8-2 (CONTINUED)

Product/Service Category	Examples
Voice Processing Systems & Services	Network Based Voice Messaging Services 800 Service - Toll Free Inbound Calling 900 Information Services Messaging Systems (Voice Mail) Answering Machines Voice Response Systems (Interactive) Audio Text Services Automatic Speech Recognition Systems (e.g. Name Dialing Collect, Credit Card Dialing, etc.) Custom Calling Services (e.g., Call Waiting, Call Forwarding, Call Tracing, Call Return, Repeat Calling) Wide Area Telephone Calling Services Audio Teleconferencing Network Services Directory Assistance Services 700 Personal Numbers (Personal Communications Service)
Transmission Equipment	Cellular Transmission Systems Long Distance and Local Carrier Systems Wireless Adjuncts for PBX's and Key Telephone Systems Fiber Optic Systems Main Connecting Frames (for Central Offices and PBX's) Channel Banks Subscriber Loop Multiplex Systems Multiplexers Repeaters Microwave Radio Systems Communication Satellites Satellite Earth Stations Undersea Carrier Systems Cable Placing Equipment (e.g. Cable Ships, Undersea Robots)
Outside Plant Equipment	Cable Splice Cases and Systems Serving Area Interfaces (Connection Boxes) Cable Vaults (manholes) Telephone Pole Platforms Microwave Towers
System and Network Management	Network and Traffic Monitoring Management Systems Switch and Adjunct Administration Applications Troubleshooting Systems Trouble Tracking and Ticketing Systems System Configuration Management (Wire, Equipment Inventory Tracking) Call Accounting & Billing Systems

3.1 End Users

The end user is the largest and most familiar category for telecommunications products and services. This includes residential users of consumer products and services -- in addition to business users, who range from the small store owner with only a two line Key Telephone System KTS to the professional worker in a large company with a 15,000 line Centrex or PBX system. Often equipment is designed for "casual" users for whom the telephone, voice messaging system, or fax represent only a small fraction of the user interfaces they interact with at work or home. These casual users rarely get formal training and will often use only a small subset of communications features that are especially intuitive. Features that are not intuitive, or require high levels of cognitive processing, are often ignored.

3.2 Expert Users

There is a special category of experts who use telecommunications equipment and services as the primarily tool for productivity in their work. Expert users usually have access to large multiline-multifunction voice terminals, PC-based workstations, fax machines, and data communications equipment. Specific examples of expert users include:

3.2.1 Secretaries. Secretaries usually have complex equipment configurations to handle a large number of lines with many specialized calling features such as Call Transfer, Conference Calling, Hold, Automatic Callback, etc.

3.2.2 Telemarketing agents. Telemarketers make or receive calls from clients to make sales, answer questions, make billing inquires, solicit donations etc. Often they are individuals in a pool who have calls directed to them via a toll-free 800 number and a PBX switch that has ACD Automatic Call Distribution functionality.

3.2.3 Attendants (Operators). Traditionally attendants were called "switchboard operators" and spent most of their work day answering calls in a business establishment. The title "receptionist" has also been used. Attendants also transfer calls, take messages, perform paging and setup teleconferences among other tasks. The equipment for attendants usually is specialized. A common name for a popular piece of specialized equipment is the attendant console. Network services operators perform tasks such as directory assistance, facilitating special calls such as collect and credit card calls and handling international call completion.

3.2.4 System Administrators. System Administrators are another special class of expert users who have specialized, computer-based interfaces to telecommunications systems. Common tasks are performed through either PC interfaces or dumb terminals and include adds, moves and changes of lines, network trunks and features for voice, data and video terminals. Additional tasks involve using call accounting systems to make inquires of equipment data bases to produce department billing records, investigating toll fraud, etc. System Administrators use a variety of PC tools or Operations Support Systems OSS that can be categorized as follows.

3.2.4.1. System Administration. Feature or equipment additions, moves and changes. It can include the bulk administration of groups of extensions and end user features for a system.

3.2.4.2 Configuration Management. Systems that maintain records on telephone wire, equipment and cable inventories and numerical identification schemes.

3.2.4.3 Maintenance Management. Troubleshooting and ticketing systems for equipment and service maintenance.

3.2.4.4 System Performance Management. Systems that monitor and report on network traffic data.

3.2.5 Servicing (installation/maintenance) personnel. Servicing personnel, sometimes called craftworkers, have a wide variety of tasks for installing, configuring, operating, and maintaining telecommunications equipment and services. The user interface includes all of the system administrator tasks described above plus additional specialized tasks for testing individual system components, circuit cards, loops, trunks, modems etc. Maintenance craftworkers often have specialized software access permission to examine equipment error logs or to set up special software traps to capture data needed to do troubleshooting. Israelski (1988) summarizes the results of a large number of job and task analysis studies of telecommunications craftworkers. Outside plant technician is one of the more complex jobs. This job has a wide variety of equipment related tasks for outside plant craft personnel who perform fiber optic and cable system installation, splicing, and maintenance. Other craftworker jobs include: central office technicians, video technicians, microwave technicians, transmission repair technicians, and PBX installation and repair technicians.

3.2.6 Telecommunication Managers. Telecommunications Managers represent a specialized user group that requires recurring, as well as ad hoc, reports on a telecommunication system's performance. These reports include data on equipment usage, traffic and fault management. The user interface for "Telcom" managers is a specialized subset of the UI for system administrators described previously.

4.0 Special Usability Attributes

Scerbo (Chapter 4) and others Nielsen (1993) have clearly stated the benefits of usability engineering. The telecommunications field is no exception in its need for the application of usability engineering. Specifically for telecommunications, the following benefits can be achieved for the user interfaces to products and services.

1. Increased user productivity and performance (Repeat sales and increased network usage and profit).
2. Decreased user error and task time (Reduced unnecessary and unprofitable network holding times).
3. User interface matches user capabilities and limitations.
4. Increased customer satisfaction (Increased sales of communications products and usage sensitive services).
5. Decreased need for user training (Decreased training costs for telecommunication service providers and product vendors).
6. Increased ease of use (Reduces costs of maintaining costly hotline staffs).
7. Increased consistency with user expectations (100 plus years of telephone technology has shaped many aspects of human communication behavior).
8. Increased conformity to user stereotypes about how things work (e.g. The Touch Tone Dial Pad has already created stereotypes about how services work).
9. Reduced development time and costs because user interface development rework is greatly reduced (design errors are caught before release).

4.1 Usability Principles as Applied to Telecommunications

There are special considerations in applying usability engineering principles to the design of telecommunications products and services. The following are definitions of core usability engineering principles as they are applied to the planning, design, and evaluation of telecommunications products and services.

4.1.1 Customer models (User Profiling)[1]. Customer models are detailed descriptions of typical customer telecommunications system and network configurations. They include descriptions of different classes of users and the communications features they would use. Interactions of communication features and their frequency of use are also specified.

4.1.2 User scenarios. User scenarios are detailed descriptions of the actual sequence of communication tasks users would follow in accomplishing an information exchange goal using the telecommunication product or service as described in the customer model. User scenarios are derived from detailed task analysis data[2]. These task analyses emphasis the communication and information management and movement aspects of users tasks.

---

[1] Chapter 4, section 6.1, provides an in-depth discussion of the construction of user profiles.

[2] For information on performing a task analysis, see Chapter 2 of Banks, W.W., & Weimer, J. (1992). *Effective Computer Display Design*. Prentice-Hall: Englewood Cliffs, NJ. For general information on task analysis, see Drury, C.G., Paramore, B., VanCott, H.P., Grey, S.M., and Corlett, E.N. (1987). Task analysis. In Gavriel Salvendy (Ed), *Handbook of Human Factors*. Wiley-Interscience: New York.

4.1.3 Usability objectives or goals. Usability objectives are quantified criteria for describing a typical user's performance (speed, accuracy and communication productivity) and satisfaction (survey ratings) in performing the user scenarios that were derived from the customer models. These usability objectives should be validated with customers and against competitive benchmarks. Table 8-3 shows illustrative examples of usability objectives that are appropriate to telecommunications.

4.1.4 Rapid prototyping (Iterative Design). User interface prototypes are simulations of the user interface of a communication product or service that can be produced by software tool kits, which do not require extensive programming skills[3]. Typically, no production code is generated, and the user interface is easily modified to allow rapid iterative design after testing with representative users. Solid physical models of communications products can also be produced with some types of rapid CAD/CAM tools and laser lithography. Initial designs can also be programmed to appear on touch-sensitive computer screens for early user testing, where the simulation fidelity does not need to be high. For example, a simulation of a voice telephone faceplate can be used to test early design concepts on a touch-sensitive computer screen in advance of early solid physical models.

4.1.5 Usability testing[4]. Usability testing is the actual testing of representative user's ability to use a telecommunication product or service. Results of usability testing are compared to the pre-established usability objectives. Usability testing is optimally carried out in two phases of design: 1) early in the design cycle, using simulations, before final requirements are specified and 2) later, during system test of the extended product, including its documentation and training materials.

Table 8-3: Usability Objectives for Telecommunications

Quantified usability criteria for performing key user scenarios:
• Human performance (e.g., learning time, task time, and accuracy)
• User satisfaction and preference (e.g., survey ratings after usability testing)
• Should be validated with customers
• Should be established against competitive benchmarks

[3]For more information on the creation of software prototypes, see Chapter 4, section 4.0, and Chapter 5, section 4.7.1.

[4]Chapter 4 provides a thorough overview of usability testing methods.

Table 8-4: Usability Engineering Methods For Telecommunications

Methodology	Example
Natural Observation of Users in Field Settings	Observing user's of a video teleconferencing system
Field Experiments[5]	Users rating PBX switch performance while system is being slowed down by an artificial call load generator
Laboratory Experiments[6]	Assessing Speech Quality through MOS , Mean Opinion Score Ratings, under different levels of speech distortion.
Focus Groups[3]	Demonstrating a multimedia conferencing system simulation and recording group reactions to the concept and its user interface.
Interviews	Individual interviews over the telephone with Long Distance Network users inquiring about delays in establishing connections.
Task Analysis	Studying and quantifying, by subject matter experts, the job tasks, knowledge, skills, and abilities needed to be a telephone operator.
Questionnaires[6]	Paper surveys given to purchasers of telephone answering machines inquiring about user interface and document quality.
User Checklists, Logs and Diaries[7]	Users of interactive multimedia services log their usage and problems encountered.
Participatory Design[5]	A small team of representative users, product developers, and a human factors specialist design on paper the user interface flow of a directory assistance system that is accessed from a PC with a modem.
Directed Dialog (Thinking Aloud)[8]	Recording users describing their thoughts while performing system administration of a video switch.
Cognitive Walkthroughs[9]	Developers and human factors specialists analyze the task sequences user must follow to initiate a data call from a cellular telephone.
Heuristic Evaluation	Human factors experts evaluate the user interface flow in setting up a fax call to a broadcast group of recipients.
Wizard of Oz[10] (Human simulating a system before it exists)	Recording user's behavior while speaking commands to an Automatic Speech Recognition System ASR, simulated by a human listener.

[5] See Chapter 9, Case Studies 1 and 3 for examples of field research and user participative design. See Chapter 9, section 3.1, Chapter 12, section 7.0, and Chapter 7.0, section 3.2 for a discussion of focus groups. For information on how focus group information can be used in the design of a product, see sections 3.2 and 3.3 of the Chapter 9.

[6] Chapter 4, section 7.0 shows a typical AT&T usability lab.

[7] For more information, see Chapter 4, section 7.5

[8] Chapter 4, section 7.4 presents a detailed discussion of the use of think aloud protocols.

[9] See Chapter 10, sections 4.2.3 and 4.3 for more information on walkthroughs.

[10] For more information on the Wizard of Oz technique, see Chapter 9, Section 3.4, Case Study 4.

4.1.6 Illustrative examples of usability objectives

- An experienced network manager would, after 10 hours of training, be able to configure a fault management network map with 30 switching nodes and 4 types of transmission systems in 60 minutes with a 99% accuracy rate. Average user satisfaction ratings for ease of use after completing this task would be 4.2 on a 5 point satisfaction scale.
- A new telephone operator, after reading a quick reference card for 5 minutes, would-be able to make a conference call and then transfer one caller within 15 seconds with a less than 1% rate of dropping calls.
- A new voice mail user, with one hour of training, would be able to create 2 personal greetings, within 3 minutes, with no errors. They would have a feature ease-of-use satisfaction rating of 4.5 or better on a 5 point satisfaction scale.
- A new user, interacting with a video messaging system would be able to retrieve 3 video messages (each less than 1 minute in duration.) They would be able to delete one message, store the second and forward the third with a short voice annotation. Ninety-five percent of users would perform this task accurately in less than 5 minutes with 2 or fewer requests for on-line help. Average ease of use rating for this system would be 4.3 on a 5 point satisfaction scale.
- For a new video teleconferencing service, operating at 384 Kb/second, 95% of first time users would rate the video signal quality as Excellent on a 5 point scale with labels of Excellent, Good, Fair, Poor and Unacceptable.

4.2 Usability Methodologies as Applied to Telecommunications

In addition to variations on classic usability principles, there are variations on the way human factors methods are employed to study communications behavior. These methodological variations are seen in the nature of the stimuli material, the level and types of independent variables, and in the types of dependent variables. Table 8-4 lists usability engineering methodologies that are commonly used by human factors specialists in the area of telecommunications.

5.0 Special Usability Methods

In the early days of telecommunications there were some specific human factors methodologies applied uniquely to the design of the user interface to telephony. Special methods of assessing speech intelligibility and quality were developed specifically to study how to design telephone networks that were acceptable to most users. Similarly, new methods had to be developed to assess the quality of visual communications. Short et al. (1976) describe some of these earlier methodologies used in the speech and visual areas. As new technologies such as multimedia advance, the lines of distinction among human factors specialty areas are becoming very fuzzy. For example, ASR Automatic Speech Recognition is now being applied to user interfaces for computers, consumer products for the home, access to network based telecommunications services, medical systems, as well as to aerospace and military systems. Other technologies (e.g. CD-ROM- based, multimedia user interfaces and full motion video) are being applied to many specialty areas such as: training, military systems, home entertainment systems, multimedia teleconferencing systems, and computer-based information systems. The spread and general applicability of advancing user interface technologies to many specialty areas makes it difficult to describe a unique set of human factors research techniques for any particular specialty. However, I will outline some special considerations that human factors specialists need to understand when investigating communications systems.

5.1 Speech Quality[11]

Speech quality is usually measured against two types of criteria: speech intelligibility and user acceptability. Speech communication requires a standard voice channel that passes approximately 3.5 KHz (i.e. 180 Hz to 3600 KHz). Digital audio compression has advanced from simple PCM (Pulse Code Modulation) to much more sophisticated coding algorithms such as LD-CELP (low delay, code excited linear prediction). These coding techniques, known as perceptual coding schemes, take advantage of human cognitive processing mechanisms for filling in missing speech and visual elements. The TSS (Telecommunications Standards Sector) of the ITU (International Telecommunications Union), formerly the CCITT (Communications Committee for International Telephones and Telegraphs) has recommended a widely used rating scale for judging speech and audio quality acceptability:

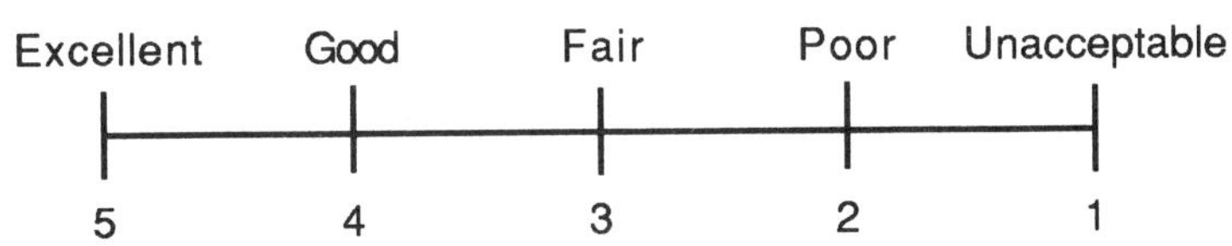

Other variations on this scale include 7 and 9 point scales. An example of a 9 point rating scale is shown below (See Kotsonis et al., 1989).

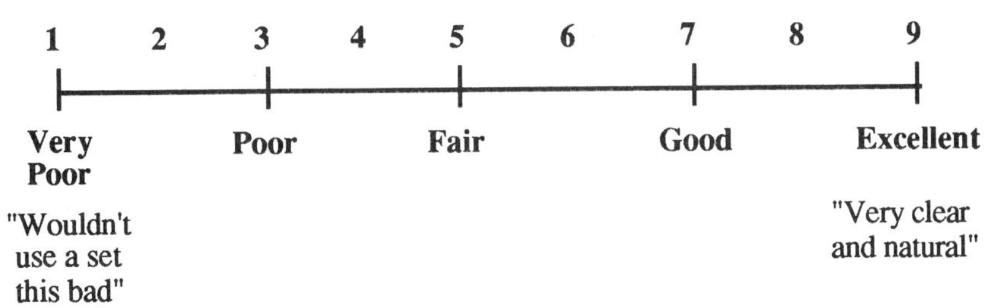

The type of data collected using the above scales is often called the MOS (Mean Opinion Score). MOS is defined as the average score when any subjective dimension of a communications system is evaluated. Many aspects of speech and audio quality can be measured by asking a panel of

---

11 Material in sections 5,6,7, and 8 are adapted from Israelski (1995) with permission of Marcel Dekker.

evaluators to listen to speech or auditory signals and to rate each sample. Sometimes the panel is a group randomly chosen from the user population. Other times, trained expert evaluators are needed to study subtle differences in network performance caused by a complex interaction of network or system impairments.

Often acceptability is measured using MOS for impairments such as:

1. Noise
   - Continuous background noise
   - Peak or Impulse
   - Quantizing (from digital encoding and decoding)
   - Speech correlated noise
2. Distortion (Especially due to different coding algorithms)
3. Echo (Hearing a repeated voice delayed in time)
4. Interference (e.g. 60 Cycle Power Line Hum)
5. Crosstalk (Hearing another conversation from a second voice channel)
6. Clipping (Distortion from transmission loss of high amplitude portions of signal)
7. Attenuation Loss
   - Overall
   - Frequency Band Specific
8. Delay

While MOS can also be gathered in the field, using conversational speech, MOS is often measured in a laboratory setting so that the levels of impairment, and any other independent variables of interest, can be controlled. A useful source of controlled speech samples is phonetically balanced speech fragments that are usually read alternatively by male and female speakers. Small, basic fragments of speech, called phonemes, are balanced across the passages. English contains 13 phonemes with vowel sounds and 25 with consonant sounds, plus several diphthongs or double vowel sounds. Some examples of phonetically balanced speech samples that are used in listening tests are:

- A dash of pepper spoils beef stew.
- A vent near the edge brought in fresh air.
- A zestful food is the hot-cross bun.
- Prod the mule with a crooked stick.
- The brass tube circled the high wall.
- The room was crowded with a wild mob.

Phonetically balanced passages may not always make logical sense, but, syntactically, they are sentences. These passages test the system for all the most common sounds and articulations used in American English. A typical lab test will present at least 20 of these passages to a subject for each impairment condition being tested. More research is now being done to understand speech quality impact in other languages that have tonal and speech qualities that differ from American English. Another type of laboratory test is a conversational test in which pairs of subjects have a natural conversation on a test circuit prior to rating its quality. Yet another procedure to judge speech quality is Voiers' (1976) Diagnostic Acceptability Measure (DAM). In this test evaluators listen and then rate a sample of sentences on speech and background attributes. Some examples of *speech* characteristics are: fluttering, thin, nasal, or muffled. Some background characteristics that are rated include: hissing, buzzing, and rumbling.

Subjective ratings are combined by weighing the magnitude and importance of the various impairments to produce the DAM score that typically ranges from 40 to 70. Speech intelligibility is another important metric and is measured by asking subjects to reproduce words, phrases, or sentences after they are presented through a system containing impairments. Typically speech intelligibility does not suffer until MOS acceptability scores are very low (e.g., below 2 on a 5 point scale). Measures of Speech Intelligibility are covered in section 5.4.

5.2 Telecommunications Network Transmission Objectives

In telecommunication networks, a concept called Grade of Service has been used to determine acceptable network transmission impairment objectives (Bell Labs, 1977). The grade of service concept mathematically combines the distribution of MOS (mean opinion scores) for transmission impairments, such as crosstalk level or clipping, with the distribution of actual network performance measures to obtain the expected percentage of customer ratings in a given opinion category (e.g. speech quality that is "Good" or better). The mathematical process involves integrating the two distributions of interest. The actual network performance distributions are obtained from objective network performance measurement surveys obtained with electronic measurement instruments.

Grade of service is defined mathematically by the integral:

$$\int_{-\infty}^{\infty} P(R|x)f(x)dx$$

where:

P(R|x) = probability a user would place a given impairment in a given opinion category

R and f(x) = probability density function of obtaining that stimulus.

The distribution function P(R | x) is obtained through subjective tests that yield MOS rating distributions, while the density function f(x) is obtained from objective network performance measurements.

5.3 Text-To-Speech Quality Measurements

Synthesized text-to-speech is a more recent technology that is being used in telecommunications systems. Synthesizers (synthesis-by-rule) being used in the early 90's still have a sound quality that many users evaluate as being artificial and robot like. A related form of speech is digitized concatenated speech (synthesis by analysis), where communications is accomplished by assembling pre-recorded digitized speech fragments to make understandable whole sentences or meaningful phrases (e.g. voice prompts in a voice messaging system). Concatenated speech can sound very natural and intelligible if speech cadence, prosody (rhythm and/or singsong quality of natural speech), inflections and coarticulation (natural blending and appropriate modifications of sequential speech sounds) are handled well when the fragments are played back in sequence. See Michaelis and Wiggins (1992) for additional details. High intelligibility of synthesized speech can be accomplished if the synthesizer is programmed to make proper inflections, accents and stresses on appropriate syllables or phonemes. These concepts are described in the following section.

5.4 Measurement of Speech Intelligibility

Speech intelligibility can be measured with a test called the DRT (Diagnostic Rhymes Test) and its derivatives (e.g. the extended DRT(Van Santen, 1991; Voiers, 1993) and the MRT Modified Rhymes Test). The extended DRT uses the following protocol for data collection:

1. Alerting tone is presented to "subject"
2. Test sentence played (e.g. "stringy banners bind the hair")
3. Pause of about 1.5 seconds
4. Message displayed on screen to subject "WAIT FOR ALTERNATIVES"
5. Pause of 3 seconds
6. Two response alternatives displayed

   q: banners
   p: badgers
7. Subject selects "q" or "p" on a keyboard type device.

The DRT in its original form presented single words rather than embedding the stimulus words in syntactically correct sentences. Test items embedded in sentences create a more natural phonetic context for the stimulus items. Important phonetic speech classes that can be tested by the DRT include (Bennett et al. , 1989):

1. Weak fricatives (such as: f, r, th, dh)
2. Strong fricatives (s, z, sh, zh)

3. Stops (b, d, g, p, t, k)
4. Nasals (m,n)
5. Liquids and glides (w, r, l, y)
6. Affricates (ch, j)

In addition to the DRT there are other speech intelligibility tests that have been used including the Phonetically Balanced (PB) monosyllabic word test (ANSI Standard S3.2-1960) and the AI, Articulation Index (ANSI S3.5-1969).[12] The AI can be calculated by taking objective electrical measurements without the need for any subjective data.

5.4.1 Future research needs for speech quality assessment. Although, much previous work has been done in the area of speech quality assessment, more research is needed. Some of these future research needs include:

1. MOS distributions of new speech coding algorithms (e.g. LD-CELP) and the impact of interactions and the additive effects of common transmission impairments (e.g. noise, echo, time delay, etc.)
2. Impact on MOS of multiple encodings of speech that occurs when speech files (e.g. voice mail messages) are transmitted as digital and decoded to analog form and then recorded to digital if forwarded to another system
3. Effect of varying transmission delays due to satellites or CPU intensive coding/decoding computations on speech quality assessments and human performance measurements where communication involves delayed speech.
4. Effect on speech intelligibility and acceptability from the use of alternating speech prompt patterns (e.g. alternating male and female voices.)
5. Effect of increased speed of speech playback (with pitch correction) on comprehension and acceptance.

5.5 Automatic Speech Recognition

Automatic Speech Recognition is an area of technology that has made some significant advances recently. ASR has two main categories: 1) speaker dependent, which requires a user to train the system to their own particular speech patterns through speech template matching, and 2) speaker independent, where large vocabularies are built with many speech samples taken from a population that has similar speech characteristics to the target users, (e.g. having similar accents). Technological advances are being made to expand usable vocabulary sizes for ASR systems (See Wattenbarger et al , 1993). Some of these technological advances that improve usability when interacting with ASR systems are:

1. Connected Digit Recognition - Allows continuous speech input as opposed to forcing users to tediously speak one digit at a time separated by pauses.

---

[12] ANSI Standards can be obtained from the American National Standards Institute, Washington, D.C.

2. Barge-In - the ability to interrupt a voice prompt at any time with speech input (ASR equivalent to allowing Touch-Tone, dial-through of announcements)
3. Word Spotting - the ability for an ASR system to ignore extraneous speech and recognize certain key words.
4. Concept Spotting - This accepts responses to prompts with alternate words, phrases and sentences that express the same intent.
5. Sub Word Recognition - the ability to create sets of recognizable vocabulary by using internal representations of words based on phonemes instead of whole word templates. These phonemes can be combined in a large number of ways to create word lists for the ASR system to recognize without the need to train for specific speakers.
6. Early Decision Rules - ASR systems that respond immediately to a user's utterance that matches a template, rather than waiting until a recognition time window has ended.

The long-term goal of ASR is to produce natural language processing so that machines would "understand" user's complete thoughts without any ambiguity. Today's ASR technology, even with recent advances, must be designed very carefully using the principles of usability engineering to avoid systems that are frustrating to use. Prompts, menus, and user feedback must be designed to guide users or chaos can result. In the meantime, ASR can be used as a limited alternative to Touch-Tone input for rotary dial customers and for speaker verification in security systems.

You need to address the impact of several important variables when designing user interfaces with ASR technology. Some of the more important variables described by Wattenbarger et al. (1993) are:

1. Length of system response delays
2. Recognition accuracy (current systems range from 60 to 95% recognition rates with large differences among individual speakers)
3. Types of recognition errors (e.g., substitution of wrong words for target words or false rejections of valid words)
4. Forms of error correction
5. Continuous versus discrete word speech
6. System vocabulary size
7. Human ability to constrain speech in terms of vocabulary, syntax and speaking patterns

The "Wizard of Oz" technique[13] is a popular methodology for studying ASR systems. Instead of using working prototypes for early user testing, this method substitutes a human listener for the prototype ASR system. The human controls feedback and prompts given to the test subjects often

[13]For more information on the Wizard of Oz technique, See Chapter 8, section 3.4.

through keyboard input to a speech output system. The test subjects are led to believe they are interacting with a machine rather than a human. Wattenbarger, Garberg, Halpern and Lively (1993) summarize laboratory research on ASR that has led to a prompting style that is more conversational. The example they use is from a telecommunications network service. The new, more effective, and better accepted prompting style is in the following form:

1. PROMPT IS GIVEN
2. PAUSE FOR USER SPEECH INPUT
3. GIVE ALTERNATIVES

For example instead of:

"Welcome to AT&T. Please say collect, calling card, third number, person to person or operator, now."

The more effective prompt would say:

1. "Welcome to AT&T. What type of call would you like to make?"
2. PAUSE (for a short period)
3. "Please say collect, calling card, third number, person to person or operator, now."

This question and pause style can accomplish three objectives:

1. By using barge-in, more experienced users are encouraged by the pause to give the desired response without waiting to hear all the alternatives.
2. Novice users wait through the pause, hear, and learn all of the options for future reference.
3. All users would find the question helpful in planning what to do next and to avoid user "freezes", where nothing gets said at all.

5.5.1 Future research needs for automatic speech recognition. Many uninvestigated ASR usability issues remain to be more thoroughly investigated. Among the many research areas, there are:

1. How to design user interface mode switching between ASR, Touch-Tone®, and GUI input modes? Under what task conditions are these various modes either singly, or in combination, optimized for the user? Under what circumstances is a modeless user interface suitable?
2. How do we design prompts and logic flows of user interactions with ASR systems to best approximate true natural language systems?
3. What are the best language analysis rules to allow ASR systems to optimally do concept spotting?
4. How to design the user interface to real time foreign language translations systems that use ASR technology?
5. How do we optimize the use of ASR technology for systems that aid the speech impaired to improve their communications skills?

5.6 Interactive Voice Response

Interactive Voice Response (IVR) technology has spread rapidly, because it has the power to unite flexible and rapidly updatable computer databases with a simple Touch-Tone® or push button dialpad telephone. ASR technology extends IVR to rotary telephone dial users, but Touch-Tone® input is the predominant access method today. There are many examples of poorly designed IVR systems -- often they are the butt of jokes and newspaper columns written by humorists, because they can put users into "voice mail jail." This happens when menu choices (e.g. "For Billing Press 1, For Refunds press 2, etc.") lead a user into an endless loop with no escape other than to hang up. Usability engineering that includes adequate user testing of prototypes is the way to avoid confusing and frustrating users. There are many possible applications of IVR. These applications can be classified into several categories.

5.6.1 Repeated requests for frequently changing information.

Sports Schedules

Homework Assignments

Bus Schedules

Movie Timetables

Price Lists

Current Inventory

Stock Quotes

Interest Rates and Loan Terms

Equipment Repair Status

5.6.2 Transaction processing.

Employee Flex Benefit Registration

Stock and Bond Purchases

Registration for Courses

Rental Car Reservations

Restaurant Reservations

Ordering and Purchasing from Catalogs

5.6.3 Retrieving information from large databases. Sometimes called Audiotext, text is browsed using Text-to-Speech (TTS). Users can listen to selected articles, also via TTS, or have them delivered via E-mail or fax. Examples include:

Magazine Articles

News Wire Articles

Information from On-Line Encyclopedia's

5.6.4 Information input transactions.

Political Opinion Gathering

Stockholder Balloting

Market Research Surveys

Consumer Feedback or Complaints

User-centered design has increasingly been applied to IVR. Tobias (1993) and Gardner-Bonneau (1992) have outlined how to apply usability to IVR design. Gardner-Bonneau (1992) has summarized the following usability problems with many IVR applications (many of these problems apply to voice-messaging systems also):

1. Lack of consistency or logic in the assignment of caller response options
2. Ambiguous prompts
3. Discourteous or curt system responses
4. Assuming too much or to little knowledge on the part of the user
5. Inappropriate timing of prompts and time-out periods
6. Failure to consider the caller's environmental context.
7. Requiring the caller to respond in awkward ways due to technology limitations
8. Ignoring human limitations in memory and information processing capacity
9. Failure to consider individual differences among user populations
10. Poor or no error handling. Not giving useful instructions in an error message.
11. Applications driven by technology or company needs, rather than by user needs
12. Failure to consider the amount of time needed to complete an IVR transaction.

Tobias (1993) gives the following tips to address these usability issues.

1. Know your callers[14]
   a. Know their education, language, age, gender and other personal attributes
   b. How often do they call?
   c. Why are they calling?
   d. How knowledgeable will users be?
   e. Will they have access to a user documentation?
2. Use simple and natural dialogue
3. Minimize the caller's short term memory load
   a. Menus should not exceed four of five choices
   b. Present option information first and then present the action (e.g. "For Billing information . . . press 2")
4. Be consistent
   a. Use consistent language in the voice prompts
   b. Keep Touch-Tone® options the same as far as possible (e.g. Listening is always the "2" digit on the dialpad)
   c. Provide global commands or responses that can be used at any time (e.g. " * D" always deletes the last entry)
5. Provide feedback to users wherever possible for conforming or rejecting their input commands
6. Provide easy exits to a live operator or to a main menu to avoid "voice mail jail"
7. Offer shortcuts for expert users
8. Provide useful error messages
   a. Give instructions on what to do next (e.g. don't just say "Invalid command")
9. Prevent user errors
10. Use professional speakers
11. Consider offering a User Guide or a quick reference card
12. Consider offering brief Caller Training
13. Provide an attendant as an escape at any time

A basic limitation of voice response systems is that human short term memory is very limited for temporal events. Humans are better information processors if some information can be presented visually. Because large area display technologies are becoming more economical, and because more and more desktops are being equipped with PC's, IVR and voice messaging systems will be achieving higher levels of usability as they take advantage of visual displays for the manipulation of such things as menu choices, random access of voice messages and selection of multiple personal mailing lists.

[14]See information on user profiling in Chapter 4, section 6.1.

5.6.5 Future research needs for IVR. Many of the future research needs mentioned earlier for ASR systems also apply to IVR systems as they begin to apply ASR technology. Some additional research considerations for IVR include:

1. More research is needed on how deep and wide auditory menu structures should be as a function of the nature of the IVR tasks being performed.
2. What are the best design implementations for using visual display input to IVR?
3. How should mode switching between Touch-Tone®, speech, touch-sensitive screens, and pen-based input be implemented for IVR systems?
4. How might expert systems be used to increase IVR user performance?

5.7 Simple Voice Telephony Services

One of the earliest applications of human engineering in telecommunications was to traditional simple voice telephony; what is somewhat humorously called POTS (Plain Old Telephone Service). The design of the ubiquitous Touch-Tone®, or push button, dialpad is one of the earliest examples. Deininger (1960) at AT&T Bell Labs conducted a comprehensive study of alternative designs for the push button dialpad. After pilot testing, subjects compared the five most promising design alternatives. User performance and preference data were collected as follows:

1. Dialing time in seconds for representative strings of telephone numbers
2. Errors (percentage of digits dialed wrong)
3. Preference (votes for best and worst alternatives)

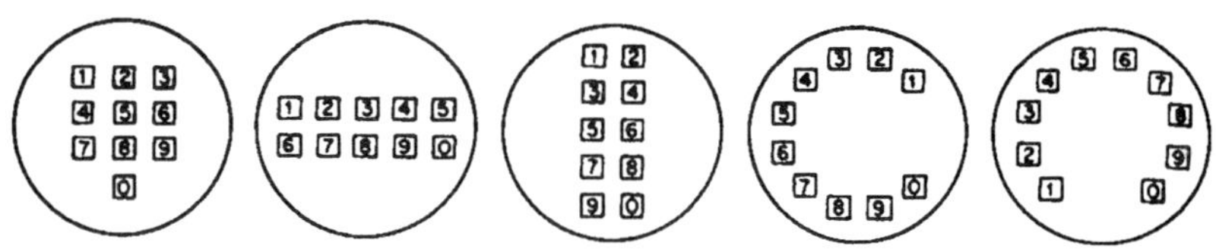

	1. Reversed adding machine	2. Two horizontal rows	3. Two vertical columns	4. Telephone	5. Speedometer
Keying time	6.01 sec	6.17 sec	6.12 sec	5.90 sec	5.97 sec
Percent errors	2.5%	2.3%	1.3%	2.0%	3.0%
Votes for	3d	1st (most)	5th (least)	2d	4th
Votes against	2d	4th	1st (most)	5th (least)	3d

Figure 8-1 Results of Dialpad Studies (From Deininger, 1960)
(Reprinted by permission of the copyright owner, AT&T)

As seen from the data in Figure 8-1, the currently used design (reversed adding machine) was chosen, not because it was best in all categories (none of the alternatives was best) but because it was a reasonable compromise. Subsequent studies by Conrad and Hull (1968, See Figure 8-2) compared the current telephone dialpad and the adding machine style and showed the current dialpad to produce significantly fewer errors, but take a slightly longer time to dial telephone numbers.

Adding Machine	Telephone
7 8 9	1 2 3
4 5 6	4 5 6
1 2 3	7 8 9
0	0

Style	Percentage Errors	Speed (Seconds)
Adding Machine	8.2	7.4
Telephone	6.4	7.8

Figure 8-2. Results of Adding Machine Vs. Telephone Dialpad Study

5.8 Distinctive Sounds for Telephone Tone Ringers

In crowded office environments it is useful to have telephone set ringing tones that allow identification of the call's origin and the call's destination. Roberts and Angiolillo-Bent (1988) conducted systematic studies of many tone ringer alternatives. Call origin alternatives included:

1. Inside building call
2. Outside call
3. A transferred call
4. A priority call

Call destination alternatives are also called personalized ringing choices and can often range from 2 to 8 choices. In their study, Roberts and Angiolillo-Bent assessed 9 different dimensions of sound quality. These results have been used to select tone ringers for current telephones, as well as being generalizable for future designs. Table 8-5 below outlines the 9 different sound dimensions, where each had four experimental levels. These experimental combinations were investigated in a series of 5 laboratory studies.

The dependent measures in the study included percentage of target sounds identified correctly and a pleasantness rating on a 5 point scale (See Figure 8-3). The data show the tradeoffs between distinctiveness (higher identification) and preference (pleasantness).

Table 8-5. Dimensions Assessed in the Tone Ringer Sound Study
(Reprinted by permission of the copyright owner, AT&T).

The tone alerting signal study assessed nine dimensions and used the following criterion for the levels to be measured:
1. Single frequency- Four frequencies, ranging from 300 to 1200 Hz, were equally distant from each other (in terms of musical scale), and were in the most pleasing pitch range (determined in pilot work).
2.Two-note melody- Four different musical intervals (two-note "melodic") sequences were chosen; two were "consonant" (e.g., the major third), and two were "dissonant" (e.g., the major second).
3. Octave- Four patterns consisting of melodic sequences, where the tones were in an octave relationship, were used.; two of the patterns contained four-note sequences, and two patterns had five-note sequences.
4. Three-note melody- Each pattern consisted of a three-note melodic sequence, where each sequence differed in its pattern of "ups and downs."
5. Four-note melody- Each pattern consisted of a four-note melodic sequence. Each of the three-note melodies had a unique contour.
6. Warble- The same frequencies were used as in the "melody" condition. All patterns were frequency modulated at a 15-Hz rate.
7. Timbre- Four preprogrammed timbres of the Yamaha DX7 sound synthesizer were selected. Each timbre had the same pitch.
8. Modulation rate- Four different frequency modulation rates were selected, ranging from very slow (5 Hz) to very fast (17 Hz). The interval of a major third was used for each pattern.
9. Rhythm- A single frequency was used for all patterns. The four patterns were: one short tone, two short tones, three short tones, and one long tone.

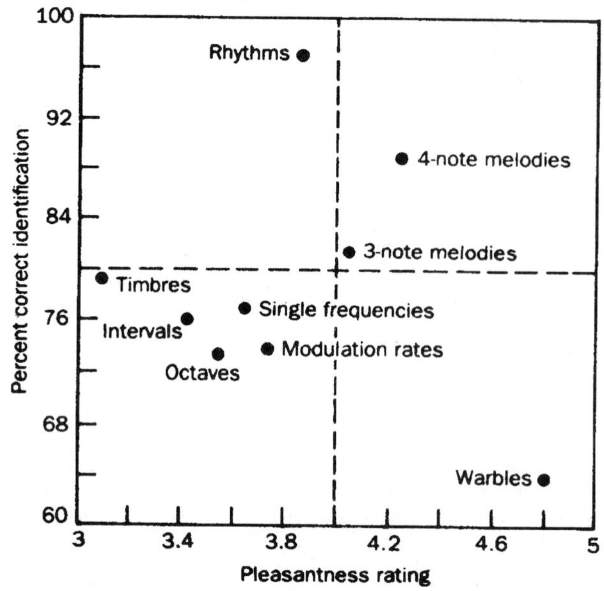

Figure 8-3. Mean Pleasantness and Correct-Identification Ratings for Nine Dimensions of Tone Ringer Sounds.

(Reprinted by permission of the copyright owner, AT&T).

5.9 Additional Telephone Design Issues

Some more frequently studied areas of terminal interface design are:

1. Softkeys - A large area LCD display (at least 10 cm x 10 cm) with dynamically relabeled buttons arranged on the sides of the display.
2. Membrane Buttons vs. Full Motion Buttons - Membrane buttons are flat, surface buttons with a covering seal or membrane to keep out unwanted dirt and liquids. These buttons give no motion feedback when pressed, so a short tone is delivered as an alternative, following the principle that all user actions require feedback. Loeb (1983) found that users rapidly adapt to the use of membrane buttons.
3. Telephone Line Status Indicators - Various technologies have been used including flashing red and green LED's as well as LCD displays with status symbols. A common problem that usability engineers must test is the most effective way of using status indicators at a variety of flashing rates to indicate various telephone states such as: incoming call, line on hold, line held by another extension, conference call, transferred call, or line busy.
4. Telephone State Indicators - LED's, LCD's, and physical position are used to indicate additional terminal states such as: speaker on, microphone on/muted, ringer on, volume level, or message waiting.

5. Speakerphone Design - Modern speakerphones have greatly improved switching characteristics that minimize speech clipping, by switching in and out of microphone and speaker, during normal conversation, to avoid creating an unstable acoustical feedback loop. Often speech quality testing is done with "Golden Ear" evaluators in addition to samples of representative users. "Golden Ears" are highly trained to evaluate the many subtle speech quality variables impacted by speakerphone design.

5.10 Complex Voice Telephony

Human factors studies on Key, PBX and Central Office switching systems are often done, both in the laboratory and in the field, to establish system performance criteria. Some of the design criteria that directly affect user perception of product quality are shown in Table 8-6, with accompanying illustrative values (percentile values indicate that all performance times are the illustrative time values or below).

Eigen (1991), in the Encyclopedia of Telecommunications, covers in some detail the human factors issues associated with ISDN (Integrated Services Digital Network) telephone sets and the usability advantages of screen-based telephony. The visual-based media of a large display telephone, or a PC interfaced with a telephone, can make tremendous improvements in usability.

5.10.1 Future research needs in voice telephony. The introduction of new technologies to voice telephony will offer great opportunities to improve the usability of terminals that have long suffered the reputation of being difficult to use. Complex voice telephony features often go unused because of the limitations of old technology. It is almost impossible to design highly intuitive steps involving push buttons and LED indicators to activate complex telephone features such as conference and transfer. Even designers of these complex features will offer apologies to a caller whom they are about to transfer to another extension by saying something like, "Please give me your number, so that I can call you back if I drop your call while I am attempting to transfer you...Sorry." New technologies, such as ASR and large screen GUI-based interfaces, are now being used to make complex voice telephony features easy to use. Some of the areas that are in need of additional human factors research include:

1. How can large area displays best be used to improve complex voice telephony feature usability? What information should be displayed? Should users be able to customize their telephone displays? If so, then how?
2. How should expert systems update information in softkey displays to best match individual user's dynamic needs? (e.g. How should a user's personal telephone directory show most recently and frequently called numbers?)
3. How should context sensitive, on-line help systems be employed for display and voice-based complex telephony systems?

Table 8-6: User Perceptible Complex Telephony Design Criteria

User Perceptible Telephone System Design Criteria	Time	Percentile Value
1. Dial Tone Delay - Response delay from voice terminal handset off hook to onset of dial tone	4 sec	98.5
2. Remove Dial Tone - Response delay from dialing of first digit to removal of dial tone.	400 msec	99
3. Post Dialing Delay - Response delay from signaling information being recognized by the switch to the application of station alerting or the trunk being seized	600 msec	99
4. Ring Trip Delay - Response delay from answer at called voice terminal to removal of ringing signal		
a. Regular telephones	100 msec	99
b. Switch attendant (operator)	160 msec	99
c. Special terminals (e.g. digital)	300 msec	99
5. Remove Ringback - Response delay from answer at called station to removal of ringback at calling station.		
a. General user to attendant calls	160 msec	99
b. General user to general user	400 msec	99
6. Close Speech Path - Response delay from answer at called station to closing of speech path between called station and calling station or facility. (also called Voice Path Cut Through - Delay. See Israelski et al. (1989) for a detailed discussion of methodologies used to study this parameter.)		
a. Calls to switch attendant	160 msec	99
b. Calls to general users	400 msec	99
7. Disconnect Delay - Response delay from recognition of valid disconnect to all equipment and network connections idled.	300 msec 500 msec	50 99
8. Lamp Appearance Delays - Response delay from button depression until an indicator lamp goes on or off. (e.g. line status lamp, hold status lamp, message waiting lamp.)	100 msec 300 msec 700 msec	50 95 100

4. What auditory cognitive processing mechanisms are responsible to the human perceptions of annoying echo when single channel speakerphones are used? How can this knowledge of auditory cognitive processes be used to reduce speakerphone echo, distortion, and clipping?
5. For GUI PC-based telephony applications (also called CTI Computer Telephony Integration), what are the best user interface metaphors that are readily apparent and highly intuitive? How do we make CTI applications work seamlessly with all of the many computer applications that will also be used on the same PC workstation?
6. In the area of wireless or portable communications, what are the behavioral issues that must be addressed in the design of complex telephony devices to best match the needs of the mobile user?
7. How can gesture-based telephony technologies, such as pen-based input to telephony screens, best be implemented? See Millen (1993) for a thorough discussion of pen-based communications devices.

6.0 Usability Evaluation of Emerging Technologies

6.1 Video Communications

In the mid 1990's, video teleconferencing is at long last beginning to penetrate the market. There are well over 10,000 video teleconferencing rooms world wide in 1993. Desktop video systems are starting to appear, although not yet in large numbers. For many years, pundits have unsuccessfully predicted the rise of video telephony, while others such as Noll (1992) have said that there is no need for face-to-face visual communications. Angiolillo, Blanchard and Israelski (1993) give an overview of human factors issues for video telephony

Some of the added values posited for non-verbal information proposed by Angiolillo et al. include:

1. Adding information not available from audio alone, such as nodding one's head, expressing disgust or impatience that cannot be picked up in the tone of voice.
2. Providing redundant or complementary information, such as a smile and a laugh together.
3. Enhancing information by adding emphasis, punctuation, or phrasing to an aural message.
4. Enhancing a person's memory of a communication event.
5. Creating a sense of presence, which may encourage the speaker and the listener to be more attentive.
6. Increasing the efficiency of group decision making. (See Weimer, 1988).

Some of the most common sources of non-verbal communications are:

1. Face and eyes - The eyes are the most expressive indicator of interest and emotions. Other aspects of facial expressions, such as position of the eyebrows and shape of the mouth are also important sources of information.
2. Gestures - Movement of the hands and other so called "body language" convey vast amounts of information and help speakers reinforce their messages. McNeill (1992) offers a comprehensive summary of the none-verbal language of human gestures.
3. Appearance - Involuntary aspects, such as signs of age, weight, height, scars, etc. Voluntary aspects such as choice of dress, hairstyle, and wearing of glasses, etc.

Studies by Ochsmand and Chapanis (1974), of the impact of various media on task performance, demonstrated that information exchange tasks usually do not show a performance advantage for video plus voice as compared with voice only communications. However, for interpersonal tasks such as negotiation, the face-to-face (or video) channel is superior to voice only (See Weimer, 1988). It appears that users can pick up non-verbal messages from the video channel to enhance interpersonal interaction.

6.1.1 Image quality. Image quality is an important area of usability for visual communications. Commercial NTSC television is the 4.2 MHz analog system that unavoidably becomes the "standard" to which video telephone systems are compared. The most important aspects of video quality include:

1. Spatial Resolution
   a. Total pixels (picture elements) per frame
   b. Number of lines of horizontal and vertical resolution
2. Color Accuracy
   a. Color saturation error
   b. Hue phase error
   c. Chroma differential gain (how color saturation varies with brightness)
   d. Chroma differential phase (how hue varies with brightness)
3. Motion Reproduction Accuracy (temporal resolution)
   a. Amount of motion jerkiness or smearing

Analog TV (NTSC) has little perceptible motion impairment, due to its high frame rate of 29.97 frames/second. Spatial resolution for NTSC is often expressed in lines of horizontal resolution (426 is considered the maximum). However, digital compression, which makes economical video transmission possible, also produces a wide variety of impairments. Corruption of digits due to line error or pulse jitter can result in large rectangular blocks appearing on the screen, edge blurring, streaking, edge business, tiling, ghosting, mosquitoing, and image persistence (Wolf, et al, 1991).

As with speech impairments, MOS mean opinion scores, are obtained to measure image quality as well as video impairment ratings. The following rating categories are often used:

Excellent	Good	Fair	Poor	Bad		
Imperceptible	Perceptible but not annoying	Slightly annoying	Annoying	Very annoying		
Much Better	Better	Slightly better	Same	Slightly worse	Worse	Much worse

The greatest difficulty with measuring motion impairments for compressed digital video systems is the dependency on the exact nature of the motion in the source material being viewed. A talking head video from a business teleconference may provide acceptable motion and spatial resolution at 112 Kbs, but an action-packed sporting event would be completely unacceptable. Research by Wolf et al. (1991) is underway to develop objective performance measures of compressed digital video that would be highly correlated with subjective ratings, while not at the mercy of the vagaries of specific video scenes as source material.

Another impairment that results from digital video compression is the introduction of video signal delays of 200 to 400 msec because of extensive digital processing time requirements. As a result of video signal delay, the audio signal must also be delayed to synchronize picture and sound (e.g. lip movement synchronization with the voice signal). Lip sync delays of less than 50 msec, where the video leads the audio are not perceptible. The IEEE has recommended that audio does not ever lead video by more than 20 msec, since this is not a naturally occurring synchronization sequence. More research is needed to understand these delay parameters and their impact on communications performance and acceptability.

6.1.2 Video ease of use. Video telephony has a number of unique and important usability issues. Angiolillo et al. (1993) describe some of these issues and propose user interface design alternatives (See Table 8-7).

The eventual success or failure of video telephony will result from the interaction of many variables including:

1. Overcoming behavioral barriers
2. Marketing and positioning
3. Businesses' desire to save time and costs
4. Usability of video products

It will take great effort to make video telephony as easy to use as regular voice telephony. See Eigen (1983), Garberg et al. (1989) and Klemmer (1989) for additional discussion.

Table 8-7: Video Telephony Usability Problems and Design Alternatives.
(As described by Angiolillo et al., 1993)

Usability Problem	Design Alternative
Spontaneity of Communication	- Portable Cellular Terminals - No Call Blocking
Video Call Setup	- Simple dialing - Intelligent network identifies mode (video, voice graphics) and type of terminal equipment
Privacy	- Begin call as voice only - User controls transmission and reception
Self-view	- No surprises such as being seen unintentionally while in the self-view mode - Mirrored view for personal self-view - Non-mirrored view for document viewing - Supply intuitive controls to transmitted view and/or local views
Delays and Lip Synch	- Reduce transmission delays - Preserve lip sync (IEEE recommends -20 msec to +40 msec differences between audio and video).
Camera Controls	- Natural control of remote end camera (e.g. zooming, as well as pan and tilt).
Physical Environment	- Design video environment to avoid poor lighting and poor acoustical treatment.
Multiple Video Source Control	- Provide intuitive control of which video sources are transmitted (e.g. GUI control over document cameras, VCR's etc.)

6.1.3 Future research needs for video communications. There are many vast uncharted areas of research needed in the field of visual and video communications. As video products become more widely accepted, additional user problems will surface as experience is gained with these technologies. Some of the areas that will need additional research include:

1. Image quality metrics, such as identifying critical subdimensions of video quality of moving images. What will be the impact of impairments introduced by new transmission systems such as, ATM (Asynchronous Transfer Mode)?
2. Social psychological implications of visual communications on individual and group communications (See Weimer, 1988), performance and acceptability. What tasks are suitable for video communications and when are they suitable?
3. All of the usability problem areas outlined in Table 8-7.
4. What is the effect of multiple video channels in a conference setting, where each conference participant might have a continuously present video signal? (Also called continuous presence video).
5. What is the impact of having stereo sound imaging associated with large screen video displays, where the sound imaging aids in locating the current speaker, among a group of speakers at a conference table?
6. What other interface metaphors are likely to aid usability of video systems? Do systems that digitize the location of a user's images, and use hand gestures derived from these digitized images as input information, increase usability?
7. Do systems that electronically alter video images to simulate close eye-to-eye contact among participants provide a better communications experience?
8. Does 3 dimensional video provide added value to video communications?

6.2 Multimedia Communications

Multimedia communication is the natural evolution of video telephony, bringing together multiple types of media (e.g., audio, voice, text, graphics, animation, full motion video (real time and stored), and fax). The merging of media is best exploited in an interactive communications environment, as described by Benimoff and Burns (1993). Multimedia systems, although richer, are potentially more natural because of an expanded range of input devices (e.g. natural speech and pen-based gesture input; See Millen,1993). However, multimedia's inherent complexity poses special usability challenges (See section 6.2.1). The outcome of developing highly usable multimedia systems can be powerful new communications products and services such as:

1. Multmedia-based distance learning
2. Multimedia, multipoint teleconferencing
3. Interactive information services
4. Interactive entertainment services
5. Electronic job performance support (Integrating job related training, documentation, and on-line help)

6.2.1 Future research needs for multimedia communications. The research needs for fully exploiting multimedia will become clearer as experience is gained from real users performing actual communications task scenarios. Unlike the voice and speech areas of telecommunications, which have been in existence for many years, there is a much smaller volume of human factors research devoted to emerging areas such as video and multimedia. Some of the many areas that need exploration are:

1. A deeper understanding of how multimedia communications can aid collaborative group activities, such as when a group is on a video teleconference and is interactively editing shared text or a spreadsheet.
2. How should a cursor be controlled in a multimedia collaborative group session?
3. At what group size does chaos begin in a multimedia conference and how is that a function of the mix of media?
4. In general, what are the interactions among various media types on communication task performance and acceptability? (e.g. Is a voice annotated spreadsheet sent as a multimedia message, as good as a marked up fax of a printout of the same spreadsheet, followed by video message from the annotator?)

7.0 Summary of Methodologies

The preceding sections have outlined past research in the many areas of telecommunications. Each section has described some of the research methodologies as they have been applied to human engineering problems in the telecommunications field. Table 8-8 serves as a chapter summary of the various research techniques used by past researchers. Research methodologies, as applied to telecommunications, are not unique, but are in reality merely variations on research techniques that are described elsewhere in this book. In particular, there is a growing fuzziness in methodological differences between telecommunications and the allied human engineering specialties of human-computer-interaction and consumer products. This lack of clarity is due primarily to the fact that modern electronics technology has blurred the user interface distinctions among these specialty areas. Nonetheless, Table 8-8 is offered as brief summation of some of the ways that human engineering research techniques are uniquely applied to the field of telecommunications. Table 8-8 also outlines typical sets of dependent and independent variables that might be measured and controlled in studies of various user interface areas.

Table 8-8: Summary Of Methodological Considerations

User Interface Area	Common Methods	Dependent Variables	Independent Variables	Considerations
Speech Quality	1. Lab or field studies using phonetically balanced speech segments	1. Mean Opinion Scores	1. Noise 2 Distortion 3. Echo 4. Crosstalk 5. Clipping 6. Delay 7. Attenuation Loss	Special apparatus needed to acoustically match physical attributes of human ear and mouth
Speech Intelligibility	1. Diagnostic Rhymes Test 2. Modified DRT 3. Articulation Index	1. Correct identification of rhyming speech alternatives	1. Noise 2. Distortion 3. Echo 4. Crosstalk 5. Clippings 6. Delay 7. Attenuation Loss	Usually not degraded until MOS scores drop significantly
Automatic Speech Recognition	1. Wizard of Oz lab studies 2. Field studies with prototypes	1. Percentage of words/commands recognized correctly 2. User satisfaction level	1. Background impairments 2. Speaker dependent training level 3. Size of vocabulary	Accuracy depends on circuit quality
Interactive Voice Response	1. Wizard of Oz lab studies 2. Field studies 3. Directed Dialog	1. Task time 2. Task accuracy 3. Preference ratings	1. Prompt wording 2. Availability of help 3. Training availability	Many systems are poorly designed
Simple Voice Telephony Services	1. PC screen-based simulations of telephones	1. Dialing time 2. Accuracy 3. Features used	1. Faceplate arrangement 2. Feature labels 3. Handset design	
Telephone Tone Ringers	1. Lab studies 2. Field trials	1. Accuracy of discrimination 2. Latency of choices 3. Preferences	1. Background noise 2. Mechanical design of terminal 3. Acoustical properties of ringers	

Complex Voice Telephony	1. Simulated office ask scenarios in a lab study 2. Field studies 3. PC-based simulators that produce various system performance impairments	1. Long term memory for features 2. Noticeability and Objectionability ratings of performance impairments 3. Preferences 4. Task completion time and accuracy	1. Performance delays 2. Number of complex features signed.	Features are usually numerous and very complex.
Visual Communication	1. Simulated group meetings 2. Lab studies 3. Field trials	1. Frequency of use 2. MOS of video quality 3. Task times and accuracy 4. Feature preferences	1. Video bandwidth 2. Compression algorithms 3. Amount of delay 4. Level of impairments - Spatial - Temporal	Motion impairments are specific to content of material being view.

8.0 The Future

Futurists predict that artificial and virtual reality (VR) technologies may be part of future communications product offerings. Virtual reality is a technology where the user wears some type off Head Mounted Display in which 3D visual displays are presented and changed dynamically as a function of head movement and hand gestures, typically using a data glove. (Sometimes experts distinguish this previous description of VR as immersive VR as distinct from non-immersive VR, as might be experienced by the desktop metaphor exemplified by the Apple Macintosh). It is likely that interactive entertainment systems will be the earliest product realization successes and may potentially involve multiple players using a telecommunications network. But VR could also be successful in other areas such as exploring architectural design, pre-travel planning, safe virtual exploration of hazardous environments, and many others.

Another future technology is the potential employment of artificial intelligent agents. These virtual agents would be given instructions via natural speech input (ASR) to carry out user's desires (e.g. find all members of a family and arrange a common time for a multimedia teleconference reunion). Another example would be for a book chapter author to instruct the intelligent agent to research a topic area, such as "Human Factors in Communications" and return an annotated bibliography complete with an outline of an interesting book chapter.

9.0 Additional Readings in Telecommunications

For more information on the human factors issues in the design and evaluation of telecommunications systems, consult the following publications:

Day, M. C. (Sept/Oct 1989). Designing the human interface: An overview. *AT&T Technical Journal*, 68(5), 2-8.

Farber, J.M. (May/June, 1993). Using technology to achieve ease of use. *AT&T Technical Journal*, 72(3), 4-6.

*Fourth International Symposium on Human Factors in Telephony, (*1968). Bad Wiesse, Germany: (Proceedings published by VDE-Verlag Gmbh, Bismarkstrasse 33, 1 Berlin 12, Germany).

Hanson, B. L., & Israelski, E. W. (1977) Human factors engineering in the outside plant: Bringing out the best. *Bell Laboratories Record*, 55(2), 30-35.

Riley, C. A., & Schwartz, B. K. (July 28, 1988). *Evolution or extinction? A case study of decentralized human factors in a telecommunications R&D company* (Bell Core TM-TSV-01203),. Presented at Human Factors in Telecommunications '88, The Hague, Netherlands. (Available from author at Bell Core, Red Bank, NJ.)

10.0 Biography

Edmond W. Israelski is technical manager of the Human Factors Systems group in the Global Business Communications Systems unit of AT&T Bell Labs. He supports the design and evaluation of user interfaces for large customer communications products and adjunct systems such as multimedia messaging, video conferencing and operations support systems. Dr. Israelski received a B.S. in Electrical Engineering from NJIT, an M.S. in Operations Research from Columbia University and a Ph.D. in Industrial and Engineering Psychology from Stevens Institute of Technology. He joined AT&T in 1970 and has worked as a systems engineer, product manager, market researcher, industrial/organizational psychologist as well as a human factors engineer. He has authored 4 other book chapters and a variety of journal articles and conference proceedings articles. He is an active member of the Human Factors and Ergonomics Society. where he has held a wide variety of elected and appointed offices.

REFERENCES

Angiolillo, J. S., Blanchard, H. E., & Israelski, E. W. (May/June, 1993). Video telephony. *AT&T Technical Journal*, 72(3), 7-20.

Benimoff, N. I. & Burns, M. J.(May/June, 1993). Multimedia user interfaces for telecommunication products and services. *AT&T Technical Journal*, 72(3), 42-49.

Bennett, R. W., Greenspan, S. L., Syrdal, A. K. Tschirgi, J. E., & Wisowaty, J. J. (Sept/Oct, 1989). Speaking to, from, and through computers: Speech technologies and user-interface design. *AT&T Technical Journal*, 68(5), 17-30.

Conrad, R. & Hull, A.J. (1968). The preferred layout for numerical data entry keysets. *Ergonomics*, 11(2), 165-173.

Deininger, R. L. (1960). Human factors engineering studies of the design and use of push button telephone sets. *Bell System Technical Journal*, 39(4), 995-1012.

Eigen, D. J. (1991). Communications human factors. In F. E. Froehlich & A. Kent (Eds.). *The Encyclopedia of Telecommunications: Vol 4.* (pp. 1-49). New York: Marcel Dekker.

Eigen, D. J. (July/August 1983). Methods for field testing new telephone services. *Bell System Technical Journal*, 62 Part 6(3), 1591-1616.

Garberg, R. B., Lincoln, C. E., & Millen, D. R. (September/October 1989). Human factors in the design of telephone features. *AT&T Technical Journal*, 68(5), 56-68.

Gardner-Bonneau, D. J. (Oct., 1992). Human factors problems in interactive voice response (IVR) applications: Do we need a guideline standard? *Proceedings of the Human Factors Society,* (pp. 222-226.) Santa Monica, CA: Human Factors & Ergonomics Society.

Hanson, B. L. (July-August 1983). A brief history of applied behavioral sciences at Bell Laboratories, *Bell System Technical Journal,* 62(6) , 571-590.

Israelski, E. W. & Reilly, R. R. (1988). Telecommunications craftworkers. In S. Gael (Ed.). *Job Analysis Handbook for Business, Industry and Government, Vol 2.* (pp. 1265-1286). New York: John Wiley & Sons.

Israelski, E. W. (1995). Methods for usability engineering in equipment design, *The Encyclopedia of Telecommunications*, Vol 6 (In press). New York: Marcel Dekker.

Israelski, E. W., Angiolillo, J. S., Brehms, D. J., Hoag, L. L, Roberts, L. A., & Wells, R. S. (September/October, 1989). Generalizable user-interface research. *AT&T Technical Journal*, 68(5), 31-43.

Klemmer, E. T. (Ed). (1989). *Ergonomics: Harness the Power of Human Factors in Your Business.* Norwood, NJ: Ablex Publishing.

Kotsonis, M. E., Abramson, S. R., Loeb, K. C. & Wattenbarger, B. L. (1989). In the customer's hands: Making the most of user feedback, *AT&T Technical Journal*, 68 (5), 69-79.

Loeb, K. M. Cohen. (July-August, 1983). Membrane keyboards and human performance. *Bell System Technical Journal*, 62 Part 6(3), 1733-1750.

McNeill, D. (1992). *Hand and Mind.* Chicago: University of Chicago Press.

Members of the Technical Staff. (1977). *Engineering and Operations in the Bell System,* (pp. 603-608). Murray Hill, NJ: Bell Telephone Laboratories, Inc. Author

Michaelis, P. & Wiggins R. (1982). A human factor's engineer's introduction to speech synthesizers. In A. Badre & B. Shneiderman (Eds.) *Directions in Human Computer Interaction,* Norwood, NJ: Ablex.

Millen, D. R. (May/June, 1993). Pen-based user interfaces, *AT&T Technical Journal*, 72(3), 21-27.

Nielsen, J. (1993). *Usability Engineering.* San Diego, CA: Academic Press.

Noll, A. M. (May/June 1992). Anatomy of a failure: Picturephone revisited. *Telecommunications Policy*, 16(4), 307-316.

Ochsman, R. B., & Chapanis, A. (1974). The effects of 10 communication modes on the behavior of teams during co-operative problem solving. *International Journal of Man Machine Studies*, 6, 576-619.

Roberts, L. A., & Angiolillo-Bent, J. S. (Oct., 1988). The relative pleasantness and distinctiveness of a variety of auditory patterns. *Proceedings of the Human Factors Society 32nd Annual Meeting*, Santa Monica, CA: Human Factors & Ergonomics Society.

Scerbo, M. (1994) Usability Techniques. In J. Weimer (Ed.) *Research Techniques in Human Engineering.* Prentice-Hall: Englewood Cliff, NJ.

Short, J., Williams, E., & Christie B.(1976). *The Social Psychology of Telecommunications.* London: John Wiley & Sons

Tobias, S. B.(1994). *CONVERSANT® VIS Release 4.0 Application Design Handbook*, AT&T Technical Document 585-350-501. (Available from AT&T Customer Information Center, +1-800 432 6600)

Van Santen, J. P. H. (1991). *Expanded Diagnostic Rhyme Test for Text-to-Speech Evaluation*, Internal AT&T Bell Labs publication. (Available from E. W. Israelski, AT&T, 200 Laurel Ave., Middletown, NJ.)

Voiers, W. D. (July, 1976). Methods of Predicting User Acceptance of Voice Communications Systems, (Final Report of Contract No. DCA 100-74-C0056). Reston, VA: Defense Communications Agency.

Voiers, W. D. (Jan/Feb 1983). Evaluating processed speech using the Diagnostic Rhyme Test. *Speech Technology,* 30-39.

Wattenbarger, B. L., Garberg, R. B., Halpern, E. S., & Lively, B. L. (May/June 1993). Serving customers with automatic speech recognition. *AT&T Technical Journal*, 72 (3), 28-41.

Weimer, J. (1988). *Machiavellianism and Computer Mediated Communication*. Unpublished doctoral dissertation, Texas Tech University: Lubbock, Texas.

Wolf, S., Pinson, M. H., Voran, S. D., & Webster, A. A. (May 9-10, 1991). Objective quality assessment of digitally transmitted video, *IEEE Pacific Rim Conference on Communications, Computers and Signal Processing,* (pp. 477-482.)

Wolf, S., Dvorak, C. A., Kubichek, R. F., South, C. R., Shaphorst, R. A., & Voran, S. D. (Oct., 1991). How will we rate telecommunications systems performance? *IEEE Communications*, 23-29.

Chapter 9
Consumer Products Techniques

Peter P. Mitchell
Ergo Research, Inc.

1.0 Introduction

Human factors research in consumer products has evolved significantly within the past five to ten years. Companies have become sensitive to the need for easy-to-use products primarily by the pressure placed upon them by the marketplace. Prior to this recent concern for usability, the common practice for most consumer products designers and manufacturers had been to concentrate solely on product appearance and consumer preference issues and ignoring the issues related to ease of use of the product. This attitude has changed, particularly in the field of consumer electronics. The marketplace has dictated that if a product does not meet consumers' expectations for ease of use, it will not be successful. As an example, the cover of *Business Week*, April 29, 1991, read in large print, "I Can't Work This ?#!*% Thing!" (Nussbaum, 1991). This article documents repeated cases where consumer products have been designed more with the engineer than the end user in mind, and it highlights the need to evaluate new product ideas through testing with typical consumers to ensure that the product is going to meet their needs and be easy to use. In recent years marketers and product managers have become aware of the need for human factors in consumer product development and have allocated research and development resources for human factors in the development process.

This chapter discusses the types of human factors research being done in the "real world" on consumer products. In writing this chapter, my emphasis has been to use case studies of actual products to illustrate the types of human factors research and usability testing that is going on in industry today. I describe some of the newer, innovative techniques, as well as the more traditional human factors and usability testing approaches.

The chapter is presented in two broad sections: (1) Informal research techniques in which, normally, just one product (variable) is tested and the primary objective is to get consumer reaction to a new product idea, and (2) formal research techniques in which independent variables are manipulated and formal dependent variable measures are obtained. Each section will describe the typical research techniques that are used, the issues that are studied, and the user population that is commonly recruited for the research. I hope that this chapter will provide students and other readers with practical and interesting information about some of the research issues relative to human factors in consumer product development as well as the procedures to follow in conducting human factors research in the area of consumer products.

2.0 Nature of Consumer Products Research

In developing new products, the researcher would always prefer to have the time and resources to conduct thorough, controlled studies in which all relevant aspects of the product are studied and evaluated by typical end users of the product. Human factors engineers in the field of consumer product development rarely have this luxury. It is normally the case that tight scheduling and cost constraints force you to conduct only limited research, and this research is often just a "sanity check" to make sure that there are no critical shortcomings with the product before sending it to production.

While not an ideal situation, this is reality, and the human factors researcher and product developer must work within these constraints. This does not mean that you cannot conduct useful and important research; it simply means you have to be resourceful and persistent in working with management and the product development team to carry out the necessary research.

3.0 Informal Techniques

This section presents a number of informal techniques that are currently used in industry to help improve the usefulness and ease of use of new consumer products. Case studies of specific products are presented in order to illustrate how human factors engineers in this field go about the business of researching and evaluating new products. Some of the examples come from work done by Ergo Research, while others come from speaking with colleagues and drawing upon their experiences and research.

3.1 Focus Groups[1]

In developing any new product there is a temptation to grab an idea and start designing the product. However, it is important to have a complete understanding of the customer's needs and preferences before beginning the product and user interface design stages. No matter how well you think you understand what the final product should look like and how it should operate, it is essential that you spend the time, effort, and money to conduct a systematic evaluation of your users' needs and preferences, as well as the human factors requirements of the product. This research task is normally assumed by the marketing research staff, and occasionally they allow the human factors group to participate. This section discusses some of the research issues associated with this initial stage, including the ways in which

[1] For more information on the use of focus groups as a technique, see Chapter 7, section 3.2.

human factors and marketing research teams should interact, and some of the data gathering techniques that can be used to achieve this initial goal.

One means of assessing customer needs is to borrow a research technique from marketing research: The focus group discussion. In the past, this technique has been used primarily to examine people's preferences regarding initial product concepts and ideas. However, focus groups can also be useful in assisting the human factors practitioner in developing the best user interface for a new consumer product. The reference to the "user interface" is made in the broadest of terms. We usually think of computer screens and keyboards when we refer to the "user interface", however, in consumer products the "user interface" may be the handle on a milk container or the flap on a cordless phone.

Stan Caplan (1990) at Kodak describes how the focus group technique can be used by the human factors professional to obtain an understanding of customer needs and help develop solutions to user interface design problems; he has used this approach in the development of cameras, copiers, and other office products at Kodak. Focus groups are small groups (usually 8 to 10 people, or mini-groups of 3 to 5 people) of typical users who are assembled in a room to discuss a concept for a new product or to examine the methods of operation of a prototype of a new product. Typically, this is done in a conference room or a focus group facility complete with a two-way mirror for observation by others on the product development team in an adjacent room. However, groups can sometimes be most effectively conducted in a living room environment since this type of setting helps put people at ease.

Typically, the focus group participants are recruited using a screener, which is a questionnaire that qualifies people for inclusion in the group based upon marketing's demographic requirements for the product. An example of a screener for a new banking product is given in Appendix 9-1; for confidentiality reasons the name of the bank has been replaced by an "X". Normally this recruiting is handled by a special field recruiting firm. By using test participants who fit the marketing department's research criteria, human factors researchers can provide valuable input to marketing, creating a useful synergy and feeling of cooperation between the two groups.

A moderator's guide is then created which contains questions aimed at addressing the important variables and issues relative to the development of the product. The participants are also often given hands-on exposure to the new product so that they may experience how it works and get a "feel" for the user interface. The moderator then directs the discussion and gets the participants to talk about what they like or dislike about the product and its user interface. As Caplan explains (1990, p. 527), "the moderator must be skilled in getting people to discuss their ideas, feelings, anxieties, frustrations, and convictions in a relatively unstructured free-flowing session". The moderator needs to be knowledgeable about the operational details of the product in order to direct the discussion effectively, however, the moderator should not have so much involvement with the product that he or she introduces a bias into the discussion. A balance must be achieved. Sometimes the human factors specialist on the development team brings the right amount of balance and, providing he or she has good interpersonal skills as mentioned by Caplan, can be a good choice for a moderator. Regardless of the moderator, it is recommended that the product development team (marketing, engineering, and management) view the sessions from behind the two-way mirror to gain a firsthand understanding of the product design needs expressed by the consumers in the group.

The way to add the human factors element to the focus group technique is to have the participants actually use the product, or a prototype of the product, during the session so that the moderator can observe their performance with the product and so that the participants will have enough information to form an opinion of the ease of use of the interface. You have to be careful in providing this hands-on exposure during the group; each person needs to spend enough time with the product to be able to make enlightened comments, but spending too much time with the product may destroy the flow and continuity of the group. In doing these types of sessions, you may want to consider having a smaller number of people in the group (3 to 5 people) in order to control these potential problems.

An example of the use of this technique involved work done by Ergo Research in the development of an information and point of sale kiosk by a U.S. computer manufacturer that would be placed in malls and large stores. The unit provided multi-media information and had both a touchscreen and a keyboard interface. The unit had credit card reading and printout capabilities. The participants were first given a concept statement to get their reaction to the idea, before seeing the model of the product concept. The prototype of the kiosk was then shown to the participants and initial reactions were obtained. Each person then went to the kiosk and used all features of the unit to experience its user interface. Following this, each aspect of the unit was discussed in the group session.

The questions of interest (variables) to the client in this study were:

1. What was the reaction to the size and appearance of the kiosk?
2. What type of input method (touchscreen vs. keypad) would be optimal?
3. What is the ideal location for the printer and credit card reader?
4. What is the reaction to its multimedia presentation capabilities?
5. What type of information or services would the customer want to access?

The focus groups produced valuable information on each of these issues which provided input to the industrial design and marketing groups on ways to improve the ease-of-use of the product.

Case Study #1: Developing a New Lunchbox

Butler, Welker, and Chan (1992) reporting on research conducted at Fitch RS in Worthington, Ohio, describe the steps involved in developing a new lunch kit for the Thermos company. This research is significant in that it illustrates how human factors can interact with marketing research, industrial design, strategic marketing, and project management to develop an innovative, easy-to-use, and appealing new product. Pictures of the final product of this research are shown in Figures 9-1, and 9-2.

The project was structured as an interdisciplinary approach from the beginning, and there was a significant amount of overlap between groups; designers contributed to the research, and researchers and human factors engineers contributed to design. It is important for human factors researchers to appreciate that you can and should have a contributing role in the design process, using the information obtained from the field research and the data gathering.

Figure 9-1: Lunchbox (Carried by Corner Handle)

The first phase of the project consisted of field research with children and parents to discover their reaction to and feelings about existing lunch kits. An examination of how kids used lunch kits was conducted and ideas were sought on how this experience could be improved. The human factors staff participated in this by conducting interviews with children in several schools and developing a survey to be sent home for completion by the parents. On-site observations were also made in school' cafeterias. The researchers studied how children use their lunch kits and made structured observations to ensure that the same kind of information was gathered by all of the research team members at the different sites. Finally, students were asked to sketch what they thought the ideal lunch kit should look like and to describe the features it would possess.

Following this initial field research, brainstorming sessions were held with the research and design groups to develop concepts for the new lunch kit (for a discussion of brainstorming, see Tull & Hawkins, 1987, p. 623, and Byrne & Barlow, 1993). The design group repeatedly referred to the field research for direction regarding the shape and size of the new lunch kit and to specify its features. Review meetings were held with Thermos to refine concept sketches and develop ideas to be reviewed with children and parents.

In the next phase, the human factors group, led by Liz Sanders, took the nine lunch kit concept models, developed in the previous phase, to schools to have them evaluated by kids. Small groups of three to six children were given the models to handle and use. In this usability testing phase, the children's use of the models was observed and comments about each of the models were recorded. One of the purposes of this phase was to determine which of the concepts was found to be most usable and to determine which of the ideas children felt were "cool" and which were felt to be too "weird". Another objective was to study and understand children's preferences regarding color and other design features of the lunch kit. Structured observations were made and the human factors group summarized their findings to provide feedback to the design group.

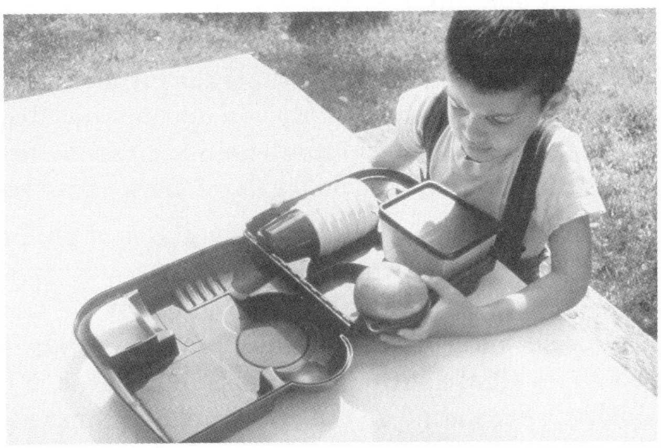

Figure 9-2. Lunchbox Compartmentalization

Concurrent with this research, mini-focus groups with the parents were conducted to obtain general reactions to the concepts and to evaluate the usability of each model. Typical lunch time foods were made available in these groups for parents to test the ease of packing the lunch kit. An interesting finding was that while children liked compartmentalization (See Figure 9-2), parents felt that the structured compartments of some of the models were too restricting; they preferred a more open format. Parents also felt that the lunch kits were too large.

All of these findings were summarized by the human factors research team and suggestions for redesign were made. The final changes made included: reducing the overall size by 10%, modifying the compartment walls inside the kit, placing the handle on the corner of the kit rather than running full length, and making one side of the kit flexible to accommodate a larger variety of objects.

3.2 The "Rapid Fire" Review Technique

In addition to product functionality, one of the fundamental issues confronting product developers is product appearance. While this is normally the domain of the marketing staff and industrial designers, it is important to recognize that there is an interaction between the appearance of the product and human factors (ease of use). Often times people form an initial negative reaction to a product based upon its appearance, and this creates a barrier to successful use of the product. You can become a more effective product developer if you could determine which product appearance factors convey ease of use and which convey complexity and thus send the message, "this product is hard to use". What is needed is a means of studying the ways in which people perceive a product and form an opinion about whether or not it is easy to use. It is appropriate for human factors professionals to contribute to this area of consumer product research.

A new technique, "Rapid Fire Review", has been developed to help industrial designers and marketing specialists understand the process by which product appearance opinions are formed; this information can then be used to help direct the industrial design program. This technique was used by Ergo Research in developing new portable phone concepts for Motorola and in researching new postage meter concepts for Pitney Bowes. The Rapid Fire Review method allows you to tap into the unconscious decision making processes that people use in determining their preference for one product over another. This is useful information for developers and researchers alike.

In the Rapid Fire Review, participants view slides of products presented for a very briefly, and then rate each product based upon its perceived ease of use. It should be noted that this same technique can be used to test the image of "quality" projected by a new product concept. Thus, the technique can be designed to evaluate either "perception of ease of use" or "the appearance of quality", depending on the development team's requirements.

The technique entails the creation of approximately fifty 35mm slides similar to and including the development product. The slides are placed in every other slot in a carousel slide tray; this ordering is used so the screen will go blank between slide presentations. A rating form is developed, numbered from 1 to the number of product images. A group of 8 to 10 individuals, matching the demographics of the target market segment, are assembled and given a brief description of the task. At Ergo, typically, a rating scale of 1 to 10 is used since this seems to be a familiar approach for most people and it is easy to remember. They are told that they will be shown one slide at a time for a very brief exposure (approximately 2 seconds), after which they are to place a number from 1 to 10 on the rating scale next to the number for that product, where 10 = the product is perceived to be very easy to use (or have the perception of high quality), and 1 = the product is perceived to be very difficult to use (or have a poor quality look). They are told not to discuss the products or their reaction during the Rapid Fire slide sequence, however, a space is left next to the rating for the participants to jot down one or two word associations for the product just viewed.

After the first pass through the slides, they are presented a second time and participants discuss why they gave a product a certain rating. Participants can refer to their rating sheets and word associations to describe their feelings and reactions to each product. Industrial designers, graphic designers, and marketing staff should view the sessions from behind the two-way mirror to learn firsthand the product appearance characteristics that convey "ease of use" or "quality" to the consumer. Subsequently the rating data are summarized, and each rating summary is associated with its respective product. In this way trends and patterns can be identified and used to help direct the product design and marketing.

3.3 Voice of the Customer

Case Study #2: Developing a New Circular Saw

Another approach to human factors testing is used at Black & Decker. Their approach, which they refer to as "Voice of the Customer", has been described by Don Zurwelle as utilizing a quality function deployment (QFD) approach in conjunction with traditional human factors research and testing methods (Zurwelle, 1993). Black & Decker used this technique in the development of a new line of circular saws. A photograph of the final product is shown in Figure 9-3.

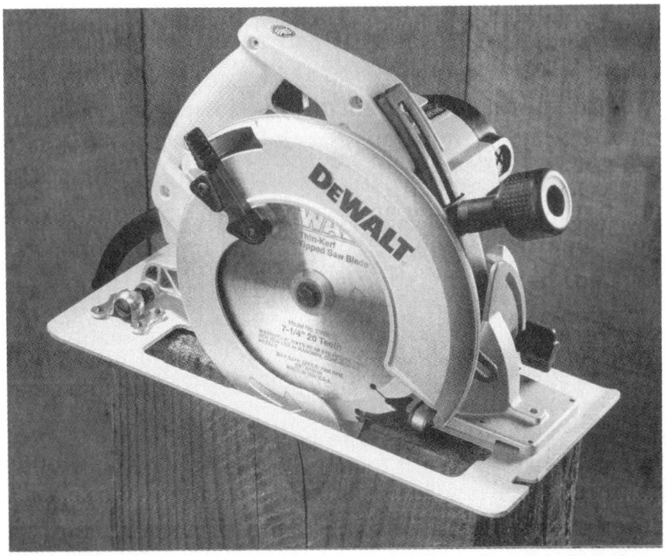

Figure 9-3. Voice of the Customer Final Saw Design

This product represented a completely new line of circular saws, including a completely new motor and a new housing for the product, and thus it was felt that a completely fresh look at the customer and his/her needs was called for. The first step in the process was to visit numerous job sites, service centers, and retail outlets to talk with end users of existing products to determine what they like as well as what aspects they feel could be improved upon. A total of approximately 400 users were interviewed, and the findings of these sessions were compiled into a requirements document, which provided the foundation for the development process. It is important to remember that these types of requirements documents are "living" documents; they should be viewed as a guideline as to the needs and preferences of the end user/marketplace and you should not hesitate to update and/or modify them as new information is obtained throughout the development cycle. These requirements formed the basis for a design guide for the product. This guide prioritized the saws potential features and provided a baseline for the product's durability, reliability, usability, and safety features.

At this time B & D purchased competitor's circular saws and put them through a series of in-house tests to determine how well they stacked up against the features and capabilities outlined in the design guide. From this testing the design guide was refined to specify the features required for the new B & D line of circular saws.

Concurrent with this effort, Zurwelle and his associates used the literature and standards on ergonomics to specify the weight, balance, and force-to-operate factors for the product. This information fed into the design of the handles, the trigger, the housing, and the controls on the saw.

Once all of these aspects of the product had been specified, true-to-life weighted models were built. These models possessed all of the handleability characteristics of the final product, including changing the angle of cut; however, they were not functioning saws. These models were initially evaluated in focus group research sessions. The B & D research team also took the models to job sites and specialty dealers to get users' reactions to the balance and ease of holding the product. Although this kind of "touchy feely" user preference research may fall sort of the standards for objectivity associated with most usability testing, Zurwelle notes that this kind of data gathering can often identify relevant issues and problems that can be addressed and corrected prior to conducting formal usability testing[2].

Finally, working prototypes of the product were constructed and usability testing was conducted with a large number of typical end users. The tests required users to make various types of cuts, use different types of wood, and set different angles on the saw. Structured observations were made of the participants' performance during the testing, and a number of specific findings were fed back to the design group. An example of a finding from the usability testing was that the amount of saw dust produced by the saw was greater than anticipated. The existing design of the saw dust chute was such that projected saw dust interfered with the safe and accurate operation of the product. Based on the usability testing, the saw dust chute was redesigned so that this problem was eliminated in the final product.

[2] This is one source of the "bug list" discussed in Chapter 2.

3.4 One-Person Research

Case Study #3: Follow-me-home Technique

In some instances, the best way to test the ease of use of a new product is by conducting the usability sessions directly in the consumer's home. An example of this was the "Follow-Me-Home" research conducted for Prodigy Services Company to evaluate the packaging and instructional material as well as the initial steps that new members follow in installing the software and enrolling on the service. The "Follow-Me Home" approach was used in this case since it was important to have the participants use their actual home phone and their home number in order to get a realistic measure of ease of use of the enrollment software. The goal of the research was to ensure that new members have a quick and enjoyable first experience with the PRODIGY service. A potential drawback to this technique is that people may be suspicious, and this may make them uncooperative. Thus, you should do everything possible to allay their apprehensions.

In the PRODIGY service study, people representative of the target user group were contacted by a recruiting firm and appointments were made to go to their home and observe them using the PRODIGY service, from the first step of opening the package all the way through the completion of the enrollment steps. As with most usability testing an observation form is used to structure the objective data recording, and the researcher did not coach or direct the participant unless they became stuck. A total of 21 people participated in the study.

The research issues covered in this study included: (a) Is the package easy to open and does it convey the benefits of the PRODIGY service? (b) Is the instructional material clear and does it effectively tell the user the specific steps to follow up to the point where instructions are presented on the screen? (c) Are the directions on the screen for installing the software easy to follow? (d) Are the directions on the enrollment screen easy to follow? (d) How easy was it to find the correct phone number to use for the service? and (e) How easy was it to provide the personal data requested on the initial screens?

After each installation and enrollment task, the participants were asked to provide a rating on a 1 to 10 scale on the ease of completing the task, and they were asked for their opinions regarding the design of the package, the instructional materials, as well as the design of the computer screens. Thus, in addition to obtaining observational information, subjective rating data and user comments were obtained for all of the tasks. A number of the sessions were videotaped for subsequent analysis. From all of the information obtained in the study, a number of recommendations were made to enhance the design of the screens and the instructional materials included in the package.

Case Study #4: Wizard of Oz Used in a Mall Intercept Environment

This case study describes combining the "Wizard of Oz" technique with a mall intercept approach to test a speech recognition user interface for new, residential telephone services. In mall intercept testing, people are approached in a shopping mall and asked to participate in a study by experiencing the new product while they are in the mall. They are usually taken to a quiet room, just off the mall, and given the product and a set of tasks to complete. The researcher provides an introduction to the testing, and then tell the user to begin completing the tasks. As with other usability testing, the respondent's performance is monitored and measured. Upon completion of the tasks, they are asked their opinion of the new product. The advantage of mall intercept testing is that a large pool of respondents is readily available, which results in a faster turn around time for the study and lower costs. The disadvantages of mall intercept testing is that there is often less control over the type of person included in the research since a comprehensive screener is not normally administered. Also people usually do not have a great deal of time, which means that the test session must be relatively short.

The Wizard of Oz approach (Kelley, 1983) enables you to simulate a user interface and let users experience it without having to build a fully functional system. In the case of speech recognition telephone services, the participant carries out the tasks and gives various commands, and a technician at the other end of the line controls the system so that it provides the appropriate feedback to the participant's command. The unusual aspect of this study was that the Wizard of Oz approach, which is traditionally used in lab settings, was conducted in a mall so that a relatively large sample size could be obtained in a short period of time. For further discussion of the Wizard of Oz technique, see Green and Wei-Haas (1985).

Speech recognition user interfaces have a unique set of issues and problems. However, a number of studies (Franzke, et. al., 1993, Gould and Alfaro, 1984, and Casali, et al., 1990) have found that speech recognition can be an effective means of controlling a computer or other electronic product, however, further work is needed in the development of speech recognition interfaces for consumer products. Telephone services, such as Repeat Call, Return Call, and Speed Dialing lists are the types of consumer services that might be ideally suited for speech recognition providing that the interface is easy to use.

The research issues, specified jointly by the client and Ergo Research included:

(a) What kind of introductory signal would most effectively communicate that users are to speak a command?

(b) How should the prompts be worded in order to get the user to say the right prompt at the right time?

(c) Do users need a signal (a beep) in order to get them to say a command?

(d) Should prompts be broken up with a "pause" to allow users to respond, or will users know to "barge-in" whenever they are ready to respond?

Answers to each of these questions was obtained through the research, and the Wizard of Oz approach in the mall intercept setting proved to be an effective combination.

4.0 Formal Techniques

Formal techniques refer to research in which two or more different product design alternatives are being considered and will be subjected to a usage evaluation by a test population. The different versions are created in prototype form, with some aspects of each being manipulated as the independent variables and performance measurement as the dependent variable. While it is normally preferable to have the time and the resources to conduct this type of controlled research in the development of new products, this is usually a luxury that is not available in the "real world". There are a number of instances in which this type of research was called for and carried out in the development of a new product. One such instance was the development of the sequence of use for building lists for the CLASS services offered by many of the Bell telephone companies around the country.

4.1 One Person Research

Case Study #5: The CLASS Services

The CLASS services allow residential customers to monitor and control their phone service to make the telephone more convenient and efficient. Although this is a communications product, it is marketed to the general residential customer which categorizes it as a consumer product. Several of the CLASS services, Call Blocking, Selective Call Forwarding, and Distinctive Ringing, allow customers to create lists of phone numbers. In the case of Distinctive Ringing, customers put the phone numbers of important or special callers on a list, and when these people call, the customer's phone sounds a distinctive ring indicating that the call is from someone on the list. In order for these services to be successful they must be easy to use. Ergo Research was commissioned by Bell Labs to ensure that the list creation aspect of the service would be easy to learn and use.

Two different methods of creating lists of phone numbers had been developed, one by Bell Labs and the other by Bellcore. The purpose of the research was to determine which of the two approaches was easiest for customers to learn and use. Ergo Research designed a controlled laboratory study in which a total of 33 participants were tested using the two different methods of creating and modifying lists of phone numbers. Typical consumers were recruited and were brought into a testing room. They were given a set of tasks to complete, directed to get to the instructional prompt for the service, and were then told to complete the tasks. They were given no coaching on completing the tasks, and performance measures (numbers and types of errors) were obtained. The sessions were audio taped for data analysis purposes.

The independent variables of the research, which were established through joint Ergo Research and Bell Labs planning sessions, where the key sequences required by these two methods were to:

(a) activate the service,

(b) put a name on the list,

(c) delete a name from the list, and

(d) hear the instructions.

The dependent variable measures were: (a) errors and (b) inefficiencies. Errors were cases in which an incorrect choice was made, while inefficiencies were instances in which the participant did not necessarily make an error, but they completed the task in an inefficient manner, indicating that they probably did not understand the conceptual model behind that particular interface. It was felt that 'inefficiencies" were an important measure of the usability of the interface in addition to the simple measurement of errors.

The research produced a clear indication of which of the two different methods resulted in the best user performance. More importantly, observing all of the participants during the testing produced a number of ideas for the development of a third version of the interface for creating lists. This third version was eventually adopted for the final product. This research effort clearly indicated the benefits that can be obtained from controlled usability testing[3].

Note: The Overlap Between Marketing and Human Factors

This research also highlights the important interaction between human factors and marketing. It is clear that human factors work should not be done in isolation from the marketing efforts in developing a new product. However, in most cases these two groups carry out their respective research independently of each other. As the human factors researcher, you can minimize or eliminate this problem by developing research methods that incorporate both human factors and marketing techniques and by being aware of the issues that affect both disciplines. There is a dynamic interaction between these two areas of product development, and this interaction should be taken advantage of to build better products and not be a source of conflict and division.

For example, in the case of the CLASS services, the length of the list (a marketing issue) interacts with the operation of finding and erasing numbers from the list (a human factors issue). That is, if the marketing requirements specify that consumers want large lists, then the user interface might be designed one way. If consumers only require a short list, then a different user interface design would be more appropriate. Thus, marketing requirements and decisions affect human factors and vice versa. You need to be aware of these interactions and use them to your advantage to create products that are easy to use and meet customer's expectations. See Sanders (1992) for additional discussion on this concept.

---

[3]For more information on usability testing, read Chapter 4.

Case Study #6: A Cordless Phone

Multiple product alternatives were also compared in a controlled study involved a cordless phone for consumers which had a built-in pager. This product was developed by Motorola; the testing was done by Ergo Research, Inc. Photographs of the product are shown in Figures 9-4 and 9-5. The phone and the pager could be turned on and off independently of each other. The question was how to best turn both the phone and the pager on and off without having to dedicate two separate keys for each on/off function.

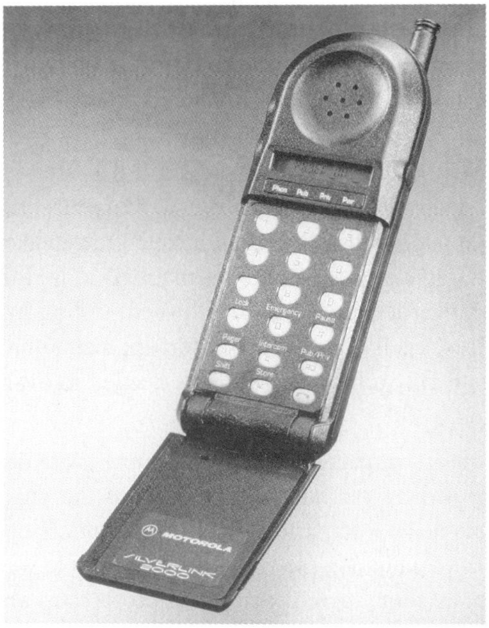

Figure 9-4. "Shift" + "on/off" Key for Pager (Method A)

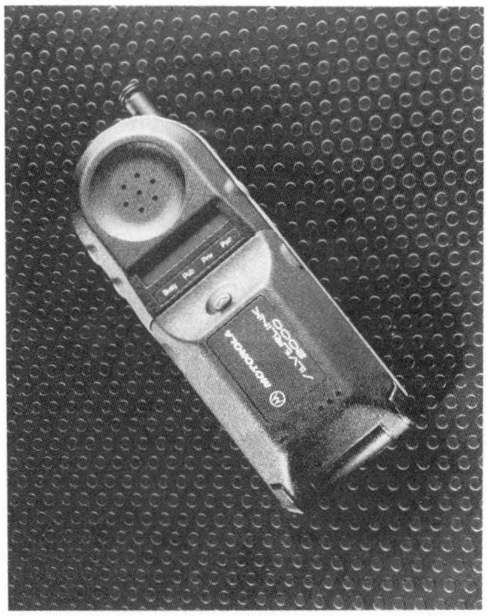

Figure 9-5. Press and Hold for Pager (Method B)

Two different methods of turning each of these functions on and off were developed. The two different on/off sequences were as follows:

Method A: Press "on/off" key for phone; press "Shift" + "on/off" key for pager

Method B: Press and hold (long press) "on/off" key for phone; quick press for pager. Thus, the human factors issue here was very specifically defined by the client, and the research challenge was to determine which of two different methods would be easiest for consumers to learn, remember, and use.

The target market for the product was the general population; users with no particular training or experience with computers or communications equipment. Thus, the requirement was that general consumers be used for the research. As in most cases, it was also a requirement that the research be completed as quickly as possible and within fairly tight budget constraints. Because a mall provides a ready supply of potential respondents for conducting research, mall recruiting and testing is generally less expensive and quicker than telephone recruiting and off-site testing. However, mall research is normally effective only in those cases where the test session is of short duration; people tested in malls generally do not have a great deal of time to sit down and evaluate a complex new product, which is often required in traditional usability testing. For those cases where longer test sessions are required, testing in the lab or some other facility is preferable. It was felt that the mall intercept technique would be appropriate for this research in which only a brief session was needed to evaluate the two interface design alternatives.

For this cordless phone project, working prototypes were developed using both of the methods of turning on and off both the phone and the pager. Test scripts were developed to instruct people how to perform both of the on/off operations. A test room was set up in the mall for conducting the test sessions. People were then recruited from the mall, brought to the test room, given each of the prototypes, and told to complete the tasks as instructed. Each participant used each of the prototypes; the order of use of each of the prototypes was counterbalanced to eliminate any order bias. They used each prototype several times to perform each of the on/off actions. They were then given a rating scale to determine their on/off sequence preference. Thus, although two different versions of the product were compared, a subjective measure, rating scale, was used as the dependent variable. The results produced a clear preference for one of the on/off sequences, which provided management and the engineering group with objective data upon which to base a decision.

4.2 Two-Person Research

A useful variation of traditional one-person usability testing is to have two participants use the product together in a usability testing session. The advantage of this approach is that the two people can talk to each other about what they are thinking and feeling about the product, and its user interface, as they progress through the test session. This provides very valuable insight into the cognitive processes of users, and this information can be very useful in making design changes to improve the product. This is referred to as the Co-discovery Technique at Philips Laboratories and is used regularly in the development of new consumer products. The two-person approach has also been used in developing a new portable phone for Motorola, in which the product was mocked up on a PowerBook and two-person sessions were conducted to evaluate the ease of operation of the phone, and for the Prodigy Service Company to evaluate the ease of using enrollment software for new members. For further discussion of two-person testing, see Dumas (1988).

5.0 The Reality of Usability Testing

Case Study #7: Human Factors at Philips Laboratories, USA

Philips Electronics North America Corporation makes consumer electronic products under the brand names, Magnavox, Philips, Philco, and Sylvania. The human factors group at Philips Laboratories in Briarcliff Manor, New York is involved in developing and testing many of their new products. While Philips conducts human factors on most of its new products, Jhumkee Iyengar, a user interface designer at Philips notes that usability engineering in the real world rarely works as smoothly as it is described in textbooks. She has summarized a number of human factors "realities" that she feel apply to research in consumer product development:

- iterative design rarely occurs; you get one shot at research during the development cycle
- testing is too time consuming and too expensive to be done often
- customers expect consumer electronic products to be inherently easy-to-use, they will not pay extra for it
- geographic and organizational barriers physically separate the human factors group from the product group and hinder textbook-type product design
- products are continuously evolving, thus the human factors researcher must adapt a testing program to be consistent with this approach
- human factors is often viewed as a service cost at the end of the product cycle; convincing management of the need for early human factors involvement is a hard sell
- engineers and managers consider themselves to be user interface experts since they use consumer electronic products like everyone else; the human factors professional must convince them of the value-added benefits of human factors analysis and testing.

While these comments may seem discouraging, they should be viewed as a challenge to adapt to meet the needs of a demanding business environment. These constraints do not prevent Philips from conducting effective human factors research; they simply challenge researchers at Philips to use their resources wisely. A human factors research and development program must be configured so as to work within the constraints of the organization. The human factors researcher must identify the tangible benefits of the human factors effort and sell these benefits to management. The better you understand your role and the ways you will and will not be utilized within the corporation, the greater will be the impact of your human factors research.

5.1 How to Get Buy-in from Management

There are a number of strategies to utilize in getting management's attention for the need for the research. Here are a few thoughts:

- Stress the importance of usability evaluations; emphasize that human factors analysis and usability testing is just as important as other engineering fundamentals in the development of the product;
- Encourage conducting the usability evaluations as early in the development process as possible; doing it as early as possible and repeating it throughout the cycle is the goal, and emphasizing it early will increase the probability of it happening at all;
- Develop an alliance with marketing and marketing research; in many instances affiliating with marketing research will get you more clout;
- Try to get the ear and the attention of upper management; human factors often has an intrinsic appeal, and having their support and backing is often times all that is needed;
- Suggest short, manageable steps in the human factors program; emphasize that the usability evaluations can be done concurrently with the other efforts, they will not upset the development schedule, and the results will provide immediate feedback to the developers.
- Present a business case for usability by talking to management in *their* language not yours. Use cost justification (See Chapter 4, section 8.0) to show that usability studies, particularly those done early in the product development cycle, *save* the company money.

These are the kinds of issues that are likely to be important to the management in charge of developing the new product, and employing these strategies is likely to increase the chances of getting the time and resources needed to conduct useful human factors analysis and testing.

6.0 Biography

Peter Mitchell is president of Ergo Research, Inc., a human factors and marketing research consulting firm, founded in 1981, and located in Norwalk, Connecticut. He has previously held the positions of Public Relations chair of the Human Factors and Ergonomics Society, and President of the Metropolitan Chapter of the HFES. He received his M.A. in Experimental Psychology from Victoria University of Wellington, New Zealand, in 1975, and his Ph.D. in Human Factors from Stevens Institute of Technology, Hoboken, N.J. in 1982. He has received the CHFP certification from the Board of Certification in Professional Ergonomics in December 1993. He has published a number of articles on human factors issues in human factors and marketing research publications.

As the head of research and user interface design at Ergo Research,he has completed numerous human factors and usability testing studies for a wide range of Fortune 500 companies. These include: a speech recognition interface for network-based telephone services such as Speed Dialing and Call Return, electronic banking services, home entertainment systems, on-line information services, patient monitoring medical equipment, PCS communication products and services, the CLASS telephone services, smartcard public telephone services, stock and options trading systems, and 2-way radio/cellular phone products.

If you have questions or comments about this chapter, or would like to know more about Ergo Research, Inc., you can e-mail Peter at: drwb55a@prodigy.com, if you are an Internet user, or just drwb55a if you are a PRODIGY user.

REFERENCES

Butler, B., Welker, K., and Chan, P. (1992). Inventing a New Kind of Lunch Kit. *Statements*, Fall.

Byrne, J.G. and Barlow, S.T. (1993). Structured Brainstorming: A Method for Collecting User Requirements. In *Proceedings of the Human Factors and Ergonomics Society 37th Annual Meeting* (pp. 427-431). Santa Monica, CA: Human Factors & Ergonomics Society.

Caplan, S. (1990). Using focus group methodology for ergonomic design. *Ergonomics,* 33, (5), 527-533.

Casali, S.P., Williges, B.H., and Dryden, R.D. (1990). Effects of Recognition Accuracy and vocabulary size of a speech recognition system on task performance and user acceptance. *Human Factors*, 32, (2), 183-196.

Dumas, J.S. (1988). *Designing User Interfaces for Software*. Englewood Cliffs, N.J.: Prentice-Hall,

Franzke, M., Marx, A. N., Roberts, T.L., and Engelbeck, G.E. (1993). Is speech recognition usable? An exploration of the usability of a speech-based voice mail interface. SIGCHI Bulletin, 25, (3), 49- 51.

Gould J.M. and Alfaro, L. (1984). Revising Documents with text editors, handwriting- recognition, and speech-recognition systems. *Human Factors,* 26, (4), 391-406.

Green, P. and Wei-Haas, L. (1985). The rapid development of user interfaces: Experience with the wizard of oz method. In *Proceedings of the Human Factors Society 29th Annual Meeting* (pp. 470-475). Santa Monica, CA: Human Factors Society.

Kelley, J.F. (1983). An Empirical Methodology for Writing User-Friendly Natural Language Computer Applications. *Proceedings of the CHI'83 Conference on Human Factors in Computing Systems* (pp. 193-196). New York: Association for Computing Machinery, Inc.

Nussbaum, B. (1991). "I Can't Work This Thing". *BusinessWeek*, April 29.

Sanders, E. (1992). Converging Perspectives: Product Development Research for the 1990s. *Design Management Journal*, Fall.

Tull, D.S. and Hawkins, D.I. (1987). *Marketing Research: Measurement and Method*. New York: Macmillan Publishing Company.

Zurwelle, Donald W., "The User as Partner in the Product Development Process", in *Proceedings of the 37th Annual Meeting of the Human Factors and Ergonomics Meeting*. Seattle, Washington, October 11-15, 1993.

Appendix 9-1
Typical Screener

SCREENER 3/6/92

PAY-BY-PHONE KIOSK STUDY:ROUND 2

Name____
Address____
Home Phone____
Interviewer_______________Date_________Time_________________

Hello, this is______________from the Ergo Research Group and we are conducting a study with bank customers. We would like to ask you a few questions.

1. Are you the principal bill payer in your household?
   [ ] YES
   [ ] NO If NO, may we contact the bill payer in your household?
      [ ] YES, Contact___________________________
      [ ] NO (TERMINATE)

2. On average, how many bills do you pay a month?
   [ ] 1 to 6 (TERMINATE)
   [ ] 7 to 12
   [ ] 13 or more

3. Which bank or banks do you currently use for your personal banking; i.e. where you have your primary checking account?
   [ ] "x"
   [ ] Other RECORD ______________________________

4. Have you signed up for the Pay-By-Phone service offered by "x" , or by some other bank, to pay bills, transfer funds, and check balances using your telephone? (To do this you fill out a form indicating the merchants you would like to pay, along with the account numbers.)
   [ ] YES Go to Question 5
   [ ] NO Go to Question 7

5. Do you use this service?
   [ ] YES, to pay bills and to make transfers
   [ ] YES, but only to make transfers (not to pay bills)
   [ ] NO

6. How many times have you used it in the last 3 months?
   [ ] More than 10 times
   [ ] 5 to 9 times
   [ ] 1 to 4 times
   [ ] Have not used it in the last 3 months

7. Do you use the Automatic Teller Machines (ATMs) available to you at your bank?
   [ ] YES
   [ ] NO

8. How frequently do you use ATM's?
   [ ] Light use, 1 time per month
   [ ] Moderate use, 2 to 4 times per month
   [ ] Heavy use, 5 or more times per month

9. What is your current occupation?
   RECORD____
   (RECRUIT A MIX OF OCCUPATIONS)

10. Note Respondent's Sex:
   [ ] MALE (RECRUIT 40%)
   [ ] FEMALE (RECRUIT 60%)

11. Into which group does your age fall?
   [ ] Under 18 (TERMINATE) [ ] 36 - 45
   [ ] 18 - 25 [ ] Over 45 (TERMINATE)
   [ ] 26 - 35
   (RECRUIT AN APPROXIMATE EQUAL AGE DISTRIBUTION)

12. Into which range does your household income fall?
   [ ] Less than $15K (TERMINATE) [ ] $35K to $49.9K
   [ ] $15K to $24.9K (TERMINATE) [ ] $50K to $74.9K
   [ ] $25K to $34.9K [ ] Over $75K
   (NOTE: FOR GROUPS 1, 2, AND 4 MUST HAVE $35K OR GREATER)

There is another part of this study I think you will find very interesting. We are inviting selected bank customers to ask their opinion regarding some new banking services. The interview will last approximately one hour; for your participation you will receive ________.

Would you be able to help us with our study? YES NO
May I have your name and address to send you a reminder letter.

Your interview will take place on __________ at ___________

Give Directions to Research Location: The "x" building at the corner of 23rd and Park Avennue.
Thank you for agreeing to help with our survey.

RECRUITING SPECS.

"x" customers (a list will be provided) and non-customers

Ages 18 to 45, recruit approx. equal number in each age group

Higher income households - over $35K

Principal bill payer in the household; pay a minimum of 7 bills/mo.

Approximately 60% women and 40% men

"x" CUSTOMERS

Group 1: Not signed up for Pay-By-Phone (N = 14)

Group 2: Signed up for Pay-By-Phone, but use it only for Transfers, or have not used it in the last 3 months. (N = 18)

Group 3: Signed up for Pay-By-Phone, and use it for bills and use it on a regular basis. (N = 8)

NON- "x" CUSTOMERS

Group 4: Non-"x" customers, may or may not use a Pay-By-Phone service at their bank. (N = 14)

Objective of the research is to evaluate a demonstration kiosk which describes and promotes the Pay-By-Phone service; the kiosks will be placed in branches.

Chapter 10
Human-Computer Interaction Techniques

Deborah A. Boehm-Davis
George Mason University

1.0 Introduction

During the 25 years from the development of the first computer until about 1970, research in the computer field focused largely on the development of better hardware and on programming methodologies to use hardware more efficiently. Little thought was given to the investigation of human skills and capacities for using computers.

It is not surprising, therefore, that in the 1960's, the involvement of human factors specialists in computing systems was largely limited to the traditional ergonomics role of designing the keyboards for computer terminals. Some comparisons of programming languages and batch versus timesharing systems were reported by Sackman (1970), but serious empirical research in other areas did not appear until after 1970.

The 1970's saw the emergence of serious scientific inquiry into human-computer interface and software engineering issues. Martin's (1972) *Design of Man-Computer Dialogues* was the first book to elevate the human-computer interface to the level of an independent area of study. Weinberg's (1971) *The Psychology of Computer Programming* emphasized the importance of controlled experimentation in evaluating performance in computer-related tasks, such as programming. In turn, Shneiderman's (1980) *Software Psychology* was the first to use the term "software psychology" to refer to studies of the performance of people using computer systems.

The technology revolution of the 1980's gave rise to the microcomputer. Computers became parts of systems ranging from everyday appliances such as microwave ovens to large-scale systems such as submarines or spacecraft. Research was done on many of these systems, and the importance of the computer component was not ignored. Further, the technology revolution provided the grist for research in software psychology and user interface design.

In the 1980s, the term "human-computer interaction" emerged as the terminology of choice to represent a discipline that combined the expertise of researchers from a wide range of disciplines who were interested in the behavioral aspects of users' interactions with computers. For the first time, computer scientists, graphics designers, human factors engineers, information systems specialists, linguists, mathematicians, and educational, cognitive, and experimental psychologists were all working to develop methods to improve the usability of computer systems for a wide range of users. Users were now not just the handful of dedicated hardware and software engineers of the 60's and 70's, but millions of more casual home and business users.

In the 1990's, we see evidence of the emergence of human-computer interaction as a mature field of endeavor. A number of national and international conferences have grown around this field (e.g., CHI, INTERACT, Empirical Studies of Programmers); a large number of books discussing these issues have recently been released (see, e.g., Dix, 1993; Hix and Hartson 1993; Laurel and Mountford, 1990; or Shneiderman, 1992) and new journals emerged (e.g., *ACM Transactions on Human-Computer Interaction, Interacting with Computers, International Journal of Human-Computer Interaction*).

2.0 Scope of the Chapter

The breadth of research techniques available for studying human-computer interaction is rivalled only by the variety of computing systems available to users to perform tasks and to researchers to study. As the field of human-computer interaction has matured, researchers have begun to specialize and apply their expertise to particular components of the human-computer system. These components include: the system hardware and the environment in which it is used, the interface between the system and the user, system users, and the software that runs the systems. Specialists in hardware study the devices that make up a computer system, such as the keyboard, mouse or monitor, as well as the ways in which these components are physically configured in a workstation within a working environment. Interface design specialists are concerned with developing the "look and feel" of an application such as Lotus™ or WordPerfect™. These researchers are concerned with generating the commands or icons people use to interact with applications programs as well as with the display and arrangement of those components on the computer screen. Other research has been focused on the characteristics of users that enhance or inhibit their performance in using computer systems. Finally, some researchers are interested in the characteristics of software that make it easier or more difficult for programmers to comprehend.

The research associated with each of these components of computing systems has its own set of unique research approaches and design issues. In the remainder of this chapter, the research techniques associated with each of these component areas will be discussed and critiqued. Within each area, the major research issues will be identified. Then, the major dependent variables (measures) used in the research will be described, along with the methodological approaches used to collect these dependent measures and examine the research issues. The advantages and disadvantages of each measure and approach will also be discussed to provide some indication of the generality of the conclusions that can be drawn from studies using these measures or designs as well as a framework for choosing from among the alternative methods and measures available.

Further, each section will include a description of case studies which illustrate the work being conducted in that area. These case studies were chosen to give the reader a flavor of the context within which the issues are being studied, not to provide the reader with design guidelines for future system development.

It is not possible in one chapter to describe the research techniques used to evaluate every application of computers in products. Rather, the focus of this chapter will be on the use of computers as personal computing workstations, not on their use as an integral part of other systems. Further, it should be made clear at the outset that this chapter is primarily for the researcher in theories of human-computer interaction, not the practitioner. It focuses on research methods used to evaluate and predict performance using computing systems in the developmental stages, primarily in a laboratory setting. The goal, then, is to guide the new researcher in this field to the research issues within the field of human-computer interaction, to the dependent measures and methodological approaches typically used to examine those issues, and to the advantages and disadvantages of using each of these measures and methodological approaches. Practitioners who want to evaluate products that are at the prototype stage or beyond should refer to the chapters on ergonomics (Chapter 11) and usability (Chapter 4) in this volume.

3.0 Hardware

The explosion in computer hardware capabilities over the past 20 years has forever changed the interaction of humans and computers. These changes have had a direct influence on user performance. The physical characteristics of the devices that comprise the system, the arrangement of these devices in the workstation, the user's position relative to the system, and the surrounding environment (including lighting, noise, etc.) have all changed dramatically. All these characteristics have been shown to influence performance (e.g., speed and accuracy of use) or physical comfort in using the system. However, the research methods used to investigate hardware have changed little in the same time span.

3.1 Major Research Issues

Within the domain of hardware, there are two major issues that are the focus of interest: (1) overall hardware configuration, and (2) device design. Hardware configuration research is concerned with arranging the physical components of a computer system (monitor, keyboard, mouse) to achieve maximum comfort, safety, and performance of the user. However, little rigorous empirical research is currently being conducted in this arena. Instead, most of the work in this area consists of evaluations of systems based on guidelines coming from earlier research.

The design of specific input and output devices has been the subject of more empirical research, particularly input devices. Much of this research has been summarized in chapters on keys and keyboards (Potosnak, 1988) and on input devices (Greenstein and Arnaut, 1988; Shneiderman, 1992). Although these chapters do an excellent job of summarizing the research on devices, they do not describe the measures that can be used to evaluate hardware, nor do they outline the methodological approaches for such evaluations.

3.2 Anthropometry: Measures and Methods

There is an extensive literature on anthropometry (See Chapter 11, section 6.4), and the goal here is to report on that portion of it relevant to computing systems. Kroemer (1988), and Kroemer, Kroemer, and Kroemer-Elbert (1990) provide an overview of the issues involved in workstation design; the American National Standard for Human Factors Engineering of Visual Display Terminal Workstations (1988) and MIL-STD-1472D provide standards for engineering visual display terminals, associated workstation furniture, and the surrounding work environment.

3.2.1 Measures. Anthropometric measures are measurements of physical characteristics of the body, taken either at rest (static) or in motion (dynamic). The measures most often used for evaluations of a hardware configuration are those related to the seated posture of an adult and the relationships between the user's eyes and the monitor and between the arms and the keyboard. These measures include elbow rest height, thigh clearance height, screen height, viewing angle, and elbow angle.

These measurements are crucial to the correct positioning of equipment. In turn, proper positioning of equipment is critical to the user's health. Improperly positioned equipment can not only cause irritation and inefficiency, but long-term medical problems, such as carpal tunnel syndrome. Unfortunately, few individual users are able either to calculate them accurately or apply them in adjusting their personal computing equipment. Baecker and Buxton (1987) state that these measures need to be "appropriately applied" (p. 103), yet they typically are not. One reason is that the measurements found in guidelines documents need to be representative of the individual who is setting up the particular piece of equipment. However, they point out that some of the measurements found in design documents were taken roughly 40 years ago from North American men, who are not representative of today's North American men or many of today's computer users. Further, they argue that even if users are armed with the appropriate data, they may not be able to apply them correctly. To support this point, they cite the example of a trade show of ergonomic furniture where the majority of the furniture being demonstrated by the sales staff was incorrectly adjusted. Finally, they point out that the adjustments provided by guidelines documents assume that computer users will remain in recommended postures, which has not been borne out by research. This suggests that anthropometric measurements are not as easily applied as might be imagined.

3.2.2 Methods. It is difficult to find a journal report that illustrates the approach typically taken in evaluating the hardware configuration of a computing system. Nonetheless, it is important to discuss the typical approach used in evaluating the overall configuration of hardware in a computing system. In a typical evaluation, users are seated in front of a console so that anthropometric measurements may be taken. The equipment is arranged according to available guidelines and the user proceeds to complete tasks while seated at the workstation. These tasks should be completed over a period of time that is representative of the amount of time users will typically spend at the workstation in their daily activities. Periodically, subjective measures of comfort and fatigue may be elicited either orally or through a written questionnaire (sometimes presented on the computer monitor) and measures of speed and accuracy on a task are usually collected through the computer itself. Thus, the primary independent variable addressed in these evaluations is the physical configuration of the system, while the primary dependent variables are subjective comfort, fatigue and performance (speed and accuracy).

Studies of this sort can be useful in applied settings, they are generally of limited value in research settings. Although it is not that difficult to select a set of representative tasks for a study of this sort, users are aware that they are being studied, which may affect their performance of the tasks[1]. To the extent that the equipment is novel, the users will also be measured as they become familiar with the new system. ***Note:*** Measures of comfort taken while the users are still relatively unfamiliar with the equipment may not be representative of later comfort. However, observations of user comfort and performance with the actual equipment provided better prediction of actual performance than approaches that do not include observational data. Thus, studies of this sort can provide useful information, even if it is somewhat limited.

3.3 Human Performance: Measures and Methods

3.3.1 Speed and accuracy. The most common dependent measures found in research on devices (both input and output) are speed and accuracy. For example, MacKenzie, Sellen, and Buxton (1991) compared performance for pointing and dragging tasks using three input devices: a mouse, a trackball, and a stylus with tablet. In this study, users were presented with two rectangular targets. In the pointing task, users were asked to alternately select between the two targets. In the dragging task, an object appeared on one of the targets and it had to be dragged to the other target.

[1]This phenomenon is referred to as the Hawthorne effect. For more infromation on the Hawthorne effect, See Cahpter 2, section 5.2.3.

Users were asked to perform both tasks using each of the three input devices, following practice using the device. The computer used for these tasks was instrumented to collect movement time and errors from each of the input devices. Movement time was calculated as the time required to move the input device from the location of the first target to the location of the second target. Errors consisted of selecting a location outside of the target or "dropping" the object during the process of dragging. Analyses of variance were computed for both measures.

Although studies sthat examine speed and accuracy provide some interesting data, a question remains about how useful speed and accuracy (and indeed, any performance measures) are as general measures of performance in using computer systems. First, no single input device is likely to be both the fastest and most accurate for a particular task. As in many other areas of psychological research, there is often a speed-accuracy tradeoff, so that you must decide whether speed or accuracy is more important for the task at hand. Further, the "best" input device for a particular task is unlikely to be the best for all tasks. For example, a device that performs quite well for a selection task might not be the best for a drawing task. Finally, absolute speed or accuracy may not be that critical for some systems. Unless an individual is performing a task repetitively without a break, the absolute speed of the input device may not have much of an impact on overall system performance. One partial solution to this problem is to develop a set of benchmark tasks that have been shown to cover a wide range of human performance[2]. Unfortunately, a commonly-accepted set of benchmark tasks has not yet been developed for the research community.

3.3.2 Methods. This case study also demonstrates the most typical research approach to the study of devices. The research design uses a within-subjects analysis of variance framework with type of device as the independent variable. This design is advantageous over a between-subjects design because it provides more power. This is especially true where the performance of a targeted population of users of a given device is known to be quite variable. The within-subjects design allows for the estimation and elimination of between-subject variability, so the design is more sensitive, especially in situations of high between-subject variability[3].

However, it is not always possible to use a within-subjects design. Carry-over effects (See Chapter 2, section 5.2.4) from one device to another may contaminate performance or time constraints may dictate that users can only be measured using one of the devices under study. In these cases, it is

[2]See Chapter 4, sections 4.0, 5.0, and 6.2 for more information on the development of usability benchmarks.

[3]For more information on the differences between within-groups and between-groups designs, see Chapter 3, section 3.2.2.

important to use a sufficient number of subjects to ensure power[4] in testing hypotheses.

Beyond the question of experimental power, however, is the question of what is learned from comparative studies of devices. Studies such as the ones described are largely confined to devices that exist, at least at a prototype stage. Thus, they can only be used in situations where a new device is fairly close to being ready to market. By that point in time, it may not be useful to collect performance data on the device.

Further, not all input devices are easily assessed. Pausch, Vogtle, and Conway (1992) report on their attempts to evaluate an input device developed for individuals with cerebral palsy. Using a Polhemus™ tracking device attached to the user (e.g., on the wrist), they tracked user motions and mapped them as control signals for cursor movement. They then examined how well users could play a Pong-like video game using this device and the mappings. Their goal was to determine the extent to which their tracking device could compensate for the users' disabilities. Specifically, they wanted to determine if their disabled population could perform tasks as easily as an able-bodied population. They felt that the comparison of the disabled group using a new input device to the same (or a similar) group using a standard input device was not theoretically interesting because it is a given that the disabled population cannot use the standard input devices and will never be able to do so. Thus, they wanted to compare the performance of their disabled users to a group of able-bodied users. However, Pausch et al. point out that there are methodological problems arising from this comparison. If the able-bodied users were to use the input devices normally available to them (such as joysticks), the comparison of performance would have been confounded by the use of two different input devices. Even if the able-bodied users were to perform the task using the new device, they would have an advantage arising from prior experience with video games. As a result, Pausch et al. required their able-bodied users to control the device with their non-dominant hand. Although one could argue whether or not this approach appropriately controls for the differences between the two groups, the point to be made is that new input devices, especially those targeted for special populations, are still relatively difficult to evaluate.

4.0 Software Interface

After the hardware, the software interface is the next point of contact between users and their computer systems. The interface is all that the user can see of the software when working with a computer system. Although there are methods for directly evaluating the physical display of information on an interface, interfaces are often evaluated indirectly, by measuring the performance of the humans using the system.

---

[4]Refer to Cohen (1988) for a detailed discuss of the computation of pwer and ussues realted to the power of an experiment.

4.1 Major Research Issues

The measurement of user interface effectiveness is an exceedingly complex issue. The complexity arises from two primary sources -- the difficulty in defining effectiveness[5] and the difficulty in measuring effectiveness (assuming you were able to define it). One definition of effectiveness is efficiency (i.e., how quickly a set of functions can be performed using a given user interface). In this sense, effectiveness is being defined in terms of time savings. With this definition, a system that allows you to execute the commands to print out a document in five seconds would be considered more effective than one that requires 20 seconds to perform the same function. Another definition of effectiveness, though, includes the notion of functionality; this definition focuses on an interface's ability to allow the user to easily perform a set of functions. Perhaps one would want to define an effective system as one with the highest degrees of both efficiency and functionality. However, no one has, as yet, been able to define what "ideal" levels of efficiency and functionality would be. In an ideal world, a system would allow users to perform every function they could possibly want or need easily and without error. Unfortunately, it is difficult to increase the functionality of a system without concurrently increasing the complexity associated with use of the system. This typically also decreases the efficiency with which the system can be used As a result, there is a tradeoff between efficiency and functionality, and there are no guidelines for how much of an efficiency loss is acceptable for a given increase in functionality.

There are also those who would argue that the ultimate definition of effectiveness must include a measure of the extent to which users are actually willing to use the system. They point out that the most functional and efficient system cannot be effective if it is not used[6]. Thus, the problems in defining user interface effectiveness are knowing which definition is appropriate and how important each of several measures taken are. It is usually possible to determine the most appropriate definition of effectiveness within the context of the system of interest. So, for example, you may discover that although a given system saves the user three seconds in keystroke time, it does not really matter since after that entry, the user needs to wait two minutes for a response from the system. Given that you know what definition of effectiveness you are seeking, there are a number of dependent measures available for evaluating user interface effectiveness.

4.2 Measuring User Interface Effectiveness

The measures used to compute interface effectiveness can come from measuring characteristics present on the display screen of the interface, from

---

[5]See Chapter 2, section 3.1.1, for more information on operationally defining concepts.

[6]Mark Scerbo states in Chapter 4, section 1.0, that: " . . . usability is achieved: when one makes effective use of a product's full potential and does so willingly . . . Further, a product that is used for only a small fraction of the tasks for which it was designed might be considered a usability failure as well."

users' performance with an interface, or from subjective evaluations. Each of these will be discussed in turn.

4.2.1 Screen characteristics. Perhaps the easiest measures of interface effectiveness are those derived from examining the images presented on the computer monitor. For example, measures such as screen density, brightness, contrast, or character size and legibility are easy to calculate objectively. The actual values of these characteristics can be compared across interfaces directly, or they can be compared against guidelines that have been developed for interface developers. Snyder (1988) describes and evaluates a particular measure of image quality (the Modulation Transfer Function Area, or MTFA). The MTFA is based on knowledge about physical characteristics of the display and the visual system of the observer. Research has shown this measure to be a useful predictor of both subjective quality ratings of displays and of objective performance of people using displays.

If measured values are to be compared to guidelines rather than to a calculated standard such as the MTFA, this search may be aided by the use of computer-based guidelines, such as DRUID (Dynamic Rules for User Interface Design), as described by Fox (1992). Unfortunately, the people who most need to know this information often do not have access to it. These measures are most likely to be used by system designers, who decide how information will be displayed to users. However, DRUID is currently more familiar to researchers in the domain of human-computer interaction than it is to software engineers who make design decisions. Further, some software packages (e.g., WordPerfect™) allow users to select some of the characteristics of their screen display. One only needs to walk around an office where WordPerfect™ is used to recognize that users of this package are ignorant of display guidelines.

4.2.2 Behavioral measures. Effectiveness of an interface can also be measured by examining the performance of users interacting with a computer system. Although the most common measures of user performance are speed and accuracy, data can also be drawn from information about percent of tasks completed, time spent in error states, patterns of eye movements, frequency with which documentation is checked, galvanic skin response, heart rate, time devoted to the task, or verbal protocols[7].

Behavioral measures are often preferred to subjective measures as they are thought to be less "contaminated" by personal biases. However, behavioral measures can be difficult to interpret meaningfully. As described earlier, speed and accuracy data may not be a critical component of task performance and thus may not provide a good index of performance. Likewise, galvanic skin response and heart rate are difficult to interpret in relationship to task performance. The key to choosing a behavioral measure is to consider what it is important to know about the individual's

[7] See Chapter 4, section 7.4 for a more detailed discussion of think-aloud verbal protocols

performance in order to assess the issue that you would like to address. So, for example, heart rate in response to alternative interfaces might be important to a population with heart problems, but not to a healthy population[8]. Time spent in an error state, on the other hand, might be important for situations where it is dangerous to be in an error state.

4.2.3 Subjective measures. Within the area of subjective measures, the primary focus is on user reactions to a given system. Questionnaire measures such as the Questionnaire for User Interaction Satisfaction, or QUIS (Chin, Diehle, and Norman, 1985), can be used to capture users' subjective evaluations of an interface, either at a feature-by-feature level, or at an overall level of "ease-of-use". Subjective evaluations may also be obtained from interface experts, using one of a number of different techniques generally known as "walkthroughs". Although subjective measures are subject to bias, especially when the evaluator is aware of the issue being tested, they provide a reasonable alternative to behavioral measures, especially when there is no theoretical guidance about what behavioral measures are important to performance. Subjective measures are also quite useful in situations where users will have a choice about whether or not to use a system. Regardless of the objective data collected on a system, if users do not like a system, they may not use it; this information can only be gleaned from subjective measures of preference.

Sweeney, Maguire, and Shackel (1993) describe usability measures as coming from three basic design approaches: user-based evaluations, theory-based evaluations, and expert-based evaluations. User-based evaluations record data from a number of different biological or behavioral sources. Theory-based measures are predictors of performance based on an objective model of behavior. Expert-based evaluations record data on conformance with guidelines or standards, and on professional opinions regarding usability.

4.2.3.1 User-based evaluations. User performance may be measured directly by time to complete a task or number of errors. Non-verbal behaviors such as eye movements, can also be measured directly[9]. User attitudes and opinions may be measured using surverys and user cognition can be measured using verbal protocols or post-hoc comments. Stress can be measured by physiological measures such as galvanic skin response or heart rate, and motivation can be measured by indicators such as effort.

Benbasat and Todd (1993) describe two experiments that are typical of the user-based approach to evaluating interfaces. They measured task completion times and errors in using an electronic mail system as a function of interface style (direct manipulation versus menu-based interface) and

---

[8]The exception is when heart rate is used as an index of mental workload. See Roscoe (1987) and Metalis (1991) for more information on the use of heart rate for determining mental workload.

[9]See Chapter 4, sections 7 .3 for more information on eye movement recording.

information format (text versus icons). Interface style and information format were crossed to create four interface conditions. The use of an experimental design and the creation of all possible combinations of independent variables is a useful approach because it allows the researcher to tease apart the individual and joint effects of the independent variables being examined. For this reason, experimental studies have often been held up as the ideal tool for testing hypotheses. This particular study examined the four interface combinations across four different groups of subjects (a between-subjects design). Although this type of design is necessary in cases where participation in one condition has significant effects on data collected in the subsequent condition (transfer effects), between-subjects designs are generally less efficient and have less power than within-subjects designs[10].

Regardless of the design used to examine the issue, the results of experimental testing should be interpreted with some caution. Interface studies typically take place over a short period of time in a setting removed from the natural work setting. Thus, the observed performance may not be representative of performance in a more naturalistic setting over a longer period of time[11]. In addition, the types of variables that are amenable to objective measurement in an experimental setting may not be the ones most predictive of success in the work environment. Further, experimental studies can only be done when an interface is sufficiently developed to allow its use in the laboratory[12]. This, plus the cost of performing large-scale user testing, makes such empirical approaches of little use in software development[13].

4.2.3.2 Theory-based evaluations. Theory-based, analytical models are useful for situations where the interface, or a prototype of the interface, has not yet been constructed. Models allow the prediction of results without the necessity of building the interface and testing it with a set of experimental subjects. Gugerty (1993) describes four analytical models that can be used to predict the performance of people using computer systems: the GOMS, OFM, Tullis, and ANETS models. The GOMS model was proposed by Card, Moran, and Newell (1983) as an engineering model of the human-computer interface. "GOMS" represents goals, operators, methods, and selection rules. The model allows designers to represent users' goals and the operations required to carry them out. Interfaces can then be described in terms of the sequences of methods, operators, and selection rules needed to achieve the users' goals. These goals are organized into hierarchies, such that goals are decomposed into sub-goals that allow you to accomplish the next-higher goal in the hierarchy. This allows the aggregation of smaller units of actions to achieve

[10]For more information on the differences between within-groups and between-groups designs, see Chapter 3, section 3.2.2.

[11]This is know n as the Hawthorne effect. For more information on the Hawthorne effect and its implications to your study, See Chapter 2, section 5.2.3.

[12]One alternative is to construct and evaluate rapid prototypes of the interface. For more information on rapid prototyping, see Chapter 4, section 4.0 and Chapter 7, section 4.7.1

[13]Chapter 4, section 8.0 presents a method for directly calculating these costs and selling them to management.

goals. Further, by using the psychological literature to estimate times for mental operations, predictions can be made about the time required to complete tasks using alternative interfaces.

OFM, the Operator Function Model (Mitchell, 1987), was developed to describe more complex supervisory control tasks, such as satellite control. Unlike GOMS, which is strictly hierarchical, OFM is a heterarchical-hierarchical network model. The heterarchy allows multiple root nodes, each of which has a hierarchy beneath it. This allows researchers to model interfaces and make predictions about user performance for systems which contain multiple simultaneous processes.

Tullis' model (1984, 1988a) provides a quantitative operational definition for five perceptual characteristics of alphanumeric displays: overall density, local density, the number and size of perceptual groups, and layout complexity. Although this model only allows predictions to be made for very circumscribed aspects of an interface, the model has been shown to be a valid and useful predictor of performance for simple tasks.

The final model, ANETS, was designed for the domain of aviation (Chechile, Eggleston, Fleischman, and Sasseville, 1989). The ANETS (Augmented NETworkS) model allows designers to represent scenarios where an operator is in control of a complex process. In this model, the user's knowledge about the domain and about the display are represented in networks which can then be used to provide an estimate of user performance. Associative networks are useful for representing situations that are not inherently hierarchical in nature, so ANETS can represent tasks that cannot be handled by either GOMS or OFM.

All of these models require expertise both in the application domain (e.g., supervisory control) and in interface design. They also each make assumptions about the primitive operations present in the system and about their users. This requires extensive experience with the model on the part of the designer. Unfortunately, these models are still relatively new, and the models have not yet made the transition from academia to industry. In fact, even within academic circles, the models have not been extensively tested by individuals outside of the original development effort. Work is beginning to appear that exercises the models and tests their limits (see, e.g., John and Vera, 1992 for a discussion of work extending GOMS to a highly interactive task). In addition, Gugerty (1993) has described some steps that might be taken to allow these models to be successfully applied in industry. However, it will be some time before these models will be available in a form that can be used directly by systems designers to make design decisions.

4.2.3.3 Expert-based evaluations. In this approach, experts rate some aspects of an interface. For example, usability walkthroughs represent a methodology whereby experts make judgments about an interface that is under development. The goal of a usability walkthrough is to identify defects in the interface that will make the system more difficult to use. Walkthrough methods represent a process which produces a list of likely usability problems with the product[14]. The methodology requires a prototype of the system (or at least a specification of all of the screens). The interface is then examined, either in a self-guided or structured exploration by an expert.

Recent research has focused on the characteristics of walkthroughs that make them effective and on their effectiveness relative to empirical studies of user performance. For example, Karat, Campbell and Fiegel (1992) compared walkthroughs (individual and team) against empirical testing. Their data showed that empirical testing was better able to identify problems than walkthroughs, at least for the graphical user interface (GUI) systems tested. However, they found some advantages for walkthroughs conducted by teams over walkthroughs conducted by individual evaluators. Finally, when they examined the cost-effectiveness of empirical testing versus walkthroughs they found that the increased time required by empirical testing led to the identification of a larger number of usability problems. Hence, empirical testing actually cost the same or less than walkthroughs on a per problem basis. However, Jeffries, Miller, Wharton, and Uyeda (1991) and Nielsen and Phillips (1993) both report that empirical testing is more expensive than some forms of walkthroughs. Virzi, Corce, and Herbert (1993) compared heuristic evaluation, think-aloud testing, and performance testing on an extended voice mail application. They found that although all three methods were able to uncover a core set of usability problems, the heuristic and think-aloud evaluations uncovered a broader range of problems than performance testing. Further, heuristic evaluations led to possible solutions to the problems uncovered, while the other two groups were less able to do so. Virzi *et al.* conclude, based on their study, that performance testing may only be appropriate as an analysis tool when "an interface supports repetitive actions, or when small performance gains can yeild large system savings" (p. 312), and that performance testing is not an effective testing strategy for consumer-oriented products.

Another form of expert-based evaluation is the assessment of the extent to which individual features of an interface conform to guidelines or standards set forth by researchers and practitioners. Hix and Hartson (1993) point out that there are four types of information that guide development efforts: user interaction standards, user interaction design guidelines, commercial style guides, and customized style guides. They define standards, such as MIL-STD-1472D, revised (1990) and ANSI/HFES 100-1988, as "official, publicly available documents that give requirements for user interaction design. Standards must be followed when designing the user interaction; they are enforceable by contract or by law" (p. 18).

User interaction design guidelines are defined as "suggestions for how to produce a good interface" (p. 20). Unlike standards, guidelines are not enforceable. Although the Smith and Mosier (1986) guidelines for user

---

[14]This is one potential origin of the bug list discussed in section 2.3 of Chapter 2.

interface design are probably the best-known, many sets of guidelines exist (e.g., Brown, 1977; Engel and Granda, 1975; Norman, 1991; Tullis, 1988b).

Commercial style guides are defined as "documents that are typically produced by one organization or vendor and are made commercially available" (Hix and Hartson, 1993; p. 22), such as OpenLook™ from AT&T, Xerox, and Sun. However, these guidelines may be more likely to reflect the issues of the systems development department than what is needed to provide a usable interface. Customized style guides are usually developed "for a particular interface development project or for a set of projects" (p. 24), such as those developed by NASA for the Space Station Freedom (1988; as described by Gugerty, 1993).

Smith (1986) also suggests that guidelines must be "tailored" to specific applications in order to be maximally useful. This supports Hix and Hartson's notion that different levels of guidelines are useful and appropriate.

One method of determining interface effectiveness, then, is to determine the extent to which a given interface matches the guidelines relevant to the system. In practice, however, this is a very difficult measure to obtain. There are a multitude of guidelines, many of which conflict, so it is not an easy task to assess the agreement between guidelines and a given interface. Although there are tools, such as DRUID (Fox, 1992), which can help automate this process, in practice, guidelines are not widely available in a form that is usable by systems designers --as opposed to human factors practitioners.

4.3 Issues in Evaluating User Interface Effectiveness

To summarize, although it is possible to isolate and manipulate a number of the variables that have an impact on user interface effectiveness (e.g., screen layout, interface style, input devices), others are more difficult to manipulate (e.g., office policies, benefits for using the system). In addition, the isolation of individual variables in an experimental study may lead to conclusions that are not generalizable to the real world where many more variables are operational. This makes it difficult to do research with broad-ranging applicability.

Analyses based on models require a high level of expertise, both in the application domain and with the model, and therefore are not very accessible to designers. Further, all models make assumptions which, if inaccurate, may call the results into question. However, if these models can be developed to the point where they can be described in handbooks, they may be able to make a huge difference in interface design. Models do not require that a prototype of the system be available, there is no cost for subjects, and many variants of a design can be tested once the basic parameters of the model have been developed. Thus, models represent a promising direction for evaluating user interface effectiveness.

For the moment, expert-based evaluations may provide the most promising approach to predicting performance with a new system. Research on a number of different usability testing approaches suggests that walkthroughs conducted by usability experts can provide a quick and useful snapshot of likely usability problems. Given the time and budgetary constraints that limit the usefulness of experimental approaches in the human-computer interaction domain, expert-based evaluations may provide the best estimates of user-system performance.

The usefulness of guidelines is also currently limited. As Chapanis and Budurka (1990) point out, human factors considerations have not been fully incorporated into the product development cycle. As a result, human factors professionals have little opportunity to apply guidelines and standards to the development of products, as they have little influence over the entire process and are often brought in very late in the development cycle. Guidelines need to be developed so that they can be applied by designers, who have great influence over the design process. However, this will require the development of more specific guidelines and standards, as well as the specification of human-computer interface requirements. Chapanis and Budurka do propose that such a document could be produced, and they describe the contents that such a document should contain. A requirements specification document of this sort could prove to be the key to getting guidelines and standards integrated into the general product development life cycle.

5.0 Users

Research in human-computer interaction is all devoted, ultimately, to improving working conditions for the user, that is, the human in the human-computer system. Unlike the other components of human-computer systems described in this chapter, neither developers nor researchers can modify the characteristics of this component, though they often seek to do so by their expectation that documentation or training can compensate for poor design. We do, therefore, need to understand this component and how it affects the overall functioning of the system. Thus, research in this area is devoted to identifying characteristics of people that have an effect on performance.

The users of computing systems have changed over the years. In the early days of computing, very few computers existed, hardware constraints made programming difficult, and input and output device constraints made interactions with computers cumbersome. As a result, early users were limited to programmers, who were willing to spend a great deal of time learning how to work with computers. Early research on users thus focused on descriptions of personal characteristics of programmers and the relationship between these characteristics and programming proficiency. As hardware and software constraints have eased, computing technology has become accessible to a much wider audience of users, who are also less likely to have had extensive training. Most current research on users is focused on the broad scope of individuals using computing systems.

Although users can be measured and described in isolation, that activity does not contribute to our ability to understand how user characteristics affect human-computer system performance. One goal of research in this area is to describe explicitly how individual difference characteristics, such as demographics or psychographics, can be used to predict the performance of an individual using a specific product. A second goal is to use those data to generate guidelines for the design of systems.

5.1 Individual Difference Variables.

Because research on users is focused on describing characteristics of individuals that predict success in using computing systems, the measures of interest in this area are characteristics that can be used to describe individuals. These include (1) demographic variables, such as gender, age, or experience; (2) cognitive variables, such as domain knowledge, technical aptitude, verbal or spatial ability; and (3) personality and affect variables. Demographic variables are usually measured by self-report responses on a questionnaire. Cognitive abilities can be measured either by self-report or by testing in the laboratory. For example, verbal or math abilities could be measured by asking individuals to report their verbal and quantitative SAT scores. Spatial ability, on the other hand, might be assessed by asking individuals to complete one or more of the spatial abilities tests contained in the Kit of Factor-Referenced Cognitive Tests (Ekstrom, French, and Harman, 1976). Personality variables are typically assessed by having individuals complete a personality inventory, such as the Myers-Briggs, which is given by skilled administrators.

Koubek, LeBold, and Salvendy (1985) tried to identify characteristics related to how students performed in college coursework that would be predictive of programming ability. They asked students to report on a number of cognitive variables: verbal and quantitative SAT scores, rank in high school, grades from high-school physics, science, and English courses, and grades from college-level science and math courses. They also obtained measures of non-cognitive variables from the Purdue Interest Questionnaire, which is completed by all engineering students at Purdue. This questionnaire provides a self-assessment of students' abilities and assesses their specific interests within engineering. Regression analyses showed that a number of the cognitive variables, specifically grades in high school and in college science and math courses, were predictive of programming ability, as measured by performance in advanced computer science coursework.

Some early research on the "general public" as users took a similar approach to predicting performance. Egan, Bowers, and Gomez (1982) studied people of differing ages, verbal, and spatial abilities using a text-editor tutorial. The study sought to determine the extent to which these individual differences characteristics could affect performance using the system. This study was one of the first to describe the importance of spatial ability and age in predicting success in using computing systems.

Although this early work was successful in identifying characteristics of individuals that led to successful computing performance, it had little impact on the design of systems. In the long run, knowledge of individual differences must be applied to system design or even the best research on the topic will have little effect on computing performance.

5.2 Methodological Approaches

5.3.1 Regression. The case studies cited all illustrate a design approach commonly used in this domain -- the regression approach. In studies using this approach, subjects are chosen to reflect the diversity of individual differences that the researcher is interested in examining. Individuals typically come to the research laboratory and are asked to complete some measures that describe their individual difference characteristics. These tests may be computer-based, but often are paper and pencil. After completing the individual differences inventories, some measure of their performance is obtained (through experimental observation, self-report, or other-reports). Regression analyses are then carried out to determine which individual difference characteristics predict performance.

5.3.2 Analysis of variance[15]. An alternative design approach used in this area is analysis of variance. In these studies, researchers decide which individual difference variable(s) they are interested in prior to conducting the study. They then select individuals who fall at the extremes of this characteristic and examine their performance on a specified task. For example, Davis and Bostrum (1992) were interested in the role that spatial ability plays in learning how to use computers and they examined how easily individuals with differing levels of spatial ability could learn to complete particular computer tasks. Czaja and Sharit (1993) used a similar design approach when they examined the performance of older and younger adults on a series of computing tasks, including data entry, records modification, and inventory management. In both of these studies, users were placed into one of two groups (high versus low spatial ability in the first study and young versus old in the second). Performance was measured for specific computing tasks, and an analysis of variance was computed to determine if the individual difference variable had a significant impact on performance.

5.3.3 Methodological issues in evaluating users. Although studies using both regression and analysis of variance approaches can confirm performance differences between groups of people who differ on some individual difference characteristic, they can not always provide insights on how to improve the system design to accomodate both (all) groups of users.

---

[15]For more infromation on the analysis of variance procedure, See Chapter 3, section 3.2.

Studies of this sort may also take too long and come too late in the development cycle to provide useful design information. Even when they can, companies may be reluctant to implement design changes beneficial to only one segment of their user population. This may be especially true where the changes needed to accomodate a range of users are expensive or when the group who most needs an accomodation is a small fraction of the total user population. As a result, existing studies of users have not had a great impact on system design to date.

On the other hand, a broader view of this work suggests benefits to be derived from this work. If researchers can establish stable relationships between assessment tests and performance, research would not be tied to any particular design cycle, but would be available for all systems designers to use. Unfortunately, most of the existing research has found poor correlations between test scores and performance, or they have found that the regression weights calculated for an individual study hold only for the specific variables tested.

6.0 Software

Computer software is the innermost layer of the computing system. Programs are written in specific programming languages, and they are often produced by a programmer following specific design procedures, commonly called program design methodologies. Further, once generated, the code is displayed using a particular physical structure, which typically involves the use of indentation and comments to set off modules within the program. Programs provide applications software with the functionality the users need and the interface that is shown to the user. Therefore, it is imperative that software be studied in its own right. Unfortunately, it is an area that has received little attention. In 1968, Sackman, Erikson, and Grant argued (p. 3), that:

> **"Amid all [the] portents of the dominating role that computer programming will play in the emerging computer scene, one would expect that computer programming would be the object of intensive applied scientific study. This is not the case. There is, in fact, an applied scientific *lag* in the study of computer programmers and computer programming -- a widening and critical lag that threatens the industry and the profession with the great waste that inevitably accompanies the absence of sytematic and established methods and findings and their substitution by anecdotal opinion, vested interests, and provincialism".**

Although the situation is somewhat better today, the amount of research has not kept pace with the growth of the computer industry.

6.1 Major Research Issues

The major issues in this area center on the effectiveness of various program characteristics in promoting software development and comprehension. Although early research focused on describing software in terms of objective, computed complexity, more recent work has focused on physical and cognitive characteristics of the code. Work examining the physical characteristics of the code has focused on issues such as different forms of indentation. Cognitive structure has been examined through studies such as the use of mnemonic variable names, the use of specific structures (such as "if-then-else") in code, and the role of different program design approaches in creating software modules.

It is important to note that in this area, the "quality" of a piece of software is _not_ measured directly as a dependent measure. Rather, it is measured indirectly through measures of program comprehension on the part of users.

6.2 Measures Computed from the Software

6.2.1 Software metrics. One of the earliest approaches taken to examining comprehension focused on direct, objective measures for predicting software complexity based on characteristics of the code itself. It was hoped that these measures could be used as software was developed as a direct measure of software quality. However, quality cannot be assessed without knowing the effect of the complexity on users (programmers). Curtis, Sheppard, Milliman, Borst, and Love (1979) examined three objectively-computed measures of software complexity and correlated each of them with other measures of comprehension (including number of program statements correctly recalled, and time and accuracy to modify the code).

This study is typical of efforts that were devoted to the development of indices of software complexity. These indices have generally been termed metrics. In defining metrics, Dunsmore (1984) makes a distinction between a "software metric" and a "direct, algorithmic software metric". He defines a software metric to be "a rule for assigning a number or identifier to software in order to characterize the software." This number need not be based on some objective source; it may be a complexity rating assigned by a programmer to a piece of software. A "direct, algorithmic software metric" is defined as a "metric that is calculated algorithmically from the software code _only_." The metrics in this chapter are of the latter form, as they can be calculated objectively.

Algorithmic metrics differ in the type of program information they index (e.g., control structure, data structure, or composites). They also differ in the level at which they are aimed; that is, whether they are directed at the modular level (micro-level) or at the system level, cutting across modules (macro-level). This section will present a sampling of metrics that are representative of these various forms of software metrics.

One of the simplest metrics is a count of the number of lines of code. Although this would appear to be an easy task, Dunsmore (1984) and others have pointed out that it is not as simple as it first appears. In counting the lines of code, decisions must be made about how to count comments, non-executable code lines, statements that continue on for several lines in the code, or statements that invoke macros that contain many lines of code.

However, length alone does not equal complexity. The lines of code metric, for example, cannot explain the difference in complexity between the two programs shown in Figure 10-1. One way to account for the increased complexity of the second program is that program B has more choice points, or places where you cannot follow a straight path through the program. The McCabe metric (1976) accounts for these differences. The McCabe metric is a measure of "cyclomatic complexity", or the number of distinct control paths through the program, and is calculated by counting the number of decision statements (predicate nodes) in the program and adding one.

An alternative way of accounting for complexity has been suggested by Halstead (1977). His metrics focus on the number of unique elements, or tokens in the program. The two most commonly cited of his metrics are the effort (E) metric and the volume (V) metric. Each of these metrics is computed using the total number of unique operators and operands and the total number of operators and operands in the program. Operators are computations that can be carried out on the data (e.g., addition, subtraction). Operands are the structures upon which the computations are carried out. Thus, this metric provides an index of the number of variables operated on and the number of different types of operations performed on those variables.

Both the McCabe and Halstead metrics accounts fairly well for complexity differences for relatively small programs such as those shown in Figure 10-1, but not as well with large systems composed of many modules, or subprograms. Some metrics have been introduced to account for this macro level complexity. Henry and Kafura (1981) proposed a metric based on the measurement of information flow between procedures and modules in a system. This metric is composed of a measure of the complexity of each individual procedure and a measure of the complexity of the relationship between each procedure and each of the other procedures in a module.

An alternative metric that takes both micro- and macro-level complexity into account has been proposed more recently by Harrison and Cook (1986). Their "total complexity" measure takes into account both the system level complexity and micro-level complexity contributed by each subprogram in the code.

PROGRAM A

```
SUBROUTINE SHELL (X,N)
C  This program is a shell sort. The next
C  The next section initializes the variables.

   DIMENSION X(N)
   IGAP = N

C  This section sets the variables
C  for each level of the shell sort

   IF (IGAP .LE. 1) RETURN
   IGAP = IGAP/2
   LOOPMAX = N-IGAP

C  This loop exchanges out-of-order
C  elements for a given gap size

   NUMEX = 0
   DO 20 I = 1,LOOPMAX
     IPLUSG = I+IGAP
     IF (X(I) .LE. X(IPLUSG)) GOTO 20
       PHOLDER = X(I)
       X(I) = X(IPLUSG)
       X(IPLUSG) = PHOLDER
       NUMEX = NUMEX+1
     CONTINUE

C  The exchange process is repeated
C  at a given gap size until there are
C  no more exchanges

   IF (NUMEX .GT. 0) GOTO 10

C  Going to statement 5 repeats the sort
C  with gap size reduced by half

     Goto 5
     END
```

PROGRAM B

```
SUBROUTINE SHELL (X,N)
C    This statement initializes the array

     DIMENSION X(N)

C    This line initializes IGAP

     IGAP = N
     IF (IGAP-1)50,50,5

C    This statement divides the size of the
C    gap by 2

     IGAP = IGAP/2

C    This line sets the value of the last
C    item in the aaray

     IMAX = N-IGAP
     IEX = 0

C    This line initializes the variable I

     I = 1
     IPLUSG = I+IGAP
     IF (X(I)-X(IPLUSG)) 20,20,15
     SAVE = X(I)
     X(I) = X(IPLUSG)
     X(IPLUSG) = SAVE

C    This statement increments the
C    variable IEX

     IEX = IEX + 1

C    This line increments the loop counter

     I = I+1
     IF (I-IMAX) 10,10,40

C    If the number of exchanges is negative
C    or zero, go to statement 1, otherwise
C    go to statement 7

     IF (IEX) 1,1,7
     RETURN
     END
```

Figure 10-1. Two Different Versions of a Shell Sort.

Metrics were originally developed for use as indicators of development or testing time. For example, the McCabe metric was developed to allow the calculation of the number of possible paths through the code, and thus, the number of paths that would have to be tested to fully exercise the capabilities of the program. Thus, increasing complexity, as measured by these metrics, was thought to predict increasing testing, development time, and program maintenance costs. Research supported all of these relationships. Researchers in software comprehension tried to extend this work to the validation of these metrics as indicators of actual program comprehensibility. Although regression analyses suggested relationships bewteen complexity, as measured by these metrics, and comprehension, the correlations were often weak. This suggests that although these metrics do provide some indication of cognitive complexity, they do not tell the entire story.

6.3 Measures Computed from Human Performance

A major obstacle faced by pioneers in human performance research was the choice and measurement of the important variables. Given the lack of systematic research in the area, it was not clear which measures would provide the best measures of performance. As a result, early researchers measured as many variables as they could think of and tried to determine the utility of each type of measure in predicting performance (using either a regression or analysis of variance approach). As part of this approach, researchers developed programs that allowed all keystrokes entered by subjects to be captured and time-stamped so that protocol data could be automatically collected while subjects were interacting with the computer[16]. For example, Sheppard, Kruesi, and Bailey (1982) used such a system to collect data as programmers attempted to code or modify a piece of software using a line-oriented editor developed for this research. The system kept track of which editor functions were invoked (e.g., listing the program or making substitutions within a line of code) and when they were invoked. The system also recorded other entries, such as the time from the beginning of the trial until the first command was entered into the system. The researchers felt that a snapshot of the editor commands that had been invoked would provide insight into the strategies used by the subjects. However, these measures were not as interesting in practice as they were in theory. For example, the time to the first editor entry had been collected as an initial measure of study time. Although some participants did study the program at some length before entering their first command, others performed an immediate listing of the program and studied the program on-line. These actions invalidated this time measure as a study time measure. On balance, the researchers found that most of the time-stamped action data could not be interpreted without knowledge of the participants' performance strategies, and they were left with total time as their best estimate of overall performance. These difficulties are not unique to the protocols collected by

[16]For a complete discussion of recordring and analyzing keystrokc data, please See Chapter 4, section 7.1

these researchers. Rather, they are a more fundamental problem with most protocol data, whether collected by video or audio tape.

Some researchers have attempted to analyze software as prose. Curtis, Soloway, Brooks, Black, Ehrlich, and Ramsey (1986) have argued that a program is a form of text in that it is "a conceptually connected group of statements that can be understood and executed by a computer, while also being understood by other programmers who might want to modify it" (p. 1097). While this analogy might be misleading in some respects, it suggests that the comprehensibility of software can be measured directly using techniques drawn from the literature on natural language understanding. These measures include recall measures, reaction time measures, comprehension tests, cloze tests, and readability (which translates into software metrics). However, it is also possible to obtain indirect measures of program comprehensibility. These measures are obtained by examining performance on a task that is thought to require comprehension as a fundamental requirement for task completion (such as debugging code).

6.3.1 Recall tests. One very straightforward measure of program comprehension is the ability to reconstruct a program after studying it for a limited amount of time. The logic behind this measure is that the easier a program is to understand, the more that can be understood and therefore recalled given a limited amount of study time. Mynatt (1984) used this approach to study the effects of semantic features (such as the use of iteration vs. recursion in the program) on program comprehension. For this study, she constructed pairs of Pascal procedures and functions such that each member of the pair was as similar as possible in surface complexity, where surface complexity was measured using Halstead's (1977) metrics. However, each member of the pair used a different programming concept (e.g., iteration vs. recursion) to accomplish the same function. Subjects were provided with copies of the program segments and asked them to study them for four minutes. At the end of that time, she asked them to write down as much of the program as they could remember. Forty-eight hours later, subjects were again asked to recall as much of the program as possible.

This study examined the amount of the program that could be recalled immediately after study and after 48 hours had passed. The scoring of the protocols was done by counting the number of elements in the protocols that exactly matched the elements in the original program. No penalty was assessed for missing or incorrect elements in the protocols. This scoring procedure allowed the subjects to receive credit for reproducing the *elements* that existed in the program in the correct order without requiring them to produce a verbatim recall of the entire program.

This approach points out one of the difficulties in scoring recall protocols. If the program must be recalled verbatim, scoring is easy, but interpretation of the score is not. That is, verbatim scores may not reflect the amount of information actually understood about the program. This would be true, for example, if the programmer understood the program but could not remember a variable name. Scoring for gist, the method used by Mynatt, requires that the experimenter spell out the procedure they used for scoring the protocols. Although this measure may provide a good reflection of understanding, it may be more difficult to score objectively and consistently, and it may not be accepted by other researchers.

6.3.2 Comprehension tests. An alternate approach to measuring program comprehension is the use of comprehension tests. Comprehension tests usually take the form of multiple-choice or completion questions, to be answered by examining a particular program. These questions probe for understanding of different types of program information (see, for example, Pennington, 1987; Sheppard, Kruesi, and Curtis, 1981). Corritore and Wiedenbeck (1991) studied the comprehension of computer programs by novice programmers. As part of this study, they constructed a comprehension test that measured comprehension along five dimensions. These dimensions corresponded to the five categories of program information proposed by Pennington (1987): operations, control flow, data flow, state, and function.

This study is representative of research using comprehension tests. Questions are developed to elicit knowledge about the content of a program, and an objective measure of performance is calculated. This measure may be the raw number of questions correct (or incorrect), percentage of questions answered correctly (incorrectly), or it may be the number correct minus the number incorrect (raw or converted into percentages).

Brooks (1980) pointed out that although multiple-choice tests are easy to score, it is difficult to ensure that the test covers all aspects of the problem while, at the same time, not revealing answers to other questions on the test. This goal is difficult to achieve, and it requires extensive pre-testing of materials. This criticism may also apply to test constructed with completion or true/false items.

Another problem with comprehension tests is that they are typically developed specifically for a particular piece of code, and thus are not comparable across studies. This makes it difficult to determine how an individual researcher's results compare with those of another researcher.

6.3.3 Cloze tests. Another alternative to recall measures and comprehension tests is the cloze technique. The cloze technique is based on research in reading comprehension (Taylor, 1953). The technique takes a segment of text (in this case, program code) which has had certain individual words deleted from it. The subject's task is to identify the missing words based on the surrounding context. These tests are attractive to researchers because they are easier to construct than multiple-choice tests and they can be standardized across different types of material.

In the original application of this technique to programs, every *n*th token was deleted from the program code. The dependent measure created using this technique is the number of deletions successfully identified by the programmer, or the percent of deletions correctly identified. Although some researchers require that the user provide a verbatim match to the deleted word, most researchers accept synonyms of the deleted word, if it would not change the execution of the code.

However, there is a problem with the direct application of this technique from the reading domain. In the programming domain, a programmer can replace certain types of words, such as "begin" or "end", without an understanding of the functionality of the particular piece of software, while they can replace other types of words, such as variable names, only if they have some understanding of the specific code's functionality.

As a result, Hall and Zweben (1986) and Thomas and Zweben (1986) suggested categorizing words to be deleted as "program independent" or "program dependent". Program-independent deletions are words that can be supplied based on a general knowledge of programming in the given language, but without specific knowledge of the algorithm under investigation. Program-dependent deletions are those which require a knowledge of the functionality of the specific piece of code in order to be completed correctly. Thomas and Zweben (1986) directly examined this issue by creating sets of cloze tests using different numbers of each type of deletion and looking at the effect on the outcomes. Specifically, they created three cloze tests, using two different software procedures. Two cloze tests were generated by deleting every fifth token from each of the two procedures, starting with the first token in the program. The third cloze test was generated by deleting every fifth token from one of the procedures, starting with the second token of the procedure (so that a different set of program independent and program dependent items would be deleted). The programmers' task in each case was to supply the missing words in the code. Comprehension was measured as a percent of deletions correctly supplied.

Based on these results, Lewis (1986) suggests that researchers be careful to examine the number of program-dependent and program-independent items appearing in two cloze tests before comparing the results of these tests for different programs. He points out that since program-independent items are easier to complete than program-dependent items, any program whose cloze test contains more program-independent deletions than another should seem easier to comprehend, which may be a misleading result.

Further, he has cautioned that the cloze test may not really be a good measure of program comprehensibility even if the numbers of program-dependent and program-independent items are equated across tests. He argues that filling in the blanks is not the same as comprehension since program-independent items can be completed without understanding the program. Further, in some cases, program-dependent items cannot be completed even though the programmer understands the problem. This problem can sometimes be alleviated by allowing synonyms as correct responses, but this does not entirely eliminate the problem. However, cloze tests do provide an objective, measurable account of program complexity.

6.3.4 Reading time. Another measure of program comprehension can be derived from the amount of time that it takes a programmer to read the code. This can be done at a holistic level (time to read the entire program), or at a molecular level (time to read a single line of code).

Studies using reading time often use program characteristics as independent variables and speed of response as the dependent measure in an analysis of variance framework. Reaction time measures, like recall measures, assume that the more comprehensible a program or a program statement is, the more quickly you can respond to it. In some cases, such as the case study described above, the response time to a particular line of code (e.g., the time to fill in a missing line, or to recall a particular line of code) has been recorded. In others, the overall time to read a program is studied. In both types of studies, an extremely long reaction time to an individual line has been used as evidence of additional processing to re-organize or form hypotheses about the program.

Brooks (1980) has pointed out several difficulties with reaction time measures. The first is a problem of knowing what goes into the time measurement. In this regard, he points to studies where an hypothesis is made about one piece of a program (e.g., control structure), but the time is measured on the whole program. In these cases, it may be that the overall time reflects difficulty not with the hypothesized piece of the program, but with some other portion of the program (e.g., the input-output structure). Second, he points out that time measures often have skewed distributions, which make data analysis and interpretation more difficult.

6.3.5 Speed and accuracy of performing software tasks. Comprehension may also be measured in an indirect fashion. This is done by examining performance on a software task that requires comprehension as one stage in the completion of that task. Comprehension is then indexed by the ease or difficulty of completing the software task. In this research area, the tasks have been used are primarily debugging and modification tasks. For example, Boehm-Davis, Holt, and Schultz (1992) examined the modifiability of program code that had been generated following one of three specific program design methodologies. In their study, student and professional programmers were asked to make either simple or complex modifications to programs that had been generated using each of three different program structures.

6.4 Methodological Approach

The most straightforward test of the effect of a particular software characteristic (e.g., program structure) would involve a between-subjects analysis of variance design where different groups of programmers perform some software task (e.g., modification) with code created by varying a specific software characteristic. Differences in speed and/or accuracy could then be used to assess the effect of the particular characteristics under investigation. However, research in this area is complicated by the fact that it relies on programmers, who demonstrate variability on the order of 28:1 in performance (Sackman, Erikson and Grant, 1968). As a result, it is critical to use repeated-measures designs in studies examining software. The use of a within-subjects design is, however, complicated by the fact that a given programmer cannot perform the same software task on different versions of the same code without significant carry-over effects[17]. Thus, the use of a within-subjects design requires the use of multiple problems, which should be counter-balanced to prevent order of presentation effects.

The design used by Boehm-Davis et al. (1992) to test the effect of program structure on modification time demonstrates the use of one of the most common designs employed in studies of this sort. This design is a split-plot, Latin square design described by Winer (1971, p. 723). The outline of this design, specifically as used in the Boehm-Davis et al. experiment, can be seen in Figure 10-2.

In this experiment, each subject saw each type of program (inline, functional decomposition, or object-oriented) and each type of problem (student list, military address, or host-at-sea). Across the three groups of programmers (groups 1, 2, and 3), all possible combinations of problem structure and problem type were represented. However, individual programmers saw only three unique combinations of the two variables. The specific combinations of the two variables seen was different for each level of the between-subjects variable, in this case, type of programmer (student or professional).

Student Programmers

	Inline	Functional Decomposition	Object Oriented
Group 1	Student List	Military Address	Host-at-Sea
Group 2	Host-at-Sea	Student List	Military Address
Group 3	Military Address	Host-at-Sea	Student List

Professional Programmers

	Inline	Functional Decomposition	Object Oriented
Group 1	Host-at-Sea	Military Address	Student List
Group 2	Military Address	Student List	Host-at-Sea
Group 3	Student List	Host-at-Sea	Military Address

Figure 10-2. Research Design Based on Boehm-Davis, Holt, and Schultz (1992)

[17]Chapter 2, section 5.2 discusses the threats to experimental validity when repeated measures designs. See section 3.2.4 of Chapter 3 for more information on this type of experimental design.

This design allows researchers to examine the effects of a particular software characteristic (e.g., program structure) and problem type as within-subjects variables, which provides a much more sensitive design for testing hypotheses[18]. There is, however, one problem with this approach. It is possible to complete debugging and modification tasks without fully understanding the program. This makes it inappropriate to use these tasks as the sole index of program comprehension. However, in combination with other sources of data, the results from this design can be quite illuminating.

7.0 Summary

This chapter has outlined four components of computing systems that have been examined using empirical research techniques: system hardware, the user interface, the users, and software. Although each component uses slightly different variables, methods, and techniques, they all have in common the goal of identifying characteristics of the computing system that lead to the highest levels of human-system performance. The review has focused specifically on the computer portion of computing systems. Applications (such as intelligent vehicle highway system displays or intelligent decision-aiding systems) have not been addressed. The most general conclusion that can be drawn from this chapter is that each measure and methodology has flaws. However, we cannot be pessimistic about our ability to draw conclusions from studies using these approaches. Rather, we need to be creative in applying research techniques in this domain, such as combining measures to produce converging evidence to support our positions.

8.0 Issues For Further Research

Research in the field of computing systems will continue to grow at an exponential rate. However, the next breakthrough in this domain will likely come not from a piece or line of research, but rather from the development of new methodologies for evaluating computing systems or new techniques for measuring performance in using these systems. The measures and methodologies described in this chapter have all been borrowed from research in related domains, such as psychology, human factors, and engineering. None of these approaches has made a perfect transition to the field of human-computer interaction. The variables that can be measured and the research approaches taken all require some sacrifice, either in the time required to generate an answer to a question or in the lack of correspondence between what is observed in the laboratory and what occurs in actual use of the system. Thus, the most fruitful avenue for further research will be in the development of new metrics and methodological approaches.

---

[18]For more information on Latin-Suares designs, see section 3.2.4 of Chapter 3.

9.0 Biography

Deborah A. Boehm-Davis is currently Associate Professor of Psychology and Assistant Provost for Research and Graduate Studies at George Mason University in Fairfax, Virginia. She holds an A.B. (1975) in psychology from Rutgers -- the State University (Douglass College), and an M.A. (1977) and Ph.D. (1980) in cognitive psychology from the University of California, Berkeley. She has worked on applied cognitive research at General Electric, NASA-Ames and Bell Laboratories prior to joining George Mason University in 1984.

Dr. Boehm-Davis' research interests center on what information individuals need to perform efficiently and effectively. This interest has lead her to do research on the comprehension and maintenance of software and data bases, and on the role of cognition in driving and piloting performance. Dr. Boehm-Davis has received research support of over $1 million to perform this work.

Dr. Boehm-Davis was President of the Human Factors and Ergonomics Society (1994), having previously served in a number of other appointed and elected capacities, including Secretary-Treasurer. She is on the editorial boards of: *Human Factors*, *International Journal of Man-Machine Systems*, *International Journal of Human-Computer Interaction*, and *Interacting with Computers*. She has also served in appointed capacities in other professional societies, most notably Division 21 of the American Psychological Association (APA) and the Special Interest Group of Computer-Human Interaction (SIGCHI) of the Association for Computing Machinery (ACM).

Readers with questions concerning this chapter are invited to E-mail Debrah at DBDAVIS@GMU.EDU.

Acknowledgements

Portions of this chapter draw heavily upon material previously discussed in Boehm-Davis (1983) and Boehm-Davis (1988). The author would like to thank Jean Fox, Christina James, Roger Remington and Jon Weimer for reviewing earlier versions of this chapter and providing helpful feedback and guidance. Any errors that remain, however, are mine.

References

Baecker, R. M., and Buxton, W. A. S. (1987). *Readings in Human-Computer Interaction: A Multidisciplinary Approach.* San Mateo, CA: Morgan Kaufmann Publishers, Inc.

Benbasat, I. and Todd, P. (1993). An experimental investigation of interface design alternatives: Icon vs. text and direct manipulation vs. menus. *International Journal of Man-Machine Studies*, *38*, 369-402.

Boehm-Davis, D. A. (1983). On the use of psychology in evaluating software documentation. *Behavior Research Methods and Instrumentation, 15*, 217-221.

Boehm-Davis, D. A. (1988). Software comprehension. In M. Helander (Ed.) *Handbook of Human-Computer Interaction*, North-Holland, 107-121.

Boehm-Davis, D. A., Holt, R. W., and Schultz, A. C. (1992). The role of program structure in software maintenance. *International Journal of Man-Machine Studies, 36*, 21-63.

Brooks, R. E. (1980). Studying programmer behavior experimentally: The problems of proper methodology. *Communications of the ACM, 23*, 207-213.

Brown, C. M. (1977). *Human-Computer Interface Design Guidelines.* Norwood, NJ: Ablex.

Card, S. K., Moran, T. P., and Newell, A. (1983). *The Psychology of Human-Computer Interaction*. Hillsdale, NJ: Erlbaum.

Chapanis, A., and Budurka, W. J. (1990). Specifying human-computer interface requirements. *Behaviour and Information Technology, 9*, 479-492.

Chechile, R. A., Eggleston, R. G., Fleischman, R. N., and Sasseville, A. M. (1989). Modeling the cognitive content of displays. *Human Factors, 31*, 31-43.

Chin, J. P., Diehle, U. A., and Norman, K. L. (1985). Development of an instrument measuring user satisfaction of the human-computer interface. *Human Factors in Computing Systems*, New York: Association for Computing Machinery, 213-218.

Cohen, J. (1988). *Statistical Power Analysis for the Behavioral Sciences* (2nd ed.). Hillsdale, NJ: Lawrence Erlbaum.

Corritore, C. L. and Wiedenbeck, S. (1991). What do novices learn during program comprehension? *International Journal of Human-Computer Interaction, 3*, 199-222.

Curtis, B., Sheppard, S. B., Milliman, P., Borst, M. A. and Love, T. (1979). Measuring the psychological complexity of software maintenance tasks with the Halstead and McCabe metrics. *IEEE Transactions on Software Engineering, SE-5*, 96-104.

Curtis, B., Soloway, E. M., Brooks, R. E., Black, J. B., Ehrlich, K., and Ramsey, H. R. (1986). Software psychology: The need for an interdisciplinary program. *Proceedings of the IEEE, 74*, 1092-1106.

Czaja, S. J., and Sharit, J. (1993). Stress reactions to computer-interactive tasks as a function of task structure and individual differences. *International Journal of Human-Computer Interaction, 5*, 1-22.

Davis, S. and Bostrum, R. (1992). An experimental investigation of the roles of the computer interface and individual characteristics in the learning of computer systems. *International Journal of Human-Computer Interaction, 4*, 143-172.

Department of Defense (1990). *MIL-STD-1472D, Human Engineering Design Criteria for Military Systems, Equipment and Facilities, Revised.* Washington, D.C.: Department of Defense

Dix, A. (1993). *Human-computer Interaction*. New York: Prentice-Hall.

Dunsmore, H.E. (1984). Software metrics: An overview of an evolving methodology. *Information Processing and Management, 20*, 183-192.

Egan, D. E., Bowers, C., and Gomez, L. M. (1982). Learner characteristics that predict success in using a text-editor tutorial, *Human Factors in Computing Systems*, Washington, DC: Association for Computing Machinery, 337-340.

Ekstrom, R. B., French, J. W., and Harman, H. H. (1976). *Manual for Kit of Factor-Referenced Cognitive Tests*. Princeton, NJ: ETS.

Engel, S. E., and Granda, R. E. (1975). *Guidelines for Man/Display Interfaces*. (Technical Report TR 00.2720). Poughkeepsie, NY: IBM.

Fitts, P. (1954). The information capacity of the human motor system in controlling the amplitude of movement. *Journal of Experimental Psychology, 47*, 381-391.

Fox, J. A. (1992). The effects of using a hypertext tool for selecting design guidelines. In *Proceedings of the Human Factors Society 36th Annual Meeting*, Santa Monica, CA: The Human Factors Society, 428-432.

Greenstein, J. S., and Arnaut, L. Y. (1988). Input devices. In M. Helander (Ed.), *Handbook of Human-Computer Interaction*. Amsterdam: North-Holland, 495-519.

Gugerty, L. (1993). The use of analytical models in human-computer-interface design. *International Journal of Man-Machine Studies, 38*, 625-660.

Hall, W.E. and Zweben, S.H. (1986). The cloze procedure and software comprehensibility measurement. *IEEE Transactions on Software Engineering, SE-12*, 608-623.

Halstead, M.H. (1977). *Elements of Software Science*. New York: North-Holland.

Harrison, W. and Cook, C. (1986). A micro/macro measure of software complexity. *Technical Report TR-86-60-3*. Corvallis, OR: Oregon State University.

Henry, S. and Kafura, D. (1981). Software structure metrics based on information flow. *IEEE Transactions on Software Engineering, SE-7*, 510-518.

Hix, D., and Hartson, H. R. (1993). *Developing User Interfaces: Ensuring Usability Through Product and Process*. New York: John Wiley and Sons.

Human Factors Society, Inc. (1988). *American National Standard for Human Factors Engineering of Visual Display Terminal Workstations, ANSI/HFES 100-1988*, Santa Monica, CA: The Human Factors Society, Inc.

Jeffries, R., Miller, J. R., Wharton, C., and Uyeda, K. M. (1991). User interface evaluation in the real world: A comparison of four techniques. *Human Factors in Computing Systems*, New Orleans: Association for Computing Machinery, 119-124.

John, B. E., and Vera, A. H. (1992). A GOMS analysis of a graphic, machine-paced, highly interactive task. *Human Factors in Computing Systems*, Monterey, CA: Association for Computing Machinery, 251-258.

Karat, C., Campbell, R., and Fiegel, T. (1992). Comparison of empirical testing and walkthrough methods in user interface evaluation. *Human Factors in Computing Systems*, Monterey, CA: Association for Computing Machinery, 397-404.

Koubek, R. J., LeBold, W. K., and Salvendy, G. (1985). Predicting performance in computer programming courses, *Behaviour and Information Technology*, *4*, 113-129.

Kroemer, E. (1988). VDT Workstation Design. In M. Helander (Ed.), *Handbook of Human-Computer Interaction*. Amsterdam: North-Holland, 521-539.

Kroemer, E., Kroemer, K. H. E., and Kroemer-Elbert, K. E. (1990). *Engineering Physiology Bases of Human Factors/Ergonomics (2nd ed.)*. New York: Van Nostrand Reinhold.

Laurel, B., and Mountford, J. (1990). *The Art of Human-Computer Interface Design*. Reading: MA: Addison-Wesley Publishing Co.

Lewis, C. (1986). Comments on Weidenbeck and Letovsky. *Empirical Studies of Programmers Workshop*. June 5-7.

MacKenzie, I. S., Sellen, A., Buxton, W. (1991). A comparison of input devices in elemental pointing and dragging tasks. *Proceedings of Human Factors in Computing Systems: Reaching Through Technology*, Association for Computing Machinery Special Interest Group on Computer-Human Interaction: New Orleans, LA, *161-166*.

Martin J. (1972). *Design of Man-Computer Dialogues*. Englewood Cliffs, NJ: Prentice-Hall.

McCabe, T.J. (1976). A complexity measure. *IEEE Transactions on Software Engineering*, *SE-2*, 308-320.

Metalis, S.A. (1991). Heart period as a useful index of pilot workload in commercial transport aircraft. *International Journal of Aviation Psychology,* 1(2), 107-116.

Mitchell, C. M. (1987). GT-MSOCC: A domain for research on human-computer interaction and decision aiding in supervisory control systems. *IEEE Transactions on Systems, Man, and Cybernetics*, *SMC-17*, 553-572.

Mynatt, B. T. (1984). The effect of semantic complexity on the comprehension of program modules. *International Journal of Man-Machine Studies*, *21*, 91-103.

NASA/Johnson Space Center (1988). *Space Station Freedom Program Human-Computer Interface Guide (USE 1000, Version 2.1)*. Houston, TX: Johnson Space Center.

Nielsen, J. and Phillips, V. L. (1993). Estimating the relative usability of two interfaces: Heuristic, formal, and empirical methods compared. *Human Factors in Computing Systems*, Amsterdam, The Netherlands: Association for Computing Machinery, 214-221.

Norman, K. (1991). *The Psychology of Menu Selection: Designing Ccgnitive Control of the Human/Computer Interface*. Norwood, NJ: Ablex Publishing Corporation.

Pausch, R., Vogtle, L., and Conway, M. (1992). One dimensional motion tailoring for the disabled: A user study. *Proceedings of the CHI '92 Conference, Human Factors in Computer Systems*, New York: ACM, 405-411.

Pennington, N. (1987). Comprehension strategies in programming. In G. M. Olson, S. Sheppard, and E. Soloway (Eds.), *Empirical Studies of Programmers: Second Workshop*, 100-113.

Potosnak, K. (1988). Keys and keyboards. In *Handbook of Human-Computer Interaction*. Amsterdam: North-Holland, 475-494.

Roscoe, A. H. (1987). In-flight assessment of workload using pilot ratings and heart rate. In A.H. Roscoe (Ed.), *The Practical Aassessment of Pilot Workload* (AGARDograph 282), (pp. 78-82). Neuilly Sur Seine, France, North Atlantic Treaty Organization, Advisory Group for Aerospace Research and Development.

Sackman, H. (1970). *Man-Computer Problem Solving*. Princeton, NJ: Auerbach.

Sackman, H., Erikson, W. J., and Grant, E. E. (1968). Exploratory experimental studies comparing online and offline programming performance. *Communications of the ACM, 11*, 3-11.

Scerbo, M. (1994). Usability Testing. In J. Weimer (Ed.), *Research Methods in Human Engineering*. Englewood Cliffs, NJ: Prentice-Hall

Sheppard, S. B., Kruesi, E., and Bailey, J. W. (1982). An empirical evaluation of software documentation formats. In *Proceedings of the Human Factors Computer Systems Conference*, Washington, DC: Association for Computing Machinery, 121-124.

Sheppard, S.B., Kruesi, E., and Curtis, B. (1981). The effects of symbology and spatial arrangement on the comprehension of software specifications. *Proceedings of the Fifth International Conference on Software Engineering*, 207-214.

Shneiderman, B. (1980). *Software Psychology*. Cambridge, Mass: Winthrop.

Shneiderman, B. (1992). *Designing the User Interface: Strategies for Efective Human-Computer Interaction (Second edition)*. Reading, Massachusetts: Addison-Wesley.

Smith, S. L. (1986). Standards versus guidelines for designing user interface software. *Behaviour and Information Technology, 5*, 47-61.

Smith, S. L. and Mosier, J. N. (1986). Design guidelines for the user interface software. *Technical Report ESD-TR-86-278*, Electronic Systems Division, ASFC, USAF, Hanscom Air Force Base, MA (NTIS No. AD A177 1986).

Snyder, H. L. (1988). Toward the determination of electronic display image quality. *Advances in Man-Machine Systems Research, 4*, 1-68.

Sweeney, M., Maguire, M. and Shackel, B. (1993). Evaluating user-computer interaction: A framework. *International Journal of Man-Machine Studies, 38*, 689-711.

Taylor, W.L. (1953). Cloze procedure: A new tool for measuring readability. *Journalism Quarterly, 30*, 415-433.

Thomas, M. and Zweben, S. (1986). The effects of program-dependent and program independent deletions on software cloze tests. In E. Soloway and S. Iyengar (Eds). *Empirical Studies of Programmers*, New Jersey: Ablex, 138-152.

Tullis, T. S. (1984). *Predicting the Usability of Alphanumeric Displays.* Doctoral Dissertation, Rice University, Houston, TX.

Tullis, T. S. (1988a). A system for evaluating screen formats: Research and applications. In H. R. Hartson and D. Hix (Eds.), *Advances in Human-Computer Interaction, Volume 2*, Norwood, NJ: Ablex, 214-286.

Tullis, T. S., (1988b). Screen design. In M. Helander (Ed.), *Handbook of Human-Computer Interaction*. Amsterdam: North-Holland, 377-411.

Virzi, R. A., Sorce, J. F., and Herbert, L. B. (1993). A comparison of three usability evaluation methods: Heuristic, think-aloud, and performance testing. In *Proceedings of the Human Factors and Ergonomics Society 37th Annual Meeting*, Santa Monica, CA: The Human Factors and Ergonomics Society, 309-313.

Wiedenbeck, S. (1986). Processes in computer program comprehension. In E. Soloway and S. Iyengar (Eds.) *Empirical Studies of Programmers*, Norwood, NJ: Ablex.

Weinberg, G. M. (1971). *The Psychology of Computer Programming.* New York: Van Nostrand Reinhold.

Winer, B. J. (1971). *Statistical Principles in Experimental Design (2nd ed.).* New York:McGraw-Hill.

Chapter 11
Industrial Ergonomics

Anil Mital
University of Cincinnati

1.0 Industrial Ergonomics and Its Scope

Ergonomics is the name given to an interdisciplinary field involving industrial and production engineers, work physiologists, medical and occupational health and safety professionals, design engineers, industrial hygienists. It also involves all those who are concerned with the performance of humans at work and how these workers cope with the working environment, interact with machines and, in general, deal with their surroundings. The term ergonomics is coined from two Greek words ergon, meaning work, and nomos, meaning natural laws. In essence, ergonomics may be defined as a scientific discipline primarily concerned with the application of natural laws governing human work.

Ergonomics may also be defined in other ways. For instance, Singleton (1972) defines ergonomics as the technology of work design. My definition of ergonomics is the application of technology to assist the human element in manual work. Ergonomics is also known as human factors in the U.S. Even though the terms ergonomics and human factors are generally considered synonymous, many prefer to make a distinction. These individuals associate the term "human factors" with the behavioral aspects of human performance and the term "ergonomics" with the quantitative and/or health and safety aspects of humans at work in occupational and non-occupational settings. Lately more people working in this interdisciplinary field have started associating themselves with the term ergonomics than with human factors. This reality was reflected when the Human Factors Society of America recently changed its name to Human Factors and Ergonomics Society.

Regardless of name, the overall objective of ergonomics is to fit tasks to humans in order to enhance their effectiveness in the workplace. This means that ergonomics aims at:

- Eliminating or minimizing injuries, strains and sprains
- Minimizing fatigue and overexertion
- Minimizing absenteeism and labor turnover
- Improving quality and quantity of output
- Minimizing lost time and costs associated with injuries and accidents
- Maximizing safety, efficiency, comfort and productivity, etc.

Ergonomics is based on biological (natural) sciences. The main components of ergonomics are anatomy, physiology, psychology, medicine and engineering. Anthropometry is concerned with the structure of the human body (Anatomy) and involves the study of the human body size. Biomechanics involves the study of body responses when it is subjected to various internal and external forces. Work physiology is mainly concerned with how the body functions (Physiology) when performing work. The study of body functions when it is subjected to different climatological factors is called environmental physiology. Psychology is concerned with the behavioral responses of humans to work and environment. While skill psychology is primarily concerned with information processing and decision making, occupational psychology involves training, effort perception, and the study of individual worker factors. Medicine is concerned with the diagnosis, including developing invasive and non-invasive tests, and treatment of injuries (acute and chronic). Engineering provides information about machinery and assists in adapting it for human use. Engineering knowledge also assists in designing and developing equipment and devices that fit humans.

When ergonomics is applied to occupational settings, as opposed to non-occupational settings, such as homes, it is generally referred to as industrial ergonomics. Since the nature of industry and occupational settings within each industry vary considerably, the word "industrial" should be interpreted somewhat broadly (there is a tendency to interpret industrial ergonomics narrowly in the context of manufacturing industries). The domain of industrial ergonomics thus becomes quite large and includes almost any kind of industry, including agriculture, transportation, construction, forestry, manufacturing, mining, leisure, and health. Even though these industries differ from each other considerably, since the nature of the work performed is different, there are many commonalities as far as ergonomics problems are concerned. For instance, problems associated with postures; movements (joint, limb and the whole body); force exertions; work space; equipment, tools and devices; information processing; and environmental factors (noise, illumination, vibration, heat and cold, and chemicals). As these examples indicate, the scope for potential application of industrial ergonomics is very broad, perhaps broader than any other area of human factors. One can broadly group industrial ergonomics applications under the following categories:

1. Physical ergonomics
2. Interface design (information ergonomics)
3. Workspace design
4. Equipment, tool and control design
5. Product design
6. Work design (including methods engineering and participatory ergonomics)
7. Environmental ergonomics.

2.0 Scope of This Chapter

As observed above, the scope of industrial ergonomics applications is very broad. Clearly, research methodologies involving all aspects of industrial ergonomics cannot be dealt with effectively in one brief chapter and, therefore, it was necessary to restrict the discussion in this chapter to those applications that are encountered more frequently and are not covered in other chapters. Specifically, the discussion will be restricted to:

1. Physical ergonomics, including anthropometry, and
2. Certain aspects of environmental ergonomics.

3.0 The Nature of Research

As in other areas of human factors, most industrial ergonomics research is experimental. Theoretical research, such as development of models (biomechanical, simulation, optimization, fuzzy sets, etc.), are relatively infrequent, eventually requiring either experimental data for validation or a basis in experimental data (development of theories/laws, etc.). Theoretical research generally must satisfy the key concerns of accuracy and sensitivity (e.g., How accurately can we predict human responses? How sensitive is the model (theory) to independent variables?). For instance, Mital and Karwowski (1986) developed a procedure for integrating qualitative and quantitative human responses from physical, mental, behavioral, and psycho-social factors. The integrated responses were incorporated in a fuzzy sets-based model intended to optimize overall effectiveness of a human-machine system effectiveness and develop work-performance standards. Though this generalized model is based on logical deductions and mathematical principles, it can only be treated as a well-defined concept or framework. While extensive experimental data are needed to validate a model before it can be used to develop reliable, work performance standards, this should not undermine the importance of theoretical research.

Often, experimental data lead to the development of sound theories and procedures. Kopardekar et al. (1993) and Kopardekar and Mital (1993) conducted a series of experiments focused on extracting the human, intuitive, thought process in laying out parts on a sheet. They concluded that it was not only possible to extract strategies that lead to higher utilization of raw materials in the cutting stock problem, but it was also possible to express these thought process in a general theoretical algorithm. This algorithm can be used to train new operators for laying out parts of different shapes on a sheet and to maximize sheet utilization by automating the laying out process

While theoretical research is not uncommon in industrial ergonomics, most of the research is experimental. In most cases, you are concerned with quantifying/determining the effect(s) of various stressors (independent variables) on human responses (dependent variables). Frequently this data is used to develop databases and procedures for designing industrial tasks.

4.0 Experimental Design

Designing experiments that will provide needed information is perhaps the most important step in carrying out any human factors research project. It not only requires determining what responses to measure (dependent variables) and how to measure them, but also involves careful selection of stressors that must be varied systematically (independent variables), or controlled during the experiment, and planning the statistical design of the experiment. Researchers must have both broad and deep knowledge of statistics and experimental design (See Chapter 3 for an overview).

In designing the experiment, it is necessary that the goal be clear and specific (e.g., development of design database, determination of the effects of independent variables on some response, quantification of the pattern of responses, etc.). Once the goal has been clearly defined, statistical design can be chosen. The key considerations in choosing a design should be simplicity and practicality in time, cost, and analysis. For instance, if the goal is to develop a design database for industrial tasks, a large and heterogeneous sample would be necessary for generalization. Given the difficulty of recruiting reliable industrial subjects (subjects who will return to the lab day-after-day, without fail), it may be advisable to use an incomplete block design, rather than a complete block design (See Chapter 3, section 3.3.2). This would increase the sample size but reduce the number of treatment combinations each subject would need to perform. However, if the goal is to effect of certain independent variables and their variability and interactions on a response, several levels of independent variables may have to be included. In this case, a complete block factorial design may be more appropriate (See Chapter 3, section 3.3.2).

Since in most industrial ergonomics studies the intent is to predict human response(s) to a set of specified conditions, the study design should be as similar as possible to the real situation (Chapanis, 1988). Furthermore, the subject population should be representative (e.g., if the situation being simulated only involves middle aged females, there is no sense in including elderly or juvenile males in the sample).

One of the most critical questions you must answer pertains to the sample size. A small sample sizes have a large type II error (Freiman et al., 1978); the sample may fail to show the effect due to treatment combination when one is in fact present. A large sample, on the other hand, is time consuming and increases the cost of the experiment. The importance of determining the required sample size can not be overemphasized (you may wish to consult a text on statistical methods used to determine the required sample size - the text by Pocock (1983) provides reasonable coverage). The standard statistical approach for determining sample size is known as power calculation and is briefly demonstrated here.

Determining the number of subjects needed for an experiment should be based on: (1) the anticipated means and standard deviations of responses to independent variables and (2) type I (alpha) and type II (beta) errors. The relationship between the sample size and these criteria is:

$$n = [2\sigma^2/(\mu_1 - \mu_2)^2].f(\alpha,\beta)$$

where

n = sample size

μ_1 = mean response to an independent variable

$\mu_1 - \mu_2$ = change in the mean response you want to detect

σ = standard deviation of the response to the independent variable

$f(\alpha,\beta)$ = is a function of type I error, α, and type II error, β.

Suppose we are interested in determining the sample size in a study investigating the effect of physical training on maximum heart rate and oxygen consumption. Assume that the smallest differences we are interested in measuring are 0.1 lit/min. for oxygen consumption and 5 beats/min. for heart rate and types I and II errors are 5% and 10%, respectively ($f(\alpha,\beta)$ = 10.5, from Pocock, 1983). The standard deviations of the maximum oxygen consumption are 0.5 lit/min. and maximum heart rate is 15 beats/min. Plugging these values in the above equation, a sample size of 525 is obtained for oxygen consumption. For heart rate, the sample size computed is 189. Since the larger sample size obtained is 525, 525 subjects should be used.

The computation of sample size requires knowledge of mean and standard deviation of response(s) to an independent variable. In reality, this data may not be available. In such situations, a pilot study must be carried out to estimate these values. It should also be noted that the larger the accuracy needs (smallest response difference that should be detected), the larger the required sample size. At this point you must answer the question: "Do I really need this accuracy?" It should also be noted that in many instances, computation of sample size is no more than an academic exercise. Lack of funds, time needed to conduct experimentation on subjects, etc., are factors that limit the available sample size. In fact, most laboratory studies reported in the published literature suffer from these limitations. Most theses and dissertations also suffer from these shortcomings.

5.0 Experimental Variables

The experimental variables in industrial ergonomics research are classified into three categories: independent variables, response or dependent variables, and controlled variables. The independent variables may be divided into the following categories:

1. Work (task), workplace and equipment factors
2. Worker (operator) factors
3. Environmental variables..

Typical independent variables are: frequency (pace) of the task, size of the object handled, weight/force handled, floor conditions, machine (equipment) speed, type and size of tools, distances moved, posture adopted, worker height and weight, body size measures, worker age and gender, level of experience, illumination levels, sound levels (amplitude and frequency), exposure time, dry bulb temperature, etc.

Dependent variables may be broadly classified into two categories: human body responses and measures of performance. The most common dependent variables in the first category are heart rate, oxygen consumption, core temperature, muscle strengths (static and dynamic), muscle activity (magnitude of electromyographic (EMG) signal), spinal stresses (compressive and shear forces), posture resulting from performing an activity, moments and forces acting on various joints, joint angles, ratings of perceived exertion (RPE), etc.

Dependent variables that measure performance include endurance time, speed of response (such as reaction and performance times), amount of work done as indicated by indices such as the maximum weight handled and work rate (kg-m/min.), time taken to complete the specified task, accuracy of performance (as indicated by number of rejects produced, quality of work, etc.), number of items completed per unit time, etc.

Any variable expected to have a significant influence on any of the dependent variables and not classified as an independent variable, should be controlled. Typical controlled variables are humidity, experience, room temperature, level of external motivation, age and gender of the subject population, etc.

It should be noted that some of the variables can either be independent variables or dependent variables, depending upon the objective of the study. For example, weight of the object. Object weight is an independent variable if its levels are fixed and the intent is to determine human body physiological responses while handling it. It is a dependent variable if the intent is to determine the maximum weight that individuals can handle, given a set of working conditions. Similarly, body posture, joint angles, speed of performance, etc., can be either independent variables or dependent variables, subject to the objectives of the study.

6.0 Measurement of Experimental Variables

It is obvious from the above listing that the number of variables typically encountered in industrial ergonomics research is quite large. Further, many of these variables can be easily measured (e.g., items produced/time, task completion time, worker age, gender, weight and height, room temperature, humidity levels, etc.). The values of these variables can be either be determined by simple observation, subject query (e.g., gender, age, weight), or use of simple and routine instrumentation (e.g., thermometer to measure room temperature). Other variables, such as oxygen consumption and EMG, require sophisticated equipment and standardized procedures. Our discussion, therefore, will be restricted to a selected number of variables. Specifically, we will discuss some of the more commonly measured variables: human strengths, body size parameters, posture, joint angles, heart rate, oxygen consumption, EMG activity, core temperature, sound pressure level, illumination, and vibration amplitude and frequency.

6.1 Types of Human Strengths

Mital and Das (1987) and Ayoub and Mital (1989) provide an excellent review of strength definitions, measurement procedures, and equipment needed to carry out strength testing. This section is based on these references.

Knowledge of what a person can or cannot do, under specified circumstances, is necessary for designing work, equipment, workplaces and tools. Human strengths can be broadly classified into two categories: static and dynamic. Under the dynamic strength category, several different kinds of strengths are grouped: isotonic, isokinetic, isoinertial, psychophysical.

Static, or isometric, strength is the capacity of muscles to produce force or torque by a single maximal voluntary isometric exertion (Chaffin, 1975; Roebuck et al., 1975). The internal muscle effort, resulting from muscular contraction, is amplified by the mechanical advantages of the body members involved. The net effect measured is the external static effect either in the form of force or force × time. The length of the muscles involved remains constant and neither the body segment involved nor the object held moves.

In case of dynamic muscular exertions, both the body segments to which contracting muscles are attached and the objects held move. Muscle length and mechanical advantages also change continuously. Furthermore, the moment of inertia changes as the distribution of mass changes. The muscle tension also changes (isotonic strength is an exception). The various types of dynamic strengths are: isometric, isokinetic, isoinertial, and psychophysical. Isotonic strength does not have industrial applications, so it is not discussed here.

Several factors are known to influence dynamic strength exertions. In particular, the effects of the following factors have been investigated:

1. Posture
2. Reach distance
3. Arm orientation
4. Speed at which exertions are recorded
5. Duration of exertion (Mital et al., 1993a).

6.1.1 Measurement of isometric strength. The procedure for assessing isometric strengths has been summarized in considerable detail (Caldwell et al., 1974; Chaffin, 1975). According to these experts, the important factors are:

1. Exertion duration
2. Strength measuring device
3. Rest periods between repeated exertions
4. Body position or posture
5. Reporting of test conditions
6. Subject biographic data and strength data.

For strength assessment purposes, Kroemer (1970) has shown that the total duration of muscular exertion should be less than 10s if fatigue is to be avoided. In general, a 4-6s period is adequate for a person to reach peak isometric exertion. Individuals can also maintain the peak exertion for 4-6s period, permitting the recording of a 3s mean value.

The strength measuring device should be capable of recording peak and 3s time averaged exertions, should not generate discomforting localized pressure, should accommodate the population, and should permit easy adjustments for recording different types of exertions.

A break of at least 30s should be provided between successive exertions, if only a few measurements are to be made. It is necessary to increase rest duration to 2 min. if about 15 measurements are to be made in one test session. This additional rest is necessary to permit recovery from fatigue due to the isometric exertion. Longer rest breaks should be allowed if the individuals being tested so desire.

The posture assumed by the subject during isometric strength exertion influences strength. It is necessary, therefore to specify and control body position if the corresponding strength values of subjects are to be compared.

The measurement procedure requires the individual to assume the specified posture. Once this is accomplished, the individual is required to exert the force (upwards in most cases or in specified direction), build it up to the maximum exertion (over a 3-4s period, without jerking), and hold the exertion at the maximum for about 3s. Competition among individuals and environmental distractions (e.g., noise, presence of other individuals besides the experimenter, unusual temperature, verbal motivation, etc.) should be avoided. The individual should be permitted to discontinue if and when he/she so desires. The anthropometric and biological characteristics, such as age, gender, height, and weight, of the sample population must be recorded in order to describe the population and compare it with populations from other studies. The mean, standard deviation and range should be provided.

6.1.2 Measurement of isokinetic strength. Isokinetic strength is the measure of maximum voluntary muscle contraction when the involved body segments move at a constant speed. Speed control is achieved by a mechanical or hydraulic device that does not allow the body segment to move faster than the pre-selected speed.

The prime requirement of isokinetic strength measurement is that the body segment velocity should remain constant during the maximum voluntary contraction. The subject is required to assume the required posture, including the arm reach distance and arm orientation. Once the subject is ready, he/she is required to exert (pull) the handle to exert as much force as possible, without jerking (the device should not allow exertions faster than the set speed). The speed of exertion should simulate the speed of actual task being simulated (e.g., manual lifting, movements of the hand and arm in the work place, etc.). The maximum force of exertion is recorded.

Just as in the case of isometric strength measurement, rest breaks between successive exertions must be provided. The posture, speed of exertion, arm orientation, reach distance, and population must be reported with strength data distribution.

6.1.3 Measurement of isoinertial strength[1]. Isoinertial strength measures the ability of a person to overcome the initial static resistance by measuring the maximum amount of weight he or she can handle and move to an assigned point at a freely chosen speed. Actual speed of movement varies within the specified range of movement. Maximum weight is determined with the help of a lifting machine, which permits incremental weights to be lifted and lowered along guides. Weight increments may be as small as 1.135 kg (Jiang, 1984) or as high as 11.4 kg (Kroemer, 1983, 1985).

Isoinertial strength testing does not measure maximum voluntary contraction. Instead, it is a method of measuring the maximum weight a person is willing to handle, at his/her own selected speed, within a specified range of movements. The testing procedure requires the subject to grasp both handles, located 5 cm above the floor, and lift the weight to knuckle or overreach height and then lower the weight. The individual starts with an initial weight of 11.4 kg. If lifted successfully, an additional 11.4 kg weight is added. Increments of 11.4 kg weight are added until the cut-off limit is reached (77.3 kg in knuckle height tests and 45.5 kg in overhead reach height tests) or an attempt fails. According to Mital et al. (1993b), the upper limit should not exceed 27 kg. If an attempt fails, the weight is reduced by 6.8 kg. If this weight is successfully lifted then 4.5 kg is added; otherwise 2.3 kg is subtracted. This procedure results in quick determination of the weight a person can lift. The procedure, however, is restricted to singular exertions and cannot take into consideration various task factors, such as object size, work place geometry, and horizontal distance moved.

---

[1]The name, "isoinertial" is a misnomer as the moment of inertia does not remain constant and changes with the distribution of mass, which in turn changes as the weight is lifted and lowered (Mital et al., 1993a).

6.1.4 Measurement of psychophysical strength. This is the psychophysically determined maximum acceptable weight of lift and is recognized by many researchers as a measure of a person's maximum dynamic strength.

Psychophysical strength is really the maximum acceptable weight of lift. The procedural details are given by Ayoub and Mital (1989) and Mital et al. (1993b). The measurement procedure requires the subject to adjust the weight of load according to his/her perception of physical strain. All other variables, such as container size, lifting frequency, etc., are controlled. Subjects are instructed to adjust the weight to the maximum amount they can sustain without strain or discomfort, without becoming unusually tired, weakened or overheated, or out of breath. The final weight is referred to as the maximum acceptable weight of lift.

Instructions given to the subjects must be specific and carefully worded to insure complete understanding. Generally, subjects are instructed to imagine that they are on piece- work, getting paid for the amount of weight that they can lift, but working normal 8-h shift that allows them to go home without feeling excessively tired. In other words, they are asked to work as hard as they can without overexerting themselves. Subjects are encouraged to make changes in the object weight by starting them with a very light or a very heavy weight.

6.2 Electromyography (EMG)

When muscles contract, myoelectric signals occur. Electromyography is the recording and analysis of these signals. EMG can be used to assess the level of muscular activity as well as to evaluate work and performance. Generally, EMG is best suited for non-repetitive work where the activity of specific muscles is of interest. For repetitive and whole body work other physiological measures, such as oxygen consumption (metabolic energy expenditure rate), are more appropriate.

According to Marras (1990), EMG recordings can provide four types of information:

1. Knowledge whether a muscle was in use during an activity or not
2. Relative level of muscle activity, providing exertion (effort) level (not force)
3. Force generated by the muscle under static or constant velocity
4. Muscle fatigue as indicated by the shift of frequency spectrum to lower levels (Basmajian and DeLuca, 1979).

However, there are primarily two kinds of EMG analyses of interest in Industrial Ergonomics: amplitude analysis and frequency analysis. Amplitude analysis provides a measure of muscle activity for different tasks and individuals, while frequency analysis provides an evaluation of the fatigue state of the muscle. In both cases, the EMG signal must be normalized. Normalization is generally performed with respect to a reference isometric maximal voluntary contraction (MVC) and is expressed as a percentage of the MVC (see the equation below):

Relative Muscle Activity = {(Task EMG - Resting EMG)/(Maximum EMG - Resting EMG)}

Normalization permits comparison across different tasks and people. If possible, the MVC of the muscle of interest should be recorded in a position simulating the actual task position. Subtraction of resting muscle EMG from both activity and MVC provides a measure of activity specific muscle activity.

For muscle fatigue studies, the frequency spectrum (distribution) needs to be normalized. Since during the state of fatigue the frequency spectrum shifts downwards, normalization is performed over the frequency range of interest (lower ranges). The amount of frequency signal in a specific range during the state of fatigue is divided by the amount of frequency signal in that range during the beginning of the activity.

There are primarily three kinds of electrodes that are used to obtain EMG signals: surface, wire, and needle. Wire and needle electrodes, also known as inserted electrodes, are primarily for clinical purposes (e.g., studying the behavior of muscle fibers in neurological research). For industrial activities, surface electrodes are adequate. In most situations, surface electrodes are used in pairs (bipolar configuration; a third electrode is used as ground). Two kinds of surface electrodes are commonly used: dry or active electrodes, which do not require skin preparation, and passive electrodes, which require cleaning of the electrodes, application of a saline gel between the electrode and skin, and skin preparation (cleaning and light abrasion of the skin at the electrode application site). Active electrodes are preferable, since they are not only convenient to use but provide relatively greater signal fidelity (accurate transmission).

Once the electrodes are prepared, you must select the application location. The location chosen should yield the highest signal amplitude. According to Basmajian and DeLuca (1985), an electrode should be located in the region halfway between the center of the innervation zone and further tendon. Soderberg (1992a) has provided additional locations for electrodes.

For analysis and interpretation, the electrode signal needs to be amplified by preamplifiers and main amplifiers, filtered, and conditioned, depending upon the need (e.g., deriving force information, frequency information, etc.). It is suggested that readers consult the text by Basmajian and DeLuca (1985) and the recent reference published by the National Institute for Occupational Safety and Health (Soderberg, 1992b).

6.3 Joint Angles and Body Posture

Posture is the configuration the human body assumes during the course of an activity. Posture can be a dependent or an independent variable. For example, you might be interested in studying the effect of specific body postures (e.g., stoop, squat, standing, etc.) on some response (heart rate, spinal stresses, etc.), or you might want to determine what postures are encountered (result) when a specific activity is performed (using hand tools, performing maintenance activities, etc.). In either case, it is necessary to record the body posture.

You first need to determine whether you need to record a 2-D or 3-D configuration of the posture. It is also important to determine whether a static recording is sufficient or a dynamic recording (posture vs. time relationship) is required. The choice is primarily based on needs (e.g., 2-D vs. 3-D analysis, static vs. kinematic analysis, etc.) and sophistication desired.

The simplest form of posture recording can be made through photographs. Typically, the subject would have a grid pattern as their background, which can be used to assess limb and joint angles in the plane of interest. Body joints must be clearly marked. Joint and limb angles, with respect to the horizontal or vertical, can also be easily recorded by using a variety of goniometers (for fingers, limbs, etc.). The posture can be graphically depicted if both the limb and joint angles and limb segment lengths are recorded. The posture recordings in such cases are not very accurate but suffice for most industrial purposes.

For recording 3-D postures, two simultaneous photographs showing a reference system (typically a graduated (in inches or centimeters) 3-axes coordinate system - Kromodihardjo and Mital, 1986, 1987) are needed. The body joints must also be clearly marked. Contrary to what many ergonomists believe and state, the two cameras need not be at right angles. In fact, as long as both views include the reference frame, angle between the cameras is unimportant. Simple geometric transformations must be performed to determine joint coordinates (x,y,z) from the two photographs (Kromodihardjo and Mital, 1986, 1987). For dynamic recording, synchronized video or high speed movie cameras should be used (Please refer to Kromodihardjo and Mital (1986, 1987) for details). The recordings in these cases are quite accurate and sophisticated. Many popular systems are also available to record dynamic postures. Among the popular ones are SELSPOT®, MOTION ANALYSIS®, WATSMART® and ELITE®.

Corlett (1990) and Kroemer (1991) have summarized other techniques for recording body postures. One such method is the development of "posturegram" (Priel, 1974). A posturegram records the deviation from some basic postures. A variation of this method is posture targeting (Corlett and Bishop, 1976; Corlett et al., 1979). Starting from a basic posture (standing), deviations of 8 major limbs (lower legs, thighs, forearms, and upper arms) and head and trunk are recorded. Movements are recorded on concentric circles (each representing a 45 degree displacement) along a marked axis; axes are marked at 45 degree intervals and include the horizontal and the vertical. Sideway movements are indicated on the horizontal axis.

There are many other techniques (OWAS - Karhu et al., 1977, 1981; TRAM - Berns and Milner, 1980; ARBAN - Holzmann, 1981; VIRA - Kilbom et al., 1986; PENGUIN - Kroemer, 1991) which primarily record postures in terms of deviations from standardized postures.

6.4 Measurement of Body Size Parameters

The study of the methods dealing with the measurement of human body size is known as engineering anthropometry. Physical growth is a continuous process for individuals. Until individuals reach adulthood, the body size keeps on increasing (beyond a certain age, certain body dimensions, for instance stature, may also decline due to the natural aging process). Furthermore, the type and rate of growth are gender and race dependent. Consequently, you must be aware of differences between individuals, changes within the individual, differences in intraindividual change, and the methods to record these growths and changes.

The various body size parameters can be broadly classified into two categories: static and dynamic. Static measurements include measurements of linear dimensions, area and volume measurements, and reach envelops. The dynamic characteristics typically measured include moments of inertia, locations of the centers of mass, and body segment angular measurements. The numerous experimental techniques that measure these characteristics are impossible to cover in the limited space of this chapter. Therefore, you should consult the authoritative reference by Roebuck et al. (1975).

Linear dimensions, which include lengths of the limbs, breadths and depths of the body, and body projections (e.g., nose, ears, etc.), are most commonly required in industrial applications. Body landmarks should be clearly marked before making measurements. For most industrial applications, quite accurate measurements can be made by marking the landmarks and measuring the distance between them (for instance, marking the elbow and wrist joints to measure the forearm length). A grid, affixed to the wall, may be used for measuring heights (sitting, standing, etc.). Circumferential dimensions can be measured reasonably accurately by a tape measure. In such cases, the location at which the circumference is to be measured should be clearly marked. It is also important to standardize the procedure by ensuring the relaxed/flexed status of the muscles and whether the measurement is being taken before or after inhaling/exhaling. If these precautions are not taken, measurement accuracy will be significantly affected. For instance, chest circumference will change with breathing and biceps circumference will change with the contraction/relaxation of biceps.

Static and dynamic characteristics may also be estimated from various regression models developed for this purpose. The two excellent sources of such models are NASA Anthropometric Sourcebook (1978) and McConville et al. (1980) and you should consult them.

Techniques to measure body contours vary quite a bit. Traditional techniques[2] (Roebuck et al., 1975) are quite cumbersome and, by and large, have been replaced by techniques that are convenient and fast. Some of the methods that have been used are biostereometrics (Whittle et al., 1977), structured light computer imaging (Dunn et al., 1989), X-ray Computerized Axial Tomography (CAT) scan (Arridge et al., 1985), radiography (Fanibunda, 1983), Facial Plethysmograph (Milles et al., 1985), Nuclear Magnetic Resonance (NMR)(Arridge et al., 1985).

6.5 Heart Rate

When humans engage in work, their cardiovascular system is strained. Heart rate and oxygen uptake are two responses that are frequently measured to provide an indication about the demands (physical stress) humans are being subjected to (Astrand and Rodhal, 1986). Heart rate can be measured either directly or indirectly (telemetry). The simplest direct method is by taking the pulse once steady state has been reached. The pulse rate should be recorded for full minute to avoid the effect of sinus arrythmia. If the pulse is being recorded at the work period, 15s sample is sufficient. Longer duration samples tend to project into the recovery period. A 3-minute average at the steady state should be recorded.

The other method for recording heart rate is somewhat similar to recording EMG in that active and passive electrodes are used. Two electrodes need to be placed on the rib cage, fairly far apart; the ground is placed on a bony landmark. The skin must be lightly abraded if passive electrodes are used; the electrodes in this case are covered with an adhesive collar filled with electrode cream.

6.6 Oxygen Consumption

Oxygen consumed by an individual is influenced by the intensity of the task he/she performs. Typically, oxygen consumption is compared with physical work capacity (PWC). PWC or maximum aerobic capacity (power) is the maximum amount of oxygen that an individual can consume per minute (maximum oxygen uptake/minute). The higher the percentage of PWC a task requires, the higher the resulting physical stress and fatigue.

PWC can be measured by maximal or submaximal methods (Astrand and Rodhal, 1986). In the maximal method, the subject is stressed to the maximum and oxygen consumption at that level is recorded. In submaximal methods, individuals are required to perform at least three workloads. At each workload, heart rate and oxygen consumption are required to stabilize before they are measured. The individual begins with the lightest workload

---

[2];Traditional techniques include the template, shadow, and casting methods (Roebuck et al, 1975). The template method employs small pieces of cardboard or plywood, or strips of lead or soft aluminum wire, fitted over the contour of the body. In the shadow method, a shadow is projected on a grid and traced. As the name implies, a mold of the contour made out of plaster of paris in the casting method.

and once the measurements are taken, the workload is increased to the next higher level. The procedure is repeated until steady state heart rate and oxygen uptake values at all workloads are recorded. The recorded heart rates and oxygen uptake values are plotted on an x-y graph (e.g., heart rate on x-axis and oxygen consumption on y-axis) and a straight line is drawn through the plotted points. Next, the value of maximum heart rate for the subject is determined and plotted on the x-axis. There are several formulas that provide the value of an individual's maximum heart rate. The formula that is perhaps the most accurate is:

Max. Heart Rate = [214 - 0.71 * Age in Years] (Cooper et al., 1975).

A vertical line is projected from the maximum heart rate point. A horizontal line is projected from the point of intersection of the vertical line and a straight line drawn through the plotted points. The value given by the point of intersection of the horizontal line and the y-axis is the PWC of the individual.

It should be noted that PWC is activity dependent and can vary quite a bit. Therefore, standardized activities should be used to measure this value. The recommended activity is graded treadmill walking (Mital et al., 1993b).

As in the case of heart rate, oxygen consumption should be recorded once the steady state is reached. A 3-minute average should be taken to reflect the individual's oxygen uptake for the activity and workload being investigated.

6.7 Core Temperature

The subcutaneous part of the body is referred to as the core. The temperature of the core rises when the heat accumulated within the body exceeds the heat loss by evaporation, radiation, and convection. If the body's core temperature rises more than a few degrees from the normal (37°C), serious adverse consequences may result. These may range from confusion to exhaustion to death. Core temperature can be accurately measured orally by a clinical thermometer or other more sophisticated devices (See section 7.7).

6.8 Sound Pressure Level

Sound pressure level (SPL) is an index of the amplitude of a sound, relative to the reference level amplitude at the threshold of hearing (2×10^{-5} N/m^2). Generally, sound pressure levels are measured on a decibel scale weighted to match the characteristics of the human ear. Three weighting scales (A, B and C) have been developed to simulate the response of the human ear to low (up to 55 dB), medium (between 55 and 85 dB) and high (above 85 dB) intensity sounds. Most of the time, however, sound pressure levels are measured using the A scale. This is because the sound levels measured using the A scale are more highly correlated with noise-related annoyance and perception of sound loudness.

Sound levels are measured using sound level meters, which consist of a microphone to convert the pressure variations into electrical signals, an amplifier, and a display device. In order to measure the overall sound level, a 'slow' setting should be used. Often, the sound may have to be averaged over a longer period (Mital et al., 1992). The sound level meter should be calibrated prior to use, and the sound should be recorded at the level of the ear. It may also be necessary to prepare a noise map of the workplace to identify areas that pose noise-induced hearing loss hazard.

6.9 Illumination

Illumination is the most critical element in the visual environment. Inadequate lighting impairs performance and causes visual fatigue. Too much light causes glare which, if discomforting or disabling, also hampers performance. In general, it is necessary to determine average illuminance within the workplace. The workplace should be divided into a grid and illumination level should be measured at grid points at the work height. The minimum number of measurements may be as few as 4, if the wall length and ceiling height ratio is less than 1, or 25 if the wall length and ceiling height ratio is greater than 6 (Howarth, 1990). The greater the number of measurements, the greater the accuracy. Measurements can be made by a digital or analog light meter.

6.10 Vibration

Vibration can be segmental or whole body. The extremities most susceptible to segmental vibration are hands, so hand tools pose the greatest health risk to the operator. Typically, accelerometers are used to measure vibration frequency and acceleration; acceleration represents the energy input to the hand or the whole body. The energy input to the hand must be assessed according to the method described by ISO (1986). For measuring whole body vibration, a triaxial accelerometer may be used.

7.0 Instrumentation

A variety of instruments are available to measure the variables described in this chapter. Only a selected few are discussed.

7.1 Human Strengths

7.1.1 Static (Isometric) strength. Primarily, two kinds of forces need to be measured: tensile forces and compressive forces. Both can be measured with the help of a load cell (cost varies from a few hundred dollars to a couple of thousand dollars). You can either build a system, which permits forces in different postures to be exerted through coupling devices (handles, etc.) and records them, or buy one of the commercially available systems. One popular static strength measuring device (ISTU - Isometric Strength Testing Unit;

cost can vary from \$ 2,000 to \$ 25,000$^+$, depending upon the attachments) is marketed by Ergometrics, Inc. (Ann Arbor, Michigan). The device allows measurement of push/pull/lift and other types of forces through an adjustable frame. The frame permits adjustments in the horizontal and vertical distances. The device also comes with a personal computer and data analysis software.

A similar device is available from Lafayette Instrument, located in Lafayette, Indiana. This device is relatively cheaper but is also has limited in terms of applications.

7.1.2 Isokinetic strength. As is the case of isometric strength, you can either build a device consisting of a load cell and speed control (clutch) or buy a commercially available unit. One of the devices is "Super II MiniGym". It is inexpensive (approximately \$300) and reasonably accurate for most industrial applications. CYBEX, located in Bay Shore, New York, also builds isokinetic systems.

7.1.3 Isoinertial strength. A device for measuring isoinertial strengths is not commercially available but can be easily built for under \$2,000. Details of the equipment needed are provided by Kroemer (1983, 1985). In principle, the device is very similar to the equipment used for bench pressing

7.1.4 E.M.G. EMG recording equipment can be obtained from a variety of medical equipment manufacturers. The basic set up consists of electrodes, preamplifiers, amplifiers, filters, oscilloscope, analog-digital converters, and computers for data processing and analysis. Among the manufacturers are Lafayette Instrument, Narco Bio-Systems (Houston, Texas), and Therapeutics Limited (Iowa City, Iowa).

Equipment is also available to record EMG through telemetry. Transkinetics Systems, Inc. (Canton, Massachusetts) builds a telemetry system that can simultaneously transmit up to 14 data channels.

The cost of the equipment can vary from \$ 10,000 to \$ 30,000, depending upon the number of channels, quality of preamplifiers, type of electrodes, etc.

7.2 Joint Angles and Body Measurements

Joint angles are measured by goniometers. A variety of goniometers are available (e.g., Lafayette Instrument) for measuring finger and other body segment flexion/extension, and include the mechanical analog and digital types. Most of these can be obtained for under \$500. Computer interface and associated software are also available for storing and processing data.

The simplest device to measure body size characteristics (linear dimensions) is the Harpenden Anthropometer (marketed by Pfister Import-Export, Inc., Carlstadt, New Jersey). It includes attachments for recording heights, widths, circumferences and depths.

7.3 Heart Rate

Heart rate recording devices vary from simple and inexpensive (under $600), such as Polar and Quinton Heart Rate Meters -- which only provide rate -- to physiographs and datagraphs, which can be used to record ECG (upwards of $15,000). The choice of equipment depends upon the nature of analysis planned. A number of companies provide devices for recording heart rate including Lafayette Instrument, Quinton (Seattle, Washington), Narco Bio-Systems, and Beckman (Schiller Park, Illinois).

7.4 Oxygen Consumption

Several devices are available for accurately recording oxygen consumption. Among the popular ones are Morgan Oxylog, marketed by Ambulatory Monitoring, Inc. (Ardsley, New York), and the MRM-1 Oxygen Consumption Computer, marketed by Waters Instruments, Inc. (Rochester, Minnesota). Also available is Beckman's Metabolic Measurement Cart (MMC). Of all these devices, the MMC is most expensive (approximately $50,000); other devices can be obtained for under $10,000.

Oxygen consumption can also be recorded by telemetry. A telemetry system (K2 System), although quite expensive (approximately $150,000), is available from Vacumed (Ventura, California).

7.5 Sound Level

A variety of devices are available for recording sound levels. Inexpensive ones (under $400), for instance those marketed by Radio Shack, can not be used for frequency analysis. More sophisticated devices (e.g., Precision Sound Level Meter, Bruel and Kjaer, Naerum, Denmark) can be used for measuring sound levels and frequency analysis and can cost as much as $5,000.

The recent trend is to record the noise using microphones and a tape recorder and then perform Fast Fourier Transformation (FFT) for frequency and amplitude analysis. This eliminates sound level meters entirely.

7.6 Illumination

Light meters are typically used to measure illumination levels. These relatively inexpensive and accurate devices are widely available and can be either analog (General Electric) or digital. The cost is generally under $150.

7.7 Core Temperature

Core temperature can be recorded by a clinical thermometer (a few dollars). A telemetry system (CorTemp) is also available (Human Technologies, Inc., St. Petersburg, Florida). This system is quite economical (approximately $4,500) but does require the use of disposable temperature sensors (approximately $20/capsule) which must be ingested orally.

7.8 Vibration

The primary equipment for measuring vibration frequency and acceleration are accelerometers. From these, a vibration meter can be constructed (under $1,000).

8.0 Major Research Issues

Industrial ergonomics covers a very broad range of topics, and it is not possible to cover all the major research issues in a chapter of this kind. This chapter, therefore is limited to a discussion pertaining only to selected topics within physical and environmental ergonomics.

8.1 Human Strengths (Based on Mital, et al., 1993)

8.1.1 Static vs. dynamic strengths. The major distinction between static and dynamic strengths is an absence of body segment, object, and muscle movement during maximal voluntary contraction when assessing static strengths. Since there is no effective limb-object-muscle movement in case of static strengths, these strengths cannot account for the effect of inertial forces. This leads to underestimating musculoskeletal joint loading during the performance of a dynamic task (Leskinen et al., 1983; Hall, 1985; McGill and Norman, 1985; Bush-Joseph et al., 1988). Clearly, for this reason alone, the static strength exertion capability of individuals should not be used to assess their capability to perform dynamic tasks. Furthermore, since most industrial processes require a force application through a range of motion in a continuous activity, the design of tasks based on static strengths in a fixed posture has lost its relevance.

A number of recent studies have shown that dynamic strengths of individuals are more highly correlated to their task performance capabilities than their static strengths (Kamon et al., 1982; Kroemer, 1983; Aghazedeh and Ayoub, 1985; Mital et al., 1986a,b and 1987; Dales et al., 1986; Smith and Ayoub, 1989). It has also been shown that even though two individuals might have the same static strength, their dynamic lifting capabilities could be substantially different (Mital, 1987). Furthermore, static strengths tend to underestimate low-back joint loading estimated from psychophysical maximum acceptable weight of lift (Garg et al., 1982; Freivalds et al., 1984; Mital and Kromodihardjo, 1986; Kromodihardjo and Mital, 1987) and may underpredict or overpredict a person's capability to perform physical tasks (Garg et al., 1980; Kamon et al., 1982; Kroemer, 1983; Kumar et al., 1988).

These recent studies clearly indicate that dynamic strengths, not static strengths, are more appropriate measures of a person's work performance capabilities and, therefore, should be used in worker screening and form the basis for designing industrial jobs, work places, tools, equipment, and controls.

8.1.2 Dynamic strengths: Requirements and measurements. While the preceding argument rationalizes the use of human dynamic strengths in industrial applications, several questions remain. What type of dynamic strength should be used? Should we use peak strength or average strength? How should we measure dynamic strength? What type of device should be used to measure dynamic strength?

8.1.2.1 Job Simulated Strength. Logic would dictate that dynamic strengths that simulate the job should be used. It is critical that the measured strength be job specific, due to the large variability in the measured strength of an individual or within a given population. For example, many factors influence an individual's dynamic strength exertion capability and vary from job-to-job. In addition, since muscular strength is significantly affected by motivation and instructions given to subjects to perform (Kroemer, 1970; Caldwell et al., 1974; Miller and Nelson, 1976; Kroemer and Marras, 1981), standardization of dynamic strength measurement procedures is essential.

8.1.2.2 Peak versus average strength. In spite of a reasonable clarity and general agreement among the experts regarding the definition of various terms, ambiguity remains regarding the aspects or derivations of such characteristics to be employed in design or safety consideration. The most obvious is "peak or average" dilemma. Given any set of conditions for exerting maximal voluntary effort, we always obtain one reading for peak and another for average. So far, considerable emphasis has been placed on the peak value. Most of the studies have emphasized this variable, and most industrial applications have used it as a design criterion. While it is reasonable to use the peak value as a design ceiling, its use is arguably inappropriate for designing jobs that must be performed for a prolonged period of time and that require sustained strength.

The use of peak strength in gauging exertion/overexertion is, however, difficult to judge. Whether peak strengths or average strengths are appropriate in such situations is yet to be established. It appears that strengths that take into consideration the effect of repetition (lower than peak strength values) correlate better with a person's capability to perform heavy manual materials handling tasks repeatedly. However, an individual's ability to determine when an exertion becomes overexertion, and, thus, potentially hazardous, is yet to be demonstrated.

8.1.2.3 Dynamic strength measuring devices and their applications. Several different devices have been developed to measure dynamic strengths. Some of these devices include LIFTEST equipment (Kroemer, 1983; 1985), B200 Isolation (a triaxial dynamometer from Isotechnologies, Inc. - Parnianpour et al., 1988), a servo-controlled motorized dynamic strength tester (Kumar et al., 1988), a modified mini-gym (Pytel and Kamon, 1981; Kamon et al., 1982; Mital et al., 1986b; Mital and Faard, 1990), a Cybex II isokinetic dynamometer (Langrana and Lee, 1984; Smith et al., 1985), and a Biokinetic ergometer from Isokinetic Inc. (Garg et al., 1988). Some applications of dynamic strength include measurement of whole body lifting strength (Pytel and Kamon, 1981; Kamon et al., 1982; Kroemer, 1983; 1985; Mital et al., 1986b; 1987); back and arm lifting strengths (Kumar et al., 1988); trunk flexion, extension, and rotation strengths (Smith et al., 1985); lifting strength in teamwork (Karwowski and Mital, 1986; Karwowski and Pongpatanasuegsa, 1988); one-handed pull-up and pull strengths (Mital and Genaidy, 1989; Mital and Faard, 1990). Marras et al. (1984, 1985) have used isokinetic devices to study the effects of trunk angle and speed on the torque production capability of the back and the relationship between the onset of intra-abdominal pressure and torque produced by the back. Several studies have demonstrated a correlation between actual maximum lifting capability and isokinetic strengths (Pytel and Kamon, 1981; Kamon et al., 1982; Mital et al., 1986c) and maximum acceptable weight of lift for repetitive tasks and repetitive isokinetic strengths (Mital et al., 1986b; 1987c). Langrana and Lee (1984) attempted to identify those individuals who are at risk because of weak trunk muscles. Attempts have also been made to distinguish between submaximal and maximal efforts using Trunk Extension/Flexion and Liftask machines (Lumex, Inc. - Hazard et al., 1988). The B200 isolation system has been used to study motor output and movement patterns (Parnianpour et al., 1988). Garg et al. (1988) used one-handed pulling strength to simulate starting of lawn mower engines.

Dynamic strength measurements can be either force-produced at some point (either on the body or in spatial reach) or moment or torque produced about a given body joint. Both of these measures are equally important depending upon the particular application. Force measures are generally used for whole body/segment exertions (such as load lifting or pulling chords). Moment or torque measures are generally used to study muscle moment capability of a specific body joint in developing biomechanical human strength models and to describe specific body action such as turning a screwdriver or a knob. Since most industrial jobs involve different motion trajectories and ranges, durations, velocities, and accelerations, the dynamic strength measuring device should permit accurate simulation of job conditions. Also, since the force output varies with the velocity of exertion (Kumar et al., 1988; Garg et al., 1988), which may change with time for a given exertion or may differ from exertion-to-exertion, the measurement device should be sensitive to fluctuations in the force output. At present no such device is available.

8.1.2.4 Limitations of dynamic strength measurements. Given the difficulties described above, researchers have adopted some simplifications and used isoinertial and isokinetic strengths for industrial applications. Both of these, however, have some serious limitations.

The use of isoinertial strength has been limited to only one type of industrial activity. (i.e., predicting a person's capability to lift loads infrequently). While this method tends to simulate the velocities and accelerations involved, it makes no provision for the trajectory of motion, duration of the activity, technique, coupling or other important job parameters. However, it does appear to provide a better worker screening alternative than static strengths (Kroemer, 1983; 1985; Dales et al., 1986; Smith and Ayoub, 1989).

Isokinetic strength is more flexible and has been used to assess workers' capacity to do a variety of jobs. While it can simulate job velocity, frequency, posture and range of motion, it also has some serious flaws. The most serious limitation is the failure of isokinetic strengths to account for motion acceleration and deceleration. The other occasional limitation could be the inability of isokinetic strengths to simulate the trajectory of motion. This means that the effective force output, which varies throughout the motion, is not recorded.

In spite of these difficulties and limitations, major progress has been made in the use of dynamic strengths for industrial applications. Some notable accomplishments are:

1. Development of screening procedures for frequent and infrequent manual lifting activities (Kamon et al., 1982; Kroemer, 1983; Aghazadeh and Ayoub, 1985; Mital et al., 1986a,b; Dales et al., 1986; Kumar et al., 1988; Kumar, 1990; Smith and Ayoub, 1989).
2. Development of design databases for a variety of maintenance and work place activities (Mital and Genaidy, 1989; Mital and Faard, 1990).
3. Development of criteria for work and equipment design (Karwowski and Mital, 1986; Karwowski and Pongpatanasuegsa, 1988; Kumar 1987a, b; Garg et al., 1988, 1989).

However, much remains to be done.

8.1.3 Future needs. The discussion has pointed out the research needs in the area of human dynamic strengths. But before dynamic strengths can be effectively used in industrial applications, at least the following must be accomplished:

1. Development of a measuring device that can simulate all aspects of the job and its motion characteristics.
2. Development of a standardized dynamic strength testing procedure that can lead to safe, repeatable, and simple tests.
3. Development of dynamic strength tests, for applications in industry, that can correlate with injury risk potential.
4. Development of design databases for a variety of industrial applications.
5. Development of generalized physical capability models and dynamic strength thresholds (job severity indices) for screening workers for physically demanding tasks.

It is imperative that dynamic strength measurements be related to job physical demands. A number of factors influence the dynamic strength exertion capability of a person. These factors include velocity, acceleration, type of motion (smooth vs. jerk), motion trajectory, distance of movement, duration of exertion, horizontal and vertical locations of the object, body posture, arm orientation, reach distance, etc. These variables need to be related to dynamic strength exertion capability and job physical demands.

8.2 Hand Tools

Based on an extensive review of literature, Mital and Kilbom (1992) have identified the following areas in which knowledge is limited:

1. Grip design and force exertion capabilities with different kinds of precision grips
2. Grip surface characteristics, for all types of grips but especially for gripping contaminated handles.
3. Hand sensitivity and occupational injury risk with localized pressure concentration while exerting for prolonged periods and/or repeatedly.
4. Optimum weight of hand tools for precision as well as power.
5. Occupational injury risk during work with high demands on precision.
6. Optimum work-rest regime, with regard to short-term recovery and long-term musculoskeletal disorders.

8.3 Anthropometry

Among the several issues that need to be addressed are the following:

1. Development of non-contact methods for measuring linear dimensions, curvatures, areas, and volumes that are convenient, simple, fast and are capable of producing accurate pictographs.
2. Detection of volumetric changes when in space.
3. Recording of kinematic data (displacement, velocity and acceleration) of limbs and joints in space using non-contact methods.
4. Development of prediction models for dynamic characteristics for females and different races.

8.4 Noise

The use of computers in the workplace has become quite prevalent. Mital et al. (1992) have shown that computer rooms have more noise energy at higher frequencies, particularly at 4000 Hz and higher. This is just the opposite of office noise, which generally has most of its energy at the lower frequencies. The noise energy level in computer rooms does not always increase with frequency. It first declines with frequency, reaching its minimum level at around 1000 Hz, and then increases, peaking out at 8000 Hz. This pattern is quite distinct from that observed for open-plan offices. It appears that equipment noise plays a more prominent role in defining the noise spectrum for computer rooms than it does in the case of offices. Fans used to cool the computers, printer, air conditioning equipment and conversational noise appear to be the main sources of user annoyance. Furthermore, user performance in such rooms may be negatively influenced by the noise levels and associated distractions. In order to provide a productive and more comfortable atmosphere, engineering and administrative controls must be found to attenuate the noise in open-plan computer rooms.

There is also an attempt to revise the noise standard downwards to 85 dBA for 8 hours of exposure. Furthermore, the exposure time must be cut in half for every 3 dBA increase in noise as opposed to the current practice, which requires 50% reduction in exposure duration for every 5 dBA increase in noise. Research is needed to determine economical ways to reduce noise emission from equipment to comply with this recommendation.

8.5 Illumination

Realistic illumination level recommendations for the elderly need to be developed. This is particularly critical with more elderly entering the workforce. Not only are the existing IES recommendations inadequate, but the relationship between object size, contrast, age and luminance (Fortuin, 1970) does not hold true when applied to people 70 years and older (Mital et al., 1991).

8.6 Musculoskeletal Injuries

Reduction in occupational musculoskeletal injuries is one of the major goals of industrial ergonomists. The two most critical areas are: the lower back and the upper extremities. There is still considerable debate about the levels of weight that can be handled safely. Reduction in cumulative trauma disorders (CTD) of the upper extremities is also a major issue. It is still not known what are the acceptable exposure levels for different applications, as expressed in terms of frequency, force and exposure duration combinations. See Ayoub and Mital (1989) and Mital et al. (1993b) regarding the issues pertaining to the lower back. For issues related to upper extremity CTDs, refer to Mital and Kilbom (1992).

9.0 Biography

Anil Mital is professor of Industrial Engineering and Director of the Ergonomics and Engineering Controls Research Laboratory at the University of Cincinnati. He received his Ph.D. in Industrial Engineering from Texas Tech University in 1980, a MS in IE from Kansas State University in 1976, and a BE in mechanical engineering from Allahabad University in 1974. In addition to being Editor-in-Chief of the *International Journal of Industrial Ergonomics*, Anil is the author of over 300 publications, including 13 books.

Anil is the recipient of numerous professional honors including: Junior Morrow Research Chair, University of Cincinnati, 1982-83; Outstanding Contributions Award, Human Factors Society Tri-State Chapter, 1983-84;

Young Engineer of the Year, Engineers and Scientists of Cincinnati, 1984; The 1984 Sigma Xi Distinguished Research Award; 1985 Ralph R. Teetor Award, SAE; Pride Award, Institute of Industrial Engineers, 1987-88; Chairman's Award, The Industrial Commission of Ohio, 1988; 1988 Eugene L . Grant Award, American Society of Engineering Education; 1989 Ergonomics Division Award for Outstanding Accomplishments in Ergonomics, Institute of Industrial Engineers; Distinguished Accomplishment Award 1993, International Foundation for Industrial Ergonomics and Safety Research.

REFERENCES

Aghazadeh, F. and Ayoub, M.M (1985). A comparison of dynamic and static strength models for prediction of lifting capacity. *Ergonomics*, 28, 1409-1417.

Arridge, S., Moss, J.P., Linney, A.D. and James, D.R. (1985). Three dimensional digitization of the face and skull. *Journal of Maxillo-Facial Surgery*, 13, 136-143.

Astrand, P.O. and Rodhal, K. (1986). *Textbook of Work Physiology*. New York: McGraw-Hill.

Ayoub, M.M. and Mital, A. (1989). *Manual Materials Handling*. London: Taylor & Francis.

Basmajian, J.V. and De Luca, C.J. (1985). *Muscles Alive: Their Functions Revealed by Electromyography*. (5th ed.) Baltimore, MD: Williams & Willkins.

Berns, T.A.R. and Milner, N.P. (1980). *TRAM: A Technique for the Recording and Analysis of Moving Work Posture*. Report No. 80:23, Ergolab, Stockholm, Sweden, pp. 22-26.

Bush-Joseph, C., Schipplein, O., Andersson, G.B.J., and Andriacchi, T.P. (1988). Influence of dynamic factors on the lumbar spine moment in lifting. *Ergonomics*, 31, 211-216.

Caldwell, L.S., Chaffin, D.B., Dukes-Dobos, F.N., Kroemer, K.K.E., Laubach, L.L., Snook, S.H. and Wasserman, D.E. (1974). A proposed standard procedure for static muscle strength testing. *American Industrial Hygiene Association Journal*, 35, 201-206.

Chaffin, D.B. (1975). Ergonomics guide for assessment of human static strength. *American Industrial Hygiene Association Journal*, 36, 505-511.

Chapanis, A. (1988). Some generalizations about generalization. *Human Factors*, 30(3), 253-267.

Cooper, A.H., Prvoy, J.C., White, S.R., Pollock, M.L. and Linnernd, A.C. (1975). *Age-Fitness Adjusted Maximal Heart Rates*. Institute for Aerobic Research, Dallas, Texas.

Corlett, E.N. (1990). Static muscle loading and the evaluation of posture. In J.R. Wilson and E.N. Corlett (Eds.) *Evaluation of Human Work: A Practical Ergonomics Methodology* . London: Taylor & Francis, pp. 542-570.

Corlett, E.N. and Bishop, R.P. (1976). A technique for assessing postural discomfort. *Ergonomics*, 19, 175-182.

Corlett, E.N., Madeley, S.J. and Manenica, I. (1979). Postural targeting: A technique for recording working postures. *Ergonomics*, 22, 357-366.

Dales, L.J., MacDonald, E.B., and Anderson, J.A.D. (1986). The "LIFTEST" strength test-An accurate method of dynamic strength assessment? *Clinical Biomechanics*, 1, 11-13.

Dunn, S.M., Keizer, R.L. and Yu, J. (1989). Measuring the area and volume of the human body with structured light. *IEEE Transactions on Systems, Man, and Cybernetics*, 19, 1350-1364.

Fanibunda, K. (1983). Photoradiography of facial structures. *British Journal of Oral Surgery*, 21, 246-258.

Fortuin, G.J. (1970). Lighting: Physiological and psychological aspects - optimum use - Specific industrial problems. In *Ergonomics and Physical Factors*, International Labour Office, Geneva, pp. 237-259.

Freiman, J.A., Chalmers, T.C., and Smith, H. (1978). The importance of beta, the Type II Error and sample size in the design and interpretation of the randomized controlled trial. *New England Journal of Medicine*, 290, 690-694.

Freivalds, A., Chaffin, D.B., Garg, A., and Lee, K. (1984). A dynamic biomechanical evaluation of lifting maximum acceptable loads. *Journal of Biomechanics*, 17, 251-262.

Garg, A., Mital, A., and Asfour, S.S. (1980). A comparison of isometric strength and dynamic lifting capability. *Ergonomics*, 23, 13-27.

Garg, A., Chaffin, D.B., and Freivalds, A. (1982). Biomechanical stresses from manual load lifting: A static vs. dynamic evaluation. *Transactions of the Institute of Industrial Engineers*, 14, 272-281.

Garg, A., Funke, S., and Janisch, D. (1988). One-handed dynamic pulling strength with special application to lawn mowers. *Ergonomics*, 31, 1139-1153.

Garg, A., Funke, S., and Janisch, D. (1989). An ergonomic evaluation of lawn mowers' startability and controls. *International Journal of Industrial Ergonomics*, 3, 207-220.

Hall, S.J. (1985). Effect of attempted lifting speed on forces and torque exerted on the lumbar spine. *Medicine and Science in Sports and Exercise*, 17, 440-444.

Hazard, R.G., Reid, S., Fenwick, J., and Reeves, V. (1988). Isokinetic trunk and lifting strength measurements: Variability as an indicator of effort. *Spine*, 13, 54-57.

Holzmann, P. (1981). ARBAN - A new method of analysis of ergonomic effort. *Applied Ergonomics*, 13, 82-86.

Howarth, P.A. (1990). Assessment of the visual environment. In *Evaluation of Human Work: A Practical Ergonomics Methodology* (Eds.: J.R. Wilson and E.N. Corlett). London: Taylor & Francis, pp. 351-386.

ISO (1986). Guidelines for the measurement and assessment of human exposure to hand transmitted vibration. *ISO/DIS 5349.2*, International Standards Organization, Geneva, Switzerland.

Jiang, B.C. (1984). *Psychophysical Capacity Modeling of Individual and Combined Manual Materials Handling Activities*. Ph.D. Dissertation, Texas Tech University, Lubbock, Texas.

Kamon, E., Kiser, D., and Pytel, L.J. (1982). Dynamic and static lifting capacity and muscular strength of steelmill workers. *American Industrial Hygiene Association Journal*, 43, 853-857.

Karthu, O., Kansi, P. and Kurinka, I. (1977). Correcting working postures in industry: Practical method for analysis. *Applied Ergonomics*, 18, 199-201.

Karthu, O., Karkonen, R., Sorvali, P. and Vepsalainen, P. (1981). Observing working postures in industry: Examples of OWAS application. *Applied Ergonomics*, 12, 13-17.

Karwowski, W. and Mital, A. (1986). Isometric and isokinetic testing of lifting strength of males in teamwork. *Ergonomics*, 29, 869-878.

Karwowski, W. and Pongpatanasuegsa, N. (1988). Testing of isometric and isokinetic lifting strengths of untrained females in teamwork. *Ergonomics*, 31, 291-301.

Kilbom, A., Persson, J. and Jonsson, B. (1986). Risk factors for work-related disorders of the neck and shoulder - with special emphasis on working postures and movements. In E.N. Corlett, J. Wilson and I. Manenica (Eds.)*The Ergonomics of Working Postures*. London: Taylor & Francis, pp. 44-53.

Kopardekar, P. and Mital, A. (1993). *Cutting Stock Problem: A Heuristic Solution Based on Operators' Intuitive Strategies*. Technical Report, Ergonomics and Engineering Controls Research Laboratory, University of Cincinnati, Cincinnati, Ohio.

Kopardekar, P., Mital, A., Allada, V., and Anand, S. (1993). Human strategies in cutting stock problem. *Proceedings of the Industrial Engineering Research Conference,* Institute of Industrial Engineers, pp. 183-186.

Kroemer, K.H.E. (1970). Human strength: Terminology, measurement, and interpretation of data. *Human Factors*, 12, 297-313.

Kroemer, K.H.E. (1983). An isoinertial technique to assess individual lifting capability. *Human Factors*, 25, 493-506.

Kroemer, K.H.E. (1985). Testing individual capability to lift material: repeatability of a dynamic test compared with static testing. *Journal of Safety Research*, 16, 1-7.

Kroemer, K.H.E. (1991). Sitting at work: Recording and assessing body postures, designing furniture for the computer workstation. In A. Mital and W. Karwowski (Eds.)*Workspace, Equipment and Tool Design* . Amsterdam: Elsevier Science Publishers, pp. 93-112.

Kroemer, K.H.E. and Marras, W.S. (1981). Evaluation of maximal and submaximal static muscle exertions. *Human Factors*, 23, 643-653.

Kromodihardjo, S. and Mital, A. (1986). Kinetic analysis of manual lifting activities: Part I - development of a three-dimensional computer model. *International Journal of Industrial Ergonomics*, 1, 77-90.

Kromodihardjo, S. and Mital, A. (1987). Biomechanical analysis of manual lifting tasks. *Journal of Biomechanical Engineering*, 109, 132-138.

Kumar, S. (1987a). Arm-lift strength variation due to task parameters. In P. Buckle (Ed.) *Musculoskeletal Disorders at Work*. London: Taylor & Francis, pp. 37-42.

Kumar, S. (1987b). Arm-lift strength at different reach distances. In S.S. Asfour (Ed.)*Trends in Ergonomics/Human Factors IV* . Amsterdam: North-Holland, pp. 623-630.

Kumar, S. (1990). Cumulative stress as a risk factor for low-back pain. *Spine*, (In Press).

Kumar, S., Chaffin, D.B., and Redfern, M. (1988). Isometric and isokinetic back and arm lifting strengths: Devices and measurement. *Journal of Biomechanics*, 21, 35-44.

Langrana, N.A. and Lee, C.K. (1984). Isokinetic evaluation of trunk muscles. *Spine*, 9, 171-175.

Leskinen, T.P.J., Stalhammer, H.R., Kuorinka, I.A.A., and Troup, J.D.G. (1983). The effect of inertial factors on spinal stress when lifting. *Engineering in Medicine*, 12, 87-89.

Marras, W.S. (1990). Guidelines: Industrial electromyography (EMG). *International Journal of Industrial Ergonomics*, 6, 89-93.

Marras, W.S., King, A.I., and Joynt, R.L. (1984). Measurements of loads on the lumbar spine under isometric and isokinetic conditions. *Spine*, 9, 176-187.

Marras, W.S., Joynt, R.L., and King, A.I. (1985). The force-velocity relation and intra-abdominal pressure during lifting activities. *Ergonomics*, 28, 603-613.

McConville, J.T., Churchill, T.D., Kaleps, I., Clauser, C.E. and Cuzzi, J. (1980). *Anthropometric Relationships of Body and Body Segments' Moments of Inertia*. Report No. AFAMRL-TR-80-119, Air Force Aerospace Medical Research Laboratory, Wright Patterson Air Force Base, Ohio.

McGill, S.M. and Norman, R.W. (1985). Dynamically and statically determined low back moments during lifting. *Journal of Biomechanics*, 18, 877-885.

Miller, D.I. and Nelson, R.C. (1976). *Biomechanics of Sports*. Lea and Febiger, Philadelphia.

Milles, M., Desjardins, P.J. and Pawel, H.E. (1985). The facial plethysmograph: A new instrument to measure facial swelling volumetrically. *Journal of Oral Maxillofacial Surgery*, 43, 346-352.

Mital, A. (1987). patterns of difference between the maximum weights of lift acceptable to experienced and inexperienced materials handlers. *Ergonomics*, 30, 1137-1147.

Mital, A. and Das, B. (1987). Human strengths and occupational safety. *Clinical Biomechanics*, 2(2), 97-106.

Mital, A. and Faard H.F. (1990). Effects of sitting and standing, reach distance, and arm orientation on isokinetic pull strengths in the horizontal plane. *International Journal of Industrial Ergonomics*, 6, 241-248.

Mital, A. and Genaidy, A.M. (1989). Isokinetic pull-up strength profiles of men and women in different working postures. *Clinical Biomechanics*, 4, 168-172.

Mital, A. and Karwowski, W. (1986). Towards the development of human-work-performance standards in futuristic man-machine systems: A fuzzy modeling approach. *International Journal for Fuzzy Sets and Systems,* 19(2), 133-147.

Mital, A. and Kilbom, A. (1992). Design, selection and use of hand tools to alleviate trauma of the upper extremities: Part II - The scientific basis (Knowledge Base) for the guide. *International Journal of Industrial Ergonomics*, 10, 7-21.

Mital, A. and Kromodihardjo, S. (1986). Kinetic analysis of manual lifting activities: Part II - Biomechanical analysis of task variables. *International Journal of Industrial Ergonomics*, 1, 91-101.

Mital, A., Aghazadeh, F., and Karwowski, W. (1986a). Relative importance of isometric and isokinetic lifting strengths in estimating maximum lifting capabilities. *Journal of Safety Research*, 17, 65-71.

Mital, A., Channaveeraiah, C., Faard, F., and Khaledi, H. (1986b). Reliability of repetitive dynamic strengths as a screening tool for manual tasks. *Clinical Biomechanics*, 1, 125-129.

Mital, A., Karwowski, W., Mazouz, A.K., and Orsarh, E. (Mital, 1986c). Prediction of maximum acceptable weight of lift in the horizontal and vertical planes using simulated job dynamic strengths. *American Industrial Hygiene Association Journal*, 47, 288-292.

Mital, A., Wang, L.W., and Fard, H.F. (1987). Boundary line between the strength and endurance regions in manual lifting. *Clinical Biomechanics*, 2, 220-222.

Mital, A., Ayer, L. and Goreman, J. (1991). A lighting evaluation of a facility for the elderly. *Journal of Human Ergology*, 20, 171-180.

Mital, A., McGlothlin, J.D. and Faard, H.F. (1992). Noise in multiple-work station open-plan computer rooms: Measurement and annoyance. *Journal of Human Ergology*, 21, 69-82.

Mital, A., Garg, A., Karwowski, W., Kumar, S., Smith, J.L. and Ayoub, M.M. (1993a). Status in human strength research and application. *Transactions of the Institute of Industrial Engineers*, In Press.

Mital, A., Nicholson, A.S. and Ayoub, M.M. (1993b). *A Guide to Manual Materials Handling*. London: Taylor & Francis.

NASA (1978). *Anthropometric Source Book*. Publication No. 1024, National Aeronautics and Space Administration, Johnson Space Center, Houston, Texas.

Parnianpour, M., Nordin, M., Kahannovitz, N., and Frankel, V. (1988). The triaxial coupling of torque generation of trunk muscles during isometric exertions and the effect of fatiguing isoinertial movements on the motor output and movement patterns. *Spine*, 13, 982-992.

Pocock, S.J. (1983). *Clinical Trials: A Practical Approach*. New York: John Wiley & Sons.

Priel, V.Z. (1974). A numerical definition of posture. *Human Factors*, 16, 576-584.

Pytel, L.J. and Kamon, E. (1981). Dynamic strength as a predictor for maximum acceptable lifting. *Ergonomics*, 24, 663-672.

Roebuck, J.A., Jr., Kroemer, K.H.E. and Thompson, W.G. (1975). *Engineering Anthropometry Methods*. New York: John Wiley & Sons.

Singleton, W.T. (1972). *Introduction to Ergonomics*. Geneva: World Health Organization.

Smith, J.L. and Ayoub, M.M. (1989). Isoinertial strength-best predictor of infrequent manual materials handling capacities. Technical Report, Department of Industrial Engineering, Texas Tech University, Lubbock, Texas.

Smith, S.S., Mayer, T.G., Gatchel, R.J., and Becker, T.J. (1985). Quantification of lumbar function. Part I: isometric and multispeed isokinetic trunk strength measures in sagittal and axial planes in normal subjects. *Spine*, 10, 757-764.

Soderberg, G.L. (1992a). Recording Techniques. *In Selected Topics in Surface Electromyography for Use in the Occupational Setting: Expert Perspectives* (Ed.: G.L. Soderberg), DHHS(NIOSH) Publication No. 91-100, Cincinnati, Ohio, pp. 24-41.

Soderberg, G.L. (1992b). *Selected Topics in Surface Electromyography for Use in the Occupational Setting: Expert Perspectives* (Editor), Department of Health and Human Services, National Institute for Occupational Safety and Health, Publication No. 91-100, Cincinnati, Ohio.

Whittle, M.W., Herron, R. and Cuzzi, J. (1977). Biostereometric analysis of body form. In R.S. Johnston and L.F. Dietlein (Eds.) *Biomedical Results from Skylab*. National Aeronautics and Space Administration, Publication SP-377, Chapter 22, pp. 198-202.

Chapter 12
Medical Techniques

Paula Sind-Prunier
ErgoMed Analytics, Inc.

1.0 Introduction

This chapter takes a two-fold approach to the topic of human factors research techniques in medicine: First, the role of human factors and ergonomics in enhancing medical technology is discussed. In doing so, the definitions of medical technology proffered by the Office of Technology Assessment (1976, 1982) will be applied to include the techniques, drugs, equipment, and procedures used by health care professionals in delivering medical care to individuals, and the systems within which care is delivered. Second, the topics of health care technology assessment, and what it might have to offer applied ergonomics practice, are addressed.

1.1 Human Factors in Health Care: Quo Vadis?

In 1968, Dr. Maurice Rappaport presented a challenge in an address before Division 21 (Applied Experimental and Engineering Psychologists) of the American Psychological Association. He identified five areas as prime territory for human factors engineering efforts. Since then, some of his ideas have been realized, some are in the process of being implemented, and others remain dreams. But this remains clear after nearly a quarter of a century: The medical arena is ripe for the infusion of human factors expertise.

The United States health care system has been the subject of heated criticism that has intensified in recent years, as plans for widespread health care reform are debated in the 1990's. Skyrocketing costs, denial of treatment, and litigation against health care providers and medical equipment manufacturers are too common. Despite these criticisms, the standard of care in the United States is unparalleled, and the life expectancy of Americans has been extended as a result of medical advances. The problems plaguing American health care can partially be attributed to:

1. Health care personnel shortages
2. Shortcomings in medical education
3. Medical information and communication system deficiencies
4. Diagnostic and treatment equipment deficiencies
5. Lack of assessment of the effects of medical procedures on performance
6. Lack of emphasis on comprehensive medical technology assessment.

The first five problems were among the needs identified by Rappaport.

2.0 Health Care Personnel Shortages

The supply of qualified health care providers (physicians, nurses, skilled technicians) in critical specialties and geographic locations is insufficient to meet demand. The problem is not simply a matter of numbers, but one of productivity shortcomings. Rather than adding health care providers to the system (which will increase costs, as more salaries will need to be paid), an emphasis on increasing the productivity of current providers is more likely to yield a greater return. Health care providers are sensitive to the inefficiencies that misuse their talent and prevent them from accomplishing their professional tasks. Rappaport (1970) stressed the need for delegation of tasks to the provider with the least surplus of expertise needed to accomplish them. He advocated the reassignment of some physician duties to medical personnel with training between that of a physician and that of a nurse. Today, we know these individuals as physicians' assistants and nurse practitioners, with certain medical specialties evolving their own levels of providers with intermediate levels of expertise. These health care providers have helped to alleviate personnel shortages in some areas. Nonetheless, the productivity of health care providers could be further enhanced by redesigning their tasks and the equipment they use, to promote efficiency.

It is estimated that medical personnel spend better than one-half of their time performing information collection and management tasks. Furthermore, there is substantial duplication of effort in most instances, which greatly erodes the personnel resources available. If the amount of time health care providers spent obtaining, documenting, and communicating patient data were reduced, significant savings could be realized.

Inefficiencies resulting from failed equipment also take their toll on personnel resources. Although increasing device reliability may not be within the purview of human factors engineering, increasing the reliability of the interaction between the practitioner and the device certainly is. An analysis of FDA device failure incident databases by Bassen (1986) found that 7.7% to 18.3% of all reports revealed "user error" as the cause of failure. Reducing incidents of user/device errors would eliminate the additional time required by medical personnel to:

1. Attend to automated systems that have failed
2. Determine that the device actually failed
3. Restart failed devices
4. Render additional care necessitated by a failed device
5. Attend to the documentation requirements resulting from the failure event

Not only could the quality of care be improved, but the time demands on health care providers could be reduced. Suggested research issues and methods for increasing the efficiency of health care providers by improving equipment interfaces are discussed later.

From a human factors perspective, personnel shortages in the medical field can be somewhat mitigated by improving health care providers' efficiency in provider/equipment, provider/provider, and provider/patient interactions. One means for studying ways in which this might be accomplished is to look toward other fields where similar efforts—improving personnel coordination—are underway. This is exactly what researchers at the U.S. Army Research Institute (USARI) are doing (Howse, 1993).

For years, the aviation community has been immersed in the idea of improving personnel interaction in the cockpit. Referred to as Crew Coordination or Cockpit Resource Management (CRM)[1], the concept grew out of intensive study of the reasons why aviation mishaps occurred. Lack of communication and coordinated efforts were seen as common problems, worthy of remediation. CRM training was developed to teach air crew members new strategies for better communication and improved team performance. The CRM concept has been widely adopted in the civilian and military aviation sectors.

Yet the same problems—lack of communication and coordinated effort—have been observed in the health care environment. Specific examples of these problems include:

- Use of subjective or ambiguous descriptions of patient history
- Use of non-standard abbreviations or notations that can be misread by others
- Failure to adequately document physician orders or the patient's response to specific treatments
- Unclear or incomplete discharge instructions that might be misunderstood and not followed (USARI, 1993).

Through its research, USARI is identifying the antecedent factors that cause an otherwise highly qualified physician to overlook or misjudge a critical aspect of the patient's care in the emergency department, its operating procedures, the utilization of medical or surgical consultants from other hospital services, the utilization of the nursing and medical technician staff, the flow of patient care information, and the personality dynamics among staff members. The charge of USARI is to implement a three-phased effort to evaluate the transfer of CRM-based practices from the aviation to the emergency medicine arena. In the first phase, researchers will seek to identify and document team coordination error patterns unique to emergency medicine and surgery. This will involve an in-depth review of hospital quality assurance records (archival analysis, discussed later), direct observation of emergency room operations, and structured interviews with each component of the emergency department staff.

---

[1]For more information on Cockpit Resource Management, see Chapter 5, section 2.4.

In the second phase, the error patterns identified in the first phase will be used to develop a team coordination evaluation instrument. Subject Matter Experts (SMEs) from participating hospitals will assist in this process. Baseline performance data from each of the participating hospitals will be obtained, and used to identify the training needs unique to each hospital, as well as to provide a comparative basis for assessing the impact of subsequent training.

In the final phase, Crew Coordination training will be implemented at the hospitals. USARI will train senior hospital physicians and nurses who, in turn, will train other members of the staff. Post-training performance measures will be collected to measure the impact of the training. Criteria for evaluation will include both a reduction in team error and basic measures of patient care.

3.0 Shortcomings in Medical Education

The rapid pace at which new knowledge comes into existence makes it very difficult for physicians and other health care providers to stay current in their field. This is perhaps not so much a shortcoming in medical education, but a limitation of knowledge acquisition. Health care providers must continuously strive to update their knowledge, yet to do so effectively would leave them with little time to tend to their patients. Rappaport (1970) called for the evaluation of training techniques and educational tools by human factors engineers as a means for increasing the effectiveness of medical education. Although this task has not been undertaken by human factors engineers specifically, some evaluations have been carried out and some modifications to training techniques have been implemented, but questions as to the effectiveness of medical education and training remain. Other demands, such as the need for hands-on experience and additional practice while limiting the exposure of patients to inexperienced providers, adhering to ethical considerations, and minimizing consumption of valuable resources, have opened inquiry into new technologies, such as virtual reality and various other simulations as training technologies. The development and continued evaluation of educational technologies remain an area with fruitful prospects for human factors engineering contributions.

Other attempts to augment the knowledge of health care providers continue. Zimny (1992) discusses the development and assessment of a "problem-knowledge coupling" (PKC) system for physical therapists. The system is based in an attempt to overcome the perceived inaccessibility and irrelevance of the scientific literature to the practicing therapist. The PKC concept is intended to provide information to the therapist, not to solve problems or make treatment decisions. This is one example of attempts to deal with the information overload brought about by the increasing size of specialized knowledge bases in health care and the limitations on human memory. However, just how successful such systems are, and how they might be improved, remains to be determined.

There has been an increasing reliance on "intelligent" aids, designed to bring the latest in medical knowledge to practitioners, coupled with information management and decision-making capabilities. Such systems have benefited from human factors engineering in a variety of application areas, medicine being just one of them. Yet, there is still much more to be done. Intelligent aids can not only support medical decision-making and information management, they may also facilitate the integration of medical planning factors with operational considerations, leading to better resource utilization. This could have the effect of increasing efficiency and decreasing the cost of care.

The use and human-computer dynamics of automated information and decision-aiding tools are critical to their ultimate utility and effectiveness in any environment. Current limitations of the accuracy of such systems, coupled with the practical and legal ramifications of decision errors, make this a critical human factors engineering issue. Weaver (1991, p. 43) notes, "Since no [computerized decision support (CDS)] system will operate independent of humans, the real test is whether, to what extent, and at what cost human performance benefits from interaction with the CDS system." As Rappaport (1970, p. 29) stated, "The computer should be his aid—his idiot savant," identifying a crucial element of the interaction dynamics of medical decision aiding. Sind and Stetson (1991) noted that such systems may become "wolves in sheep's clothing," when an easy-to-use, well-designed interface camouflages limitations in the system's accuracy or ability. Human factors engineering philosophies of system design for medical (and other types of) decision making advocate maximizing improvement of the human-computer interface. This often occurs without due concern for the ultimate effect that improved usability and credible "appearance" may have on user behavior, particularly "trust" or confidence in the system. These factors have not been adequately investigated.

Anecdotal and empirical support has been shown for the notion that users are unable to objectively assess the utility and accuracy of such systems, and that *improving the human-computer interface may effectively camouflage other types of system shortcomings.* For example, Chouinard, Ryack and Stetson (1991) evaluated three versions of a user interface for a medical diagnostic system and found that subjects (U.S. Navy submarine-fleet hospital corpsmen) held significant preferences for interfaces. Moreover, the preference for the version of the interface was highly correlated with users' perceptions of the accuracy of the DSS, although the knowledge base underlying the systems under investigation was the same. This suggests that increasing preference for a system will lead to increasing perceptions of accuracy, regardless of the true accuracy of the system. However, because Chouinard et al. (1991) varied several parameters simultaneously among the interfaces tested, it is not possible to isolate the specific factor(s) which influenced users' perceptions of accuracy, or trust, of the system. The role of individual interface design parameters in overall usability and in affecting users' trust needs further study. Significant information could be obtained through a replication of the study reported by Chouinard et al. (1991), using versions of a DSS (or simulated DSS) which unconfound the interface parameters investigated in their study.

A better understanding of human/computer decision-making dynamics is vital to ensure that the computer becomes a useful aid to the health care provider, rather than a sly, deceiving, and potentially dangerous "aid" that actually degrades the practitioner's performance. By systematically investigating human-computer interaction parameters (computer response time delays, use of color, command-language versus graphical interface, ordering of questions in a query-based system, just to mention a few), the relative contributions of individual parameters can be evaluated. Guidelines for facilitating improved human-computer decision-making could then be formulated.

With decision support systems, it is important to distinguish between true accuracy and perceived accuracy. True accuracy is an objective, measurable quantity—typically the ratio of correct decisions (diagnoses) to the number of cases evaluated. Perceived accuracy is a subjective assessment made by the user and which may or may not reflect the true accuracy.

A system that delivers results of low accuracy will be of little utility to the user. Significant experience with a system of low perceived accuracy will likely lead to non-use of the DSS when its employment is optional. "Significant experience" has yet to be defined—will one negative experience discredit the user's perception of the system's integrity? Once a user has lost confidence in the integrity of a DSS, is it possible for the DSS to regain the trust of the user? And if so, what is necessary to facilitate its occurrence? These questions might best be answered through research using a simulated DSS that allows the manipulation of responses by the experimenter. By having subjects provide indicators of perceived accuracy, the experimenter can selectively degrade and improve the true accuracy of the system and monitor the response, perceived accuracy. This might effectively be done using the "Wizard of Oz"[2] paradigm discussed by Green and Wei-Haas (1985). Concurrent verbal protocol or "think aloud" procedures[3] might be useful for obtaining subjects' assessments of accuracy. Ericsson and Simon's (1983) seminal monograph details verbal protocol analysis, an extremely useful procedure used to probe the mechanisms and internal structure of cognitive processes, in this case, the formation of trust or confidence in response to interaction with a decision-support system.

Appropriately designed, DSSs have extreme potential to facilitate consistently good thought processes and medical decisions and, ultimately, to integrate such decisions within a larger operational framework. Yet, the

[2]For more information on the Wizard of Oz technique, see Chapter 9, Section 3.4, Case Study #4.

[3]For more information on think aloud and verbal protocols, See Chapter 4, section 7.4. A special type of think aloud protocol, where two users discuss an interface while interacting with it, is called the Co-discovery method. For more information on this technique, see Chapter 9, section 4.2.

extent to which that potential may be realized is heavily dependent upon the system's design. And, research suggests that training and other factors interact with the utilization and dependence on technology in medical practice, opening new questions in need of answers by the human factors discipline.

For example, Merrill, Laux, and Thornby (1991) evaluated medical students' reliance on technology using a psychophysical scaling instrument. They found that reliance on technology was greatest when experience was lacking (i.e., medical students with little clinical experience), and was correlated with choice of specialty. In particular, those with a greater reliance on technology migrated to careers in anesthesiology, general surgery and radiology, as compared to obstetrics/gynecology, internal medicine, and pediatrics. This suggests that greater understanding of such user-class specific characteristics is necessary to develop effective technologies and ensure their intended use.

From a research perspective, this finding is important in that it may limit the ability to generalize conclusions drawn from research addressing one population (e.g., anesthesiologists) to another (e.g., pediatricians), even though the design issues may appear similar and the populations may seem compatible in many other ways. The need to replicate research and demonstrate the ability to generalize its findings across different populations is nothing new. The findings of Merrill et al. (1991), however, serve to emphasize the importance of this pursuit, one which presents many opportunities for novice and seasoned researchers alike. Simply put, the methods and protocol described for an existing study can be repeated with modifications, employing a different subject population.

4.0 Medical Information and Communication System Deficiencies

Much effort and time are wasted due to the limitations and inefficiencies in medical information and communication systems. A patient's time is also valuable, and often needlessly wasted. In many instances, patients must provide redundant information about their medical history, or undergo repeated diagnostic tests because the results were misfiled, located elsewhere and thus unattainable, or the conduct of prior testing was unknown to the practitioner now treating the patient because it was done in another place by someone else. More obvious, perhaps, is the compromised care that results from the lack of information being where it is needed. Documenting a patient's allergy to a medication may prevent him from experiencing a serious reaction at a later point in time, but only if that record is readily accessible at that time and place. Although the electronic storage and transmission of medical data and images are now possible, such capabilities have yet to be exploited. While cost is the primary factor which has limited the adoption of advanced technologies, it is the lack of perceived benefit relative to cost that is perhaps more to blame.

Human factors engineering is needed to ensure that the benefits of advanced technologies can be realized. For example, appropriate benchmarks and minimum system requirements for electronic medical imaging systems (e.g., computerized axial tomography [CAT] scanners and similar devices) are best derived psychophysically from systematic evaluations of image interpreters' (human) performance, rather than driven by the technology. Human factors engineers can aid in quickening the pace of performance enhancements by identifying imaging parameters for which improvement would yield not just the greatest gain in machine capability, but those which would yield the greatest performance increment. This necessarily requires that the medical device and its operator be considered as a unit, rather than trying to evaluate the technology independently of its user.

Medical images posses a number of characteristics, such as contrast, resolution, color, uniformity, etc. Through technological advances, these characteristics can be refined: increased contrast, finer resolution, more accurate colors or different application of color, etc. Yet such refinement is short-sighted if it is not matched by improvements in performance; in other words, the refinements must be behaviorally validated. Snyder (1985) discusses the utility of psychophysical research and several image quality metrics, recognizing image quality to mean more than simply preference for one image over another, but rather performance differences due to the ability to perceive information in the image.

Psychophysical methods are discussed in a number of leading texts, among them, Stevens (1960), and Gescheider (1985). Techniques such as the Method of Constant Stimuli, the Method of Limits, and the Method of Adjustment are the foundation for the determination of absolute and differential thresholds, the basis for system performance benchmarks. Where measurement of sensory attributes is desirable, psychophysical scaling techniques can be used to quantitatively assess attributes with more precision and utility than qualitative rating affords.

Whether the technology is used for information and communication purposes or diagnostic and treatment purposes, the same concept applies—decisions regarding technology assessment must include human factors/usability considerations if an impact on productivity and cost effectiveness is to be realized. This theme is discussed in greater detail, in section 7.0.

5.0 Diagnostic and Treatment Equipment Deficiencies

User problems, rather than equipment malfunction, can account for half of all equipment problems in the acute care environment (Ostrander, 1986). This adversely and seriously affects patient monitoring, diagnosis, and therapy. If a product is found to posses a serious safety concern, it may be recalled. An estimated 12% of medical device recalls are the result of "human factors problems," according to Hyman & Schlain (1986). (The technique used by Hyman et al., archival records analysis, is discussed in section 7.1). Systematic consideration of human factors issues and comprehensive performance evaluations are needed to reduce human factors problems in medical equipment. Where equipment requirements are particularly challenging (e.g., medical equipment for field use; equipment intended for naïve or incapacitated users), the importance and scope of human factors considerations are intensified. So, too, is the need for consideration and realistic representation of situational variables which would affect the validity of assessments.

In an evaluation of several blood and urine analysis devices for proposed use by military medical personnel in the field, investigators discovered serendipitiously, that the temperature of specimens and ambient temperature and humidity affected the test results (Perrotta, Bolecek, Christ and Hobson, 1994). This has two important implications for testing and subsequent use of the devices in field settings. Because it is acknowledged that temperatures and humidity in a field environment could vary significantly, changes in field operating procedures may be necessary. For example, where the specimen temperature must be controlled, it may be necessary to require that fresh specimens be tested immediately (when they are still at or near body temperature), or placed in a temperature-controlling environment (i.e., a refrigerator). Otherwise, the temperature of the specimen could vary, depending on the ambient temperature and the elapsed time since the specimen was collected. This could cause erroneous results for some tests. Yet, such restrictions on field operations may not be possible. In that case, thorough evaluation of the devices would necessarily include specimens of varying temperatures, conducted under varying temperature and humidity conditions. These additional requirements would increase the cost and time required for testing. Perrotta et al. (1994) found that some equipment was more sensitive than other equipment, with regard to temperature and humidity factors. Knowledge of specific differences would be extremely valuable in decisions to adopt one piece of equipment over another for field use. Devices which are more resistant to changes in environmental conditions would provide greater latitude for use in a field setting. Thus, the integrity of the evaluation and utility of the resulting information could benefit from a factorial (or comparable) experimental design.

Despite a myriad of international and domestic standards, guidelines, recommended practices, and regulations for most aspects of medical equipment design, specific human factors guidance is sorely lacking. The Association for the Advancement of Medical Instrumentation (AAMI) published the first set of guidelines for human factors engineering of medical equipment in 1988 (AAMI, 1988). The *Guidelines* (which evolved into a second revision, which was adopted by the American National Standards Institute in 1993 as ANSI/AAMI HE48-1993) were developed with the participation of medical device industry representatives and physicians. They were derived from MIL-STD-1472, several other Department of Defense

(DOD) standards and resources, and suggestions of the designers and physicians who participated in their development. While extremely beneficial, potential weaknesses of ANSI/AAMI HE48 (1993) should be noted.

Although physicians (one class of end users) contributed significantly to the development of the standard, the physicians were, almost exclusively, anesthesiologists. As such, the homogeneity of the users involved and their input may limit the utility, applicability, and appropriateness of the standard as applied across all types of medical equipment, which is the stated scope of the document. The findings of Merrill et al. (1991) add credence to this concern.

In addition, information extracted from sources such as MIL-STD-1472 was selectively "adapted" when it was agreed that the information was inappropriate (e.g., specifications based on anthropometric data collected from a military population). These adaptations were opinion-based rather than empirically-based, and have not been validated. To do so would require empirical evaluation, or in limited instances, the judicious application of established models for extrapolating human performance data. In addition to the need for anthropometric data which is more representative of the user population, attempts to guide medical equipment designers would benefit greatly from basic and applied research addressing visual and audible alarms, as well as discipline-specific and general stereotypes for coding. To be useful, however, the methods employed must be sound.

Schulte and Block (1992) present an example of an effort to evaluate "sound" issues, using a potentially "unsound" methodology. Schulte et al. (1992) conducted a simple study to test their observations that people are unable to perceive the pitch changes of a variable-pitch pulse oximeter. A pulse oximeter is commonly used to monitor oxygen saturation in conjunction with heart rate. The device presents a tone which corresponds temporally to the patient's heartbeat. The pitch of the tone varies on each heartbeat as a function of the oxygen saturation. The pitch falls as O_2 saturation decreases, and rises as O_2 saturation increases, creating an efficient, dual-coding scheme that helps to limit the proliferation of auditory signals and alarms in the patient care environment. Schulte et al. (1992) acknowledged several apparatus concerns (e.g., they used tape recordings of simulated tones, hence, the stimuli may have been compromised in the recording process. It was also noted that the tones might not be necessarily representative of the spectral characteristics of actual pulse-oximeter tones, although selection of stimuli frequencies were based on one such device). Additionally, the methodology employed (a single, descending trial using the Method of Limits and the same initial value for all subjects) might benefit from refinement. Because the Method of Limits is particularly susceptible to errors of habituation and expectation, repeated measures consisting of both ascending and descending trials, with random initial values, is generally recommended. This protocol is sometimes called the "random staircase method," and its controls are considered useful in combating the inherent biases in the Method of Limits.

The paucity of human factors research directed toward the development of medical device design criteria and recommendations often necessitates the reliance on data and criteria derived from military systems and other pursuits. Some validation and research directed at specific issues for medical equipment design are needed before ANSI/AAMI HE48 (1993) can be implemented with confidence. Moreover, blind adherence to any published guideline does not ensure a better, safer, more productive, "human-engineered" product. Although ANSI/AAMI HE48 includes an overview of the design process with the role of human factors engineering defined throughout (adapted from military specifications and handbooks), ANSI/AAMI HE48 remains just a guideline. Live human factors engineers need to be involved in the design and evaluation of medical devices, even when guidelines and standards are followed. Human factors educators have not yet managed to reduce human factors engineering to a cookbook that any designer can pick up and follow, and it is unlikely that we will be able to do so in the near future.

Indeed, more research is needed to provide a solid foundation for design guidelines and standards. To be truly useful, however, such research must be rigorously conducted and appropriately documented. An important consideration in any research is that the methods chosen provide an objective and unbiased means for studying the phenomenon of interest. Experimenters must always ask themselves (and impartial colleagues) whether the ultimate results will be totally the result of the manipulation of the independent variable, or whether the chosen methods may bias the results in favor of one particular outcome.

For example, Farris (1993) investigated color-coding stereotypes for continuous dimensions, a concept of potential interest in the medical field. Color might be used as a coding scheme for time, a continuous variable—as the color of an indicator progresses from one color to the next, the passage of time can be observed. In a complex display system, such coding would be far superior to numerical coding, reducing display clutter and capitalizing upon the superiority of color as a coding mechanism for visual search.

Color might also be used as a coding scheme for the direction and magnitude of patient variables. Lesser (personal communication, February, 1994) has developed a graphical language (GIFIC or Graphical Interface For Information Cognition), which is proposed for use in the intensive care setting for communicating patient status information. The system uses a patient metaphor icon, with various regions and areas of the icon representing specific diagnostic test results. Green represents test results which are within norms, red is used to identify results which are above norms, and yellow to indicate below-norm values. Missing results are represented by blank (black) areas on the display, signaling the health care provider that the datum is absent. The system is remarkably easy to interpret and learn (indeed, individuals with no medical knowledge were able to differentiate a patient with myocardial infarction from another with renal dysfunction in seconds, after only a 10-minute explanation of the system). This ease of learning is owing in part to the metaphor concept and the simplistic use of color. The colors were selected by the developer based on hypothesized color stereotypes. Validation of the color scheme by testing novice users from the intended user population—physicians, nurses, and certain specialty personnel—would be beneficial. This might be accomplished by using verbal protocol to elicit patient evaluations based upon interpretation of the graphical display and monitoring specific errors/delays in reporting. For example, if a subject states "uric acid level is high . . . no . . . it's low," this could indicate a potential problem with the RED-GREEN-YELLOW coding of HIGH-NORM-LOW, at least for that dimension.

Returning to the example of Farris' (1993) research on color as a coding scheme for a continuous dimension, however, the problem of color assignment becomes more complex when there is a desire to code several levels of a continuous dimension, using color. Farris believed that subjects' assignment of colors along a continuous dimension would follow the spectrum, although the direction (red to violet versus violet to red) was uncertain, and suspected of varying, depending on the dimension of interest. Farris initially considered a test wherein subjects would be required to order the six basic colors of the spectrum (red, orange, yellow, green, blue, and violet) in relation to two adjectival endpoints, for example HOT-COLD or FAST-SLOW. Care to avoid order effects by counterbalancing presentation order of endpoint pairs (e.g., COLD-HOT versus HOT-COLD) was implemented. Yet a test which presented all six colors simultaneously might bias the results toward the spectral organization, as subjects might have considered it an underlying order (because of its obvious visual presence), whether or not related to the endpoints (which would be of more interest in a design scenario). Thus, use of such a technique would not permit unbiased testing of the hypothesis that ordering along a given dimension would follow the spectral order. Moreover, if the spectral ordering was followed, it would essentially reduce the test to one of the spectral endpoints and their relation to the adjectival endpoints, as the other colors would follow in intermediate, spectral order.

Instead, Farris (1993) used a paired-comparison technique, presenting two colors at a time and instructing subjects to order the colors according to the adjectival endpoints. Analysis of the results showed that when so presented discretely, subjects did not follow the spectral ordering. Moreover, a consistent directional ordering among subjects did not exist, suggesting that comprehensive color ordering stereotypes for the dimensions used may not be implicit in the population.

Farris concluded that a study addressing simultaneous presentation of all colors and concurrent ordering by subjects would be necessary before one could conclude that subjects will not follow the spectral ordering. Yet, in a design situation where a discrete indicator is used to code an underlying continuous dimension, the paired-comparison methodology was a more stringent and unbiased test. Her results do not indicate that color should be avoided in coding continuous dimensions; rather, the indication is that a strong stereotype is not ingrained in the population and a logical, easily-learned ordering of the colors (spectral or otherwise) could be considered for use.

Clearly, the methodology employed can affect the results, as is suspected here. The question then becomes, which methodology is the appropriate one to use? When color is used discretely and independently as a coding scheme for a continuous dimension, the paired-comparison technique is perhaps very appropriate. In another situation, the simultaneous presentation and ordering methodology might appear more appropriate.

Finally, Farris' (1993) study used "general" dimensions such as HOT-COLD, etc., and introductory psychology students as subjects. Replication of her study using specific dimensions unique to medical practitioners, and an appropriately homogeneous subject pool (e.g., color coding of oxygen (O_2) saturation by anesthesiologists) might yield different results. Consideration of a subset of the colors and their ordering might also indicate usable information for the design of color coding of continuous dimensions where fewer than six levels are required.

6.0 Assessment of the Effects of Medical Procedures on Patient Behavior and Performance

Advances in medical technology (including pharmaceuticals) have had exciting and beneficial effects on patients. Outpatient surgery is the norm for many procedures which once required expensive, lengthy hospital stays, and there is an emphasis on early release, home care, and self-care, primarily as cost-saving measures. Moreover, diabetes, epilepsy, allergies, high blood pressure, and other disorders that once killed or severely restricted lifestyles, are now controllable (although not necessarily curable), due to a proliferation of prophylactic and maintenance drugs. Millions of Americans now live longer, with an enhanced quality of life, provided they take their medication—the consequence of which is that the number of people on medication is growing. And, while pharmaceutical manufacturers have demonstrated the efficacy and safety of their product in accordance with U.S. Food & Drug Administration requirements, the behavioral and performance implications of many of these drugs is not as well known. It is in this domain that the DOD community has led the civilian sector in research, as a result of concerns about the performance of service personnel when sleep-deprived, subjected to the influence of various pharmaceutical agents, affected by stress or other task characteristics, or a combination of such factors[4]. This information is equally beneficial in understanding the effects of these drugs (and other medical procedures) on an individual's ability to drive, perform

[4]For more information on the DOD's research into the effects of drugs on user performance,, see Chapter 13, sections 4.4.1 and 4.42.

cognitive and physical requirements on the job, partake in recreational activities such as scuba diving, etc. Finally, those concerned with the abilities of medical personnel to remain alert, capable, and proficient over extended periods of duty can look to the DOD community for advice, which has perhaps the longest standing and most productive program of research on the problems (and improvement strategies) of sustained and continuous operations. Continued efforts involving the human factors community to evaluate the performance effects of specific medical procedures, pharmaceutical agents, and various medical conditions would be quite beneficial. This is an area amenable to technology transfer and cooperation between the DOD and civilian communities.

Using a series of standardized human performance metrics, Rice (1993a, 1993b) investigated the effects of Hismanal (astemizole) and Benadryl (diphenhydramine) in a placebo-controlled study of human performance[5]. Astemizole is a long-acting, selective histamine H_1-receptor antagonist, prescribed for long-term use. It provides symptomatic relief of seasonal allergic rhinitis and chronic idiopathic hives. Diphenhydramine is an antihistamine with anticholinergic and sedative effects. Like astemizole, it is commonly prescribed for management of allergies. Unlike diphenhydramine, astemizole is not believed to possess sedative effects.

Rice used portions of the Unified Tri-Service Assessment Battery (UTC-PAB) and the Complex Cognitive Assessment Battery (CCAB) to evaluate performance effects of the drugs[5]. These batteries measure complex cognitive abilities, and were originally developed to assess the effects of prophylactic drugs used as counteragents in chemical warfare. The tests used by Rice included tests of route planning and direction following, choice reaction time, temporal interval production, time anticipation, serial pattern comparison, logical reasoning, spatial perception, serial addition and subtraction, code substitution, an unstable tracking task, a Sternberg memory search/tracking combination task, and a visual search task. Also administered were the Mood Scale II, the Profile of Mood States (POMS), the Stanford Sleepiness Scale, a self-evaluation of perceived performance, and an a self-assessment of subjects' belief as to whether they had received the drug or the placebo. These tests included some from the UTC-PAB and CCAB and others, and are described in Rice (1990).

Rice found performance decrements post-diphenhydramine ingestion on three tasks. No performance decrements were found following ingestion of astemizole. Subjective effects of mood were found for both antihistamines, an effect more pronounced following ingestion of diphenhydramine. The results are described in greater detail in Rice (1993a, 1993b).

Similar studies, using standardized metrics of human performance (such as the UTC-PAB, CCAB, and others used by Rice) in a laboratory environment, would be extremely worthwhile. Criteria for drug selection

[5]For an analogous military study on the effects of these drugs on performance, see Cahpter 13, section 4.4.2.

might include those which are currently or are projected to come into widespread use (e.g., antihypertensives, cold preparations, analgesics), and for which the performance effects are not clearly understood. Placebo-controlled studies are vital in establishing validity of the results. Additionally, fasting, or caffeine or alcohol ingestion, might be simultaneously evaluated with selected drugs (those considered "safe" for use under such conditions) to evaluate possible potentiation of performance effects. As the number of people on prophylactic and therapeutic drugs continues to rise, the importance of such studies will escalate.

7.0 Health Care Technology Assessment

There is no clear understanding nor widespread acceptance of a definition or scope of technology assessment in health care (c.f., Goodman, 1992; Lumsdon, 1992; Hansen, 1992). While some argue that the future of technology assessment will see growth in scope and interaction among various disciplines (e.g., Hansen, 1992), others argue that this broader definition of health care technology assessment was the intent at its inception, and it is only now running full circle (Goodman, 1992). Many of the criticisms of technology assessment in health care (e.g., an over reliance on randomized clinical trials (RCT), and their inherent methodological shortcomings) stem from a perceived myopic view of technology assessment. Using a broader definition quells some of the criticisms of health care technology assessment and underscores the need for human factors engineers in such assessments.

For virtually any technology to be taken seriously, it must prove to be efficacious, effective, and efficient. A technology is efficacious if it demonstrates (usually under ideal circumstances, such as in a controlled setting) the *capacity* for effectiveness. It is effective if it achieves the desired results. In distinguishing these terms, effectiveness is subjected to the rigors and confounds of an operational environment, whereas efficacy is usually limited to carefully-controlled conditions. In other words, efficacy is established when patient compliance is strictly controlled—if the patient follows the treatment protocol precisely. In reality, however, patients forget to take medications, miss appointments for therapy, use a home device improperly or for a longer or shorter period of time than prescribed, etc. Because some technologies are more resilient to such variations, evaluating both efficacy and effectiveness is important. Efficiency relates to the consumption of resources, the most efficient technology being the one which consumes the least. *Human factors engineering, by its orientation, is most apt to address concerns related to effectiveness and efficiency.*

Human factors engineering efforts to enhance effectiveness and efficiency through the reduction of errors and control of training costs is a difficult challenge. One factor in this challenge is the lack of standardization of medical equipment in current use. Standardization, viewed by some device manufacturers as burdensome and restricting, is well-established in human factors philosophy as a viable and necessary mechanism for reducing instances of human error and limiting training demands. Standardization capitalizes on the efficiency of human resources, particularly the limited cognitive resources of humans. When properly implemented, standardization can achieve its objectives with minimal impact on the industry. The prospect of implementing standards broadly and across all types of medical equipment would be virtually impossible, and perhaps is unwarranted. Rather, an emphasis on task analysis within defined user classes, and on equipment use within a user class, may enable limited standardization which achieves the anticipated benefits of a more comprehensive standardization program.

For example, Hähnel, Friesdorf, Schwilk, Marx and Blessing (1992) describe their efforts to assess the amenability of the intensive care unit (ICU) workstation to standardization. They believed that if physicians could reliably predict, at the time of admission, a patient's equipment needs, ICU workstations could be equipped permanently, in a standardized manner, with electronically linked modules. Currently, independent, free-standing equipment modules are introduced to the workstation as needed. The lack of cohesion of these modules sometimes leads to conflicts and incompatibilities—different user interfaces make their operation error-prone. A workstation equipped with all ICU equipment modules would be a costly waste of resources.

Hähnel et al. (1992) interviewed ICU physicians within 24 hours of patient admission, asking them questions regarding anticipated patient outcomes, equipment needs, duration of artificial ventilation, and duration of hospitalization. Their results suggest that equipment currently found in the ICU can be grouped into two levels of use, rendering ICU workstations amenable to standardization within those two levels. Similar efforts to ready other workstations for standardization may be feasible. This "incremental" approach to standardization might limit resistance to standardization by making standardization needs-driven, rather than done as a matter of principle. This would also eliminate the unnecessary standardization of independent elements, e.g., pieces of equipment used exclusively in different settings, with no common personnel.

Without a doubt, the human element plays an extremely important role in health care, both from the perspective of the patient and the provider. The human factors discipline has much to offer health care technology users, both patients and providers. The user-centered design concept must be integrated into health care technology assessment; the critical role that the user plays in proper use of medical technology and patient compliance emphasizes the impact of human factors considerations on effectiveness and efficiency.

When Batavia and Hammer (1990) attempted to develop user-based criteria for evaluating assistive devices. By observing the use of assistive devices by persons with disabilities, they noticed a common pattern of adoption and abandonment of such devices. If they could identify the factors associated with abandonment, then future design efforts could strive to avoid these factors. In all, 17 factors were identified and ranked by experts (individuals with mobility and/or sensory disabilities) using a small focus group[6] process based on a modified version of the Delphi Method. The Delphi Method, a useful procedure for facilitating consensus-building among small groups of experts, is detailed in Linstone and Turoff (1985). Batavia and Hammer (1990) developed a preliminary list of evaluation factors based upon their experiences in evaluating assistive devices. Next, two groups (one group of individuals with mobility impairments and one with sensory impairments) met independently. In the first phase, group members identified their own criteria used in evaluating specific technologies (e.g., motorized wheelchair by the group of mobility-impairment experts; a type reader by the group of sensory-impairment experts). In the second phase, group members prioritized the criteria developed in Phase I. The authors caution that their study should be regarded as preliminary in nature. It used a relatively small sample of consumers of assistive devices who are not necessarily representative of the population of long-term users of such devices. Moreover, the researchers did not test the validity and reliability of the factors identified and prioritized. Nonetheless, the study illustrates one example of how human factors engineering might be applied proactively—by developing criteria for the design and evaluation of assistive devices used by persons with disabilities.

Batavia and Hammer recommend future research to quantitatively assess the relative importance of specific usability criteria. Psychophysical techniques such as magnitude estimation (Gescheider, 1980) might be useful in this regard. In a magnitude estimation experiment, the subject makes a direct numerical estimation of the magnitudes of several stimuli. In this case, a subject might be asked to rate the magnitude of importance of various criteria. For example, the subject might state that ease of maintenance is a "10" in importance, but affordability is, in their opinion, 2.5 times as important, so they would give it a "25." In this manner, not only can the ordering of criteria importance be established, but the magnitude of their importance can be determined. They further recommend training recently-disabled persons to use such criteria, once validated, in the selection of assistive devices, and to test the value of the criteria in making such decisions.

Similarly, the criteria for health care technology assessment need further development and refinement to include user-based criteria. It must be kept in mind that many types of medical equipment have multiple classes of users, each user class with its own needs and requirements. Such user classes would include the operator of the equipment, and the patient with whom it is used. Maintainers of the equipment might be considered yet a third class of user. For improved use, the needs of all such user classes must be identified and addressed in design. Moreover, equipment employed by a

[6]For more information on the use of the focus group technique, see Chapter 7, section 3.2 and Chapter 9, section 3.1,

diverse user group (e.g., an external pacing/defibrillator device may be used by any member of the medical team certified in its use—which may include physicians, nurses, emergency medical technicians, and others) must be developed with the diversity of that group in mind.

7.1 The Methods of Technology Assessment

Health care technology assessors and human factors engineers would do well to pool their various tools and methods, with the objective of identifying those which show promise for improvements in health care technology assessment. More importantly, these methods need to be further developed and defined, and standard protocols established, so as to enhance the ability to compare evaluations and outcomes across studies. Deusinger (1992) discusses how the analysis of errors that occur in practice may be used for assessing and enhancing the quality of care—an axiom well established in classical human factors thinking. Using open-ended questions in a telephone interview with licensed physical therapists, she collected information on self-reported incidents from the therapists' careers that had caused (or had the potential to cause) negative outcomes for patients. She chose to use open-ended questions, which previous research suggested facilitate the reporting of socially undesirable behavior by making questions appear less threatening. Deusinger then classified the type, environment, perceptions of severity, and error responsibility attributions, and analyzed these factors, allowing her to draw conclusions about errors in the practice of physical therapy.

Thrush (1992) explains how automated anesthesia records can be used to detect and aid in the diagnosis of problems in anesthesia practice. Automated anesthesia records can be used to document the course of events, allowing the reconstruction and analysis of incidents. In the case study presented, a comparison of data manually recorded by physicians and that recorded automatically by the device, showed that a discontinuation of ventilation to the patient was apparently unnoticed, as it was not recorded by the physician. The physician attributed the resulting episode of hypotension and O_2 desaturation to an unusual drug reaction or pulmonary embolization instead of its true cause, the discontinuation of ventilation, and implemented an inappropriate treatment protocol. Similar means of instrumented performance could be beneficial in other domain, and would be similarly useful.

Wall (1991) argues in favor of the use of randomized clinical trials (RCTs) to evaluate clinical information systems, as well as other techniques for assessing the efficiency and effectiveness of such systems. RCT protocol is the most widely used evaluative vehicle in the medical discipline, and is a virtual prerequisite in studies carried out to obtain the approval of the Food and Drug Administration for medical technologies used in the United States. Although it could be argued that RCT protocol is contrary to classical human factors engineering philosophy -- it isolates the analysis, ignoring the interaction of real and important influences -- randomized clinical trials might be useful nonetheless. If nothing else, RCTs can be used to establish efficacy, which becomes the basis against which analyses of the effectiveness of alternate implementations of the technology can be compared. Moreover, because of the staunch, loyal following of randomized clinical trials as an assessment tool, this method is not likely to fall into disuse in the near future.

Antczak-Bouckoms, Burdick, Klawansky and Mosteller (1991) and Blais (1991) discuss the possibility of using medical registries and administrative data bases for technology assessment. They selected several registries (such as the International Bone Marrow Transplant Registry, IBMTR) and obtained a list of articles emanating from the registries obtained in a literature search. They selected those articles which were specifically related to technology assessment and developed 75 questions as the basis for a standardized review of the articles. The questions covered 10 topic areas, including: description of the technology, disease or condition, data collection, data analysis, comparisons, RCTs, costs, diagnostic tests, non-medical aspects, and general evaluation. (The actual questions included in the researchers' protocol are presented as an appendix in their 1991 article). This protocol and its implementation became the basis for several additional articles addressing the specific utility of each of the registries selected, for conducting technology assessment.

Bassen's (1986) analysis of device failures is another example of the use of archival data techniques (using previously-collected information to answer new questions, sometimes in a retrospective nature). Bassen reviewed the device failure incident databases maintained by the Food and Drug Administration, collecting information about the reported causes of device failures. Of particular interest to him were device failures where "user error" was the failure attribution. Analyzing archival data sources has the advantages of being non-intrusive, inexpensive, and facilitating the analysis of information collected from a large population over a long period of time. Such archival techniques, however, are limited by the lack of standardization in terminology and classification schemes among different data bases. Often, complete information is lacking, as the objectives of current research were not defined when the data base was conceived. Additionally, the need to conduct independent validation of the data in such archives cannot be overemphasized. Legal considerations may prevent access to some types of information, or may dictate limitations upon its usability. Information from many U.S. Government archival sources including the Food and Drug Administration, however, is available under the Freedom of Information Act (see Section 9.1).

Expert opinion has been used as another basis for evaluating technology effectiveness (e.g., Panerai, Almeida, Portela, de Carvalho, Coura-Silho and da Costa, 1991). This type of analysis may be limited, however, in assessing some human factors aspects of health care technology, but is nonetheless useful as a preliminary or supplemental technique.

Problems in concurrent combination of various approaches to assessment must also be evaluated, particularly when a multidisciplinary approach to health care technology assessment is advocated. For example, Evans and Robinson (1980) raise concerns of atypical practice in the context of clinical trials, expressing doubt as to the ability to generalize economic data derived from clinical trials. Drummond and Davies (1991) discuss methodological issues when attempting to analyze economic factors in conjunction with clinical trials, and concede that several issues remain to be resolved.

Workload issues also confound various approaches to health care technology assessment. Because the physical and cognitive workload of operators using various medical technologies is so dependent on the situation and environment under evaluation, care in generalizing assessments must be exercised. A new bedside monitoring technology might receive different reviews in one setting compared to another, if it provides useful, necessary information in one and redundant or conflicting information in another. The enhancements of a new system may go unrealized if the cognitive complexity of the use environment is such that cognitive overload results, and the full benefits of the enhancements are never exploited. What is to be gained and lost in terms of cognitive and physical demands on the operator must be evaluated in order to anticipate the conditions under which overload situations are likely to occur.

Unfortunately, the factors that influence workload are innumerable and complex. It is particularly difficult to assess workload effects in the context of typical clinical trials, with all their inherent constraints on fidelity. In RCTs, the unnatural structuring, added monitoring and reporting requirements, and rigid adherence to conditions different than those found in typical practice settings affects the workload distribution and characteristics; it becomes impossible to separate the effects on workload of experimentation or monitoring from the effects of the technology and its features and capabilities.

An important phenomenon that has been observed, and which challenges the utility of technology assessment in health care (and particularly workload estimations), is the failure of advanced technologies to replace their predecessors. Even when new technologies offer improved capabilities, many practitioners are reluctant to discard older practices. Refusal to abandon previously-learned skills, as well as concern over legal liability that encourages the proliferation of diagnostic clinical data, are but two explanations for this phenomenon. As a result, technological advances often become additions to, rather than replacements for, older technologies. The amount of information to be attended to, synthesized, understood, and acted upon, increases accordingly.

Because health care technology assessment necessitates a systematic rather than a piece-wise approach, the systems engineering-based philosophy of human factors test and evaluation methods could be very beneficial and appropriate. Usability testing (Chapter 4) is one technique available for technology assessment. Rice (in press) discusses how usability testing can be used in the particular case of assistive equipment for disabled persons. Relman (1988) describes health care technology assessment as the "third revolution in health care," due to its current stance as a potential way to ensure cost-effectiveness in adopting medical technology. Roper, Winkenwerder, Hackbart and Krakauer (1988) note that while health care technology assessment can provide a sound basis for economic decision making, can improve the quality and effectiveness of health care, and can enhance safety for both the patient and provider, the methods of data acquisition and processing for evaluating medical technology safety and effectiveness are lacking. However, human factors engineers have been involved in related activities for non-medical systems for over half a century. Thus, filling the methodological void may not be so terribly difficult. Future research should address means for transferring human factors evaluative methodologies extant, to the problems of health care and medical technologies. There continues to be a great need for human factors involvement in health care and medical applications, as medical technology continues to outpace our knowledge of its relative effectiveness and usability.

7.2 Technology Assessment and Ergonomics Practice

Since its inception, the field of human factors/ergonomics has progressed from a principally scientific orientation to become more practitioner-based. As the knowledge base of the profession increased, some individuals continued basic and applied research in human capabilities and limitations, the cornerstone areas of the discipline. Others, however, focused their efforts on the application of this newly-synthesized knowledge, some involving themselves little, if at all, in evaluating the fruits of their work. Technology assessment needs to become an important and consistent complement to occupational ergonomics, where practitioners recommend and effect changes that reduce errors, prevent injuries, and maintain or improve productivity.

Presently, there is a significant lack of knowledge as to the efficacy of many implementations of ergonomics technology. This problem is not unique to this discipline, however. Mace (1991) identifies similar shortcomings with regard to the discipline of behavior analysis, using the medical field and its assessment of technology as a model from which to gauge the differences in assessment. Mace (1991) notes, "Technological advances in medicine... are the result of continuous, and often purposeful, interaction among basic scientists, technology developers, clinical researchers, clinicians, and theory builders. There are well-trodden pathways connecting all of these areas that are essential to the ultimate goal of advancing medical technology. Some phases of the process are so well defined that they are regulated by the federal government." (p. 433) There has been a growing sentiment within the human factors community of a "researchers versus practitioners" mentality, contrary to the type of interaction necessary for continuous technology development and assessment. Understandably, the human factors discipline, barely a half-century old, is still trying to establish itself, make its mark, and contribute where it can. This haste in implementing ergonomics technologies comes at the expense of their rigorous assessment. Inevitably, the assessment of ergonomics technologies will need to be addressed. This assessment may take the form of that which is used currently in the medical arena, as described below. More likely, a modified approach would better serve the discipline.

The first stage in the building of technology is the accumulation of fundamental knowledge of the subject matter. This is derived from basic research in related disciplines. The human factors discipline has operated in this stage since its inception. It has successfully increased the fundamental knowledge regarding human capabilities and limitations, and how this information might be useful in system design. This is an on-going stage; nonetheless, it is a stage in which the discipline has proven a degree of competence in executing. Progress in this stage is hindered and responsiveness to practical needs is slowed, however, when basic and applied research are not clearly linked[7]. The lack of data to support the recommendations of practitioners in many application areas, including occupational ergonomics, is evidence that this link is deficient.

In the second stage of technology building, a technology is formulated as a possible solution to a problem, and demonstrated experimentally. A technology that exhibits potential merit becomes a candidate for further development and testing in clinical trials. It is in this stage that many ergonomics technologies remain, from an assessment perspective. Although the technology may be implemented (and claims made concerning its success, based on theoretical relationships and preliminary evidence), few ergonomics technologies have faced assessment equivalent to the rigors of clinical trials. This is most unfortunate, when one considers that it is through the rigors of such testing that technology is refined, proven, and its limitations identified.

Clinical trials involve a multiple-phase assessment. In the first phase, parametric investigations of implementation of the technology are evaluated, usually with a small number of subjects, and careful documentation of implementation parameters and results. Phase I clinical trials are the first step in establishing efficacy. Some human factors technologies have been subjected to an evaluative process similar to Phase I clinical trials. Yet the medical area regards this stage as “over-a-hurdle,” yet not finished with the race. In other words, progress in assessment to this degree is necessary, but not sufficient, to demonstrate the efficacy of the technology. Those technologies which hold promise after the close scrutiny of Phase I enter Phase II clinical trials. In Phase II clinical trials, the technology is evaluated under much of the same conditions as in Phase I, although a double-blind methodology is usually employed to render the findings with objectivity. For

[7]For more information on the distinction between basic and applied human factors research, see Chapter 2, sections 1.1 and 1.2.

technologies which demonstrate objective potential, Phase III clinical trials evaluate the technology on a much larger scale and under less-controlled conditions, those which are more typical of the use environment. Phase III clinical trials are the first step in establishing effectiveness.

This evaluative process continues, however, with parametric and case studies on sub-group effectiveness and long-term implications, evaluations which are undertaken after the technology is in wide-spread use. This is termed the "post-approval" phase, referring to approval from the Food & Drug Administration for distribution and use of the technology.

This deliberate strategy for technology building is far more complex than that typically employed within the human factors discipline. Ergonomics technologies often progress through equivalents of the pre-clinical trial phases, and may be evaluated in a manner similar to medical technologies in the post-approval phase; yet the rigors of clinical trials are unmatched in the evaluation of most ergonomic technologies.

An ergonomics technology that illustrates this progression is the keyboard wrist rest. The wrist rest (sometimes called a palm support) is a device routinely prescribed by many practicing ergonomists, as a means for maintaining a "neutral" wrist posture when typing on a keyboard. Basic research in biomechanics and medicine established that pressures within the carpal tunnel were higher when the wrist is severely flexed (c.f., Gelberman, Hergenroeder, Hargens, Lundborg & Akeson, 1981; Smith, Sonstegard, and Anderson, 1977). The reasoning followed, then, that flexion of the wrist might contribute to the development of carpal tunnel syndrome, since carpal tunnel syndrome was determined to result from pressure on the median nerve, which passes through the carpal tunnel. Observing that some keyboard users flex and/or extended their wrists while typing, the wrist rest was proposed as a means for maintaining the "neutral" wrist posture, by aligning the heel of the hand with respect to the keyboard. Theoretically, the wrist rest would solve the "problem" of wrist posture.

Without the benefit of assessment, approximating the rigors of clinical trials, wrist rests appeared on the desks of keyboard users by the thousands. In 1987, a case study was published which identified potential problems (Sauter, Chapman, Knutson, and Anderson, 1987). The case study presented evidence of injury to the pisiform and dorsal sensory branch of the ulnar nerve in a keyboard user who habitually rested her wrists against the proximal edge of the keyboard. The researchers called for further evaluation of the dynamics of wrist rest use in light of their observations, realizing that wrist rest users might be susceptible to injuries similar to the subject in their case study.

The case study published by Sauter et al. (1987) is similar to the post-approval mechanism (i.e., on-going feedback or subsequent inquiry which serves to question, refine, and/or illuminate a potential contraindication or complication that was not raised during preceding evaluative phases). Although the case study did not directly show that wrist rests were unequivocally inadvisable, it did raise questions that might have influenced the design of wrist rests, the conditions under which they might be recommended, etc. In terms of the evaluative process, this subsequent communication illustrates the relevant lack of rigor and the numerous questions left unanswered in the typical technology building process used in many disciplines, including some areas of human factors and ergonomics.

Technology assessment serves several purposes. Wolf (1992) discusses the relationship between technology assessment and utilization, favoring consideration of the findings of technology assessment in making utilization and reimbursement decisions. In his example, electromyographic biofeedback and its utilization in physical therapy, the need for demonstrating efficacy as a prerequisite to effectiveness, was shown. Wolf (1992) also alludes to the problems which result when technology assessment is lacking. Technology assessment is critical to refinement of the technology, which yields a better widget as a result. Technology assessment ensures not only the safety and well-being of potential users of the technology, it also safeguards the integrity of the discipline, by eliminating the "snake oil" and adding credence to proven technologies.

You could argue that the process of technology evaluation used in the medical area is not clearly transferable to human factors technologies. Mace (1991) describes an adaptation of clinical trials, as outlined in Table 12-1. This investigative sequence is more generic than the medical evaluation process, and Mace argues it is applicable to most applied areas.

Table 12-1: Technology Building Investigative Sequence for Assessing Human Factors Technologies

I	An initial experimental demonstration of the effects of a novel procedure or a method or process of investigation on a single subject.
II	Systematic replications that parametrically vary subject, setting, and response variables (four or five replications per experiment is probably sufficient).
III	Demonstration of the short- and long-term maintenance of the intervention effects with 4 or 5 subjects per experiment.
IV	Detailed analysis of factors predicting favorable and unfavorable responses to the intervention with several subjects (i.e., specification of the conditions necessary and sufficient for the behavioral operation to invoke the behavioral process)
V	Large-scale studies documenting the percentage effectiveness in the population and consisting of single-case experiments in numbers sufficient for accurately estimating population success rates.
VI	Large-scale studies comparing the effectiveness of alternative interventions, under optimal conditions and in numbers permitting comparative success rates in the population.

(From Mace, 1991, p. 435)

8.0 Summary

The human factors discipline has, and will likely continue to make contributions of increasing importance in the health care arena. The receptivity to human factors input by the medical community, with its pragmatic orientation, would be greatly enhanced by adherence to a more rigorous and deliberate strategy for evaluating human factors technologies. The form that this strategy should take is a major area for investigation.

Human factors researchers can make great strides in addressing problems facing the health care field, assuming due concern for methodological and evaluative issues. This chapter discussed six major areas where human factors efforts could be beneficial:

1. Mitigating or alleviating health care personnel shortages through improvements in the provider/equipment, provider/provider, and provider/patient interfaces;
2. Improving medical education and training;
3. Ameliorating medical information and communication system deficiencies;
4. Improving diagnostic and treatment equipment through performance benchmarking;
5. Assessing the effects of medical procedures and technology on behavior and performance;
6. Improving the evaluation process by integrating human factors concerns throughout.

The examples and suggested areas for pursuit outlined in this chapter are not inclusive and represent only a few illustrations of human factors achievements and needs in the medical arena. There is so much more to be done. Health care will present significant opportunities for increased human factors research and engineering efforts in the future, and may ultimately replace national defense as the driving force behind human factors engineering development and innovation.

9.0 Resources

The following information resources may provide guidance to the human factors researcher, novice and seasoned alike, in learning more about important, potential avenues to pursue. Some of the research discussed in this chapter was unpublished at the time of this writing. Therefore, information for contacting the principal investigator(s) is included, to facilitate on-going monitoring of the progress of their efforts.

9.1 Public and Private Organizations

The **Office of Technology Assessment** (OHTA) evaluates the safety and effectiveness of new or unestablished medical technologies that are being considered for coverage under federally financed health programs. OHTA publishes Health Technology Assessment Reports, which form the basis for the Public Health Service's recommendations to government health care financing agencies. These reports are available to the public once a coverage decision regarding the subject technology has been made. Copies of the reports may be obtained at no charge from the Division of Information and Publications, Agency for Health Care Policy and Research, 5600 Fishers Lane, Parklawn Building, Room 18-12, Rockville, MD 20857; Telephone: (301) 443-4100. Copies of Health Technology Assessment Reports are also available from the National Technical Information Service, Springfield, VA 22161 (703/487-4650).

The **U.S. Food and Drug Administration**, Office of Consumer Affairs Information Line can be reached at: (301) 443-3170; Unfortunately, human factors researchers will likely find the Information Line to be of limited utility, unless their request deals with information of a supplemental or general nature rather than human factors-specific inquiries. The Office of Consumer Affairs Information Line is the starting point for identifying basic FDA information resources such as press releases, consumer publications, speeches, and congressional testimony. Under the Freedom of Information Act, additional information not normally prepared for public distribution may also be available. Freedom of Information requests must be made in writing, to: U.S. Food and Drug Administration, Freedom of Information Staff (HFI-35), 5600 Fishers Lane, Rockville, MD 20857. Requests should include the requestor's name, address, and telephone number, along with a statement of the records being sought, identified as specifically as possible. Note that the Freedom of Information Act pertains only to existing records. The staff cannot compile information that is not already available and identifiable. Fees for search and review time, photocopying, microfiche, certifications, and computer charges may apply to Freedom of Information requests. Contact the Freedom of Information Staff Office for additional information on submitting a request.

The **Emergency Care Research Institute** (ECRI), is a health research institute which publishes a variety of information concerning standards and recommended practices, research reports, medical technology recalls, and hazard reports. For more information, contact ECRI at: 5200 Butler Pike, Plymouth Meeting, PA 19462; Telephone: (215) 825-6000.

Arkansas Children's Hospital has established a computer bulletin board system with the ultimate goal of linking all hospitals' biomedical engineering departments. The BBS can be used for evaluation of equipment, safety topics, job placement and parts allocation. For more information, contact: Jack Jenkins, Director, Biomedical Services, 800 Marshall Street, Little Rock, AR 72202-3591; Telephone: (501) 320-1463, or call "CHILD-LINK" at (800) 444-4124.

The **Association for the Advancement of Medical Instrumentation** (AAMI) published the *Human Factors Engineering Guidelines and Preferred Practices for the Design of Medical Devices* (ANSI/AAMI HE48—1993). Copies of the standard are available from AAMI, 3330 Washington Boulevard, Suite 400, Arlington, VA 22201-4598; Telephone: (800) 332-2264 or (703) 525-4890. The cost of the standard is $59 (or $39 for AAMI members) plus $5 postage and handling. AAMI also publishes a membership directory ($100 per copy or $20.00 for AAMI members), and numerous other standards and documents. Contact the number listed above for more information.

The **Society for Technology Assessment in Anesthesia** (STA) publishes a newsletter as a companion to the Journal of Clinical Monitoring. Several STA members are strong advocates of human factors in anesthesiology technology, and the topic has received some treatment in the STA newsletter. For more information on STA membership and publications, contact Jerry Wilhoit at (804) 379-5513.

The **International Society for Technology Assessment in Health Care** (ISTAHC) publishes the *International Journal of Technology Assessment in Health Care* and the *ISTAHC Newsletter,* and hosts an annual meeting and periodic symposia. For more information contact: ISTAHC Membership Office, Cambridge University Press, 110 Midland Avenue, Port Chester, NY 10573.

9.2 Research in Progress

For more information on the USARI Team Coordination Training Development Project for Hospital Emergency Departments, contact: Dennis K. Leedom, Ph.D., U.S. Army Research Institute, Aviation R&D Activity, Fort Rucker, AL 36362; Telephone: 205/255-5227.

For more information on *GIFIC: Graphical Interface For Information Cognition*, contact: Michael F. Lesser, M.D., Osler Medical, 930 S. Harbor City Blvd., Melbourne, FL 32901.

9.3 Publications (see also 9.1)

The works of Ericsson and Simon (1983) and Stevens (1960) referenced in this chapter, were, at the time of this writing, out of print. Nonetheless, they are available through most libraries.

9.4 Additional Information

Additional information is available upon request from the author. Inquiries may be directed to: Paula Sind-Prunier, Ph.D., ErgoMed Analytics, Inc., 5275 Babcock Street, N.E., Suite 11-138, Palm Bay, FL 32905; E-Mail (CompuServe): 73234,3104.

10.0 Biography

Paula Sind Prunier is President and Scientific Director of ErgoMed Analytics, Inc. Formerly, she was Chair of the Engineering Psychology Graduate Program at Florida Institute of Technology and was on the faculty at the University of Massachusetts—Amherst. She received her Ph.D. in Industrial Engineering & Operations Research with a specialization in Human Factors Engineering from Virginia Polytechnic Institute and State University. She holds a bachelor's degree in Industrial Psychology and an M.S. in Engineering Psychology from the University of Detroit and Florida Institute of Technology, respectively. Her primary research areas are medical device displays and controls, instrumented studies of occupational injuries, and decision-making, productivity, and user error in health care applications. Dr. Sind-Prunier serves on the ANSI/AAMI Human Engineering Standards Committee and is a member of the Association for the Advancement of Medical Instrumentation, the Human Factors and Ergonomics Society, and the International Society for Technology Assessment in Health Care.

REFERENCES

Antczak-Bouckoms, A., Burdick, E., Klawansky, S., and Mosteller, F. (1991). Using medical registries and data sets for technology assessment. *International Journal of Technology Assessment in Health Care,* 7(2), 123-128.

Association for the Advancement of Medical Instrumentation (1988). *Human Engineering Guidelines and Recommended Practices for the Design of Medical Equipment.* Alexandria, VA: AAMI.

Association for the Advancement of Medical Instrumentation (1993). *Human Factors Engineering Guidelines and Preferred Practices for the Design of Medical Devices,* (ANSI/AAMI HE48-1993). Alexandria, VA: AAMI.

Bassen, H.I. (1986). From problem reporting to technological solutions. *Medical Instrumentation,* 20(1), 17-26.

Batavia, A.I., and Hammer, G.S. (1990). Toward the development of consumer-based criteria for the evaluation of assistive devices. *Journal of Rehabilitation Research and Development,* 27(4), 425-436.

Blais, R. (1991). Using administrative data bases for technology assessment in health care. *International Journal of Technology Assessment in Health Care,* 7(2), 203-208.

Chouinard, E.F., Ryack, B.L., and Stetson, D.M. (1991). *A Comparison of Three Versions of a Computerized Medical Diagnostic Assistance Program for Abdominal Pain.* (Report No. 1172). Groton, CT: Naval Submarine Medical Research Laboratory.

Deusinger, S.S. (1992). Analyzing errors in practice: A vehicle for assessing and enhancing the quality of care. *International Journal of Technology Assessment in Health Care,* 8(1), 62-75.

Drummond, M.F., and Davies, L. (1991). Economic analysis alongside clinical trials: Revisiting the methodological issues. *International Journal of Technology Assessment in Health Care,* 7(4), 561-573.

Ericsson, K.A., and Simon, H.A. (1983). *Protocol Analysis: Verbal Reports as Data.* Cambridge, MA: MIT Press.

Evans, R.G., and Robinson, G.C. (1980). Surgical day care: Measurements of the economic payoff. *Canadian Medical Association Journal,* 123, 873-880.

Farris, D.R. (1993). *Color Ordering Stereotypes Along Ten Continuous Dimensions.* Unpublished Master's Thesis, School of Psychology, Florida Institute of Technology, Melbourne, Florida.

Gelberman, R.H., Hergenroeder, P., Hargens, A., Lundborg, G.N., and Akeson, W.H. (1981). The carpal tunnel syndrome: A study of carpal canal pressures. *Journal of Bone and Joint Surgery,* 63A(3), 380-383.

Gescheider, G.A. (1985). *Psychophysics: Method, Theory, and Application* (2nd Edition). Hillsdale, NJ: Lawrence Erlbaum Associates.

Goodman, C. (1992). It's time to rethink health care technology assessment. *International Journal of Technology Assessment in Health Care,* 8(2), 335-358.

Green, P., and Wei-Haas, L. (1985). The rapid development of user interfaces: Experience with the Wizard of Oz method. In: *Proceedings of the Human Factors Society 29th Annual Meeting,* (pp. 470-474). Santa Monica, CA: Human Factors Society.

Hähnel, J., Friesdorf, W., Schwilk, B., Marx, T., and Blessing. S. (1992). Can a clinician predict the technical equipment a patient will need during intensive care unit treatment? An approach to standardize and redesign the intensive care unit workstation. *Journal of Clinical Monitoring,* 8(1), 1-6.

Hansen, E.H. (1992). Technology assessment in a user perspective—experiences with drug technology. *International Journal of Technology Assessment in Health Care,* 8(1), 150-165.

Howse, W. (1993). *Dual-Use Team Technologies.* Briefing presented at the Department of Defense Technical Group Meeting, Biomedical Applications Subgroup, November 16, 1993, San Diego, California.

Hyman, W.A., and Schlain, L.A. (1986). User problems and medical device recalls. *Medical Instrumentation,* 20(1), 14-16.

Linstone, H.A., and Turoff, M. (1985). *The Delphi Method: Techniques and Applications.* Reading, MA: Addison-Wesley.

Lumsdon, K. (1992). Beyond tech assessment: Balancing needs, strategy. *Hospitals,* 66(15), 20-26.

Mace, F.C. (1991). Technological to a fault or faulty approach to technology development?. *Journal of Applied Behavior Analysis,* 24(3), 433-435.

Merrill, J.M., Laux, L.F., and Thornby, J.I. (1991). A measure of excessive "reliance on high technology" (RHT) in medicine and what it means. *Southern Medical Journal,* 84(1), 101-102.

Ostrander, L.E. (1986). Attention to the medical equipment user in biomedical engineering. *Medical Instrumentation,* 20(1), 3-5.

Panerai, R.B., Almeida, R.T., Portela, M.C., de Carvalho, M., Coura-Silho, O., and da Costa, T.P. (1991). Estimating the effectiveness of perinatal care technologies by expert opinion. *International Journal of Technology Assessment in Health Care,* 7(3), 367-378.

Perrotta, P., Bolecek, C., Christ, E., and Hobson, D. (1994). *Evaluation of Field Clinical Laboratory Equipment for Fleet Marine Services.* (Report No. 1191). Naval Submarine Medical Research Laboratory, Groton, Connecticut, February 2, 1994.

Rappaport, M. (1970). Human factors applications in medicine. *Human Factors,* 12(1), 25-35.

Relman, A. (1988). Assessment and accountability: The third revolution in medical care. *New England Journal of Medicine,* 319(18), 1220-1222.

Rice, V.J.B. (1990). Comparison of the effects of two antihistamines on cognitive performance, mood, and perceived performance. In: *Proceedings of the Human Factors Society 34th Annual Meeting* (pp. 598-601. Santa Monica, CA: Human Factors Society.

Rice, V.J.B. (1993a). The effects of Benadryl and Hismanal on mood, physiological measures, antihistamine detection, and subjective symptoms. *Aviation, Space & Environmental Medicine,* 64, 717-725.

Rice, V.J.B. (1993b). The effects of Benadryl and Hismanal on psychomotor performance and perceived performance. *Aviation, Space & Environmental Medicine,* 64, 726-734.

Rice, V.J.B. (1993a). The effects of Benadryl and Hismanal on psychomotor performance and perceived performance. *Aviation, Space & Environmental Medicine,* 64, 726-734.

Rice, V.J.B. (in press). Human factors and medical rehabilitation equipment: product development and usability testing. In: K. Jacobs and C. Bettencourt [Eds.], *Ergonomics for Therapists.* Stoneham, MA: Butterworths.

Roper, W.L., Winkenwerder, W., Hackbart, G., and Krakauer, H. (1988). Effectiveness in health care: An initiative to evaluate and improve medical practice. *New England Journal of Medicine,* 319(18), 1197-1202.

Sauter, S.L., Chapman, L.J., Knutson, S.J., and Anderson, H.A. (1987). Case example of wrist trauma in keyboard use. *Applied Ergonomics,* 18 (3), 183-186.

Schulte, G.T., and Block, F.E., Jr. (1992). Can people hear the pitch change on a variable-pitch pulse oximeter? *Journal of Clinical Monitoring,* 8 (3), 198-200.

Sind, P.M., and Stetson, D.M. (1991). *Human Factors Issues in the Development, Evaluation, and Deployment of a Medical Diagnostic Decision Support System for Use by Submarine Medical Corpsmen.* Briefing presented at the Department of Defense Human Factors Engineering Technical Group Meeting, Biomedical Devices Subgroup, November 4, 1991, San Antonio, TX.

Smith, E., Sonstegard, D., and Anderson, W. (1977). Contribution of flexor tendons to the carpal tunnel syndrome. *Archives of Physical Medicine and Rehabilitation,* 58, 379-385.

Snyder, H.L. (1985). Image Quality: Measures and Visual Performance. In: L. Tannas [Ed.], *Flat Panel Displays and CRTs.* New York: VanNostrand-Reinhold.

Stevens, S.S. (1960). *Handbook of Experimental Psychology.* New York: Wiley.

Thrush, D.N. (1992). Automated anesthesia records and anesthetic incidents. *Journal of Clinical Monitoring,* 8(1), 59-61.

U.S. Army Research Institute for the Behavioral & Social Sciences (1993). *Team Coordination Training Development for Hospital Emergency Departments: A Training R&D Investment for Improving Patient Care and Reducing Hospital Costs* (Brochure). Fort Rucker, AL: USARI.

U.S. Congress, Office of Technology Assessment (1976). *Development of Medical Technology: Opportunities for assessment.* Washington, DC: U.S. Government Printing Office.

U.S. Congress, Office of Technology Assessment (1982). *Strategies for Medical Technology Assessment.* Washington, DC: U.S. Government Printing Office.

Wall, R. (1991). Computer Rx: More harm than good? *Journal of Medical Systems,* 15(5/6), 321-334.

Weaver, R.R. (1991). Assessment and diffusion of computerized decision support systems. *International Journal of Technology Assessment in Health Care,* 7(1), 42-50.

Wolf, S.L. (1992). The relationship of technology assessment and utilization: Electromyographic feedback instrumentation as a model. *International Journal of Technology Assessment in Health Care,* 8(1), 102-108.

Zimny, N.J. (1992). Making information accessible and useful to practicing clinicians: Problem-knowledge coupling. *International Journal of Technology Assessment in Health Care,* 8(1), 109-117.

Chapter 13
Military Systems Techniques

William F. Moroney
University of Dayton

Alvah C. Bittner, Jr
Battelle

1.0 Overview

The interaction between HFE and DOD has historically been synergistic. Indeed, as reported by Christensen (1987, p.5):

> **". . .to their credit, it was the authorities in the Department of Defense who first actively supported the human factors profession. Even today many industries are not yet at the stage of development with respect to human factors that DOD was a generation ago."**

This chapter provides a broad overview of selected areas in which Human Factors Engineering (HFE) personnel from a variety of disciplines have supported the acquisition, development, and deployment of a wide variety of military systems. Most of the efforts described were performed by the DOD or funded by the DOD within the last three to five years. We elected to report on what we consider to be the major contributions by HFE personnel to military systems. This chapter is not intended to be comprehensive, but rather to provide the reader with a sense of the breadth and tools of military HFE research. Selected areas, to which DOD has contributed significantly, such as advanced displays and Human Computer Interaction (HCI) are not addressed at all because of their clear overlap with the civilian sector and their coverage in other chapters in this text (e.g. Chapter 10). Similarly, readers are referred to other chapters in this text for details on the DOD's contributions in areas such as training and teamwork (see Chapter 14) and aerospace (see Chapter 5). DOD's historical interaction with HFE has been discussed earlier in Chapter 1. Because of its complexity, the acquisition process will not be addressed; interested readers can consult Driskell and Olmstead (1989) or the developing Smart Contract Preparation Environment (SCOPE) described by McCommons and Cofod (1992).

We hope that this chapter will allow you to:

1. Appreciate the uniqueness of military HFE
2. Understand the DOD's emphasis on systems
3. Become familiar with experimental design/statistical issues unique to DOD
4. Become familiar with selected DOD areas of interest
5. Be informed of selected HFE technology/tools
6. Better understand the unique environments in which DOD's personnel work
7. Appreciate the DOD's concern regarding the use of human subjects
8. Access a bibliography which identifies critical DOD reports in selected areas
9. Identify key DOD HFE organizations
10. Become more aware of some of the DOD's contributions to the civilian sector
11. Have a sense for DOD's future direction

Military Human Factors Engineering is both the most diverse and challenging area of HFE; it is also the area which has contributed most to the development of human factors. HFE within the Department of Defense (DOD) has but one focus: Performance. In wartime, combat performance is the focal point; in peacetime, readiness to perform in combat is the focal point. The Departments of the Army, Navy and Air Force (and in wartime the Coast Guard) are always on duty and must be ready to respond. Within the United States, that performance is delivered by systems operated by members of an all-volunteer force. Performance is expected from personnel with diverse backgrounds in a wide variety of environments. Let's build a context by briefly examining two scenarios: an aircraft carrier and rapid deployment troops.

1.1 The Aircraft Carrier

An aircraft carrier is a nuclear powered, transportable airfield, operated by approximately 5000 personnel. This airfield has the maintenance facilities/personnel for a variety of high performance airplanes and helicopters and their sophisticated sensors and communication equipment. The airfield, with 1100 feet of runway, four catapults, and four arresting wires is expected to operate 24 hours a day in frigid North Atlantic gales and sweltering Indian Ocean calm. Like all airports, it has its own fire, police, and medical departments. However, unlike most airports, it has conventional and nuclear weapons and provides food and housing for its employees. The vessel can remain at sea almost indefinitely because it is constantly resupplied by tankers, ammunition and refrigeration ships. The crews must perform as a professional team to meet mission demands while under considerable psychological and physical stress for an indefinite period of time. They are exposed to combinations of stressors including: acceleration, noise, heat, cold, hazardous material, toxic fumes, radiation, and the dangers of working at sea and on a flight deck. Aircrew are exposed to these hazards as well as to those peculiar to aviation: vertigo, loss of situational awareness, and the high stress associated with night carrier landings. Finally, carrier personnel realize their "home" is the prize target.

1.2 Rapid Deployment Forces.

Given varying amounts of lead time (more often short than long), soldiers may be transported by air from the southeastern United States to any trouble spot and expected to perform. Within a few hours, they may suddenly be confronted with mountain sickness and frostbite or heat and dehydration. Ground soldiers may be expected to perform in protective clothing that stores body heat, restricts movement, inhibits communication, and reduces visibility. Armor crews will be exposed to noise, vibration, and propellant gases. Airborne troops will experience forces that may induce motion sickness as they are transported to landing zones in terrain-following helicopters. Finally, all of these individuals may be required to engage in round-the-clock comba, using night vision and infrared devices. Military personnel must perform for indeterminate periods under circumstances and in environments which are unmatched in the civilian sector.

Military personnel are expected to receive an input, correctly analyze the situation, and execute an appropriate output under a wide variety of stressors. Not the least which is the enemy's attempts to deny or confuse that input, disrupt the analysis, and prevent the execution of the appropriate response. To properly execute its combat readiness mission, the DOD must be constantly at the leading edge of technology. However, this technology must be operable and maintainable by members of the all-volunteer force. Given the capabilities of some modern systems, the human operator has often been portrayed as the system's "limiting factor". However, the unique contributions of humans to systems cannot be ignored; indeed with weapon systems, the ability of a human operator to intervene is crucial. In recognition of these facts, the DOD has institutionalized (DODINST 5000.2. 1991a and b) the activities of HFE personnel in the research, development, test, and evaluation (RDT&E) of systems (also see Chapter 1).

2.0 Uniqueness of the Military

The DOD is the mother of all corporate giants. It is an organization of 1.7 million active duty, 1.0 million full time Guard and Reserve personnel, and 854,000 civilian personnel[1] with a 1992 fiscal year budget of $278 billion according to the General Accounting Office (GAO, 1992a). However, unlike other corporate giants, its productivity and effectiveness are not measured by the number of units produced or profit margins. DOD's mission is to maintain the security of the United States and support national policy. DOD's bottom line is mission accomplishment.

[1] Data provided by the Department of Defense Manpower Data Center are current as of May 1993.

2.1 Systems Considerations

The DOD is perhaps the world's major developer of new systems. Requiring as much as seven years for development, these usually expensive systems are designed to respond to a threat or to use more efficient and effective technology. Sometimes the orderly development process may be complicated or redirected by changes in knowledge about an adversary's capabilities or intentions, funding levels, or national priorities. Despite these, the DOD needs highly reliable systems (including people) to accomplish its mission. Indeed, given the rapid pace of modern warfare, DOD personnel may get only one opportunity to accomplish their mission.

When the total life cycle cost of a weapon system is examined, the importance of considering individual operators and maintainers early in the system development process becomes apparent. Graine (1988) reported that approximately 60 percent of the weapon system life cycle costs are related to people or training requirements. Consequently considerable savings can be attained if the design requirements specify: 1) reduced crew sizes and 2) a reduction in the skill level required to operate and maintain the system.

2.2 Personnel/Selection Considerations

Driskell and Olmstead (1989, p.46) describe the military as "*the largest employer of initially unskilled labor in the nation*". Unlike civilian organizations, the DOD rarely hires personnel with the required skills. Rather, selection batteries such as the Armed Services Vocational Appitude Battery (ASVAB) and follow-on selection tests are used to identify individuals with the required aptitudes and abilities to meet organizational needs. They are then trained and assigned to appropriate positions. Most individuals will serve only three to six years, after which they return to the civilian sector. Other individuals, who receive specialized training (pilots, nuclear power personnel, military academy graduates), commit themselves for somewhat longer periods. Thus, there is often only a short period during which an individual's training can be amortized. These factors, combined with DOD's 'Up or Out' policy (be promoted or be put out) accounts for DOD's very high turnover rate. During Fiscal Year (FY) 1992, 202,464 personnel joined DOD while 335,276 departed DOD. The number of entering personnel is 83,096 fewer than the number recruited during FY 1988, and 29,071 fewer than the number recruited in 1990. This decline can be clearly attributed to the reduction in DOD manpower requirements. Furthermore, the number departing is inflated by the early-out program for career personnel.

In addition to decreases in the number of personnel entering and increases in the number departing the Armed Forces, DOD must also be concerned with the quality of the personnel it recruits. Since the demise of the draft, the military has become an all-volunteer force and therefore must compete with the civilian employment market for personnel. The services prefer to recruit high school graduates, however when they are not available, individuals who have not completed high school may be accepted.

The criticality of proper selection becomes apparent when the cost of specialized training is examined. Driskell and Olmstead (1989) report that the Air Force trains 1,600 new pilots and 750 new navigators yearly, at a cost of $1.3 million for each EF-111 pilot and $700,000 navigator.

2.3 Training Considerations[2]

The Department of Defense is the world's largest school with a broad curriculum. It employs unique pedagogical techniques, relying heavily on simulation, because simulation:

- is less expensive (Stinger missiles cost $60,000 each; armor piercing tank rounds cost $1964 each; and 120mm training rounds cost $737 each)
- is safer
- does not consume assets
- reduces wear and tear on real equipment
- has significantly less environmental impact than real combat.

The importance and validity of simulation was confirmed in a GAO (1992b) report on training for Operation Desert Storm. Their report attributed success to both the emphasis on individual/ small unit and battle staff training in command and control. Details on this simulation technology are delineated in Alluisi's (1991) history of the development of SIMNET (Simulation Networking). But not all training can be accomplished in simulators. Ranges such as the 200,000 acre maneuvering training area at the National Training Center where real wind driven sand abrades personnel and equipment, systems are exposed to heat and cold, and equipment must be operated, maintained and repaired in the field are essential to maintaining mission effectiveness.

Considering the large investment in training, the emphasis of DOD sponsored training research on "reducing training time and cost and increasing training effectiveness (Driskell and Olmstead (1989, p 48)" is to be expected. Additional details on DOD training and training systems are described in Chapter 14 and are available from MATRIS[3].

2.4 Military Personnel

The DOD is not a microcosm of U.S. society, differing from it in many significant ways, as illustrated in the following tables. Table 13-1 provides data describing the total number of personnel within each branch of the military and the percentages of each gender in each branch.

---

[2] For more information on performing research in the area of training and training effectiveness, see Chapter 14.

[3] Details on Manpower and Training research are also available from MATRIS (Manpower and Training Research System), DTIC-DMA, San Diego, CA 921152-6800 or by calling (619) 553-7000. MATRIS also publishes a useful directory listing DOD researchers in the area of Manpower, Personnel, Training and Human Factors.

Table 13-1. Gender Distribution of Active Duty Military

Service	% Male	% Female	Total Number
Army	87.70	12.30	580,073
Navy	89.49	10.51	510,029
Air force	85.12	14.88	444,542
Marine	95.58	4.42	179,456
Total	88.39	11.61	1,714,100

(Based on May 1993 Data)

In the immediate future, the total number of personnel can be expected to decrease while the percent of females will likely increase. Not only does DOD differ from U.S. society in gender, but also in racial mix (Table 13-2).

Table 13-2. Racial Distribution of Active Duty Military

Service	% White	% Black	Other	Unknown
Army	64.16	27.97	7.72	.15
Navy	77.15	16.48	6.21	.16
Air force	81.03	14.84	4.12	.00
Marine	75.13	17.00	7.86	.01

(Based on May 1993 Data)

Finally, an examination of the age distribution of active duty DOD personnel (Table 13-3) reveals that the DOD is primarily an organization of young personnel. On the basis of these data, it is clear that DOD active duty military personnel are not representative of U.S. society. Moroney and Reising (1991) have cautioned against the inappropriate use of data reported in human factors and ergonomics research. That same caution also applies to generalizing from data based on DOD personnel to the population in general.

Table 13-3. Age Distribution of Active Duty Military

Service	Mean	Mode	Median	Standard Deviation
Army	28.23	22	27	7.48
Navy	28.01	22	26	7.30
Air force	29.83	22	29	7.28
Marine	25.58	21	23	6.37
Overall	28.30	22	27	7.34

(Based on May 1993 Data)

2.5 Funding of Human Factor Engineering Related Activities

Unlike other organizations, the DOD maintains a budget line for HF research and development (R&D). The related congressional budget categories are: education and training, human factors, manpower and personnel, and simulation and training devices. In 1992, 54.9, 76.0, 29.6 and 129.1 million dollars were allocated to these areas respectively for a total of 289.6 million dollars. In 1993, a total of 304.3 million dollars were planned for allocation. To put these number in context, in 1987 almost 400 million dollars had been allocated, while in 1990, only about 290 million was allocated.[4] Driskell and Olmstead (1989) provided a detailed description of the budgeting process and listed the major behavioral science R&D organizations in the DOD. An updated listing is included as Tables 13-5, 13-6, and 13-7 (**Note:** In addition to these R&D organizations, HFE personnel are also employed by non-R&D programs associated with emerging systems or the upgrading of existing systems. Many of these personnel are engaged in system testing and evaluation (T&E)).

2.6 Human Factor Engineering's Areas of Responsibility

HFE researchers supporting DOD examine many of the same dependent variables (i.e. reaction time, speed, accuracy, frequency) as do their non-DOD counterparts. Often, however, these variables are couched in operational terms such as time-on-target, rounds on target, convergence time, number of targets detected/recognized/identified, etc. Likewise, some of the independent variables addressed by human factors personnel are also common to both groups: levels of temperature, humidity, and noise. However, some are unique and include not only wider ranges of the previously listed independent variables but also unique accelerative forces, radiation environments, sustained operations (well in excess of the civilian eight hour workday), and stress. Given these requirements, the DOD maintains unique facilities in which the effects of stressors can be evaluated. These facilities, for both basic and applied research, include shipboard motion simulators, man-rated centrifuges, linear accelerators, dynamic flight simulators, hypobaric and hyperbaric chambers, heat and cold chambers, etc. In addition to using these facilities, HF researchers, often as team members, are expected to apply their research skills in the not-so-neat operational world where data are often gathered during operations on a 'not-to-interfere-basis'. Military personnel often work in harsh environments at the leading edge of technology, and supporting HFE personnel must also be capable of applying their talents there.

---

[4] Based on data provided by MATRIS, dated 24 July 1992.

Table 13-5. Major Human Factors Research and Development Organizations in the Army[5]

Organization	HF Point of Contact	Areas of Responsibility
U.S. Army Research Institute for the Behavioral and Social Sciences	ATTN: PERI-PO 5001 Eisenhower Ave. Alexandria, VA 22333-5600	Manpower and Personnel; Education and Training; Simulation and Training Devices
U.S. Army Research Laboratory	Human Research & Engineering Directorate ATTN: AMSRL-HR Aberdeen Proving Ground, MD 21005-5001	Human Engineering; Manpower & Personnel; Training; System Safety; Health Hazards; Soldier Survivability; Robotics
U.S. Army Research Institute of Environmental Medicine	Commander U.S. Army Natrick RD&E Center Building 42 Natick, MA 01760	Impact of environmental stress on human health and performance
Walter Reed Army Institute of Research	ATTN: Information Office Washington, DC 20307-5100	Performance Measurement
U.S. Army Aeronautical Research Laboratory	P.O. Box 577 Fort Rucker, AL 36362-5000	Medical, Physiological, and Psychological research related to aviation

Table 13-6. Major Human Factors Research and Development Organizations in the Air Force[5]

Organization	HF Point of Contact	Areas of Responsibility
Armstrong Laboratory	Human Resources Directorate (AL/HR) 7909 Lindbergh Dr. Brooks AFB, TX 78235-5340	Logistics, Human Factors, Manpower & Personnel, Technical Training, Aircrew Training and Simulation devices
Armstrong Laboratory	Crew Systems Directorate (AL/CF) 2610 7th St. WPAFB, OH 45433-7901	Human Factors, Biodynamics, Biocommunication, Protective Equipment
USAF School of Aerospace Medicine	USAFSAM/EDB Aerospace Physiology Branch Education Division USAF School of Aerospace Medicine Brooks AFB, TX 78235-5301	Medical issues related to aviation
Air Force Office of Scientific Research	Director of Life Sciences Boiling AFB, DC 20332-6448	Neuroscience, Perception, Cognition, Spatial Awareness

[5]Updated from Driskell & Olmstead (1989) in *American Psychologist*. Some organizations are in the process of being consolidated and the names may change.

Table 13-7. Major Human Factors Research and Development Organizations in the Navy[5]

Organization	HF Point of Contact	Areas of Responsibility
Office of Naval Research	CODE 342 800 N. Quincy Arlington, VA 22217-5660	Basic Research in Cognitive Science, Perceptual Science, and Computational Neuroscience
Office of Naval Research	CODE 461 800 N. Quincy Street Arlington, VA 22217-5660	Applied Research in Manpower and Personnel, Human Factors, Education and Training, and Simulation and Training Devices
Navy Personnel Research and Development Center	Technical Information Office Code 04 San Diego, CA 92152-7250	Manpower and Personnel, Education and Training, Logistics
Naval Command Control and Ocean Surveillance Center	RDT&E Division 44 53370 Silvergate Ave San Diego, CA 92152-5146	Command and Control Systems, Decision Support Systems, HCI, Advanced Displays, Simulation and Modeling
Naval Aviation Systems Command	Crew Systems 5313 1421 Jefferson Davis Hwy Arlington, VA 22243-5310	Human Engineering, Aviation Psychology, Environmental Effects, Crew Survivability
Naval Air Weapons Center Aircraft Division	Crew Systems NAS Patuxent River, MD 20670-5304	Human Factors, Air Vehicle Systems, Biodynamics, Protective Equipment, Aeromedical Issues
Naval Air Weapons Center Training Systems Division	Human Systems Integration 12350 Research Parkway Orlando, FL 32826-3224	Simulation & Training Systems Team Training & Performance Training Technology
Naval Air Weapons Center Weapons Division	Crew Interface Systems NAS China Lake, CA 93555-6000	Airborne Weapon Systems, Modeling, Decision Making
Naval Health Research Center	Chief Scientist (001) P.O. Box 85122 San Diego, CA 92138-9174	Biomedical and Psychological Aspects of Personnel Health and Performance
Naval Aerospace Medical Research Laboratory	Naval Aerospace Medical Research Laboratory NAS Pensacola, FL 32508-5700	Human factors Aviation Psychology Human Performance
Naval Biodynamics Laboratory	Attn: Commanding Officer P.O. Box 29407 New Orleans, LA 70189-0407	Biomechanics, Impact Acceleration

2.7 Support for a Human Factors Engineering Technical Group

Since 1976, the DOD Human Factors Engineering Technical Group (DODHFETG) has functioned as the DOD chartered mechanism for the exchange of current technical information in human factors engineering. Both the Chairperson and the biannual meeting sites are rotated among the services. Other agencies (such as NASA, FAA, and NTSB) have also participated in DODHFETG exchanges as have industry and professional societies (HFES, AIAA, IEEE, APA, among others). Over the years, a number of subgroups have emerged and have been dissolved to meet changing needs. At the November 1992 meeting, the DODHFETG Steering Committee (Miles, Deaton and Loose, 1992) proposed that the subgroups be broken into three tracks: Applications, Technology and Support:

- The Applications Subgroup would be comprised of Systems Safety and Health Hazards; Human Systems Integration; Acquisition; and Design.
- The Technology Subgroup would be comprised of Sustained Operations; User Computer Interaction and Controls and Displays; Biomedical Devices; Workload; and Manned Systems Modeling.
- The Support Subgroup would be comprised of Aviation Screening; Technical Coordinating Papers; Technical Society/Industry; and Test and Evaluation.

The titles of these groups indicate both the breadth of the interest and the responsibilities of the DODHFETG. The DODHFETG has produced a variety of products in addition to the tri-service exchanges, which occur at these meetings. These include reports on "Hot Issues" in DOD human factors, a Military Standard on Task Performance Analysis (MIL-STD-1478), a proceedings document (Reeves and Gadolin, 1989) on sustained/continuous operations (SUSOPS), two volumes on SUSOPS methodology and instrumentation edited by Sidowski (1985a and 1985b). The HFEDODTG also revised and reduced the number of human factors contract Data Item Descriptions. Finally the DODHFETG provides a ready point of contact for the HF Standardization Steering Committee which promulgates standards within the DOD.

2.8 Development of Specifications and Standards

The DOD, in its systems development role, has developed a series of contractually binding documents, assorted standards, and guidelines[6]. These address products as diverse as aircraft materials, food quality, drawing practices, and soldering. Presently, the DOD Human Factors Standardization Area includes 18 military standards and four military handbooks.[7] According

---

[6]The military documents listed in this section are listed in the reference section under the Department of Defense.

[7]Copies of these documents may be obtained for a nominal fee from the Standardization Documents Order Desk, Building D, 700 Robbins Avenue, Philadelphia, PA 19111-5094.

to Birt and Chaikin (1993), human factors design standards within the DOD originated during the late 1950s based on the same sources as those cited in the initial *Human Engineering Guide to Equipment Design* (Morgan, Cook, Chapanis & Lund, 1963). Basically, human factors Military Standards establish technical requirements for (1) HFE procedures, practices, and methods and (2) human engineering design criteria. Perhaps the most frequently referenced document is MIL-STD-1472 (presently in its fourth "D" update): *Human Engineering Design Criteria for Military Systems, Equipment and Facilities.* MIL-STD-1472 provides detailed requirements for the following areas:

- control/display integration
- visual and audio displays
- controls
- labeling
- anthropometry
- workspace design
- environmental factors
- designing for maintainers
- designing for remote handling
- hazards and safety
- aerospace vehicle compartments
- user-computer interface and visual display terminals.

Military standards have also been developed to establish and define requirements for applying human engineering to the development and acquisition of systems. Sometimes these are referred to as "tasking" or "programmatic" documents. The primary military standard used as a tasking document for acquisitions is MIL-H-46855: *Human Engineering Requirements for Military Systems, Equipment and Facilities.* MIL-H-46855[8] specifies HFE efforts in analysis (e.g. functional, information flow, task, workload), design, and test and evaluation. Military handbooks provide supplemental guidance that expands on information contained in MIL-STDs. The four HFE Military handbooks are:

- DOD-HDBK-743: *Anthropometry of US Military Personnel*
- DOD-HDBK 759: *Human Factors Engineering Design of Army Material*
- DOD-HDBK-763: *Human Engineering Procedures Guide*
- DOD-HDBK-761: *Human Engineering Guidelines for Management Information Systems*

[8] MIL-H-46855 is currently being changed into MIL-STD-46855.

Some of the documents cited above have been seminal documents used by other agencies in developing their own HFE standards (e.g. NASA-STD-3000, DOE-STD-HFAC-1) and by non-governmental organizations (AAMI-HE-88, ASTM-F1166) to meet their needs. In addition, DOD's HFE related literature is well represented in other non-DOD documents including the recently (1992) developed American National Standards Institute (ANSI) *Guide to Human Performance Measurements*. This information transfer process works both ways, for currently DOD is considering adopting ANSI/HFS-100-1988: *Standard for Human Factors Engineering of Visual Display Terminal Workstations*.

2.9 Crew System Ergonomics Information Analysis Center (CSERIAC)

The DOD sponsored CSERIAC, located at Wright Patterson Air Force Base (WPAFB) and managed by the Human Engineering Division of the USAF Armstrong Laboratory, address issues well beyond specifications, standards, and handbooks. Unlike archival based bibliographic research services that provide only abstracts and copies of referenced material, CSERIAC collects, reviews, analyzes, appraises, summarizes, and disseminates information related specifically to ergonomics and human factors. CSERIAC also performs technology assessments and critical reviews and provides a variety of other services including developing handbooks, State Of The Art Reports (SOARs), workshops, symposia, and short courses. Additionally, CSERIAC is responsible for maintaining and disseminating HFE related computer-aided design (CAD) operator models including COMBIMAN and CREW CHIEF, which are used in cockpit design and designing for maintainability, respectively. These CAD packages have been distributed to over 90 commercial users. COMBIMAN has been provided to commercial users including Boeing, IBM, Lockheed, McDonnell, and Sikorsky. CREWCHIEF has been provided to the companies cited previously and Allison Gas Turbines, Garrett, GE, Martin-Marietta, Texas Instruments, and others. Other models and software include the Subjective Workload Assessment Technique (SWAT), the Criterion Task Set (CTS), and the Psychophysiological Assessment Test System (PATS). As a focal point for HFE information, CSERIAC investigators provide not only rapid turn-around, but often perform the invaluable networking function of linking the individual who has the HFE concern with the appropriate experts. CSERIACS's SOARs provide a medium that focuses on specific topics of current concern to the HFE community. Recent SOARs include: *Naturalistic Decision Making* (Klein, 1993), *Human Factors Issues in Head-Up Display Design: The Book of HUD* (Weintraub and Ensing, 1992), *Hypertext: Prospects and Problems for Crew System Design* (Glushko, 1991). CSERIAC products and services are available on a cost-recovery basis to both government and non-government organizations.[9]

---

[9] Readers interested in utilizing CSERIAC's services can contact the CSERIAC Program Office at AL/CFH/CSERIAC, Bldg 248, 2255 H St, WPAFB, OH 45433-7022 or call (513) 255-4842.

3.0 System Development

DOD directives mandate consideration of the human operator/ maintainer domains as discussed earlier (See Chapter 1). The Army's MANPRINT (MANPower INTegration) program reflects the intent of these directives. The MANPRINT philosophy and doctrine, described by Booher (1990), embodies the following elements:

1. Provide high level visibility for people-oriented concepts
2. Multidisciplinary view of design;
3. Quantification of operator/maintainer variables;
4. Provide trade-offs early in design;
5. Communicate in the decision maker's language;
6. Ultimately reduce the demand for manpower, personnel, and training.

Critical to the success of the MANPRINT program has been the formal institutionalization of the process into policy documents. This must be strongly supported by an educational process to convince Army personnel that MANPRINT is of value to them and is an inherent part of the system development process, not an appendage. MANPRINT goals include: identifying factors that encourage human error; identifying trade-offs early in the design process; reducing manpower, personnel, and training costs; and redirecting resources rather than increasing the demand for resources. The critical question (Miles, 1976), that MANPRINT strives to answer is:

Can this soldier (...), with this training (...), perform these tasks (...) to these standards (...) under these conditions (...)?

Answering this question requires system developers to clearly identify the elements needed to complete each of the (...) sections. For example, what are the characteristics of the soldier? What are his/her strength limitations? What are the aptitudes and abilities of the intended system users?

3.1 Selected Systems

The following sections will briefly describe three ARMY systems that have used or are using the MANPRINT philosophy and doctrine. The first system is the T-800 turbine engine used in Army helicopters. In the awarding process, the integration of MANPRINT (including reliability, maintainability, and logistics support) into the development process was weighted at 25 percent of the evaluation for contract award (Weand, 1989). As a result of intensive use of MANPRINT analytical tools, supported by practical verification, the final product attained reliability and maintainability standards exceeding those standards specified in the requirements document without requiring any new maintenance skills or special tools. Some of the significant improvements included: reduction in the number of maintenance tools required at the user level from 134 tools to 6 common hand tools;

development of a single electrical harness with clearly coded connectors; reduction in the total number of maintenance tasks; consistent use of captive fasteners; and elimination of safety wiring and cotter pins (Weand and Thagard, 1989). Use of the MANPRINT approach in the design process has also given the engine manufacturer's a more competitive position in the commercial engine market.

The second system is the RAH-64 Comanche, which uses two T-800 engines. Hamilton and Metzler (1992) describe the evolution of the crewstation and avionics integration. They attribute much of the success in cockpit development to the use of MANPRINT procedures coupled with the development of a Pilot-Vehicle Interface Mechanism Specification (PIVMS). The PIVMS served as a focal point where requirements, analysis, and implementation documents could be simultaneously reviewed and evaluated. The development of the PIVMS required detailed mission analysis; use of cognitive engineering in evaluating crew expectancies; integration of crew protection; lighting, ingress/egress and anthropometric concerns; development of appropriate menu structures; task analysis; and workload prediction. Use of the PIVMS allowed early involvement and review by Army personnel and was a means of effecting changes at an early stage in system development. In the Comanche program, there were over 500 instances in which MANPRINT technology contributed directly to the success of the design.

Finally, in a more recent development, the Army awarded a contract valued at $30 billion for the Light Helicopter (LH) program. According to the program manager, while both competitors were very close in their technical and producibility proposals, the deciding factors were costs, reliability, maintainability, logistics support, training and man-machine interfaces. These factors accounted for 55% of the scoring of the development proposals (Bond, 1991). In describing some of the HFE considerations regarding the development of the LH, Kandeno (1991) reported that the vehicle can be supported by approximately 60 percent of the manpower currently required. Maintenance innovations included: extensive use of doors as work platforms; use of line replaceable avionics modules which are only one module deep; and the use of a portable intelligent maintenance aid to identify maintenance needs. Innovative changes, affecting the pilot, include the elimination of rudder (yaw) pedals, by using a sidearm controller, which is twisted for yaw control.

The importance of attending to MANPRINT requirements and the financial rewards associated with doing so are apparent to those organizations developing the systems described above. Indeed, MANPRINT's formalized user-centered process is very compatible with the philosophies of both Total Quality Management (TQM) and Concurrent Engineering. Booher (1993) argues that MANPRINT offers these approaches " ... a way of defining quantitatively what the real user requirements are, and a process for assuring that the disciplines, technology and requirements drive every technology and system designer to produce the best product possible" (p11). Some manufacturers who have seen that MANPRINT can improve their profit margin and market share have modified their organizations to incorporate parts of the MANPRINT philosophy. Recently, the Ministry of the Defence in the United Kingdom mandated the use of MANPRINT by all services. According to Booher (1993), several U.S. government organizations are evaluating or selectively adopting the MANPRINT approach. The Food and Drug Administration is studying the MANPRINT model as an aid in improving regulation of medical devices[10]. Using the MANPRINT model, the FAA has developed a human factors program with both a research component and an applications component. The FAA is also institutionalizing the MANPRINT process so that its emphasis on human factors is clearly reflected in agency strategies, policy, processes, training, and infrastructure. Many of the details of this implementation are addressed in detail in the National Plan for Aviation Human Factors (FAA, 1991). The Nuclear Regulatory Commission is also selectively applying some MANPRINT techniques to better regulate nuclear power plants.

3.2 Test and Evaluation

Today, DOD Testing and Evaluation (T&E) personnel are involved in all phases of product development (Meister, 1985, 1986; Bittner, 1993). The current involvement of T&E personnel from specification of criteria through operational deployment has been described by Meister (1985, 1986). Integral to these works is the common emphasis on measurement, in all its forms of who, what, when, where, how and why.

An excellent, more recent, HFE T&E document, detailing current procedures has been prepared for the Army Test and Evaluation Command by Carlow International (1990). This document delineates procedures for the testing of design, functional performance, and environmental considerations for the functions of operability, maintainability, transportability, portability, useability, erectability, and habitability. The two volume document also provides both test planning guidance as well as test procedures including sample data collection forms, questionnaires, checklists, etc.

Reflecting T&E's critical role in systems development are efforts such as those contained in Volume 34 # 4 of *Human Factors* (1992) edited by Meister and Enderwick, and *Ergonomics in Design* (Bittner,1993).

3.3 Statistical and Methodological Issues

HFE practitioners frequently face research problems that challenge the adequacy of many experimental and statistical methods (Meister, 1986, 1989; Bittner, 1992). The following sections will: characterize the most problematic aspects of research related to system development, delineate "robust" approaches and methods for addressing these research design and analysis

---

[10] For more information on human factors research on medical devices, see Chapter 12.

challenges, and consider some broader, collective implications of these challenges. These design and analysis methods, and associated implications, will interest researchers with similar challenges.

3.3.1 Challenge of system development related investigations. HFE practitioners are frequently challenged on three fronts. Simultaneously, they must deal with: "qualified subject limitiations", "testbed" availability, and situational demand characteristics and the flexibility of humans operating military systems.

3.3.1.1 Qualified subject limitations. The numbers of available subjects are frequently limited (e.g., $\underline{N}s \leq 5$) by the nature of the research environment (e.g., hazardous environmental research requires highly screened, "medically qualified" volunteers) and/or specialized training requirements (e.g., the evaluation of high performance aircraft requires "Test Pilot School" graduates). The numbers of available subjects are often substantially less than the numbers of equipment, environmental, or other conditions ($\underline{K}$) to be investigated: ($\underline{N} < \underline{K}$).

3.3.1.2 Testbed availability limitations. The testbed in which research must be conducted is often limited by the available windows-of-opportunity (e.g., "piggy-back" tests of new equipment during a once-a-year field exercise) and costs-of-operation (e.g., $1,000-to-$100,000/hour for multiple person and unit simulation facilities). Compounding these limitations are testbed equipment breakdowns that often reduce availability within the windows-of-opportunity and the planned data collections periods (cf., Bittner, 1992, p. 478-479).

3.3.1.3 Situational demand characteristics (Performance Flexibility). Performance, in military system studies, may often be maintained by participants via: (1) increased mental and physical efforts (up to some level of tolerable "workload") and/or (2) by strategy shifts. In studies comparing system alternatives or environmental stressors (e.g, hours of sleep loss), for example, test participants often exert themselves to obtain the best possible performance from inadequate systems or under increased stressors (reflecting the so-called "can-do attitude")[11]. Consequently, performance results may show statistically meager differences while corresponding participant "workload" variations are relatively massive (Lysaght et al., 1989, Bittner, 1992).

Both the "subject" and "testbed" limitations have directly promoted the widespread application of repeated-measures methods, i.e., within-subjects designs and statistical analysis (Campbell and Stanley, 1963; Greenwald, 1976; Winer, Brown and Michels, 1991). Qualified subject limitations, in

---

[11] The Hawthorne effect is a threat to experimental validity which occurs when subjects behave differently than they normally would, because they "suspect" or know that they are the subject of an experiment. For more information on the Hawthorne effect, see Chapter 2, Section 5.2.3.

particular, have promoted use of such methods by promising appropriately powerful statistical comparisons of many conditions using few subjects (cf., Bramwell,Bittner and Morrissey, 1992). Limited "testbed" availability also has promoted use of repeated-measures as a means to maximize sensitivity within available time and funding resources (Bittner, 1992). Because of their statistical power, repeated-measures studies[12] are the method-of-choice even when performance flexibilities may be an issue, because of the unique opportunities for statistically identifying strategy shifts (Bramwell, Bittner and Morrissey, 1992; Bittner and Bramwell, 1992). These promises of repeated-measures methods have consequently led to their widespread use in diverse military HFE applications. Repeated-measures methods have been illustrated in studies of environmental effects on performance (e.g., altitude by Banderet et al., 1992), training effectiveness and prediction (Lane, Kennedy and Jones, 1986), and differing equipment configurations (Charlton, 1992).

The widespread use of repeated-measures methods has been accompanied by an emerging appreciation of both their special "problems"[13] and robust methods to overcome these problems (Alveres and Hulin, 1972; Bittner et al., 1986; Lane et al., 1986; Morrissey et al., 1990; Bramwell, Bittner and Morrissey, 1992; Bittner, 1992). Although emerging from the challenging context of military human factors investigations, these problems and methods impact and offer promise for other domains of human factors research. Three of the most challenging repeated-measures problems are delineated in the following subsections. These problems are: Practice Effects, Carry-Over and Sensitization Effects, and Situational Demand Characteristics (performance flexibility).

3.3.2.1.1 Practice effects. Subjects can be expected to change their behavior with practice even when not exposed to any treatment conditions. For example, Bittner, Carter, Kennedy, Harbeson and Krause (1986) report that when more than 114 measures were repeatedly administered over 15 working days, without any manipulations of system variables, systematic changes were generally observed daily in:

- Mean Performance. There was typically an early non-linear period of improvement, followed by a more linear "stable' period (often apparently during an approach to an asymptote). Not surprisingly, mean performance curves were typical of "learning curves."
- Standard Deviations. Standard deviations were often, but not always, correlated with the daily means. The daily standard deviations usually became stable (constant) after a period of practice.

---

[12]For more information on repeated measures designs, see Chapter 3, Section 3.2.2.2.

[13]For more information on the problems associated with repeated measures designs, see Chapter 2, Section 5.1 and 5.2.

- Differential-Content (Context Effect). Changes in differential-content (i.e., changes in the nature of what-is-being-measured) were indicated by systematic changes in the between-day correlations across subjects (adjacent days being typically more correlated than non-adjacent days early in practice). Such changes could be due to either: 1) progressive changes in the mix of abilities used for a task, or 2) more-or-less permanent differential changes in the subjects' basic capabilities, with the mix remaining constant (Alveres & Hulin, 1972).[14] Bittner, Carter, Kennedy, Harbeson and Krause (1986) found that differential-content (what-is-being-measured) would become "stable" after a period of practice (reflected by a constant correlation between later day performance).

These and related practice effects can confound both experimental and statistical comparison of systems. With respect to mean performance changes, Figure 13-1 illustrates a comparison of two system alternatives that is confounded by non-parallel changes with practice. Perhaps reflecting a previously unpracticed or novel 'new alternative', System 2 is initially inferior (more costly) to System 1 (over the first 3 to 6 blocks). Statistically, if only the first 3 blocks were collected and conventional statistical analyses applied, it could be concluded that System 1 is superior (less costly). However, asymptotically, the reverse is true and System 2 would be concluded to be "best" if comparisons were made over the later trial blocks (i.e., 12 and beyond where System 2 is less costly). To overcome this type of confounding, asymptotic performance levels could be estimated and compared by non-typical statistical methods, if only early performance blocks were evaluated (Bittner, 1991). Extended practice would appear the better alternative for unambiguously revealing relative asymptotic performances.

Variance and differential-content (context) changes across trials can also seriously jeopardize the comparison of system variables (Bramwell, Bittner and Morrissey, 1992; Morrissey, Bittner and Ghahramani, 1990). Aside from the logical 'apples and oranges comparison' difficulties implicit with differential-content changes (i.e. in the nature of what-is-being-measured), such changes generally represent a violation of the "sphericity assumption" (Winer, Brown and Michels, 1991; Kirk, 1982) required for conventional repeated-measures analysis-of-variance (RANOVA).[15] This RANOVA violation, in contrast to the typical robustness of analysis-of-variance, can lead to inflation of a test's significance level far above the nominal 0.05 level.[16] Morrissey, Bittner, and Gharamani (1990) summarize

---

[14]A change in the mix-of-abilities would suggest that "general intelligence" is important in early, complex, psychomotor learning, while basic motor skills and other abilities progressively dominate as training progresses. Alternately, demonstration that specific task practice enhanced subjects' capabilities to perform all tasks, calling on the same abilities, would reflect development of subjects' basic abilities. Unfortunately, neither of these demonstrations would be definitive as can be inferred from Alveres and Hulin (1972).

[15]The sphericity assumption is met when between-trial correlations are constant and variances are homogeneous. Tests for sphericity are extremely subject to bias when distributions are not normal (Huynth and Mandeville, 1979)

[16] Our intention is not to discourage the use of RANOVA but to describe the importance of checking for violations of the sphericity assumption.

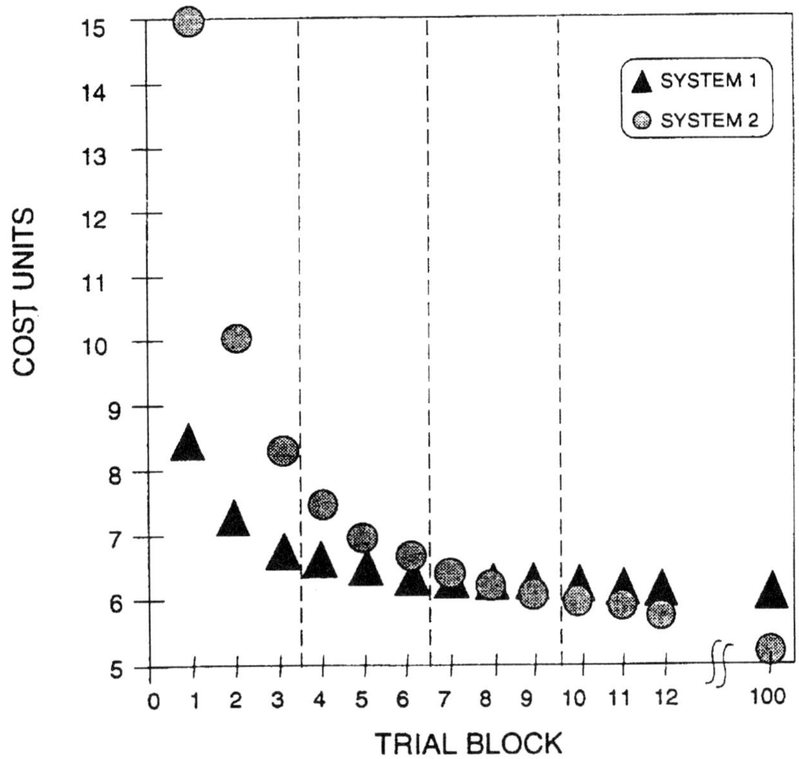

Figure 13-1. Confounding of Learning and System Differences
(Adapted from Bittner, 1991)

simulation research that points-out symmetry-violation cases where the actual levels for main-effects were as high as 0.30 when the traditional 0.05 level was used; between-within interactions had actual significance levels as high as 0.60. Prompted by the potentially dire consequences of such violations, they conducted a formal survey of the human factors literature, seeking evidence of consideration of potential symmetry violations. Their survey, based on three major human factors-ergonomics journals, published over a 15 to 18 month period, found 60 of 66 journal reported of repeated-measures experiments that did not indicate such considerations. This formal survey followed an earlier less-formal survey of military human factors studies, where symmetry considerations appeared even less frequently. These results prompted Morrissey et al. (1990) to outline a scheme for robust analysis of repeated-measures data (e.g., using RANOVA epsilon-correction methods).

Bramwell, Bittner, and Morrissey (1992) have recently amplified on this scheme for robust analysis in the broad context of repeated measures issues, and recommend use of Epsilon correction to the degrees of freedom when using a RANOVA. This correction is routinely available in statistical packages (e.g. BMDP, SAS, and SPSS).

Left unchecked, practice effects can confound experimental <u>and</u> statistical comparisons. Providing extended practice before comparisons may eliminate some difficulties, since means, variances, and differential content often become stable, reducing confounding (e.g., Figure 13-1 where mean performance is stable in later trial blocks). Practice, can also provide an opportunity to evaluate the magnitude of such effects and to estimate the measure's reliability and sensitivity (Bittner et al., 1986). However, extended practice is often not practical (e.g., testbed availability). Results must be carefully weighed if practice effects are an issue, though statistical methods may prove helpful (Bramwell, Bittner, and Morrissey, 1992; Bittner, 1991).

3.3.2.1.2 Carry-over and sensitization effects. Carry-over and sensitization effects occur in equipment-comparison, environmental stressor, and other repeated-measures investigations, when one treatment affects a subjects' behavior in other, later treatments (e.g., Poulton, 1982, Bittner & Guignard, 1988; Damos, 1985; Lewis, 1993). For example, in environmental stressor (e.g., ship-motion studies) or drug (e.g., chemical defense) investigations, if the physical effects (e.g., nausea or drug effects) induced in one treatment are not totally "washed out", they will carry over to the next period and confound potentially interesting findings. When the "carry over" is of direct interest and relatively simple, such as nausea in a ship-motion study, one method to achieve control is to use the measurement at the end of the previous period as a covariate for its measurement during the next period (e.g., Bittner and Guignard, 1988). Though frequently useful, this will be unsatisfactory when conditions <u>differentially</u> affect performance, depending on their order in a sequence of trials (Damos, 1985; Koch, Elashoff, and Amara, 1988, p.50ff). "Balanced for residual effects" experimental designs have frequently been used, to provide for assessment of and adjustment for carry-over effects (Cox, 1958, Lewis, 1993), in studies where differential carry overs are very transitory (e.g. drug studies where depressants and activators can have opposite carry overs on a following condition). Another method, albeit often impractical, for handling transitory carry-over effects is to wait until the effects of the treatment have completely dissipated before introducing another treatment (Greenwald, 1976; Drury, 1990).[17]

More difficult are investigations where differential carry-over effects are less transitory (e.g., Damos, 1985; Poulton, 1982, Carlsmith et al., 1976). A special case are "sensitization effects"; e.g., early trials give subjects clues of how to act in later ones (Bramwell, Bittner, and Morrissey, 1992). This can be a major problem in studies of social psychological phenomena, such as group productivity or perceptions of leadership (Carlsmith et al., 1976). When using repeated measures designs, the only experimental design that directly minimizes these effects, disguise the treatments so subjects do not infer the relationship between treatments (e.g., interest in group productivity might be concealed by a cover story about studying processes).

---

[17]This method is often impractical in military research because of "test-bed" availability and other limitations.

In principle, the 'best' camouflage would be derived from consideration of the research environment and the concept of interest, but this may not be possible for all studies. However, when such camouflage or other means of directly minimizing less transitory carry-overs are of concern, statistical means can be used to access their potential impacts. Basic methods for testing for 'asymmetric transfer effects' have been described by Poulton (1982).[18] Damos (1985) applied Poulton's recommendation of only using first condition results when asymmetric transfer effects are found significant (i.e., evaluating only the independent groups portion of the experimental data).

3.3.2.1.3 Situational demand characteristics (performance flexibility). The tendency for participants in military studies to strive to maintain their performance levels in very marginal systems and/or environmental conditions reflects their "can-do attitude." This attitude frequently leads participants to maintain performance through:

Increased mental and physical efforts. These operator workload (OWL) increases often result in few directly apparent performance changes, albeit these may be assessed using a variety of "empirical methods" (cf., Hancock & Meshkati, 1988; Lysaght et al., 1989; Hart & Wickens, 1990).

Strategy shifts. These shifts are often not directly reflected in mean primary performance measures, but often can be detected both by the significance of the subject-condition interaction (SxC) tests and by changes in task verbal protocols (Bittner and Bramwell, 1992). It is easy for unwary investigators, who only attends to primary performance measures, to be mislead when either or both of these performance maintenance strategies are used.

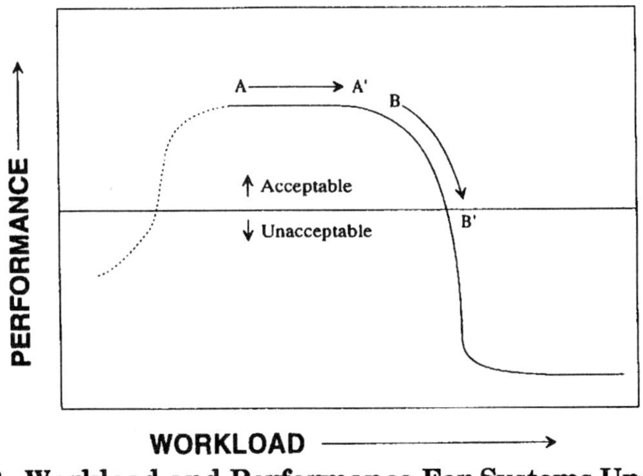

Figure 13-2. Workload and Performance For Systems Under Test and Evaluation (A&B) and Operational (A' and B') Conditions

(Adapted from Lysaght, et al., 1989)

[18]Bittner (1991) also reviewed methods for dealing with asymmetric transfer effects, including the fitting of asymptotes as a way of estimating the results of extended practice where transitory effects may be overcome.

Attending only to primary measures (e.g., speed and accuracy measures) can have potentially disastrous effects when operator workload (OWL) is ignored. Consider the situation in Figure 13-2 where two system alternatives (A and B) initially differ little in performance but substantially in OWL. Failure to attend to this OWL difference could lead to a disaster if the near-capacity system alternative (B) were selected perhaps on grounds of less initial cost. This is because performance of the near-capacity system would decline precipitously (B to B') when an operationally-experienced workload was substantially greater than that experienced during the experimental evaluation (e.g., in combat conditions). A similar situation can occur in environmental (heat) stress evaluations where a participant may be performing well one minute and collapse the next. In contrast, there is also a potential reverse "underload" problem, where OWL for a system is too low (e.g., highly automated cockpits) and operators find it difficult to transition to high workload emergencies (Bittner, Kantowitz, and Bramwell, 1993; Huey and Wickens, 1993). To begin avoiding these and other potentially disastrous OWL-related deceptions, the HF researcher needs to include OWL assessments in their investigations. Discussions of the variety of subjective and other OWL "empirical methods" applicable for this purpose are provided in Section 4.3 of this chapter and can also be found in a variety of contemporary sources (e.g., Hancock and Meshkati, 1988; Lysaght et al., 1989; Hart and Wickens, 1990; Hill et al., 1992; Wierwille and Eggemeier, 1993; Christ et al., 1993).

Strategy shifts can also confound assessments when evaluating varied environmental and/or system conditions. To maintain primary task performance (e.g., speed-of-response), for example, military participants frequently shed secondary tasks (See Chapter 5, sections 2.5.1, 3.1.3, and 3.4) and/or make trade offs with related performance metrics (e.g., trading firing accuracy for speed). Investigators can be seriously misled about the quality of performance when they fail to attend to such shifts. These specific strategy shifts can be assessed from direct changes in the relevant measures (e.g., accuracy), *when the relevant measures are assessed*. This, among other things, leads to arguments for the comprehensive assessment of measures based on theoretical and other considerations (See Kantowitz, 1992; Bittner, 1992). Unfortunately, such comprehensiveness is not always practical (due to the cost and other difficulties of assessing everything that could be potentially important). Even more challenging, many strategy shifts reflect more fundamental and internal (e.g., cognitive) changes in the way that a task is accomplished.

Table 13-4. ANOVA Source Table For a Typical Split-Plot Design With One Between and Two Within Ss Variables

Source of variation	EMS	Traditional *F*-ratio	Recommended SCWG ratios
Between subjects			
(1) A	$\sigma_e^2 + qr\sigma_\pi^2 + nqr\sigma_\alpha^2$	(1)/(2)	(1)/(2)
(2) Subj w. groups	$\sigma_e^2 + qr\sigma_\pi^2$		(2)/(11)
Within subjects			
(3) B	$\sigma_e^2 + r\sigma_{\beta\pi}^2 + npr\sigma_\beta^2$	(3)/(5)	(3)/(5)
(4) AB	$\sigma_e^2 + r\sigma_{\beta\pi} + npr\sigma_{\alpha\beta}^2$	(4)/(5)	(4)/(5)
(5) B×subj w. groups	$\sigma_e^2 + r\sigma_{\beta\pi}^2$	–	(5)/(11)
(6) C	$\sigma_e^2 + q\sigma_{\mu\pi}^2 + npq\sigma_\mu^2$	(6)/(8)	(6)/(8)
(7) AC	$\sigma_e^2 + q\sigma_{\mu\pi}^2 + nq\sigma_{\alpha\mu}^2$	(7)/(8)	(7)/(8)
(8) C×subj w. groups	$\sigma_e^2 + q\sigma_{\mu\pi}^2$	–	(8)/(11)
(9) BC	$\sigma_e^2 + \sigma_{\beta\mu\pi}^2 + np\alpha_{\alpha\beta\mu}^2$	(9)/(11)	(9)/(11)
(10) ABC	$\sigma_e^2 + \sigma_{\beta\mu\pi}^2 + n\sigma_{\alpha\beta\mu}^2$	(10)/(11)	(10)/(11)
(11) BC×subj w. groups	$\sigma_e^2 + \sigma_{\beta\mu\pi}^2$		

(Adapted from Morrisey, Bittner, and Gharamani, 1989)

Cases of strategy shifts can be generally assessed using other approaches. One approach, described by Bittner and Bramwell (1992), involves the statistical testing of subject-condition (SxC) interactions as a means of detecting the possible presence of strategy shifts. For example, in the case represented in Table 13-4, this would involve the testing of terms (5) and (8) using a conservative estimate of pure error, i.e., term (11).[19] Statistical significance of such tests would, after ruling out "scale of measurement effects", indicate the complications of strategy shifts or related condition requirement differences. The significant SxC interaction, would indicate systematic, idiosyncratic response(s) by one or more of the subjects. The examination of SxC interactions has previously been used to identify strategy shifts. For example, Bittner and Morrissey (1988) point out a case where SxC testing detected that a subject had used a novel "hand stabilizing" method to overcome the negative performance effects of whole-body vibration (subsequently leading to a "stabilizing glove system" that could be employed by other subjects for the same purpose). SxC testing has resulted in this and other system improvements as well as enhancements of theory (Bittner and Morrissey, 1988; Bramwell, Bittner and Morrissey, 1992).

A second approach for assessing the possibility of strategy shifts is by directly or indirectly asking research participants about their strategies. Meister and Enderwick (1992) elegantly argue for systematically debriefing subjects to discern their strategies (and other salient information). They also delineate a debriefing approach and recommend use of video and other event playbacks to facilitate the process. Tolbert and Bittner (1991) have also proposed similar playback evaluations using verbal protocol analysis (VPA)[20]. They report that such playback methods can reveal strategies even weeks after an event (Hill, Zaklad, Bittner, Byers, and Christ, 1988; Bowers and Snyder, 1990; Triggs, Kantowitz, Terrill, Bittner and Fleming, 1990). Triggs et al. (1990), using a playback method, have shown how VPAs collected minutes after an event can be coupled with examinations of the fine structure rapid-motor performances. Consequently, debriefing subjects may be coupled with direct experimental observations and other means of assessing strategy shifts (Bittner and Bramwell, 1992).

3.3.4 Broader implications. HFE practitioners face a variety of research problems that challenge the adequacy of traditional experimental and statistical methods. "Subject" and "testbed" limitations: 1) promote the extensive use of repeated-measures research methods and 2) bring with them a breadth of statistical and methodological problems.

---

[19]The (5) and (8) 'error' terms each contain 'pure' error variance (σ_e^2) and one source of SxC variance; while, the (11) error term is a conservative (over-large) estimate of pure error variance as it has an additional ($\sigma_{\beta\mu\pi}^2$) term.

[20]For more information on voice protocol analysis, also called think aloud protocols, see Chapter 4, section 7.4

Some HFE researchers may have been disturbed by this discussion of statistical and methodological issues. First, they may have been disturbed by the questions that repeated-measures problems present regarding the value of much of the research based on such methods. If, for example, the traditional tests of RANOVA within-between interactions can have actual significance levels approaching 0.60 (vs. a nominal .05) when assumptions are violated, then how trustworthy are the estimated 90% of the repeated-measures results in the literature where these were apparently not considered (Bramwell, Bittner and Morrissey, 1992). Second, the consideration of the performance flexibility challenges promoted by the military subjects' "can do attitude" may have been distressing to other readers. This is likely to be true, if these readers have neglected to consider potentially-confounding OWL and strategy-shift related problems in their own or colleagues' work. One of us (Bittner) has found significant SxC interactions showing some level of strategy shifts or differential task requirements in about 60% of his analyses over the last eight years. Unfortunately, this latter concern is not eliminated by the use of independent group designs; subjects in different groups can systematically work at different levels of OWL or shed tasks regardless of experimental design. Most concerned, however, are likely to be those investigators who have simultaneously exposed themselves to almost all of the potential problems delineated herein in a single study. The statistical and methodological problems addressed by military HFE investigators may be more challenging than those of their non-military colleagues, but both groups risk drawing inappropriate conclusions when these challenges are not met.

Necessity has also been the 'mother of invention' for HFE practitioners facing the particular challenges of military research environments. As evidenced by the variety of methods used to overcome specific "practice," "carry over and sensitization", and "performance flexibility" problems, military HFE practitioners have been increasingly successful in overcoming their challenges. The result of their efforts has led to the development of a framework of "robust" methods for addressing such challenges (e.g., Meister, 1986; Bittner, 1992). In some cases, these developments have led to assessments (e.g., SxC interactions) not attended to with previous methods (Bittner and Bramwell, 1992). These robust statistical and other methods that have been assembled by military practitioners are available to other HFE investigators facing similar problems.

3.4 Maintenance

Since the late 1970s, within the DOD there has been considerable emphasis on increased reliability and decreased maintainability (described as Big R/Little m). Indeed, Big R/Little m was one of the major accomplishments of the F/A-18 acquisition program. However, there are limits to increasing reliability by the use of redundant systems, improved materials, longer lasting lubricants, etc. Howell (1993) suggests that the military will need to train broadly based technicians, who, with the support of computer based diagnostic aids, can provide rapid on-site repairs. Selection and training of these types of personnel may be difficult due to the decrease in the availability of capable personnel within the US labor force.

An additional maintenance related HFE area deserving considerable attention is the design and utilization of paperless maintenance manuals. Presently, the B1-B maintenance manuals consume approximately 1,000,000 pages, while the maintenance manuals for the F/A-18 consume 500,000 pages. These numbers reflect the considerable growth in system complexity since the 1950s and 60s when the manual for the F-4 was 100,000 pages and the manual for the F-80 was less than 10,000 pages (Conway, 1992). Today, there is increased time pressure to complete maintenance, and more information is required to perform the maintenance while the average technician has poorer training and less experience. Conway suggests that a solution to this dilemma lies in the development of hypermedia interactive electronic technical manuals (essentially CD-ROM technology) combined with integrated diagnostics technologies. These technologies have been successfully demonstrated in the maintenance of C-130 auxiliary power units (Conway, 1992). The USAF is pursuing related efforts under the Integrated Maintenance Information System (Human Systems Division, 1991a).

Future efforts in the maintenance area require detailed knowledge of the maintenance task and use of that knowledge early in the design process. One related DOD success (the T-800 engine) was described previously in the System Development section. Another effort, the development of an analytical technique began with a critical review of military standards related to designing for maintainability (Loose, 1989). The analytical technique which evolved, Comparative Anatomy of Maintenance Tasks (CAMT), is applicable to both avionics and mechanical maintenance tasks. CAMT identifies "task primitives", which are reusable subtasks that apply across numerous maintenance tasks on a variety of systems. CAMT (Loose, Gentner, and Dascalos, 1993; Chenzoff and Loose, 1992) will allow HFE personnel to determine the effect of alternate designs of maintenance tasks, while the system is still in the early stages of development and HFE impact can be felt. Preliminary findings indicate that the data collection techniques utilized in CAMT are reasonably reliable, sensitive to design differences and of sufficiently limited data collection scope to be acceptable (Loose, Gentner, Chenzoff and Shipton, 1993).

In addition to developing strategies for analyzing maintenance tasks, DOD HFE personnel have developed Computer Aided Design (CAD) tools such as CREWCHIEF (McDaniel and Hoffman,1990). A related emerging effort, Design Evaluation for Personnel, Training, and Human factors (DEPTH) builds on the CREWCHIEF technology and will provide multi-person task simulations, more detailed hand and vision models and incorporate environmental factors (Boyle, Easterly, and Ianni, 1990).

4.0 HFE Tools/Techniques Developed/Utilized

As part of its emphasis on performance, the military has supported the development of many HFE tools and techniques. This section describes some of these and provides guidance to sources containing others. It also contains a section on simulation, since it is a primary tool used by the military.

4.1 Catalogs/Integration of Tools

Over the years, a number of HFE techniques and procedures have been published and evolved into guidelines (e.g. Geer's 1981 report evolved into DOD-HDBK-763). However, some of these documents are service or domain specific, of limited distribution, or not well integrated with each other or the acquisition process. Recently, there has been a major effort to catalog HFE tools to avoid some of these limitations and encourage dissemination. This on-going DOD/NATO cataloging effort intends to develop a comprehensive data base of "Liveware" information (Gentner and Crissey, 1992). The term "Liveware" encompasses the domains of: manpower, personnel, training, safety, health hazard prevention, human factors, and integration.

Specific emphasis has been placed on identifying technologies that can be used in the acquisition process. The survey and literature reviews uncovered more than 500 applicable technologies, of which 254 were HFE related (many still under development). The technologies were classified as:

- mission function and task analysis
- task performance and workload
- human-machine interface
- information transfer
- workspace and anthropometry
- environment and life support.

The liveware technology guide/database provides basic information about individual tools/techniques/databases and their applicability in each acquisition phase. Points-of-contact and their phone numbers are also identified. Illustrious of the types of material that can be found is the entry describing the 1988 ANthropometric SURvey of Army Personnel (ANSUR) by Gordon, et al.(1989) and how to obtain the data on magnetic tape. Another entry informs the reader about how to access the USAF Computerized Biomechanical Man-Model (COMBIMAN) used to evaluate the physical accommodation of the pilots in crewstations and that the ANSUR data and data from non-military populations can be entered. The user will find the Liveware database is extremely terse and is expected to obtain additional information from the designated point-of-contact. In addition, while over 80% of the techniques are listed as "ready to use", Gentner, Kancler and Crissey (1993) note that only 15.4% of these techniques haved been validated and 4.6% have validation studies in progress. Thus, users accessing this survey are cautioned to evaluate the validity of the tools/techniques/ databases.

The development of the *Directory of Design Support Methods* by Bonger, Kibbe, Laine and Hewitt (1990) is a related effort. This directory, which is to be updated regularly, was produced in response to needs identified by the DOD HFE Technical Group (DOD-HFE-TG). Unlike the terse approach in the LIVEWARE database, the current document provides a two page summary of the 74 techniques identified as useful in system design or evaluation. Each entry describes the method (uses, hardware requirements, input requirements, processing procedures, output products, etc), lists alternate approaches, and identifies the sponsor and points of contact for obtaining the technique. Techniques are classified as analytical, computer software, databases, handbooks/guides, military standards/specifications and additional design support methods. The techniques range from a PC-based software package useful for estimating manpower costs and evaluating various mixes of manpower skills to the multi-million dollar SIMulation NETworking (SIMNET).

Both the *LIVEWARE* and the *Directory of Design Support Methods* databases are accessible through the Manpower and Training Research Information System (MATRIS) Office (see footnote 3).

As described previously in the System Development section, MANPRINT is the major DOD effort to develop HFE tools and strategies for their use in systems development (Booher, 1990). While MANPRINT addresses a wide range of platforms and systems, other platform specific tool development efforts also merit attention. Specifically, the current focus is on improving the efficiency and effectiveness of the crewstation development process and is embodied in programs such as the Navy's Advanced Technology Crew Station (ATCS) program and the USAF Crew-Centered Cockpit Design (CCCD) program. Prior to these efforts, much of the skills and knowledge required to perform development tasks resided in experts, many of whom are approaching retirement age. Both programs document experts' descriptions of the cockpit development process, examine the structure of the process and its formalization. The ATCS program (Warner and Notaro, 1993) focuses on crew station development from the "operator's brain" outward and on the multidisciplinary interaction required during the crew station design cycle. While the goal of the CCCD program is to produce a "highly disciplined and traceable cockpit design process, along with supporting tools and technologies" (Human Systems Division, 1991b, p 46). As part of the CCCD program, a Performance Assessment and Workload Evaluation System (PAWES) effort to standardize the evaluation of cockpit design during flight tests is underway (Cohen, Gawron, Mummaw, and Turner (1993). Use of the tools/techniques produced by these efforts will allow DOD to avoid previous pitfalls and more completely address the cockpit/crewstation development process.

4.2 Questionnaires, Surveys, Interviews, and Verbal Protocol Analysis

4.2.1 Questionnaires, surveys, and interviews. These strategies are routinely used by DOD personnel to gather opinion data during all phases of system development. They have been used to evaluate everything from the effectiveness of night vision goggles (Crowley, 1991) to motion sickness (Kennedy, Fowlkes, Berbaum, and Lilienthal, 1992). It is essential to their reliability and validity that scientifically based techniques be used in the development of these tools. Therefore, the Army Research Institute developed a two volume set which deals with questionnaire design. One volume, the *Questionnaire Construction Manual* (Babbitt and Nystrom, 1989a) describes topics such as: structured interviews, types of questionnaire items, scaling techniques, response anchoring and bases for selection of modifiers, respondents characteristics etc. It also provides advice on physical characteristics of questionnaires and factors to consider in administering questionnaires and interviews. The second volume, the *Questionnaire Construction Manual Annex: Literature Survey and Bibliography* (Babbitt and Nystrom, 1989b), focuses on the scientific literature regarding scale categories, behavioral scales, design of questionnaire items, interviewer and respondent characteristics and questionnaire format. While many of the illustrations used in these documents have a military flavor, the principles are equally applicable in civilian settings.

4.2.2 Verbal protocol analysis[21]. Verbal Protocol Analysis (VPA) is being used more frequently by HFE personnel in the human-computer interface area as they attempt to elicit and analyze a persons verbalizations about performing a task (Ohnemus and Biers,1993). VPA has well established roots in the cognitive psychology literature (Erricsson and Simon, 1984). In the human factors area it is often referred to as a method of cognitive task analysis because verbalizations in "thinking through a task" can be analyzed to delineate the task structure (Meister, 1992). Military HFE personnel have long considered VPA-like debriefing techniques important for understanding the hidden (perceptual and cognitive) aspects of performance and have employed them for such purposes throughout the development of their systems (cf. Meister, 1986). Building on the traditions of military debriefing applications, Tolbert and Bittner (1991) have delineated the applicability of VPAs in non-military industrial environments. These techniques are applicable throughout both the military and civilian product development cycle.

[21]For more information on verbal protocol analysis, also called "think aloud protocols," see Chapter 4, section 7.4. A variant of this technique, where two subjects intereact with a system and discuss the steps they are taking is called the co-discovery technique, and is described in detail in Chapter 9, section 4.2.

4.3 Operator Workload (OWL) Measurement[22]

As technology progresses, the role of the system operator increasingly changes from primarily physical to mental. Today's weapon system operators interface with computers, multiple sensors, and multiple data and voice communication links, while functioning in stressful, physically demanding environments. The military system operator is as much a system manager as their civilian analog, but with one major distinction: The military system operator makes the crucial *friend or foe, shoot or don't shoot decision*. Thus, it is essential that the level of workload associated with a particular system be determined correctly if the system is to achieve its design goals. HFE practitioners must seek a middle ground between too little and too much workload. To achieve this, practitioners may use a combination of objective "system" measures, subjective measures, and physiological measures. Objective measures of workload (e.g. targets correctly identified, deviation from course) are system specific and are not be addressed here, due to space limitations. Recognize, however, that "objective" measures are in part subjective in that their very choice is subjective (Muckler and Seven, 1992).

4.3.1 Subjective measures. While much of the workload research has been funded by the military or NASA, it is also applicable in civilian sectors. The Cooper-Harper scale (1969), the precursor of several of today's workload measurements, was developed by NASA for evaluating aircraft handling. Today's DOD regulations require the evaluation of OWL during systems development (Christ, Bulger, Hill and Zaklad, 1990). So the Army Research Institute initiated the OWL program. The Owl program's first step was the completion of a comprehensive review and evaluation of operator workload methodologies (Lysaght, et al, 1989), which incorporated approximately 500 references. This document described analytical (predictive) techniques, such as mathematical models and simulations, and empirical (evaluative) techniques, such as subjective, secondary task, and physiological measures. It also provided recommendations for the use of these techniques throughout system development. The review was followed by a series of studies, involving several Army systems, in which workload was evaluated (Christ, et al, 1993). Among the analytical techniques evaluated were the prospective Task Load Index (TLX) and the Task Analysis/Workload (TAWL) and TAWL Operating System Simulation (TOSS) methods. Four empirical techniques were chosen for evaluation from those described in the previous work. These techniques were: Task Load Index (TLX), Subjective Workload Assessment Technique (SWAT), the Modified Cooper-Harper (MCH), and Overall Workload (OW). Each analytic technique performed well as strategies for identifying potential workload problems early in systems development. Among the empirical techniques evaluated, the TLX was consistently higher in factor validity and operator acceptance. Furthermore, the TLX subscales could provide information regarding the sources of workload.

---

[22]For more information on operator workload as a research topic, see Chapter 5.

To facilitate OWL method selection during system development, a PC-based tool knowledge-based expert system tool (OWLKNEST) was developed by Harris, Hill, Lysaght, and Christ (1992). OWLKNEST, an extension of NASA's Workload Consultant For Field Evaluation (WC FIELDE, Casper, Shively and Hart, 1986), guides a practitioner in the selection of the most appropriate workload measurement technique. OWLKNEST considers 34 different workload measuring techniques. Through a dialogue, the practitioner describes constraints (e.g. operational or laboratory test conditions, availability of subject matter experts, etc) and requirements (diagnosticity, sensitivity, ease of use, etc) that OWLKNEST reduces to an ordered listing of options. This use of expert systems can be expected to become more common and will allow DOD and other practitioners to use existing but complex bodies of knowledge in their decision making.

4.3.2 Physiological measures. "Successful physiological measurement of operator workload has, unfortunately, been easier to conceptualize than to achieve" according to Wilson and O'Donnell (1988, p. 63). However, there have been some recent breakthroughs since this assessment. Excellent reviews of the status of physiological measures of work load have been provided by Kramer (1991), while Wilson and Eggemeier (1991) have examined psychophysical measures in multi-task environments. More recently, Weirwille and Eggemeier (1993) evaluated workload metrics which could be used during test and evaluation. As described by Wilson and Eggemeier (1991), physiological measures have the advantage of not requiring overt responses from the system operator and can be monitored continuously as the task is being performed. Conversely, physiological measures have unique instrumentation requirements and may be confounded by problematic artifacts (e.g., increased heart rate may be due to environmental stressors not increased mental workload). Improved instrumentation packaging and analysis techniques (Wilson and Fischer, 1991) have resulted in significant breakthroughs in this area. Wilson (1991) has reported on data gathered from A-7, B-1, and F-4 aircrew:s

In the A-7 study, heart rate data gathered under both simulator and in-flight conditions revealed significant differences as a function of mission segment in the aircraft while no significant differences in heart rate were noted in the simulator. Under the in-flight conditions, two real in-flight emergencies did occur and resulted in an approximately 50% increase in the heart rate approximately one minute following the emergency. Thus, physiological measures can detect differences between simulators and in-flight conditions. Similarly, under the B-1 flight conditions, heart rate increased as the aircraft got closer to the target site.

During the F-4 flights heart rate, eye-blink and evoked brain potentials were recorded for both the pilot and the Weapon Systems Operator (WSO). The data show that the heart rates of the pilot or WSO increased as a function of their responsibility during the flight. The eye blink data differed from the in-flight and laboratory environments, with much lower blink rates occurring under laboratory conditions. As an additional first, auditory evoked brain potential was recorded from tactical aircrew during flight. It was determined that the amplitude of the positive component (P2) decreased during the highest workload segment.

By monitoring in-flight cardiac measures and eyeblink rates of F4 crewmembers, Wilson and Fisher (1991) have been able to differentiate between crewmembers, and eight flight segments. This suggests that eventually information regarding the status of the pilot component could be fed into the aircraft's data bus, much as engine and fuel parameters are today.

The bottom line from these studies is clearly that, if physiological measures are to be used as workload metrics then those data must be collected in the actual environment. Readers interested in using cardiorespiratory activity in performance studies would do well to consult the special issue of *Biological Psychology* edited by Wilson (1992).

4.4 Performance Test Batteries

As with other system components, operators/maintainers must be tested and evaluated by valid and reliable procedures. Since the early 1980s, microcomputer technology has provided opportunities for developing computerized test batteries for examining the behavioral effects of environmental and operational stressors (heat, altitude, sleep deprivation, accelerative forces, chemical warfare pretreatment drugs, etc). A variety of strategies have been followed in developing these test batteries: at one extreme are computerized versions of paper and pencil tests, while at the other are tests selected for their stability, reliability, and relative independence. Between these two extremes are those cognitive tests selected to detect changes in operator performance as a function of the independent variables being examined (Turnage, Kennedy, Smith, Baltzley and Lane, 1992).

Kane and Kay (1992) provide an excellent review and comparison of 13 computerized neuropsychological and performance test batteries. They point out that the use of microcomputers brings several advantages including standardized administration and scoring, rapid generation of alternate forms, precise control of stimuli, as well as more cost effective testing. However, they also offer the following cautions. The subject's prior experience or inexperience with computers and keyboards **must** be considered in test administration. Norms developed with a paper and pencil version of a test may change when that test is "computerized." The reliability and accuracy of the timing must also be considered. The human-computer input device (joystick, lightpen,or keyboard) used affects performance on computerized tests. The resolution, contrast,or brightness of a display device (cathode ray tube, liquid crystal, plasma) as well as refresh rates and decay time may also impact on subject performance. Thus, for the "same" test, normative data collected on one type of display device may not apply when the same stimuli are presented on a different display device. Recently, Kennedy, Dunlap, Turnage, Lane and Jones (1993) demonstrated that when tests using the same software were presented on two different PC platforms, the acquisition curves retain the same shape. However, mean differences in the number correct and response latencies as large as some treatment effects were found. Fortunately, the factor structure remained intact which suggests that scores obtained with one system can be transformed and normalized with respect to the other system. **Additional work is needed in this area.**

While Kane and Kay (1992) focus on the cognitive aspects of these test batteries, these batteries also address perceptual and motor output. Typical perceptual subtests include pattern matching, spatial rotation, and reaction time. Cognitive tasks include linguistic and mathematical reasoning, calculations and complex problem solving. Motor tasks include finger tapping, coordination, and tracking. A few test batteries use dual and multitasking tasks such as a combined Sternberg/tracking task. The origins of many of these tests and test batteries can be traced to DOD investigators. Due to space constraints, only three of these batteries will be considered in this chapter. All of these tests are intended for use in repeated measures design experiments. The Automated Portable Test System (APTS) described by Bittner, Smith, Kennedy, Staley and Harbeson (1985) evolved from the Navy's Performance Evaluations Tests for Environmental Research (PETER) program which was conceptualized in 1977 by Kennedy and Bittner. The Unified Tri-services Cognitive Performance Assessment Battery (UTC-PAB) was developed to provide standardization during a multilevel drug evaluation program (Englund, et al, 1987). Finally, the Advisory Group for Aerospace Research and Development (AGARD) Standardized Tests for Research with Environmental Stressors (STRES) Battery which defined "the tests most useful in a battery for stress research, provided detailed and machine independent test specifications and established a standardized data exchange format to facilitate the construction of a data base" (AGARD, 1989, p. 1). These tests have been used in a wide variety of military and non-military applications.

4.4.1 Automated Portable Test System (APTS). APTS includes 21 different tests (including finger tapping, pattern comparison, spatial rotation, and linguistic processing) from which an experimenter, using the included factor analysis, selects those tests which s/he feels best taps the constructs to be examined. The APTS evolved from a meta-analysis of 114 measures (Bittner, Carter, Kennedy Harbeson and Krause, 1986). It was recently used in a field test in Alaska to determine the effect of high altitude on climber's performance (Kramer,Coyne and Strayer, 1993). Turnage, Kennedy, Smith, Baltzley, and Lane (1992) describe several repeated measure studies in which APTS sensitivity to environmental effects have been demonstrated including: blood alcohol level, hypoxia, motion sickness prevention drugs, chemoradiotherapy, antihistamine drugs, and 1% halon gas inhalation. In a more recent study, Kennedy, Dunlap, Turnage, Lane and Jones (1993), set the ground work for evaluating the cognitive and performance readiness of space crews, and described performance decrements among aircrews engaged in transatlantic flights. Kennedy, Turnage, Wilkes and Dunlap (1993) described an exciting development in the use of these tests for evaluating fitness for duty . They indexed performance deficits due to stressors such as altitude, halon, and selected drugs against various Blood Alcohol Concentrations (BACs). This strategy, after additional validation, may allow environmental or drug effects to be described as equivalent to a specified BAC.

4.4.2 The Unified Tri-services Cognitive Performance Assessment Battery (UTC-PAB). The UTC-PAB evolved (Shingledecker, 1984) from the Walter Reed Performance Assessment Battery (WRPAB) and the Criterion Task Set (CTS). The UTC-PAB consists of 26 tests (including grammatical reasoning, complex reaction time, an alpha-numeric visual vigilance task, time estimation). Normative data obtained for tests taken from the WRPAB and the CTS may also apply to the UTC-PAB (Kane and Kay,1992). In addition, Schlegel, Gilliland, and Crabtree (1992) describe the development of the UTC-PAB normative database.

The UTC-PAB has been used in a variety of environments. Neshtus, Schiflett, Eddy, and Whitmore (1991) used the battery to compare the effect of the antihistamines, Benadryl and Seldane, on simulator-based performance of airborne weapon director teams under different levels of cognitive workload. Their conclusions supported allowing non-pilot aircrew to use Seldane, but not Benadryl, for treating seasonal allergies or other nonallergenic rhinitis symptoms. While these drugs did not impact operational effectiveness, trends in the data indicated that members of the Benadryl group were poorer performers (Eddy, Dalrymple and Schiflett, 1992). Shappel, Neri and DeJohn (1992) used the UTC-PAB to determine the effects of dextro-methamphetamine on simulated-sustained flight operations, and found that dextro-methamphetamine reduced subjective fatigue, improved performance, and reduced apparent risky behavior on two spatial memory tasks. The UTC-PAB has also been used to examine the effects of cold temperatures (4°C, 39.2° F) on cognitive performance (Thomas et al, 1990). Computerized copies of these tests and/or access to a bulletin board service by contacting the Office of Military Performance Assessment Technology (OMPAT)[23] at Walter Reed Army Institute of Research.

4.4.3 The Standardized Tests for Research with Environmental Stressors (STRES) Battery. The STRES battery consists of seven tests, and requires approximately 30 minutes for administration on a IBM PC. The tests included are: complex reaction time, serial add/subtract, Sternberg Memory search, Spatial Rotation-Sequential, Visual-Motor Tracking, Grammatical/Logical Reasoning,

---

[23] Contact OMPAT at 301 427-5210.

Combined Sternberg, and Visual-Motor tracking. These tests have been incorporated into the UTC-PAB. The STRES battery was developed to overcome the costly 'Tower of Babel' phenomenon which precludes the direct comparison of results obtained from studies examining the same phenomenon but under different protocols, data collection strategies, or testing conditions (AGARD, 1989). The strength of the STRES battery rests in its emphasis on standardization of test administration (Eglund, et al, 1987), including efforts to minimize language differences since the test is available in German, French, and English. A unique feature is the development of a standardized data base format to facilitate the exchange of performance data among investigators. The STRES battery has been used to evaluate performance in a variety of situations including sleep deprivation (Gravelle, 1993, Batejat and Lagarde, 1992) and drug efficacy (Shapppel, Kerns, DeJohn and Neri, 1993). The STRES Battery is available through CSERIAC.

4.5 Simulation

Simulation and modeling are so critical to DOD that the Defense Modeling and Simulation Office (DMSO) was established (Lilienthal, 1993). The mission of this organization is to "strengthen the use of modeling and simulation in joint education, training, and military operations; research and development; test and evaluation; analysis and production, and logistics". It is also responsible for guiding and coordinating the development of simulations and models across the military services. The DMSO contends that "Everything is simulation except combat"; everything ranges from field exercises to computerized wargames to SIMulator NETworking (SIMNET).

Simulators, properly designed and utilized, meet the goal of military training research by "reducing training time and cost and increasing training effectiveness" (Driskell and Olmstead, 1989, p 48). While the military has placed considerable emphasis on the development and utilization of simulators and simulator technology for individual systems, a major step in collective training was taken in 1983 when the ground work was laid for the SIMNET. SIMNET is capable of uniting land, sea, and aviation simulators at 18 DOD sites (11 in Europe and 7 in the U.S.) into one seamless simulation (Alluisi, 1991). The importance and validity of simulation as described in a GAO (1992) report on training for Operation Desert Storm has been discussed in the section on DOD's uniqueness. Other aspects of simulation have been discussed elsewhere in the chapters on: automotive systems (Chapter 7), training effectiveness (Chapter 14), and aerospace systems (Chapter 5). Rather than dwell on use of simulators within the military, the authors will: 1) describe the future of simulation in DOD and 2) discuss a specific HFE related concern regarding the use of simulators namely simulator sickness.

In 1992, the Director of Defense Research and Engineering (DDR&E) identified "synthetic environments" as one of seven critical Science and Technology areas that must be maintained and supported to preserve technological superiority, a key element in deterrence. Synthetic environments are internetted simulations, which represent activities at a level of realism described as "total immersion", and are the result of converging information technologies (e.g., local and wide area networks, high speed CPUs and transmission rates, improved data bases, satellite links). Synthetic environments have one focus: training military personnel, individually and in teams, through total immersion in the task. Ultimately, any military system that uses a computer will be interoperable with all other computers in the synthetic environment. The fidelity will be so high that the DDR&E predicts: "The distinction between computer-based synthetic environments and computer-based operational systems blurs in the 2000s" (DDR&E, 1993, p. II-56). Synthetic environments will provide not only a means for evaluating training and readiness, but also a means for evaluating the effectiveness of proposed and conceptual systems, as well as tactics. This area offers many challenges and opportunities to human factors personnel, not only in the areas of human-computer interface and displays, but also in the area of adapting scoring and analytical techniques for use under real training conditions (Alluisi, 1991). See Orlansky (1992) for additional details on training strategies for networked simulation and gaming.

While considerable progress has been made in simulation, it has come at a price - simulator sickness, which interferes with effective training. In 1984, McCauley edited a NRC report on research issues in simulator sickness. Since then, many of the report's recommendations have been effectively incorporated into the training procedures used by the military services. Simulator sickness is not unique to aircraft simulators and has been reported in automobile, tank, and ship simulators, though much of the research has focused on symptoms encountered by aircrew. Kennedy and Fowlkes (1992) describe simulator-induced motion sickness as a "syndrome", with a variety of symptoms including nausea, stomach awareness, sweating, pallor, eyestrain, dizziness, and occasional vomiting.

Baltzley, Kennedy, Berbaum, Lilienthal, and Gower (1989) posit that perhaps 10% of all pilots experience aftereffects for several hours after completing simulator training. Some of these aftereffects, such as improperly perceived motion, can lead to hazardous situations if an individual flies or drives a vehicle after simulator training. Indeed, McGuinness, Bouman, and Forbes (1981) have reported reduced simulator usage in simulators which induce symptoms of motion sickness. Finally, Kennedy (1990) cautions that development of more realistic displays and usage of simulators in environments that move (e.g. aircraft carriers) may increase the incidence of simulator sickness. Kennedy and Fowlkes (1992) suggest that simulator sickness is polygenic and polysymptomatic and recommend that data from large sample sizes be gathered in existing simulators to identify features that contribute to the syndrome.

5.0 Environmental Effects

DOD personnel must perform in a variety of natural and man-made environments - chemical, radiological, nuclear, laser, acceleration/vibration, altitude/depth, noise, temperature, humidity, cultural, etc. In addition to these stressors (which are often combined), they face the stresses of combat or military duties including: survival, enemy action, sustained operations, isolation, etc. Therefore, much of DOD's research has focused on penetrating the barriers unique to these environments to insure successful mission accomplishment. Detailed consideration of each of these environments is beyond the scope of this chapter; therefore, we will first direct you to relevant literature in some of these areas and then focus on three selected areas:: sustained operations, acceleration, and decision making under stress.

A number of recent publications by DOD researchers have addressed sound, group/cultural attitudes, altitude and thermal effects. Moore and Von Gierke (1991) provided an excellent review of military performance in acoustic noise environments, addressing both noise-induced hearing loss, and auditory signal and speech communication. Payments for noise induced hearing loss by the U.S. Veterans Administration exceeded 173 million dollars in 1986. Peak impulse levels of 160 dB SPL (Sound Pressure Level) for a single M-16 rifle round, while a single 90mm recoilless rifle round generates 188 db SPL. This is an area in which preventive measures could result in reduced personnel injury and considerable savings.

Taylor (1991) reviewed the literature on individual and group behavior in extreme situations and environments including: prisoners of war, wintering in Antarctica, and submarine duty. Kaplan (1991) addressed the area of cultural issues that are often ignored but which can significantly impact military and civilian personnel interacting with other cultures. His observations on stereotypes were particularly interesting, referencing Kroemer (1975) as reporting that the American and German stereotype of 'Move power switch up to turn equipment ON' does not exist in Britain where the stereotype is 'Move power switch down to turn equipment ON.

Banderet and Burse (1991) also provided a good overview of the effect of altitudes in excess of 3000m on military performance and propose countermeasures. The effects of hot and cold environments on the performance of military personnel are well addressed by Kobrick and Johnson (1991). The effect of elevated body temperatures, resulting from the requirement to wear protective clothing (Figure 13-3) against chemical attack, is a serious concern (Banderet et al., 1992; Szlyk, Caretti, Sils, Zabul, and Faughn,1992). Some of the strategies developed by the military for evaluating and countering thermal stress were used to improve the survival probability of the shuttle crew (See Figure 13-4; Askew and Kaufman, 1991; Kaufman, Dejneka, Morrissey, Bagian, and Bittner, 1988; Kaufman and Dejneka, 1987). Within DOD, an interesting development in the area of rewarming after hyperthermia has been the use of radio frequency (RF) induction coils (Kaufman, Dejneka, and Askew, 1990). In a repeated measures design, they

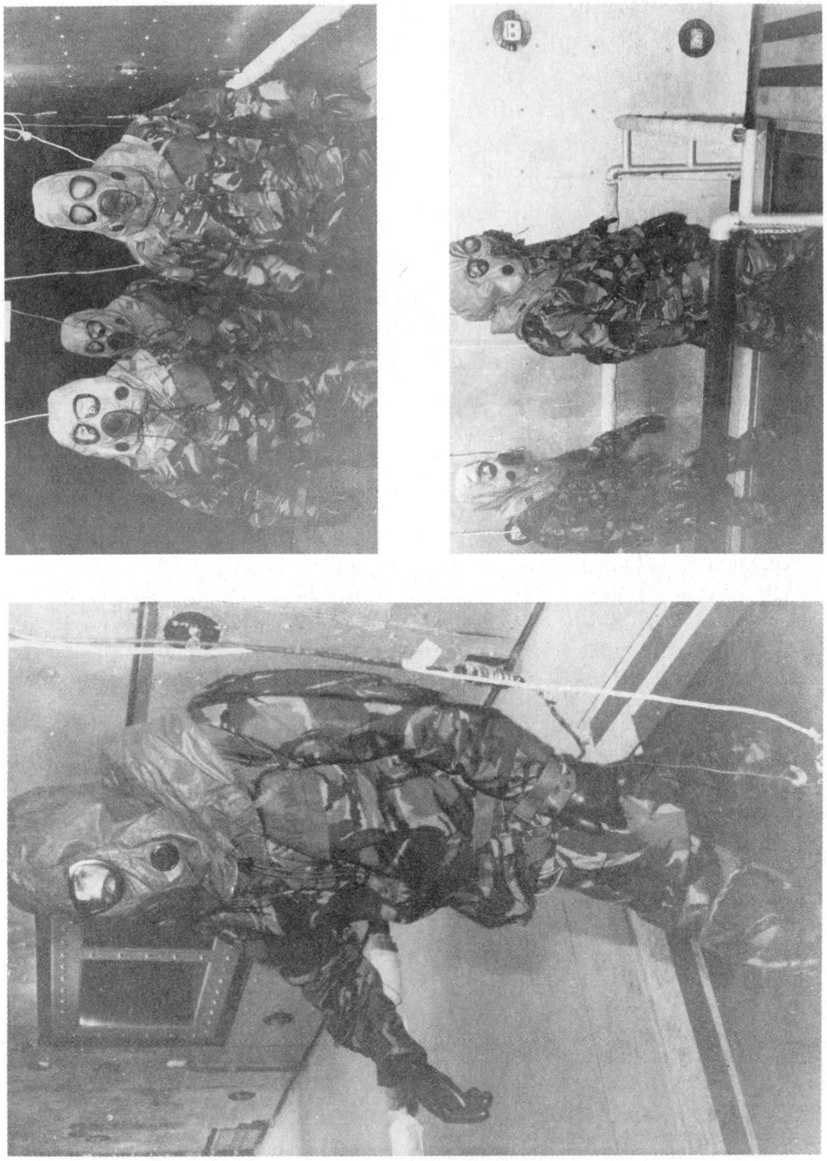

Figure 13-3. Evaluation of Protective Clothing Ensembles at US Army Research Institute of Environmental Medicine

Figure 13-4. Evaluation of NASA's Shuttle Launch/Entry Suit at Naval Air Weapons Center, Aircraft Department

rewarmed mildly hypothermic individuals using RF, warm water immersion, and an insulated mummy type rewarming sack. The warm water immersion technique proved to be the most effective while, at the frequencies and absorption rates tested, the RF rewarming technique was roughly as effective as the rewarming sack. More recently, Lloyd and Olsen (1992) reported that when the RF frequency was doubled, hands or feet could be rewarmed. Additional work is needed, but the use of RF as a warming technique could increase the survivability rate of hypothermia victims and could replace the heat loss which reduces diver dexterity and dive time.

5.1 Sustained Operations

Night vision and other sensor technologies have deprived military personnel of the respite offered by darkness. Compounding this are requirements for continuous operations (CONOPS) that require sustained performance with minimal rest for extended periods (e.g. 72-120 hours). In addition to CONOPS, military personnel also engage in sustained operations (SUSOPS) where sustained performance is again required, but relief personnel are not available at predetermined intervals and the duration of the task is determined by the time required to achieve the objective. Simply stated, these personnel are shift workers and they must work or be available to work on any or all "shifts." Since fatigue and sleep loss inevitably lead to degraded performance, accidents, and reduced effectiveness, the DOD has considerable interest in research in this area (Krueger, 1991). The deleterious consequences of fatigue and sleep loss are also of increasing concern in the civilian sector, as we enter the information age and feel the impact of the "global village." Moore-Ede, in a recent book (1993) notes that technological (telecommunications, satellites, facsimile machines, etc) and economic imperatives (Just-In-Time deliveries, round-the-clock assembly lines, 24 hour supermarkets, etc) are creating a 24 hour society in which we ignore circadian rhythms and time zones at our peril.

Kreuger (1991) provides an excellent review of this topic. He examined: the interaction between task and task duration; circadian and ultradian rhythmic changes in performance; the effect of fatigue and sleep loss; and, the restorative ability of naps. He also reviewed studies performed under CONOPS and SUSOPS conditions, strategies for sustaining military performance, for both physical and mental tasks. Regarding physical (manual) tasks in which lactic acid accumulates, Tharion, Rauch, Strowman and Shukitt (1987) reported that in the best of circumstances highly motivated, trained personnel can sustain continuous physical effort for 10-15 hours. However, there is considerable variability in the work pace. Paton, Vogel, Damokosh, and Mellow (1989) determined that artillerymen (performing a repeated lifting task), who slept for between 4.0 to 6.6 hours in each 24 hour period could sustain a high level of performance for **at least** eight days. In dealing with cognitive tasks (message handling), Angus and Heslegrave (1985) reported 30% decrements in reaction time, logical reasoning, encoding and decoding after 24 continuous hours on-duty.

Performance remained at this level for the next eight hours after which it declined an additional 10% within the next six hours. As might be expected, the greatest decrements were noted during the predawn hours. Gravelle (1993) examined the perceptual effect of one nights sleep loss and reported increased error rates accompanied by erratic, unpredictable fluctuations in response latency without overall increases in reaction time. Vigilance tasks show the well documented decline in performance within 30 minutes after the start of the task (Warm,1984, Mackie,1977). The vigilance literature may recommend watches of less than four hour durations (Warm, 1984) and rotation of personnel (Mackie,1977), but these accommodations are not available during SUSOPs.

During SUSOPS and CONOPS, the circadian rhythms of military personnel are disrupted by the lack of a formal shift schedule. Furthermore, unlike the civilian trans-meridian traveler, members of rapid deployment forces are usually involved in periods of intense preparatory activity, an additional performance degrading stressor, prior to departing for combat. Military aviation personnel transporting these deploying troops also suffer the same debilitating effects (Graeber, 1988) as do commercial airline pilots however, they may be required to fly considerably more flights than commercial airline pilots. Generally, calibration of the circadian clock to local time is most desirable before commencing military operations. However, Neri and Shappell (1992) describe the advantages to carrier based naval aviators of flying late night/early morning combat missions while their body time was closer to evening flight times. Knowledge about circadian phases is important for complete mission planning.

Krueger (1991) also discussed the increased frequency of 'microsleep' (periods of as much as 10 seconds of inactivity) as personnel are deprived of sleep. This phenomenon combined with the tendency to emphasize accuracy at the expense of speed is very problematic in CONOPS and SUSOPS and may lead to accidents, omissions, communication errors, etc. To counter this, DOD has examined sleep requirements and the effectiveness of naps. Kreuger reports that most sleep researchers have concluded that, in general, naps taken in conjunction with 4 to 5 hours of <u>uninterrupted</u> sleep will allow performance to be maintained at an adequate level. As a result, military personnel engaged in CONOPS are officially encouraged to take 'power naps' whenever it is safe to do so. Related to the issue of napping, Naitoh, Kelly and Baskoff (1991) examined the effect of napping on 'sleep-inertia' (the brief period of inferior task performance and/or disorientation occurring immediately after awakening from sleep). They discovered that the severity of sleep-inertia depended on the level of sleep from which the individual was awakened. They also noted incidents of 'sleep aversion' (i.e. resistance to take naps by personnel who realized that they were required to awaken on demand). Kreuger, Redmond, Belenky, and Leu (1988) monitored the sleep and activity of personnel engaged in simulated CONOPS during 16 days of field training exercises for armor mechanized infantry. They found that the higher the soldiers rank the less likely he was to have restorative sleep.

Thus, the senior personnel whose workload most involved decision making had the least amount of sleep. As a result of these and related studies, information on the adversive effects of sleep loss have been incorporated into training and administrative changes that allow restorative sleep have been enacted.

In addition to administrative and the other approaches mentioned above, the DOD has considered pharmacological interventions. Kreuger (1991) reports the use of sleep inducers by flying personnel in the Falklands and by Israeli troops during the Entebbe Raid. Alertness enhancers (methylphenidate and dextroamphetamine) were used by U.S. forces in Vietnam. The use of these alertness enhancers led to their abuse and ultimately to discontinuation of their use. The current DOD policy requires careful evaluation of these interventions to identify behavioral side effects. This requirement, combined with the need to evaluate the behavioral effects of chemical defense drugs and protective ensembles, contributed to the development of the test batteries described previously under tools.

5.2 Acceleration

Military personnel are exposed to a variety of accelerative environments (including vibration). Aircrew, for example, are exposed to highly dynamic G forces (both positive and negative). Ships crews are exposed to both the very low frequencies produced by gentle swells and the higher frequencies produced at higher speeds and rougher seas. Personnel in armored vehicles are exposed to accelerative forces that vary as a function of their speed, terrain type and the vehicle's energy attenuation characteristics. These forces may result in injuries ranging from spinal fractures/compression to motion sickness and drowsiness. Problems associated with this area require the interaction of DOD HFE personnel from the professions of engineering, biomechanics, biomedicine, physiology, and psychology. Rolnick and Gordon (1991) provide a fine review of the effect of motion sickness on military performance. Von Gierke, McCloskey, and Albery (1991) provide an excellent review and integration of the sustained acceleration and vibration literature. The March 1991 issue of *Engineering in Medicine and Biology*, edited by Hrebien, contains several articles which focus on the effect of forces encountered in the high G environment of fighter aviation. McCloskey, Tripp, Chelette and Popper (1992) describe test and evaluation metrics techniques that address the hydrostatic column, blood oxygen saturation and neurological models, generally used to explain the effect of G forces on aircrew.

The loss of aircrew and aircraft due to G-induced loss of consciousness (G-LOC) combined with improvements in materials and aerodynamic designs have resulted in the pilot being described as the limiting factor in today's and tomorrow's tactical aircraft. Therefore, considerable DOD HFE related assets and capabilities have been focused on this problem. Typically, sustained G-forces result in loss of blood flow to the brain, which leads to reduction of the visual field, greyout, blackout and loss of consciousness [with an average 24 second period of incapacitation (Whinnery, 1991)]. Note that under some conditions, this sequence is not followed and G-LOC can be effectively instantaneous. After recovery of consciousness, there is a period of disorientation, before the pilot regains full control of the aircraft. The time to G-LOC varies as a function of many factors (Whinnery, 1988) including rate of onset, duration of exposure, neurological and cardiovascular reserve at the time of onset, physical state of the crewmember, recency of training and recency of exposure to G, etc. Various G protective techniques (breathing and straining), devices (anti-G suits, assisted positive pressure breathing ensembles), and cockpit designs (reclining seats, elevated lower extremities) have been developed to increase G tolerance and endurance. Readers interested in a comprehensive overview would do well to consult High Altitude and High Acceleration Protection for Military Aircrew (AGARD, 1991). The increased use of data buses aboard aircraft has lead researchers to develop non-invasive strategies for detecting G induced physiological changes in the pilot control system (Albery and Van Patten, 1991). Eventually, these devices will allow the onboard computer to take control of the aircraft when the pilot has lost consciousness. An interesting development in this area has been the discovery that there are periods of "almost unconsciousness," perhaps similar to microsleep, during which the crewmember does not respond to stimuli (P.E. Whitley, personal communication, August, 1993).

5.3 Decision Making Under Stress

"Hours of boredom, punctuated by moments of sheer terror" describes the stress frequently encountered by military personnel in the operational environment. Problems associated with decision making under stress reached a critical mass during two Persian Gulf incidents in the late 1980s. In the first incident, the USS Stark sustained significant damage and loss of life because it did not shoot down an aggressor aircraft. In the second incident, the USS Vincennes mistook an Iranian commercial aircraft for an aggressor aircraft and destroyed it, killing all passengers.

In response to these and related incidents, a program to investigate Tactical Decision Making Under Stress (TADMUS) was initiated by the Office of Naval Research. The TADMUS program does not attempt to simulate conditions which may produce fear but concentrates on developing strategies to improve decision making. Specifically, the TADMUS program (Cannon-Bowers, Salas, Grossman, 1992) was designed to:

1. Define the decision problem facing Navy tactical teams
2. Develop measures of tactical decision making performance
3. Collect empirical data to document the impact of stress on decision making
4. Develop principles for decision support, information display, training system design and simulation that mitigate these stress effects.

Tolcott (1992) characterizes decision making under stress as having: short decision making time, high workload, and ambiguous and incomplete information. These characteristics are influenced by the presence of other stressors such as SUSOPS, sleep loss and auditory overload.

Tolcott (1992) described the two primary components of military decision making as situation assessment (what is happening) and action selection (what to do about it). Action selection is often addressed by prepared standard operating procedures (SOPs), while the former is more difficult to describe (Kaempf, Wolf, and Miller, 1993).

While the TADMUS program is still in progress, some interesting findings have evolved. Kaempf, Wolf, and Miller (1993) report that when faced with time pressure and ambiguity, "... decision makers rarely use analytical decision strategies, they usually satisfice rather than optimize, they rely heavily on diagnostic decisions, and they invoke singular rather than comparative evaluations of courses of action" (p 1107). Perrin, Barnett and Walrath (1993), examined decision making in anti-air warfare simulation with trained Navy personnel and determined that:

1. Decision making was significantly influenced by the order in which the information was received
2. Decision makers showed a confirmatory bias (i.e. they recalled more of the information that was consistent with their final decision).

The trend in the development of models of decision making under stress appears to be away from the rational models (Bayesian, multi-attribute utility models) and toward descriptive, naturalistic models (Tolcott,1992). Supporting this theme, Klein (1989) questioned the utility of the concept of "decision bias" and the applicability of laboratory-based findings in naturalistic settings. Critically needed information on group decision making should evolve from this program. This information should transfer to the civilian sector, particularly in areas such as nuclear powerplants and air traffic control.

6.0 Use of Human Subjects in the Military

Since DOD's primary concern is system performance, DOD must realistically test and evaluate (T&E) its systems in the environments in which they are intended for use. Operators/ maintainers are critical system components and as such are exposed to the same testing environment. The DOD is also concerned with the survivability of its personnel and therefore will expose personnel to stressful environments and scenarios during the evaluation of protective equipment. These testing requirements place special burdens on researchers and practitioners in the DOD.

Because of their professional affiliations, HFE personnel may be bound to comply with the American Psychological Association's Ethical Principles of Psychologists and Code of Conduct (APA, 1992), the Code of Ethics provided by the Human Factors and Ergonomics Society (HFES, 1993), as well as the code of ethics of other professional associations. However, these codes provide little specific guidance to HFE personnel regarding ethical issues in unusual DOD environments. The APA (1992, p.5) requires psychologists to "*take reasonable steps to avoid harming their... research participants*" (APA, p. 5), while the HFES (1993), which devotes almost 25% of its code to "Subject Precautions," states that HFE personnel have the responsibility for treating subjects " *humanely and in accordance with federal, state and local laws or regulations.*" (p. 357)

One of the most publicized ethical violations involving the use of human subjects to provide data for military use occurred in NAZI facilities during WWII when data were collected on survival rates of humans in frigid water[24]. The researchers justified their position on the basis that "such experiments yield results for the good of society that are unprocurable by other methods or means of study" (Government Printing Office, 1949, p. 181). These types of experiments resulted in the establishment of the *Nuremburg Code*, which specified 10 principles that must be adhered to when testing involves human subjects. These principles have been incorporated into the *Federal Policy for the Protection of Human Subjects* (Office of Science and Technology, 1991) to which the DOD is a signatory.

Specific DOD directives such as Directive 3216.2, "Protection of Human Subjects in DOD-Supported Research" (DOD, 1983) applies to all research involving the use of humans in situations where there is more than minimal risk and mandates the establishment of review committees similar to Institutional Review Boards (IRBs). These IRBs function much as civilian IRBs with the exception that within the DOD the approval authority is vested in a DOD approving official and not with the board members. The regulation mandates the inclusion of:

1. Nonaffiliated members not under the authority of the approving official (e.g. civilians, religious representatives)
2. Physicians on the review board.

Under this regulation, the approving official may not reduce any of the safeguards required by the reviewing committee nor serve as an investigator. Instructions unique to the departments of DOD, such as SECNAVINST 3900.39B (Office of the Secretary of the Navy, 1984) caution against the use of coercion or undue influence and require the investigator to seek consent only under circumstances which truly allow the potential subject to freely decide whether or not to participate.

As might be expected, the directives require that only persons who are informed fully and agree to participate voluntarily may serve as subjects. However, some unique distinctions are made. The term "subject" does not

---

[24] The U.S. Department of Energy is curently investigating the exposure of DOD personnel to nuclear radiation during the 1940s and 1950s (Smolowe, 1994).

include personnel who by education, training, and testing have met the criteria for formal designation as test pilots and test engineers (DOD Directive 3216.2, p. 2). Thus test pilots, test engineers, etc. are not considered subjects when data are gathered from these individuals in environments to which they would be exposed as part of their normal duties. Obviously, these individuals still need to be informed and to consent to the research; indeed they are usually part of the RDT&E (Research, Development, Test and Evaluation) team which makes the cost/benefit judgement. DOD Directive 3216.2 does not apply to research conducted as part of individual or group training (e.g. physical fitness and crew proficiency). The latter position is based on the consideration that constraints on training are well defined (e.g., limitations exist regarding performing physical fitness training above specified temperatures and humidity levels).

There has been a continuing effort within the DOD to reduce the use of human subjects in experimentation. Indeed, the principles of replacement and reduction (Russell and Burch, 1959) are embodied in DOD research. Replacement is achieved through the use of cadavers, lower level animals, models (both mathematical and physical).

Reduction in required sample size and/or frequency of exposure is achieved by *a priori* determination of the appropriate statistical power necessary for the experimental design. The model-based evaluations of environmental effects hold the promise of minimizing the need for exposing human subjects (Kantowitz, 1992; Bittner, 1992).

Data for models (Weiss, Guccione and Watkins, 1990) predicting neck injury are derived from low-level exposure research such as that illustrated in Figure 13-5. This type of data has also been used in determining the biofidelity of anthropomorphic test devices, i.e. dummies. A recent challenge was the use of lasers to degrade target detection by inducing glare. Since specific wavelengths of laser energy are damaging to the eye, the phenomenon cannot be studied directly, however a mathematical model has been developed that predicts distances at which targets can be detected (Gish, 1990). Many of the findings of these types of research have been incorporated into standards (ISO, SAE, ANSI, AIAA, etc.) used in evaluating the safety of transportation systems. For example, data gathered during ship simulator testing (McCauley and Kennedy, 1976) have been incorporated into international standards (ISO 2631\3-1985).

Methods for reducting the required number of subjects or frequency of exposure have also been developed (e.g. Bittner, 1992). These range from methods for statistically evaluating measure stability and reliability adequacy before exposing subjects to hazardous environments to robust modeling and analysis approaches for assessing the environmental effects (Bittner, Harbeson, Kennedy and Lundy, 1986; Bramwell, Bittner and Morrissey, 1992).

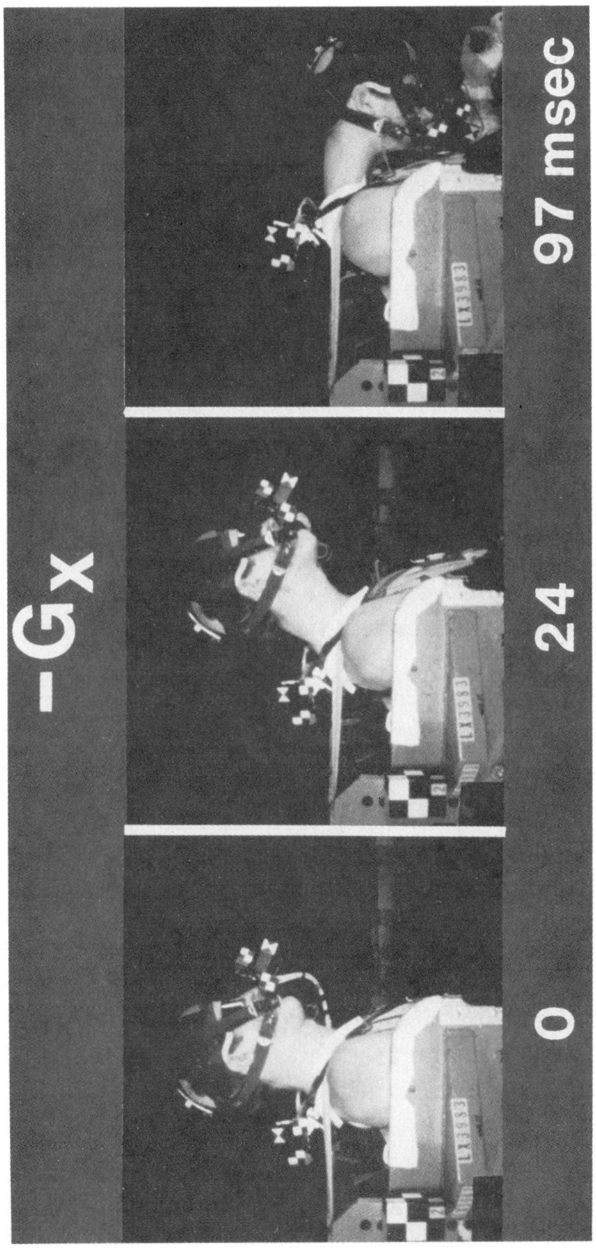

Figure 13-5. Subject Undergoing Rapid Deceleration at the Naval Biodynamics Laboratory

Despite efforts to develop human surrogates, the use of human subjects can be expected to continue, but at a decreasing rate and under closer scrutiny. In addition, as researchers become more knowledgeable about exotic environmental hazards, guidelines will be published. Recent guidelines provide data regarding the safe exposure of humans to impact acceleration (Weiss, Matson, and Mawn, 1989) and to aviation environments (Whinnery and Hamilton, 1991).

The issue regarding the use of human subjects is further complicated by both the rapid changes in medical technology and today's shifting norms and standards. While there is reasonable consensus as to what constitutes a skeletal injury as revealed by X-ray technology, that consensus doesn't always exist when more advanced imaging techniques are used (e.g. magnetic resonance imagery). Finally, Institutional Review Boards (IRBs) must be responsive to the changing norms and standards while balancing the implications of performing or not performing the research (Rosnow, Rotheram-Borus, Ceci, Blanack and Koochler, 1993).

7.0 Women in the Military

The role of women in the military and their potential involvement in combat has social, ethical and political implications beyond the scope of this chapter. Moreover, since there do not appear to be meaningful, design-related *cognitive* differences between the sexes (Ketcham-Wiedel and Bittner, 1977), this section will focus on physically-related gender differences with significant design implications: strength (anaerobic capability), endurance (aerobic capability), and anthropometric (body size) compatibility. While each service has its own physical entrance standards, Army data will be utilized to illustrate some basic gender differences. The mean female Army recruit is 4.8 inches shorter and 31.7 lbs lighter and has 8.5% more body fat then her male counterpart (Myers, Gebhardt, Crump, and Fleishman, 1984).

The upper and lower torso isometric strength of Army women is reported as being 60% to 65% that of men (Wright, Sharp, Vogel and Patton, 1985). Marcinik, Hodgdon, O'Brien, and Mittleman (1985) reported that the upper torso weight lifting strength of Navy women ranged from 46% to 58% that of men; Robertson and Trent (1985) reported only a 7% overlap in dynamic weight lifting scores of Navy men and women. Similar differences have been reported elsewhere in the literature and attributed to the male's greater mechanical advantage (larger levers) and the larger cross-sectional area of male muscles.

Maximal oxygen consumption (VO_2max) is the standard measure of aerobic capability. Vogel, Patton, Mello, and Daniels (1985) reported that the mean VO_2max of males and females entering the Army was 51 and 37 ml/kg/min - a 27% difference. Hence a woman, performing the same load carrying task at the same rate as a man is typically working at a higher metabolic rate and thus will fatigue faster. These differences are attributable to the typically lower cardiac output of a woman's smaller heart.

Robertson (1992) notes that while the selection process has emphasized technical skills, the frequency and duration of performing physically demanding tasks is irregular and likely to occur under combat conditions. What physical tasks are involved and what differences exist in the abilities of males and females to perform the tasks? Myers, Gebhardt, Crump, and Fleishman (1984), examining 1,999 critical army tasks, determined that 41% involved lifting/lowering, 30% involved carrying/load bearing, and 11% involved pushing/pulling. Subsequently, Vogel (1992) reported that for lifting, carrying, and pushing tasks, the average female strength score was 59.4%, 58.3% and 63.5% respectively that of the male strength score. In field research, Robertson (1992) used a work output index (a combination of force, distance and time) to evaluate the performance of 273 men and 259 women recruits completing shipboard tasks. The results showed that 32% of the women were below the standard for the fuel tank carrying task, 77% were below the standard for the fuel hose dragging task, 81% were below the standard for cable rigging, and none met the standard for bomb loading. During these same tests, a 10.6% injury rate was noted among women in contrast with a 0.9% rate among men. Faced with similar materials handling concerns, the civilian sector has used powered devices for lifting, carrying, pushing, etc. Unfortunately, these devices are often neither compatible with the operational environment nor available aboard ships or in the field. However, as Robertson (1992, p 1302-1303) notes the "effect of inadequate strength resulting in rapid fatigue in sustained combat or casualty conditions, in turn contributing to additional losses of life, weapons or battles is a critical concern."

What are some possible solutions? Since it is unlikely that the need for unplanned, on-the-spot "brute-force" will ever be eliminated in combat or combat-support missions, only individuals with strength appropriate for the tasks should be assigned to those occupational specialties which require strength. Robertson (1992) proposes that specific training in manual materials handling could reduce the number of individuals failing to attain established standards on criterion tasks. In addition, as technology develops more compact portable power storage devices and progresses in the use of lighter, stronger materials, we can expect the development of devices which both supplement an individual's strength capabilities and are compatible with the operational environment.

Presently there are efforts or proposals within all services to establish or maintain the currency of existing job standards for jobs demanding strength/endurance. In 1975, the USAF developed the Strength Aptitude Test (SAT). Today, each military Air Force job description specifies a minimum SAT performance score which must be attained before an individual will be considered for assignment to that position (McDaniel, Scandis and Madole, 1983). The Army's analog, Military Entrance Physical Strength Capacity Test (MEPSCAT), was developed along similar lines but was used only in an advisory category until 1990 at which time its use was discontinued. The Navy currently does not have occupational physical standards for each occupation specialty, but does have stringent physical requirements for selected programs such as divers, aviators, Explosive Ordnance Detail (EOD), and Sea, Air, Land teams (SEALs).

In addition to strength requirements, anthropometric (body-size) compatibility can also be a limiting factor. In a review of accommodation of women on a new Navy combatant (Carlow International, 1993), many anthropometric incompatibilities were noted, including the inability to reach and close hatches, operate equipment, and properly utilize protective equipment such as fire fighting gear and oxygen breathing apparatus. These incompatibilities may be attributed to ship design standards which called for the accommodation of the fifth to ninety-fifth percentile male (statures of 64 to 73 inches, respectively). Since, the stature for the fiftieth percentile female is slightly less than that of the fifth percentile male, it is not surprising that compatibility problems are encountered by at least half of the female population. This problem is not unique to ships. Aboard current military aircraft, the minimum sitting height requirement for aviators also excludes approximately half the potential female candidates (Ketcham-Wiedel and Bittner, 1977).

Changing designs to accommodate a wider range of individuals in ships and aircraft is a technical and in many cases costly challenge. In some cases, problems can be corrected easily by increasing the range of adjustments on seats or providing larger levers on tools. In other cases, such as redesigning the cockpits of tactical aircraft, the task is considerably more difficult because a shorter bodied person must sit higher (to see adequately over the nose of the aircraft) while maintaining contact with stick and rudder controls and having adequate visual and manual access to other controls and displays. The use of individual specific accommodation devices (seat pan/seat back boosters) may work in some aircraft while in other aircraft the same accommodative devices may interfere with performance or safe egress. Ejection seats are also a cause of concern since the design specifications for present day Navy ejection seats are based on a male population (5th to 95th percentile values of 140 to 203 lbs nude weight, respectively). Reflecting this, Patterson and Harbeson (1989) found the incidence of ejection induced back injuries (below Cervical-7) was significantly higher among individuals falling below the mean body weight. Since these seats have been tested to a lower limit of 136 lbs, the risk associated with ejecting lighter personnel can analytically be expected to be higher. Specifically, basic physics (Force=Mass*Acceleration) indicates that the accelerative forces imposed on a 110 pound individual would be twice that imposed on a 220 pound individual. While women may be at risk after initiating an ejection, McDaniel and Robbins (1992) has demonstrated that women have adequate strength to initiate an ejection.

Anthropometric accommodation is also a concern in the design of protective clothing (such as that shown previously in Figures 13-3 and 13-4) and transport equipment (parachutes, backpacks). To properly design these types of clothing and equipment, the military has collected considerable anthropometric data. A very complete survey of Army personnel of both sexes was completed recently by Gordon et al.(1989). Efforts in uniform clothing design (Robinette and Mellian and Ervin, 1991) and the design of unisex clothing for Army personnel (Gordon et al., 1986) will transfer into the design and the development of tariffs for protective equipment, which should facilitate the accommodation and protection of women in previously all-male workspaces and environments.

Based in part on some of the data presented above, the Presidential Commission on the Assignment of Women in the Armed Forces (1992) arrived at the following HFE related conclusions:

1. Specific requirements should be adopted for specialties in which strenght/ endurance and cardiovascular capacity are relevant. These requirements should be gender-neutral.
2. Gender-specific physical fitness test and standards should be maintained, but they must not compromise training or qualification programs for physically demanding combat or combat support jobs.
3. Entrance Standards can be gender-specific during basic training.

8.0 Opportunities for Involvement in DOD Programs

No single DOD agency serves as "the" Point of Contact for DOD R&D programs requiring HFE, however there are a variety of ways in which students, researchers and practitioners participate. The usual contracting approach requires a monitoring of Commerce Business Daily[25], which contains announcements of DOD's contractual intentions and solicits responses from potential suppliers of goods and services. An alternate approach is to contact HFE DOD personnel involved in the area you wish to research. These personnel are listed in the MATRIS directory of DOD researchers (see footnote 3) or can be identified through presentations at meetings such as the HFES Annual Meeting or through journal publications or reports available through the National Technical Information Service (NTIS). A third option is to contact the HF points of Contact listed in Tables 13-5, 13-6, and 13-7.

In addition to the above, each of the services provide post-doctoral programs, and opportunities for summer research to university faculty members.[26] For example, the Office of Naval Research and the Air Force Systems Command offer support to individuals who have completed their Ph.D program within the last five years. At the graduate student level the USAF offers a graduate student research program at a variety of laboratories.

---

[25] Available from the Superintendent of Documents, Government Printing Office, Washington,DC,20402-9371

[26] For details contact ODUSD(R&AT/RLM) Room 3E114, Office of the Secretary of Defense, Washington, D.C. 20301.

Unique opportunities also exist within the Armed Forces for individuals, who wish to serve in uniform. For example, the Naval Aerospace Experimental Psychologist program recruits psychologists with PhDs, or with Masters degrees and at least four years commissioned service. The desired areas of specialization include: experimental, engineering, industrial, personnel, training, cognition, operations research, or physiological psychology. Individuals accepted into the program must meet aviation physical standards and complete the prescribed flight training syllabus. Similar opportunities exist for research psychologists, who serve in billets supporting non-aviation areas such as underwater, surface warfare and Marine Corps. These individuals serve, as commissioned officers, in positions from bench-level researchers through executive positions at the DOD level.

9.0 Future Directions of Military HFE

"Military Human Factors Engineering (HFE) has been both the most diverse and challenging area of HFE and the area which has contributed most to the development of human factors." The truth of this paraphrase from the opening section of this chapter should be clear to readers of previous sections. It should also be clear that, as stated in the opening section, the "emphasis within the DOD has been on performance" indeed, that theme has been repeated throughout this chapter. In addition to the material described above, DOD standards, developed in response to military environments, have provided a basis for industrial, national, and international HFE standards. Many of the "products" produced by DOD's HFE personnel have been transferred to the civilian sector both in the U.S. and around the world. These include:

- Selection batteries used in industry
- Navy Diving Tables used by industrial divers
- Cabin pressurization schedules followed by commercial airlines
- Innumerable studies describing the human's performance capabilities and limitations under a multitude of environmental extremes used in the civilian sector
- INTERNET evolved from four computers linked together by Defense Advanced Research Projects Agency (DARPA), in 1969
- Research executed to support Command, Control and Communication requirements has been adopted for use by the "Information Super Highway"
- Use of Global Positioning Systems in Intelligent Vehicle Highway Systems (IVHS).
- Flight simulators, now used routinely in commercial aviation, laid the foundation for modern driving simulators, virtual reality and synthetic environments.

But what about the future? What themes and emphases are military HFE likely to pursue, and will it continue in its contributions to the broader area of civilian HFE?

One aspect of the future of military HFE is clear -- the emphasis of military HFE will continue to be on performance. However, it is also clear that this emphasis will be impacted by many factors that influence both the military and the civilian sectors. Howell (1993), in this regard, notes that skill requirements are increasing in many occupations, but that the educational level of the U.S. labor force is declining. At the same time, the workforce in the U.S. is aging and diversifying (with regard to both ethnicity and gender). The military will increasingly be influenced by these trends and by the geopolitical shifts resulting from the breakup of the former Soviet block, which lead to the reductions in global but not local area military tensions.

Based on these trends, Howell (1993) forecasts four trends for the military:

1. Emphasis on modification and maintenance of existing weapon systems with less expenditures for the development of new weapon systems
2. Smaller, more mobile special forces to complete a mission quickly and precisely
3. Limited opportunity for realistic combat training exercises due to cost and environmental constraints
4. Emphasis on technology transfer from the DOD to civilian sectors

This last trend has been reflected in the recent development of ARPA's Dual Use Technologies Program (ARPA, 1993). Anticipating this, it may be recalled from the earlier system development section, that many civilian and non-DOD government organizations have transfered MANPRINT's philosophy and selected tools to the industrial and non-DOD sectors. Related to this dual-use theme, Gal and Mangelsdorff (1991, p. XXIX) state:

> **"Military institutions present unique opportunities for developing and setting professional trends which affect civilian settings as well. Among the most significant trends are the [continued] development of occupational classification categories, increased utilization of women, better opportunities for minorities, training and utilization of para-professionals, and assessment batteries for large-scale population screening."**

The considerations listed above, coupled with the concomitant reduction in personnel, provide new challenges for military HFE practitioners. In the future, these practitioners can expect to work as team members, to interact even more closely with the ultimate user, and to justify their efforts in cost-benefit terms. In addition to the traditional areas described previously, the following areas are expected to continue to expand.

9.1 Simulation.

Simulation is used for both large group and individual training. On the large scale, simulations such as those used in SIMMNET (Alluisi, 1991) and in a recently established Close Combat Tactical Training program can be expected to increase. Furthermore, Director Of Defense Research and Engineering has made a commitment to the development-utilization of virtual environments. We have already seen the increased use of virtual mockups in development, test, and evaluation models such as CREWCHIEF (McDaniel and Hofmann, 1990). Issues related to proving and measuring effective training for large groups have been recently addressed (Moses and Alluisi, 1993; McKeever and Christ, 1993). For individual or small group training, increased use of PC-based training devices can be expected. Relatedly, Travillian, Volpe, Cannon-Bowers and Salas (1993) recently used a PC-based game to evaluate the effectiveness of cross-training team members. Analogously, Braun, Bowers, Holmes, and Salas (1993) used a low-fidelity, PC-based flight simulator to evaluate acquisition of aircrew coordination skills. Emphasis on simulation can be expected to force HFE personnel to readdress issues such as part vs. whole-task training, embedded training, transfer of training, and fidelity requirements.

9.2 Modeling.

Human operator and maintainer model development and use can be expected to increase. Both SIMNET and MANPRINT rely heavily on the use of models. The development of appropriate models would also minimize the requirement for testing humans under hazardous conditions. Proper use of validated models would considerably reduce development, test and evaluation cost. The models would address requirements ranging from biomechanical to complex cognitive applications. Currently, models such as CREWCHIEF address biomechanical applications while, on the cognitive level, models such as COGNET (COGnitive NEtwork of Tasks) developed by Zachary, Ryder and Zubritzky (1989) for anti-submarine warfare task applications have been applied to anti-air warfare tasks (Zachary, Zaklad, Hicinbothom, Ryder, and Purcell, 1993).

9.3 Workload/Situational Awareness

Workload and situational awareness are combined under the same heading, because they are often closely related, can be difficult to measure, yet must be measured. Improved workload metrics are desired to provide better estimates of personnel and team requirements for existing and upgraded systems (Christ, Zaklad, Bittner, Hill and Linton, 1989). Also needed are improvements in measuring situational awareness, since assessment and knowledge of the situation are the critical event drivers (Kaempf, Wolf, and Miller, 1993). Once decision makers are aware of and have assessed the situation, then the required actions are usually determined by standard operational procedures.

9.4 Automation

Automation is no longer seen as a panacea, for we have become aware of its deceptive capabilities, particularly when transition from automatic to manual control is required. Lockart, Strub, Hawley and Tapia (1993), for example, describe improperly designed automation that has led to degradations in manual-transitions because of its contributions to the users loss of situational awareness and manual skills. Perhaps offering one solution to the transition problem, among other, is adaptive automation, in which the automated system responds automatically to predefined situations (acute G-forces in an aircraft), pilot state variables (e.g., physiological workload measures) or performance (time to respond to alarms). Morrison (1993) provides a fine overview of adaptive automation albeit considerably more work is needed to define the "appropriate" interaction between the operator and automation. Finally, the TADMUS program (Section 5.3) may also provide guidance on decision making when using automated systems.

9.5 Expert Systems

Expert systems, like automation, are no longer seen as a panacea. However, we have realized that the appropriate use of expert systems shows considerable promise for improving/supplementing the skill level of operators/ maintainers and HFE personnel. The "Pilot Associate" program has been an attempt to use expert systems within the aviation community. The purpose of this DARPA program has been to integrate computer technology, decision support systems and artificial intelligence into an intelligent interface that could be used by pilots of tactical aircraft. Hammer and Small (in press) provide an overview of the development of the Pilot Associate intelligent interface. While, Barrett and Donnell (1990) provide a thought-provoking, reality-testing, article on fundamental issues to be considered in developing real-time expert advisory systems.

The use of expert systems by HFE personnel can be expected to become more common as the number of experienced HFE practitioners in DOD declines. Directly applicable to the selection of workload measurements is OWLKNEST (Operator Workload KNowledge-based Expert System Tool) described earlier in the tool section (Harris et al., 1992).

9.6 Personnel Utilization

Personnel utilization will require additional research over the next decade. DOD must have systems that can be operated and maintained successfully despite the impact of: 1) reductions in the overall number of military personnel, and 2) changes in the mix of personnel and their capabilities; Sharp, Rice, Nindl, and Williamson, 1993) examined the effect of mixed genders on a three person team engaged in a lifting task, while, Stone (1993) reviewed literature describing the characteristics of the aging military aviator. Additional studies examining the impact of age, gender, and ethnic differences on the design of workspaces and clothing can be expected.

9.7 Maintenance

Maintenance costs currently account for 30% of the life cycle cost of military systems and about 12% of commercial airlines operating expenses. Davis (1993) lists maintenance and inspection as the second leading cause of fatalities among commercial airlines. Thus, this area has potential for considerable savings in both cost and lives. The maintenance procedures and training strategies developed by DOD's HFE personnel will not only reduce DOD's costs but the technology transfer will increase the competitiveness of the civilian sector.

HFE personnel supporting the military can be expected to continue contributing to the human factors discipline. New systems technologies, expanding personnel diversity, increased interdisciplinary efforts, changes in funding levels, emphasis on technology transfer, and the challenges presented by the military's new directions in the changing world will continue to make it the most challenging area of HFE. Of particular note, are the unique simulation, modeling, and other opportunities described above. These challenging opportunities and the unique strengths of the military's many HFE practitioners will lead to even greater contributions in the future.

10.0 Biography

William F. Moroney served as a US Navy Aerospace Experimental Psychologist for more than 22 years in the area of human factors engineering. He has authored scientific and technical publications dealing topics as diverse as motion sickness, helmet mounted displays, laser designator systems, simulation, selection and training. He has supported the development and upgrading of a variety of advanced aircraft and systems. He taught in the Operations Research Department at the Naval Postgraduate School, the Naval Aviation Safety School and the Navy Test Pilot School. He is a founding member of the Department of Defense Human Factors Engineering Technical Group for Test and Evaluation and has served in a variety of positions on DOD, national and international human factors groups. As an Associate Professor of Psychology at the University of Dayton, he continues research in the areas of simulation, workload, cockpit design, displays, and anthropometry. He is presently serving as Chair of both the Test and Evaluation Technical Group and the Accreditation Review Committee of the Human Factors and Ergonomics Society. His E-mail address is: Moroney@udavxb.oca.udayton.edu

Alvah C. Bittner has more than 25 years of experience as a human factors and ergonomics researcher, practitioner, and manager. Throughout his career, he has been involved with the programmatic development, application, and evaluation of human factors/ergonomics tools (e.g., CAPE/CAR, CADRE, PETER, APTS, and OWL). This involvement has resulted in 67 journal and book chapter publications and more than 150 other proceedings and technical reports. In addition to his research interests, he has been involved with the development of national and international standards (DOD, ANSI, and ISO). He has also been an involved member of various technical societies, e.g., the Human Factors and Ergonomics Society (HFES) and the International Foundation for Industrial Ergonomics & Safety Research (IFIESR). He has previously served as President of the IFIESR and Chair of the HFES T&E Technical Group. Dr. Bittner is a Fellow of the HFES. His E-mail address is: Bittner@Battelle.org.

ACKNOWLEDGEMENTS

The authors wish to acknowledge the support and assistance of the many former or current HFE personnel in the Department of Defense, who graciously responded to requests for information and materials, suggested alternate sources of information and reviewed parts of this chapter. They reflect the professionalism and teamwork, which the authors have found to be characteristic of HFE personnel within the DOD. Since it would be impossible to acknowledge all of you without missing someone, we extend a global grateful "Thank You" to our many DOD friends.

The technical assistance of Joyce Cameron, Michele Hemp and Brian Moroney, who reviewed and critiqued this document is also gratefully acknowledged.

Finally, the authors acknowledge their wives, Kathleen and Catherine, who supported our efforts in completing this chapter. We thank them for their tolerance.

REFERENCES

Note: References with AD or ADA numbers may be obtained by calling the National Technical Information Service at 1-800 553-6847.

Advanced Research Projects Agency. (1993). *Program Information Package for Defense Conversion, Reinvestment and Transition Assistance.* Arlington, VA: Technology Reinvestment Project.

Advisory Group For Aerospace Research and Development. (1989). *Human Performance Assessment Methods. AGARDograph No 308.* Neuilly-Sur-Seine, France: AGARD.

Advisory Group for Aerospace Research and Development. (1991). *High Altitude and High Acceleration Protection for Military Aircrew (Conference Proceedings)* (AGARD-CP-516 ed.). Neuilly-Sur-Seine, France: AGARD.

Albery, W. B., & Van Patten, R. E. (1991). Non-invasive sensing systems for acceleration-induced physiological changes. *IEEE Engineering in Medicine and Biology*, 10(1), 46-51.

Alluisi, E. A. (1991). The development of technology for collective training: SIMNET, a case history. *Human Factors*, 33, 343-362.

Alveres, K.M. and Hulin, C.L. (1972). Two explanations of temporal changes in ability-skill relationships: A literature review and theoretical analysis. *Human Factors*, 14, 295-308.

American National Standards Institute. (1992,draft). *Guide to Human Performance Measurements. BSR/AIAA G-035-1992*. Washington, DC: American Institute of Aeronautics and Astronautics.

American National Standards Institute. (1988). *ANSI/HFS-100- 1988: Standard for Human Factors Engineering of Visual Display Terminal Workstations*. Santa Monica, CA: Human Factors Society.

American Psychological Association. (1992). Ethical principles of psychologists and code of conduct. *American Psychologist*, 47(12), 1597-1611.

American Society for Testing and Materials. (1988). American Society for Testing and Materials F-1166. *Standard Practice for Human Engineering Design for Marine Systems, Equipment and Facilities*. Philadelphia, PA: ASTM.

Angus, R. G., & Heslegrave, R. J. (1985). Effects of sleep loss on sustained cognitive performance during a command and control simulation. *Behavior Research Methods, Instruments and Computers*, 17, 55-67.

Askew, G. K., & Kaufman, J. A. (1991). *Ventilation Loss in the NASA Space Shuttle Crew Protective Garments: Potential for Heat Stress*. NADC-91129-60. Warminster, Naval Air Development Center.

Association for the Advancement of Medical Instrumentation. (1993). AAMI HE-1988. *Human Factors Engineering Guidelines and Preferred Practices for the Design of Medical Devices*. (In 1994,this document will be redesignated HE-48 by ANSI.) Arlington, VA: AAMI.

Babbitt, B. A., & Nystrom, C. O. (1989a). *Questionnaire Construction Manual*. Alexandria, VA: U.S. Army Research Institute for the Behavioral and Social Sciences.

Babbitt, B. A., & Nystrom, C. O. (1989b). *Questionnaire Construction Manual Annex. Questionnaires: Literature Survey and Bibliography*. Alexandria, VA: U.S. Army Research Institute for the Behavioral and Social Sciences.

Babkoff, H., & Kreuger, G. P. (1992). The use of stimulants to ameliorate the effects of sleep loss during sustained performance. *Military Psychology*, 4, 191-205.

Baltzley, D. R., Kennedy, R. S., Berbaum, K. S., Lilienthal, M. G., & Gower, D. W. (1989). The time course of postflight simulator sickness symptoms. *Aviation, Space, and Environmental Medicine*, 60, 1043-1048.

Banderet, L. E., Blewett, W., Gonzalez, R. R., Johnson, R. F., Redmond, D., Thornton, R., Taylor, H. L., & Orlansky, J. (1992). *Proceedings of a Symposium: Consequences of Wearing the Chemical Protective Ensemble: Illustrative Assessment Approaches*. Natick, MA: U.S. Army Research Institute of Environmental Medicine.

Banderet, L. E., & Burse, R. L. (1991). Effects of high terrestrial altitude on military performance. In R. Gal & A. D. Mangelsdorff (Eds.), *Handbook of Military Psychology* (pp. 233-254). New York: John Wiley.

Banderet, L.E., Shukitt-Hale, B., Kennedy, R.S., Houston, C.S. & Bittner, A.C., Jr. (1992). *Cognitive Performance and Affect During Ascent to 7600m Simulated Altitude: Operation Everest II.* Natick, MA: US Army Research Institute of Environmental Medicine.

Baron, S., Kruser, D. S., & Huey, B. M. (Eds.). (1990). *Quantitative Modeling of Human Performance in Complex,Dynamic Systems.* Washington, D.C.: National Academy Press.

Barrett, C. L., & Donnell, M. L. (1990). Real time expert advisory systems: Considerations and imperatives. *Information and Decision Technologies*, 16, 15-25.

Batejat, D., & Lagarde, D. (1992). Circadian rhythm and sleep deprivation: Effects on psychomotor performance. *Medical Science Research*, 20, 167-168.

Birt, J. A., & Chaikin, G. (1993). Standards activities in the Department of Defense. *Human Factors and Ergonomics Society Bulletin*, 36 (5), 3-4.

Bittner, A. C., Jr. (1993). Test and evaluation of requirements for human-in-the-loop systems. *Ergonomics in Design,* 29-32.

Bittner, A.C., Jr. (1992). Robust testing and evaluation (T&E) of systems: Framework, approaches, and illustrative tools. *Human Factors*, 34, 477-484.

Bittner, A.C., Jr. (1991). Analysis of learning-curve asymptotes: Ergonomic applications. In W. Karwowski and J. W. Yates (Eds.), *Advances in Industrial Ergonomics and Safety III* (pp. 769-776). Bristol, PA: Taylor & Francis Inc.

Bittner, A.C., Jr., and Bramwell, A.T. (1992). Subjects in human factors: Evaluation of subject-condition (SxC) interactions. *Proceedings of the Human Factors Society 36th Annual Meeting*. 1232-1236.

Bittner, A. C., Jr., Carter, R. C., Kennedy, R. S., Harbeson, M. M., & Krause, M. (1986). Performance evaluation tests for environmental research (PETER): Evaluation of 114 measures. *Perceptual and Motor Skills*, 63, 683-708.

Bittner, A.C., Jr. and Guignard, J.C. (1988). Shipboard evaluation of motion sickness incidence. In F. Aghazadeh (Ed.), *Trends in Ergonomics/Human Factors V* (pp. 529-541). New York: North-Holland.

Bittner, A. C., Jr., Harbeson, M. M., Kennedy, R. S., & Lundy, N. C. (1986). Assessing the human performance envelope: A brief guide (SAE 851776). *SAE Transactions*, 6, 375-385.

Bittner, A.C., Jr., Kantowitz, B.H. and Bramwell, A.T. (1993). *Workload Assessment of Automated Flight Decks: Analysis of ASRS Incident Reports* (Final Report). Seattle WA: Battelle Human Affairs Research Centers.

Bittner, A.C., Jr. and Morrissey, S.J. (1988). Analysis of "error" variances in repeated measures designs. In F. Aghazadeh (Ed.), *Trends in Ergonomics/Human Factors V* (pp. 15-20). New York, NY: North-Holland.

Bittner, A. C., Jr., Smith, M. G., Kennedy, R. S., Staley, C. F., & Harbeson, M. M. (1985). Automated portable test system (APTS): Overview and prospects. *Behavior Research Methods, Instruments and Computers*, 17, 217-221.

Bogner, M. S., Kibbe, M., Laine, R., & Hewitt, G. (1990). *Directory of Design Support Methods*. San Diego, CA: MATRIS, Defense Technical Information Center. AD229180; updated as AD256987.

Bond, D. F. (1993). Cost, supportability: Key to Boeing Sikorsky LH award. *Aviation Week & Space Technology*, April 15,1993, 18-19.

Booher, H. R. (Ed.). (1990). *Manprint, An Approach to Systems Integration*. New York: Van Nostrand Reinhold.

Booher, H. R. (1993).Manprint and dual use. *Army Research, Development and Acquisition Bulletin, PB70-93-6*. Alexandria, VA: HQ Army Material Command.

Bowers, V.A. and Snyder, H.L. (1990). Concurrent versus retrospective verbal protocol for comparing window usability. *Proceedings of the Human Factors Society 34th Factors Annual Meeting*. 1270-1274.

Boyle, E., Ianni, J., Easterling, J., Harper, S. & Korna, M. *Human-Centered Technology for Maintainability: Workshop Proceedings. AL-TP-1991-0010*. Wright-Patterson AFB, OH: Armstrong Laboratory. ADA239090.

Bramwell, A. T., Bittner, A. C., Jr., & Morrissey, S. J. (1992). Repeated measures analysis: Issues and options. *International Journal of Ergonomics*, 10, 185-197.

Braun, C. C., Bowers, C. A., Holmes, B. A., & Salas, E. (1993). Impact of task difficulty on the acquisition of aircrew coordination skills. In *Proceedings of the Human Factors and Ergonomics Society 37th Annual Meetings-1993*. 1262-1266.

Campbell, D.T., and Stanley,J.C. (1963). *Experimental and Quasi-Experimental Designs for Research*. Boston, MA: Houghton-Miflin.

Cannon-Bowers, J. A., Salas, E., & Grossman, J. D. (1992). Improving tactical decision making under stress: Research directions and applied implications. In S. C. Collyer (Ed.), *The 27th International Applied Military Psychology Symposium: A Focus on Decision Making Research* (pp. 49-71). Washington, DC: Office of Naval Research European Office.

Carlow International. (1990). *Human Factors Engineering: Part 1. Test Procedures; Part II: Human Factors Engineering Data Guide for Evaluation (HEDGE)*. Washington D.C.: Army Test and Evaluation Command. ADA226480.

Carlow International Inc. and Thomas Enterprises, Inc. (1993). *Human Systems Integration Assessment for Accommodating Women on the DDG-51 Class*. Falls Church, VA: Carlow International Incorporated.

Carlsmith, J.M., Ellsworth, P.C. and Aronson, E. (1976). *Methods of Research in the Social Psychology*. New York, NY: Random House.

Casper, P. A., Shively, R. J., & Hart, S. G. (1986). Decision support for workload assessment: Introducing WC Fielde. *Proceedings of the Human Factors Society's 31st Annual Meeting*. 72-76.

Chapanis, A., Garner, W. R., Morgan, C. T., & Sanford, F. H. (1947). *Lectures on Men and Machines: An Introduction to Human Engineering*. Baltimore: Systems Research Laboratory.

Charlton, S.G. (1992). Establishing human factors criteria for space control systems, *Human Factors*, 34, 485-501).

Chenzoff, A. P., & Loose, D. R. (1992). *Comparative Anatomy of Maintenance Tasks (CAMT): A Feasibility Study. AL-TR-1992-0007*. Wright-Patterson AFB, OH: Armstrong Laboratory. ADA248709.

Christ, R. E., Bulger, J. P., Hill, S. G., & Zaklad, A. L. (1990). *Incorporating Ooperator Workload Issues and Concerns Into the System Acquisition Process: A Pamphlet for Army Managers*. Alexandria, VA: U.S. Army Research Institute for the Behavioral and Social Sciences. TR 90-30.

Christ, R. E., Hill, S. G., Byers, J. C., Iavecchia, H. M., Zaklad, A. L., & Bittner, A. C. (1993). *Application and Validation of Workload Assessment Techniques. ARI-TR-974*. Alexandria, VA: U.S. Army Research Institute for the Behavior and Social Sciences. ADA264575.

Christ, R. E., Zaklad, A. L., Bittner, A. C., Hill, S. G., & Linton, P. M. (1989). The army operator workload (OWL) program: Review and prospectus. In *Proceedings of the Human Factors Society's 33rd Annual Meeting*. 1471-1475.

Christensen, J. M. (1987). The human factors profession. In G. Salvendy (Ed.), *Handbook of Human Factors* (pp. 3-16). New York: John Wiley & Sons.

Clauser, C. E., Tucker, P. E., McConville, J. T., Churchill, E., Laubach, L. L., & Reardon, J. A. (1972). *Anthropometry of Air Force Women*. Wright-Patterson AFB, OH: Armstrong Aerospace Medical Research Laboratory.

Cohen, J. B., Gawron, V. J., Mummaw, D. A., & Turner, A. D. (in press). Performance assessment and workload evaluation system (PAWES): A process and tool to evaluate cockpit design during flight test. In *Proceedings of the Seventh International Symposium on Aviation Psychology*. Columbus, OH: Ohio State University.

Conway, C. V. (1992). The role of paperless manuals and integrated diagnostics in improving maintenance. *NAECON*, 985-993.

Cooper, G. E., & Harper, R. P. (1969). *The Use of Pilot Rating in the Evaluation of Aircraft Handling Qualities. NASA-TN-D-5153*. Moffett Field, CA: NASA AMES.

Cox, D.L. (1958). *The Planning of Experiments*. New York: Wiley & Sons.

Crowley, J. (1991). *Human Factors of Night Vision Devices: Anecdotes from the Field Concerning Visual Illusions and Other Effects. USAARL-91-15*. Fort Rucker, AL: Army Aeromedical Research Laboratory. AD A237641.

Damos, D. (1985). The effect of asymmetric transfer and speech technology on dual-task performance. *Human Factors*, 27, 409-421.

Davis, R. A. (1993, October). Human factors in the global marketplace. *Keynote Address at the 37th Annual Meeting of the Human Factors and Ergonomics Society*, Seattle, WA.

Department of Defense. (1980). *DOD-HDBK-743. Anthropometry of US Military Personnel*. Washington, DC: DOD.

Department of Defense. (1983). *DOD Directive: 3216.2: Protection of Human Subjects in DOD-Supported Research*. Washington DC: DOD.

Department of Defense. (1987). *DOD-HDBK-763: Human Engineering Procedures Guide*. Washington, DC: DOD.

Department of Defense. (1991a). *DODI 5000.2. Defense Acquisition Management Policies and Procedures, Part 7, Section B, Human Systems Integration*. Washington, DC: DOD.

Department of Defense. (1991b). *DOD 5000.2-M. Defense Acquisition Management Documentation and Reports*. Washington, DC: DOD.

Department of Defense. (1984). *MIL-H-46855B; Human Engineering Requirements for Military Systems, Eequipment and Facilities*. Washington, DC: Pentagon.

Department of Defense. (1989). *DOD-HDBK-761. Human Engineering Guidelines for Management Information Systems*. Washington, DC: DOD.

Department of Defense. (1989). *DOD-HDBK-763. Human Engineering Procedures Guide*. Washington, DC: DOD.

Department of Defense. (1992). *MIL-HDBK--759B: Human Factors Engineering Design of Army Material*. Washington, DC: Pentagon.

Department of Defense. (1991). *MIL-STD-1478: Task Performance Analysis*. Washington, DC: DOD.

Department of Defense. (1992). *MIL-STD-1472: Human Engineering Design Criteria for Military Systems, Equipment and Facilities*. Washington, DC: DOD.

Department of Defense, Director of Defense Research and Engineering. (1992). *DOD Key Technologies Plan*. Washington, DC: DOD. ADA253692.

Department of Defense, Director of Defense Research and Engineering. (1992). *Defense Science and Technology Strategy*. Washington DC: DOD.

Department of Energy. (1992). *Human Factors Engineering Design Criteria: Vol. 1. General Criteria. DOE-STD-HFAC 1 (Vol. 1)*. Washington, DC: DOE, Office of Nuclear Safety Policy and Standards.

Driskell, J. E., & Olmstead, B. (1989). Psychology and the military. *American Psychologist*, 44(1), 43-54.

Driskell, J. E., & Salas, E. (1991). Overcoming the effects of stress on military performance: Human factors, training, and selection strategies. In R. Gal & A. D. Mangelsdorff (Eds.), *Handbook of Military Psychology* (pp. 183-191). New York : John Wiley.

Drury, C.G. (1990). Designing ergonomics studies and experiments. In: J.R. Wilson and E.N. Corlett (Eds.), *Evaluation of Human Work: A Practical Ergonomics Methodology*. Taylor & Francis, London.

Eddy, D. R., Dalrymple, M. A., & Schiflett, S. G. (1992). *Comparative Effects of Antihistamines on Aircrew Mission Effectiveness Under Sustained Operations*. Brooks AFB, TX: Armstrong Laboratory, AL-TR-1992-0018.

Eggemeier, F. T., & Wilson, G. F. (1991). Performance-based and subjective assessment of workload in multi-task environments. In D. L. Damos (Ed.), *Multiple-Task Performance* (pp. 217-278). Washington, DC: Taylor and Francis.

Elkind, J. I., Card, S. K., Hochberg, J., & Huey, B. M. (1989). *Human Performance Models for Computer-Aided Engineering*. Washington, DC: National Academy Press.

Englund, C. E., Reeves, D. L., Shingledecker, C. A., Thorne, D. R., Wilson, K. P., & Hegge, F. W. (1987). *Unified Tri-Service Cognitive Performance Assessment Battery (UTC-PAB) I. Design and Specification of the Battery*. San Diego, CA: Naval Health Research Center.

Federal Aviation Administration. (1990). *The National Plan for Aviation Human Factors*. Springfield, VA: National Technical Information Service. PB91-10003347.

Fleger, S. A., Permenter, F. E., & Malone, T. B. (1988). *Advanced Human Factors Engineering Tool Technologies. TM 2-88*. Aberdeen Proving Ground, MD: U.S. Army Human Engineering Laboratory. AD-A195252.

Gal, R., & Mangelsdorff, A. D. (Eds.). (1991). *Handbook of Military Psychology*. West Sussex, England: John Wiley.

Geer, C. W. (1981). *Human Engineering Procedures Guide. AFAMRL-TR-81-35*. Wright-Patterson AFB, OH: Air Force Aerospace Medical Research Laboratory.

General Accounting Office. (1981a). *Effectiveness of U.S. Forces Can Be Increased Through Improved Weapon System Design. PSAD-81-17.* Washington D.C. Washington D.C.: U.S. General Accounting Office.

General Accounting Office. (1981b). *Guidelines for Assessing Whether Human Factors Were Considered in the Weapon Acquisition Process. FPCD-82-5.* Washington D.C.: U.S. General Accounting Office.

General Accounting Office. (1985). *The Army Can Better Integrate Manpower, Personnel, and Training Into the Weapon Systems Acquisition Process.* Washington D.C.: U.S. General Accounting Office.

General Accounting Office. (1992a). *Defense Procurement Trends for 1985-93 in DOD's Spending, Employment, and Contractors.* GAO/NSIAD-92-274BR. Washington D.C.: U.S. General Accounting Office.

General Accounting Office. (1992b). *Operation Desert Storm: War Offers Important Insights Into Army and Marine Corps Training Needs.* GAO/NSIAD-92-240. Washington D.C.: U.S. General Accounting Office.

Gentner, F. C., & Crissey, M. J. (1992). Liveware survey of human systems integration (HSI) technologies: Need for comprehensive survey and available database. In *Proceedings of the Human Factors Society 36th Annual Meeting.* 1133-1137.

Gentner, F. C., Kancler, D. E., & Crissey, M. J. (in press). Search for training and HSI technologies: Analysis of DOD liveware survey. In *Proceedings of the 1993 Interservice/Industry Training System and Education Conference.* Washington, DC: Headquarters, U.S. Coast Guard.

Gish, K. (1990). Model of visual degradation due to glare. *Proceedings of the 61st Annual Scientific Meeting of the Aerospace Medical Association.* Washington, DC: Aerospace Medical Association.

Glushko, R. (1991). *Hypertext: Prospects and Problems for Crew System Design.* Wright-Patterson AFB, OH: CSERIAC.

Gordon, C. C. (1986). Anthropometric sizing and fit testing of a single battledress uniform for US Army men and women. In R. L. Barker & G. C. Colletta (Eds.), *Performance of Protective Clothing. ASTM STP 900* (pp. 581-592). Philadelphia,PA: American Society for Testing and Materials.

Gordon, C. C., Bradtmiller, B., Churchhill, T., Clauser, C. E., McConville, J. T., Tebbetts, I., & Walker, R. (1989). *1988 Anthropometric Survey of U.S. Army Personnel: Methods and Summary Statistics. NATICK/TR-89/044.* Natick, MA: Army Natick, Research Development and Engineering Center.

Government Printing Office. (1949). *Trials of War Criminals Before the Nuerenberg Military Tribunals Under Control Council Law No 10 (Vol. 2).* Washington, DC: Government Printing Office.

Graeber, R. C. (1988). Aircrew fatigue and circadian rhythmicity. In E. L. Wiener & D. C. Nagel (Eds.), *Human Factors in Aviation.* New York: Academic Press.

Graine, G. N. (1988). The engineering syndrome vs. the manpower personnel and training dilemma. *Naval Engineers Journal*, 54-58.

Gravelle, M. D. (1993). *Performance Effects of One Night's Sleep Deprivation.* Unpublished MA Thesis. University of Dayton, Dayton, OH.

Greenwald, A.G. (1976). Within-subject designs: To use or not to use? *Psychological Reports*, 83, 314-320.

Grunsten, R. C., Gilbert, N. S., & Mawn, S. V. (1989). The mechanical effects of impact acceleration on the unconstrained human head and neck complex. *Contemporary Orthopaedics*, 18, 199-202.

Hamilton, B., & Metzler, T. (1992). *Comanche Crew Station Design. AIAA-92-1049.* Washington, D.C.: American Institute for Aeronautics and Astronautics.

Hammer, J. M., & Small, R. L. (in press). An intelligent interface in an associate system. In W. B. Rouse (Ed.), *Human/Technology Interaction in Complex Systems* (Vol. 7). Greenwich, CT: JAI Press.

Hancock, P.A. and Meshkati, N. (Eds.). (1988) *Human Mental Workload.* Amerstdam: North-Holland.

Harris, R. M., Hill, S. G., & Lysaght, R. J. (1992). *Handbook for Operating the OWLKNEST Ttechnology. ARI Research Note 92-49.* Alexandria, VA: U.S.Army Research Institute for the Behavioral and Social Sciences. ADA253412.

Harrison, A. A., Clearwater, Y. A., & McKay, C. A. (Eds.). (1991). *From Antartica to Outer Sspace: Life in Isolation and Confinement.* New York: Springer-Verlag.

Hart, S.G. and Wickens, C.D. (1990). Workload assessment and prediction. In H.R. Booher (Ed.), *Manprint: An Approach to Systems Integration* (pp. 657-672). New York, NY: Van Nostrand Reinhold.

Hill, S.G., and Harris, R. (1989). OWLNEST: A knowledge-based expert system for selecting workload techniques. In A. Grenaidy and W. Karwowski (Eds.), *Computer-Aided Design: Applications in Ergonomics and Safety.* London: Taylor and Francis.

Hill, S. G., Iavecchia, H. P., Byers, J. C., Bittner, A. C., Jr., Zaklad, A. L., & Christ, R. E. (1992). Comparison of four subjective workload rating scales. *Human Factors*, 34, 429-439.

Hill, S.G., Zaklad, A.L., Bittner, A.C., Jr., Byers, J.C., and Christ, R.E. (1988). Workload assessment of a mobile air defense missile system. *Proceedings of the Human Factors Society 32nd Annual Meeting.* 1068-1072.

Holcombe, F. D., & Webb, S. C. (1991). *Human Factors Assessment of USCG 47-ft Motor Lifeboat* (NBDL-91R003 ed.). New Orleans: Naval Biodynamics Laboratory.

Howell, W. C. (1993). Engineering psychology in a changing world. *Annual Review of Psychology*, 44, 231-263.

Hrebian, L.(Ed). (1991). High-G environments. *IEEE Engineering in Medicine and Biology*, 10,1, 25-75.

Huey, B. M., & Wickens, C. D. (Eds.). (1993). *Workload Transition: Implications for Individual and Team Performance.* Washington, DC: National Academy Press.

Human Factors and Ergonomics Society. (1993). Code of ethics. *Human Factors Society's 1993 Directory and Yearbook,* 357-358. Santa Monica: Human Factors and Ergonomics Society.

Human Systems Division. (1991a). Integrated maintenance information system (IMIS). In *Human Systems Division Products and Progress* (p. 53). Brooks Air Force Base, TX: Human Systems Division

Human Systems Division. (1991b). Crew centered cockpit design (CCCD). In *Human Systems Division Products and Progress* (p. 46). Brooks Air Force Base, TX: Human Systems Division.

International Standards Organization. (1985). *Evaluation of Human Exposure to Whole-Body Z Axis Vertical Vibration in the Frequency Range 0.1 to 0.63 Hz* (ISO 2631\3-1985). Geneva: International Standards Organization.

Kaempf, G. L., Wolf, S., & Miller, T. E. (1993). Decision making in the AEGIS combat information center. In *Proceedings of the 37th Annual Meeeting of the Human Factors and Ergonomics Society*. 1107-1111.

Kandebo, S. W. (1991). Boeing Sikorsky LH technologies will increase Army combat capability. *Aviation Week & Space Technology*, April 15, 1991, 20-22.

Kane, R. L., & Kay, G. G. (1992). Computerized assessment in neuropsychology: A review of tests and tests batteries. [Special Issue]. *Neuropsychology Review*, 3 (1),1-117.

Kantowitz, B. H. (1992). Selecting measures for human factors research. *Human Factors*, 34, 387-398.

Kaplan, M. (1991). Cultural ergonomics: An evolving focus for military human factors. In R. Gal & A. D. Mangelsdorff (Eds.), *Handbook of Military Psychology* (pp. 155-167). New York: John Wiley.

Kaufman, J., & Dejneka, K. (1987). *Evaluation of Thermal Stress Induced by NASA Crew Altitude Protective System*. NADC-88070-60. Warminster, Naval Air Development Center.

Kaufman, J. W., Dejneka, K. Y., & Askew, G. K. (1990). *A Comparison of Rewarming Methods in Mildly Hypothermic Individuals*. NADC-91008-60. Warminster, Naval Air Development Center.

Kaufman, J. W., Dejneka, K. Y., Morrissey, S. J., Bagian, J. P., & Bittner, A. C., Jr. (1988). *Cold Water Evaluation of NASA Launch Entry Suit (LES)*. NADC-88017-60. Warminster, Naval Air Development Center.

Kelly, T. L., & Booth, R. (1990). *A Keyboard for Underwater Performance Assessment Battery Testing*. R90-25. San Diego. CA: Naval Health Research Center.

Kennedy, R. S. (1990). Protocol analysis of military tasks. In *Proceedings of a Conference: Motion Sickness, Visual Displays, and Armored Vehicle Design* (pp. 89-97). Aberdeen, MD: U.S. Army Laboratory Command, Ballistic ResearchLaboratory.

Kennedy, R. S., & Bittner, A. C., Jr. (1977). The development of a Navy Performance Evaluation Test for Environmental Research (PETER). In L. T. Pope & D. Meister (Eds.), *Productivity Enhancement: Personnel Performance Assessment in Navy Systems*. (pp. 393-408). San Diego, CA: Naval Personnel Research and Development Center. ADA056047.

Kennedy, R. S., Dunlap, W. P., Turnage, J. J., Lane, N. E., Jones, M. B., & Cornell, R. A. (1993). *Cognitive and Performance Readiness of Space Crews*. Orlando, FL: Essex Corporation.

Kennedy, R. S., & Fowlkes, J. E. (1992). Simulator sickness is polygenic and polysymptomatic: Implications for research. *International Journal of Aviation Psychology*, 2 (1). 23-38.

Kennedy, R. S., Fowlkes, J. E., Berbaum, K. S., & Lilienthal, M. G. (1992). Use of a motion sickness history questionnaire for prediction of simulator sickness. *Aviation, Space and Environmental Medicine*, 63, 1-6.

Kennedy, R. S., Turnage, J. J., Wilkes, R.L. and Dunlap, W. P.(1993). Effects of graded dosages of alcohol on nine computerized repeated measures tests. *Ergonomics*, 36(10), 1195-1222.

Kern, J., & Lind, J. (1990). *Human Factors Engineering Tool Evaluation, Technical Approach and Program Plan.* Warminster, PA: Air Vechicle and Crew Systems Technology Department. TR91038-60.

Ketcham-Wiedel, M. A., & Bittner, A. C., Jr. (1977). Human factors engineering design for women: A qualitative and quanitative analysis. In *Preprints of the 49th annual meeting of the Aerospace and Medical Association* (pp. 255-258). Las Vegas, NE: Aerospace Medical Association.

Kirk,R.E. (1982). *Experimental Design (2nd edition).* Monterey, CA:Brooks-Cole.

Klein, G. (1993). *Naturalistic Decision Making: Implications for Design.* Wright-Patterson AFB:OH: CSERIAC.

Klein, G. A. (1989). Do decision biases explain too much? *Human Factors Society Bulletin*, 32, 1-3.

Knight, D. R., Bryant, K., Ollayos, C. W., & Luria, S. M. (1989). *The Kinetics of Dark Adaption in Hypoxic Subjects.* NSMRL Report 1151. Groton, CT: Naval Submarine Medical Research Laboratory.

Kobrick, J. L., & Johnson, R. F. (1991). Effects of heat and cold environments on military performance. In R. Gal & A. D. Mangelsdorff (Eds.), *Handbook of Military Psychology* (pp. 215-232). New York: John Wiley.

Koch, G.G., Elashoff, J.D. and Amara, I.A. (1988). Repeated measures-design and analysis. In: *Encyclopedia of Statistical Sciences, Vol 8* (pp. 50-73). New York, NY: John Wiley & Sons.

Kramer, A. F. (1991). Physiological metrics of mental workload: A review of recent progress. In D. L. Damos (Ed.), *Multiple-Task Performance* (pp. 279-328). London: Taylor & Francis.

Kramer, A. F., Coyne, J. T., & Strayer, D. L. (1993). Cognitive function at high altitude. *The Journal of the Human Factors and Ergonomics Society*, 35, 329-344.

Kroemer, K. H. E. (1975). Muscle strength as a criterion in control design for diverse populations. In A. Chapanis (Ed.), *Ethnic Variables in Human Factors Engineering* (pp 67-89). Baltimore: The Johns Hopkins University.

Kroemer, K. H. E., Snook, S. H., Meadows, S. K., & Deutsch, S. (Eds.). (1988). *Ergonomics Models of Anthropometry, Human Biomechanics, and Operator-Equipment Interfaces*. Washington, DC: National Academy Press.

Krueger, G. P. (1991). Sustained military performance in continuous operations: Combatant fatigue, rest and sleep needs. In R. Gal & A. D. Mangelsdorff (Eds.), *Handbook of Military Psychology* (pp. 255-277). New York: John Wiley.

Krueger, G. P., Redmond, D. P., Belenky, G. L., & Leu, J. R. (1988). Sleep and activity during simulated continuous operations at thr National Training Center. Unpublished data. Presented at the Oct. 1988 poster session. *Uniformed Services University of the Health Sciences, 4th Annual Conference on Military Medicine*. Washington, DC: Walter Reed Army Institute of Research.

Lane, N. E. (1986). *Issues in Performance Measurement for Military Aviation with Applications to Air Combat Maneuvering*. Orlando, FL: Naval Training Systems Center.

Lane, N.E., Kennedy, R.S., and Jones, M.B. (1986). Overcoming the unreliability of operational measures: The use of surrogate measure systems. *Proceedings of the Human Factors Society 30th Annual Meeting*. 1398-1402.

Lewis, J.R. (1993). Pairs of Latin squares that produce digram-balanced Greco-Latin designs: A BASIC program. *Behavior Research Methods, Instruments, & Computers*, 25, 414-415.

Lilienthal, M. G. (1993). *Defense Modeling and Simulation Office (DMSO)*. Presentation to DOD Human Factors Engineering Technical Group on May 14, 1993.

Lloyd, J. R., & Olsen, R. G. (1992). *Radiofrequency Energy for rewarming of Cold Extremities*. Pensacola, FL: Naval Aerospace Medical Research Laboratory.

Lockhart, J. M., Strub, M. H., Hawley, J. K., & Tapia, L. A. (1993). Automation and supervisory control: A perspective on human performance, training, and performance aiding. *Proceedings of the Human Factors and Ergonomics Society 37th Annual Meeting-1993*. 1211-1215.

Loose, D. R. (1990). *Design for Maintainability: What Military Standards Do and Don't Say. AFHRL-TP-89-28*. Brooks Air Force Base, TX: Air Force Human Resources Laboratory. ADA221771.

Loose, D. R., Gentner, F. C., & Dascalos, C. M. (1993). Comparative anatomy of maintenance tasks (CAMT): Demonstration of field administration technique. In *Proceedings of 1993 National Avionics and Electronics Convention*, (pp. 645-653). New York: IEEE.

Loose, D. R., Gnetner, F. C., Chenzoff, A. P., & Shipton, D. L. (in press). Comparative anatomy of mainteanance tasks (CAMT): Field study results. In *Proceedings of the 1993 Meeting of the Military Training Association*. Washington, DC: Headquarters, U.S. Coast Guard.

Luria, S. M., Socks, J., & Kobus, D. (1986). *Low Level White Lighting for Submarine Control Rooms*. Groton, CT: Submarine Medical Research Laboratory. AD175505.

Lysaght, R. J., Hill, S. G., Dick, A. O., Plamondon, B. D., Linton, P. M., Wierwille, W. W., Zaklad, A. L., Bittner, A. C., Jr. & Wherry, R. J. (1989). *Operator Workload: Comprehenive Rreview and Evaluation of Ooperator Workload Methodologies*. TR 851. Alexandria, VA: U.S.Army Research Institute for the Behavioral and Social Sciences.

Mackie, R. R. (Ed.). (1977). *Vigilance: Theory, Operational Performance and Physiological Correlates*. New York: Plenum Press.

Marcinik, E. J., Hodgdon, J. A., O'Brien, J. J., & Mittleman, K. (1985). A *Comparison of the Effects of Circuit Weight Training on Navy Men and Women*. San Diego, CA: Naval Health Research Center.

MATRIS. (1992). *Research Directory for Manpower, Personnel, Training, and Human Factors*. San Diego, CA: Defense Technical Information Center.

McCauley, M. E. (Ed.). (1984). *Research Issues in Simulator Sickness*. Washington, DC: National Academy Press.

McCauley, M. E., & Kennedy, R. S. (1976). *Recommended Human Exposure Limits for Very Low Frequency Vibration*. Pt. Mugu, CA: Pacific Missile Test Center.

McCloskey, K. A., Tripp, L. D., Chelette, T. L., & Popper, S. E. (1992). Test and evaluation metrics for use in sustained acceleration research. *Human Factors*, 34, 409-428.

McCommons, R. B., & Cofod, R. K. (1992). *Smart COntract Preparations Environment (SCOPE) Delivers First Products. Gateway. Vol 3* (3), 14-15. Wright Patterson AFB, OH: CSERIAC.

McDaniel, J. W., & Hofmann, M. A. (1990). Computer-aided ergonomic design tools. In H. R. Booher (Ed.), *MANPRINT: An Approach to Systems Integration* (pp. 205-235). New York: Van Nostrand Reinhold.

McDaniel, J. W., & Robbins, G. (1992). The strength of women for activation of ejection seat controls. In S. Kumar (Ed.), *Advances in Industrial Ergonomics and Safety IV* (pp 1275-1282). London: Taylor & Francis.

McDaniel, J. W., Scandis, R. J., & Madole, S. W. (1983). *Weight Lifting Capability of Air Force Basic Trainees. AFAMRL-TR-83-0001*. Dayton, OH: Armstrong Medical Research Laboratory. ADA 129543.

McGuinness, J., Bouwman, J. H., & Forbes, J. M. (1981). *Simulator Sickness Occurences in the 2E6 Air Combat Maneuvering Simulator (ACMS)*. Orlando, FL: Naval Training Equipment Center

McKeever, K. J., & Christ, R. E. (1993). A confident measure of teamwork: The efficacy of confidence assessment and feedback enhancement for collective training. In *Proceedings of the Human Factors and Ergonomics Society 37th Annual Meeting* pp. 1181-1185).

McMillan, G. R., Beevis, D., Salas, E., Strub, M. H., Sutton, R., & Van Breda, L. (Eds.). (1989). *Applications of Human Performance Models to System Design*. New York: Plenum Press.

Meister, D. (1985). *Behavior Analysis and Measurement Methods*. New York: John Wiley.

Meister, D. (1986). *Human Factors Testing and Evaluation.* New York: Elsevier Science Publishing Company.

Meister, D. (1989). *Conceptual Aspects of Human Factors.* Baltimore, MD: The Johns Hopkins University Press.

Meister, D., Enderwick, T. P.(Eds). (1992). Measurement in human factors [Special Issue]. *Human Factors*, 34, 383-506.

Meister, D. & Enderwick, T.P. (1992). Subjects in human factors: What are they thinking? *Proceedings of the 36th Annual Meeting of the Human Factors Society*. 1237-1240.

Miles, J. L., Jr. (1976). *Manprint's Critical Question*. Letter Report to U.S. Army Operational Test and Evaluation Activity.

Miles, J. L. Jr., Deaton, J. E., & Loose, D. R. (1992). *DODHFETG: The Next Generation*. Washington, DC: DOD.

Moore, T. J., & Von Gierke, H. E. (1991). Military performance in acoustic noise environments. In R. Gal & A. D. Mangelsdorff (Eds.), *Handbook of Military Psychology* (pp. 295-311). New York: John Wiley.

Moore-Ede, M. (1993). *The Twenty Four Hour Society*. New York: Addison-Wesley.

Morgan, C. T., Cook, J. S., Chapanis, A., & Lund, M. W. (Eds.). (1963). *Human Engineering Guide to Equipment Design*. New York: McGraw-Hill.

Moroney, W. F., & Reising, J. (1992). Subjects in human factors: Just who are they ? *Proceedings of the Human Factors Society 36th Annual Meeting.* 1227-1231.

Morrison, J. G. (Ed). (1993). *The Adaptive Function Allocation for Intelligent Cockpits (AFAIC) Program: Interim Research and Guidelines for the Application of Adaptive Automation.* NAWCADWAR-93031-60. Warminster, PA: Naval Air Warfare Center, Aircraft Division.

Morrison, T. R., Dobie, T. G., Willems, G. C., Webb, S. C. *Ship Roll Stabilization and Human Performance*. New Orleans: Naval Biodynamics Laboratory.., & Endler, J. L. (1991).

Morrissey, S.J., Bittner Jr., A.C., and Gharamani, B. (1990). Options for analysis of repeated measures designs: Watching-out for the assumptions. In B. Das (Ed.), *Advances in Industrial Ergonomics and Safety II* (pp. 843-855). Bristol, PA: Taylor & Francis Inc.

Moses, F. L., & Alluisi, E. A. (1993). Issues in providing effective training for large groups (A panel presentation and discussion). In *Proceedings of the Human Factors and Ergonomics Society 37th Annual Meeting.* 1248-1251.

Muckler, F. A., & Seven, S. A. (1992). Selecting performance measures: "Objective" versus "subjective" measurement. *Human Factors*, 34, 441-455.

Myers, D. C., Gebhardt, D. L., Crump, C. E., & Fleishman, E. A. (1984). *Validation of the Military Entrance Physical Strength Capacity Test.* Alexandria, VA: U.S. Army Research Institute for the Behavioral and Social Sciences.

Naitoh, P., Kelly, T., & Babkoff, H. (1992). *Sleep Inertia: Is There a Worst Time to Wake Up?* Report # 91-45. San Diego,CA: Naval Health Research Center.

National Aeronautics and Space Administration. (1987). *NASA-STD-3000: Man-System Integration Standards.* Houston, TX: L.B. Johnson Space Center.

Neri, D. F., & Shappell, S. A. (1992). *The Effect of Combat on the Work/Rest Schedules and Fatigue of A-6 and F-14 Aviators During Operation Desert Shield/Storm. NAMRL-1375.* Pensacola, FL: Naval Aerospace Medical Research Laboratory.

Nesthus, T. E., Schiflett, S. G., Eddy, D. R., & Whitmore, J. N. (1991). *Comparative Effects of Antihistamines on Aircrew Performance of Simple and Complex Tasks Under Sustained Operations.* AL-TR-1991-0104. Brooks AFB, TX: Armstrong Laboratory

O'Donnell, R. D. (1991). *Directions in Performance Assessment: Results of the Workshop on Future Metrics and Models for Assessment of Human/System Performance in Advanced Military Systems* (CSERIAC-91-2). Wright-Paterson AFB, OH: CSERIAC.

Office of Naval Research. (1968). *U.S. Naval Flight Surgeons Manual (2nd edition).* Washington,DC: U.S. Government Printing Office.

Office of Science and Technology, Executive Office of the President. (1991). Federal Policy for the protection of human subjects; Notices and rules. In *Federal Register* (Vol. 56, #117, pp. 28001-28032). Washington, DC: Government Printing Office.

Office of the Secretary of the Navy. (1984). *SECNAVINST 3900.39B. Protection of Human Subjects.* Washington, DC: Secretary of the Navy.

Ohnemus, K., & Biers, D. W. (1993). Retrospective vs concurrent thinking-out-loud in useablilty testing. In *Procedings of the 37th Annual Meeting of the Human Factors and Ergonomics Society.* 1127-1131.

Orlansky, J. (Ed.). (1992). *Training Strategies for Networked Simulation and Gaming.* Brussels: NATO, Defense Research Group, Panel on the Defense Applications of Human And Biomedical Sciences.

Parsons, H. M. (1972). *Man-Machine System Experiments.* Baltimore: The Johns Hopkins Press.

Patterson, F. R., & Harbeson, M. (1989). An analysis of anthropometric risk factors related to back injury induced by ejection seat acceleration. *Paper presented at the Annual Meeting of the Aerospace Medical Association.* 65 Washington, DC: Aerospace Medical Association Annual meeting. p 65

Patton, J. F., Damokosh, A. I., & Mello, R. P. (1989). Effects of continuous military operations and physical fitness capacity and physical performance. *Work and Stress,* 3, 69-77.

Perrin, B. M., Barnett, B. J., & Walrath, L. C. (1993). Decision making bias in complex task environments. In *Proceedings of the Human Factors and Ergonomics Society 37th Annual Meeting*, 1117-1121.

Poulton, E.C., 1982. Influential companions: Effects of one strategy on another in within-subjects designs of cognitive psychology. *Psychological Bulletin*, 91, 673-690.

Presidential Commission on the Assignment of Women in the Armed Forces. (1992). *Report to the President.* Washington, DC: Government Printing Office. ISBN:0-16-038236-X.

Reeves, D. L., & Gadolin, R. E. (Eds.). (1989). *Sustained/Continuous Operations Subgroup of the DODHFETG Program Summary and Abstracts From the 8th Semiannual Meeting. NAMRL TM 89-2.* Pensacola, FL: Naval Aerospace Medical Research Laboratory.

Robertson, D. W. (1992). Development of job performance standards for muscularly demanding military tasks. In S. Kumar (Ed.), *Advances in Industrial Ergonomics and Safety IV* (pp. 1299-1304). London: Taylor & Francis.

Robertson, D. W., & Trent, T. T. (1985). *Documentation of Muscularly Demanding Job Tasks and Validation of an Occupational Strength Test Battery (STB).* San Diego,CA: Naval Personnel Research and Development Center.

Robinette, K. M., Mellian, S. A., & Ervin, C. (1991). *Development of Sizing Systems for Navy Women's Uniforms.* AL-TR-1991-0117. Wright-Patterson AFB, OH: Armstrong Laboratory.

Robinette, K. M., & Whitestone, J. J. (1992). *Methods for Characterizing the Human Head for the Design of Helmets. AL-TR-1992-0061.* Wright-Patterson AFB, OH: Armstrong Laboratory.

Rolnick, A., & Gordon, C. R. (1991). The effects of motion sickness on military performance. In R. Gal & A. D. Mandelsdorff (Eds.), *Handbook of Military Psychology* (pp. 279-293). New York: John Wiley.

Rosnow, R. L., Rotheram-Borus, M. J., Ceci, S. J., Blanck, P. D., & Koocher, G. P. (1993). The Institutional Review Board as a mirror of scientific and ethical standards. *American Psychologist*, 48(7), 821-826.

Russell, W. M. S., & Burch, R. L. (1959). *Principles of Humane Experimental Technique.* Springfield, IL: Charles C. Thomas.

Schlegel, R. E., Gilland, K., & Crabtree, M. S. (1992). *Development of the UTC-PAB Normative Database. AL-TR-1992-0145.* Wright Patterson AFB, OH: Armstrong LAboratory.

Shappell, S. A., Kerns, G., DeJohn, C. A., & Neri, D. F. (1993). The chronopharmacokinetics of destromehtamphetamine and it's relationship to performance and subject fatigue. *Proceedings of the 63 Scientific Meeting of the Aerospace Medical Association. A4.* Washington, DC: Aerospace Medical Association.

Shappell, S. A., Neri, D. F., & DeJohn, C. A. (1992). Simulated sustained flight operations and performance, Part 2: Effects of dextro-methamphetamine. *Military Psychology*, 4, 267-287.

Sharp, M., Rice, V., Nindl, B., & Williamson, T. (1993). Maximum lifting capacity in single and mixed gender three-person teams. In *Proceedings of the Human Factors and Ergonomics Society 37th Annual Meeting,* 725-729.

Shingledecker, C.A. (1984). *A Task Battery for Applied Human Performance Assessment Research*. AFAMRL-TR-84. Wright-Patterson AFB, OH: AMRL.

Sidowski, J. B.(Ed). (1985a). Methodological approaches to the study of sustained work/sustained opeations. [Special Section]. *Behavior Research Methods, Instruments and Computers*. 17,1 .

Sidowski, J. B. (Ed) (1985b). Methodological approaches to the study of sustained work/sustained opeations. [Special Section]. *Behavior Research Methods, Instruments and Computers*. 17, 6.

Simon, C.W. and Roscoe, S.N. (1984). Application of a multifactor approach to transfer of training research. *Human Factors*, 26, 591-612.

Smith, S. L., & Mosier, J. N. (1986). *Guidelines for Designing User Interface Software. ESD-TR-86-278.* Hanscon AFB, MA: Electronics Systems Division.

Smolowe,J. (1994). The widening fallout. *Time,* 143,3, 30-31.

Steege, F. W. (1991). Selection, classification and placement in military services. In R. Gal & A. D. Mangelsdorff (Eds.), *Handbook of Military Psychology* (pp. 1-149). New York: John Wiley.

Stone, L. W. (1993). *The Aging Military Aviator: A Review and Annotated Bibliography. USAARL Report 93-11.* Fort Rucker, AL: Army Aeromedical Research Laboratory.

Sussman, L. (1947). Evaluation of Electroroic Cooking Device (Radarrange) for Submarines. MRL Rep. 116. Groton, CN: Naval Medical Research Laboratory.

Szlyk, P. C., Caretti, D. M., Sils, I. V., Zubal, O., & Faugh, J. A. (1992). *Effect of Protective Clothing Ensembles on Artillery Battery Crew Performance.* Natick, MA: U.S. Army Research Institute of Environmental Medicine.

Taylor, A. J. W. (1991). Individual and group behavior in extreme situations and environments. In R. Gal & A. D. Mangelsdorff (Eds.), *Handbook of Military Psychology* (pp. 491-505). New York: John Wiley.

Taylor, H. L., & Alluisi, E. A. (in press). Military psychology. In V. S. Ramachandran (Ed.), *Encyclopedia of Human Behavior.* San Diego, CA: Academic Press.

Tharion, W. J., Rauch, T. M., Strowman, S. R., & Shukitt, B. L. (1987). *The Psychological Attributes of Ultramarathon Runners and Factors Which Limit Endurance*. Natick, MA: U.S. Army Research Institute of Environmental Medicine.

Thomas, J. R., Ahlers, S. T., House, J. F., Schrot, J., Van Orden, K. F., Winsborough, M. M., Hesslink, R. L., & Lewis, S. B. (1990). Adregenic responses to cognitive activity in a cold environment. *Journal of Applied Physiology*, 68,3, 962-966.

Tolbert, C. A., & Bittner, A. C., Jr (1991). Applications of verbal protocol analysis during the system development cycle. In W. Karwowski & J.W. Yates (Eds). *Advances in Industrial Ergnomics and Safety III.* (855-862). Bristol, PA: Taylor & Francis.

Tolcott, M. A. (1992). Understanding and aiding military decisions. In S. Collyer (Ed.), *The 27th International Applied Military Psychology Symposium: A Focus on Decision Making Research.* Washington, DC: Office of Naval Research, European Office.

Travillian, K. K., Volpe, C. E., Cannon-Bowers, J. A., & Salas, E. (1993). Cross-training highly interdependent teams: Effects on team processes and team performance. In *Proceedings of the Human Factors and Ergonomics Society 37th Annual Meeting.* 1243-1247.

Triggs, T.J., Kantowitz, B.H., Terrill, B.S., Bittner Jr., A.C. & Fleming, T.F. (1990). The playback method of protocol analysis applied to a rapid aiming task. *Proceedings of the Human Factors Society 34th Annual Meeting.* 1275-1279.

Turnage, J. J., Kennedy, R. S., Smith, M. G., Baltzley, D. R., & Lane, N. E. (1992). Development of microcomputer-based mental acuity tests. *Ergonomics*, 35, 1271-1295.

Vogel, J. (1992). Presentation to the Presidential Commission on the assignment of women in the armed forces (Aug 7, 1992). In *Report to the President from the Presidential Commission on the Assignment of Women in the Armed Forces.* Washington, DC: Government Printing Office. ISBN-0-16-038236-X

Vogel, J. A., Patton, J. F., Mello, R. P., & Daniels, W. L. (1985). *An Analysis of Aerobic Capacity in a Large United States Population. USARIEM Report M28/1985.* Natick, MA: US Army Research Institute of Environmental Medicine.

Von Gierke, H. E., McCloskey, K., & Albery, W. B. (1991). Military performance in sustained acceleration and vibration environments. In R. Gal & A. D. Mangelsdorff (Eds.), *Handbook of Military Psychology* (pp. 335-364). New York: John Wiley.

Warm, J. S. (Ed.). (1984). *Sustained Attention in Human Performance.* New York: John Wiley.

Warner, N. W., & Notaro, J. (in press). Navy's Advanced Technology Crew Station (ATCS) program overview: Origin, accomplishments and products. In *Proceedings of the 1993 SAFE Annual Meeting.* Yoncalla. WA: SAFE.

Weand, S. (1989, Mar-Apr). The T800 engine acquisition strategy. PB 70-89-2. *Army Research, Development and Acquisition Bulletin.* 8-11. Alexandria, VA: HQ Army Material Command.

Weand, S., & Thagard, P. (1989, July-Aug)) T800 Remembers The Soldier. PB-89-4. *Army Research, Development and Acquisition Bulletin*. 13-16. Alexandria, VA: HQ Army Material Command.

Weintraub, D. J., & Ensing, M. (1992). *Human Factors Issues in Head-Up Display Design: The Book of HUD*. Wright-Patterson AFB, OH: CSERIAC.

Weiss, M. S., Guccione, S. J., & Watkins, T. A. (1990). A kinematic/dynamic model for prediction of neck injury during impact acceleration. In *AGARD Conference Proceedings No.471* (pp. 11:1-6). Neuilly-sur-Seine, France: North Atlantic Treaty Organization Advisory Group for Aerospace Research and Development.

Weiss, M. S., Matson, D. L., & Mawn, S. V. (1989). *Guidelines for Safe Human Exposure to Impact Acceleration Update A. NBDL-89R003*. New Orleans, LA: Naval Biodynamics Laboratory.

Weybrew, B. B. (1992). *The ABC's of stress: A Submarine Psychologist's Perspective*. Westport, CT: Praeger.

Whinnery, J. (1991). Theoretical analysis of acceleration-induced central nervous system ischemia. *Engineering in Medicine and Biology*, 10,1, 41-45.

Whinnery, J. E. (1988). *On the Theory of Acceleration Tolerance. NADC-88088-60*. Warminster, PA: Naval Air Development Center.

Whinnery, J. E., & Hamilton, R. J. (1991). *Naval Air Development Center Medical Standards for Research Subjects Exposed to Hazardous Aerospace Environments. NADC-91035-60*. Warminster, PA: Naval Air Development Center.

Whitaker, L. A., & Peters, L. J. (1993). *Performance as a Function of Speech Communication: Auditory Workload and Task Performance. CSERIAC 93-1*. Wright Patterson AFB, OH: CSERIAC.

Wierwille, W. W., & Eggemeier, F. T. (1993). Recommendations for mental workload measurement in a test and evaluation environment. *Human Factors*, 35, 263-281.

Wiker, S. F., Kennedy, R. S., McCauley, M. E., & Pepper, R. L. (1989). Susceptibility to seasickness: Influence of hull design and steaming direction. *Aviation, Space and Environmental Medicine*, 50, 1046-1051.

Willems, G. C. (1989). *Closing the Loop--or Can the Ship Motion Simulator Simulate Ship Motion? NBDL-89R003*. New Orleans, LA.: Naval Biodynamics Laboratory. ADA222355.

Willems, G. C., Muzzy, W. H., Knouse, D., & Gilbreath, F. (1991). *Dynamic Response of the Hybrid III Dummy to +G_z Simulated Ship Shock--Cushioned vs. Hard Seats*. New Orleans, LA: Naval Biodynamics Laboratory.

Wilson, G. F. (1991). *Progress in the Psychophysiological Assessment of Workload*. AL-TR-1992-0007. Wright Patterson AFB, OH: Armstrong Laboratory.

Wilson, G. F.(Ed). (1992). Cardiorespiratory measures and their role in studies of performance [Special Issue]. *Biological Psychology*, 34, 91-289.

Wilson, G. F., & Eggemeier, F. T. (1991). Psychophysiological assessment of workload in multi-task environments. In D. L. Damos (Ed.), *Multiple-Task Performance* (pp. 329-360). London: Taylor & Francis.

Wilson, G. F., & Fisher, F. (1991). The use of cardiac and eye blink measures to determine flight segment in F4 crews. *Aviation, Space and Environmental Medicine*, 62, 959-962.

Wilson, G. F., & O'Donnell, R. D. (1988). Measurement of operator workload with the neuropsychological workload test battery. In P. A. Hancock & N. Meshkati (Eds.), *Human Mental Workload* (pp. 63-100). Amsterdam: North-Holland.

Winer, B.J., Brown, D.R. and Michels, K.M. (1991). *Statistical Principles in Experimental Design* (3rd ed.). New York, NY: McGraw-Hill.

Wright, J. A., Sharp, D. S., Vogel, J. A., & Patton, J. F. (1985). *Assessment of Muscle Strength and Prediction of Lifting in U.S. Army Personnel. USARIEM Report # M9/1985*. Natick, MA: US Army Research Institure of Environmental Medicine.

Zachary, W., Ryder, J. M., & Zubritzky, M. C. (1989). *A Cognitive Model of Human-Computer Interaction in Naval Air ASW Mission Management.* Spring House, PA: CHI Systems.

Zachary, W. W., Zaklad, A. L., Hicinbothom, J. H., Ryder, J. M., & Purcell, J. A. (1993). COGNET representation of tactical decision-making in Anti-air warefare. In *Proceedings of the Human Factors and Ergonomics Society 37th Annual Meeting,* 1112-1116.

Chapter 14
Training Effectiveness Techniques:

Eduardo Salas
Kerry A. Burgess
Janis A. Cannon-Bowers
Naval Training Systems Center

1.0 Overview

Organizations have begun to focus an increasing amount of attention on training their workforce; businesses are generating and implementing training programs at a rapid rate. The most common purpose of these training programs is to increase worker skills and/or knowledge levels so that on-the-job accidents can be reduced, product quality can be improved, services and management system quality can be increased, and the effects of stress on worker productivity can be ameliorated (Goldstein, 1993). Moreover, training programs have become even more crucial in response to the gradual changes in workforce demographics (e.g., diversity), globalization of world markets, and new technological advances which require different and more varied skill levels (Noe & Ford, 1992). As technological advancement continues, demand for training will undoubtedly continue to rise.

As a function of these changes, training in modern industry has become a big business. Specifically, Wexley and Latham (1991) reported that U.S. businesses have spent approximately $2 trillion over the past decade in training their employees. In 1991, it was estimated that organizations were spending approximately $30 billion on formal training, and $180 billion in on-the-job training on a yearly basis (Carnevale, Gainer, & Villet, 1990). There is little doubt that these figures will continue to rise in the next decade.

The increased reliance of organizations on training, coupled with the financial investments being devoted to training, has led to a resurgence of research examining training effectiveness. Training scientists and practitioners alike have begun to focus more on determining <u>when</u> and <u>why</u> training programs succeed or fail (Mathieu, Tannenbaum, & Salas, 1993). In fact, determining and improving the effectiveness of training programs have become particularly crucial in light of the investment in training and technological advances noted above.

Fortunately, modern training research is more dynamic, diverse, and rich with new theoretical developments, findings, and methods than ever (Tannenbaum & Yukl, 1992). One reason for this may be the greater opportunity provided by organizations to conduct research - especially since organizations, too, are beginning to realize the importance of evaluating their training programs (Goldstein, 1989). There is certainly a need for more accountability of the resources used in training. A second reason may be that there is now a trend to entwine concepts from cognitive science, educational psychology, industrial/organizational psychology, and human factors (Kraiger, Ford, & Salas, 1993). Also, a number of national societies continue to promote the science and practice of training (See Appendix 13-1). Moreover, the number of training-relevant articles being published in journals and magazines has increased (See Appendix 13-1). Indeed, there is now more communication among researchers from these different perspectives than before.

In light of the current attention on training research, this chapter has two purposes. First, to present a comprehensive framework that encompasses specific issues of concern and interest in training effectiveness research; and second, to discuss the methods, variables, and techniques necessary to conduct such research. To accomplish these purposes, we will describe what training effectiveness is, illustrate what training effectiveness research entails, and offer a set of tools necessary for conducting training effectiveness research.

2.0 Training Effectiveness

To gain a better understanding of what it takes to conduct training research, you must have a clear understanding of the components that encompass training and training effectiveness. First, it is important to define training. According to Goldstein (1993), training is defined as:

> **The acquisition of skills, concepts, or attitudes which result in improved performance in another environment.**

Therefore, training is designed to produce, for example, more competent pilots, more capable first-line supervisors, more efficient sales associates, and safer nuclear power plant operators. While there are any number of important issues to be addressed when conducting training research, perhaps the most over-arching issue is whether training is effective and if so, why. That is, determining which factors influence training effectiveness is a critical step toward developing better performing pilots, supervisors, sales associates, and so forth. We now turn our attention to the crucial topic of training effectiveness, first presenting a conceptual framework, and then discussing specific factors that affect it.

2.1 What is Training Effectiveness?

In a general sense, training effectiveness can be defined as: *The extent to which training brings desired or appropriate outcomes.* In past work, a common misconception regarding training effectiveness has been that it is a rather simple input-throughput-output process (i.e., it is often assumed that training effectiveness rests solely on the quality or nature of the training program itself). Figure 14-1 displays this relationship graphically. Inherent in Figure 14-1 is the assumption that merely exposing a trainee to a training program will yield a"trained worker". Further, suggests that the study of training effectiveness should rest on an investigation of factors associated only with the training program.

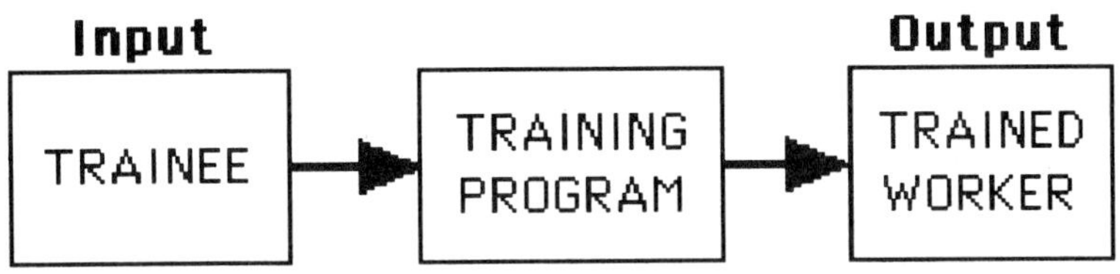

Figure 14-1: Simplistic View of the Training Process

Recently, this simplistic view of training has been called into question. Several researchers have argued that training effectiveness is dependent not only on the training program, but a host of factors associated with the trainee, the context in which training occurs, and the environment to which training must transfer (Baldwin & Ford, 1988; Cannon-Bowers, Salas, Tannenbaum, & Mathieu, in press). The implications of this position for the investigation of training effectiveness are significant. Most importantly, it suggests that training effectiveness researchers must be concerned with studying training effectiveness from multiple perspectives, concentrating on several classes of variables that can affect the outcome of training before, during, and after the training actually occurs.

Training effectiveness research is important from both practical and theoretical perspectives. On a practical level, the value of training effectiveness research is evidenced by the need to determine which factors influence the success or failure of specific training programs. For example, an organization may conclude that their unsuccessful training program failed because of the design of the program; when, in fact, it was due to low trainee motivation. On a theoretical level, we must understand the nature and impact of constructs such as self-efficacy, feedback, motivation, and learning with regard to training effectiveness because neglecting these constructs would make it difficult to ascertain why training may or may not have been successful. To delineate the various aspects of training effectiveness and describe how these variables relate to each other, Tannenbaum, Cannon-Bowers, Salas, & Mathieu (1993) developed a comprehensive, theoretical model of training effectiveness (see Figure 14-2).

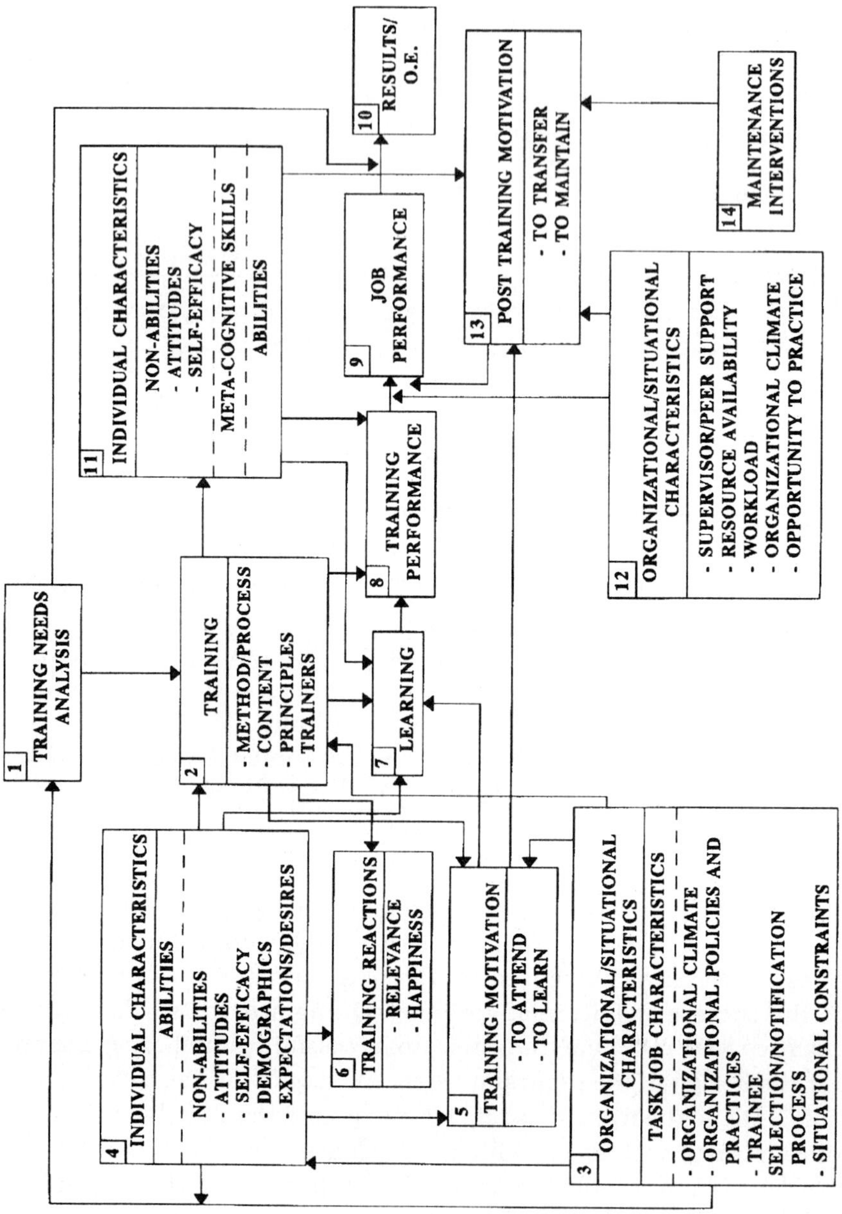

Figure 14-2. Training Effectiveness Model

To begin with, several assumptions are made in this model. First, it represents a longitudinal, process-oriented perspective. That is, it considers events before, during, and after the training. Second, it views training as a behavioral event in which the acquisition of knowledge, skills, and abilities (KSAs) is of primary concern, with emphasis on the application of these KSAs to the job environment. Third, it focuses on training within the work context. That is, it acknowledges that training is influenced by the organizational environment. Fourth, it illustrates that technology alone (e.g., intelligent systems, high-fidelity simulators) does not guarantee skill acquisition (learning) after training. Technology is an enabling tool for training, not an "end" by itself. Finally, it acknowledges the influence of often-ignored constructs such as motivation, trainee expectations, and self-efficacy on training effectiveness.

While a detailed explanation of the model is beyond the scope of this chapter (See Tannenbaum et al., 1993 for a full description), an understanding of the major variables and their relationship to each other is necessary.

In general, the model asserts that several inter-related constructs and variables affect the effectiveness of training systems. First, the training needs analysis (Box 1) influences the design and development of the training program itself (Box 2). The implementation or delivery of the training program is dependent on such organizational characteristics as previous policies and practices about training (Box 3), as well as what the trainees bring into the training program, such as their expectations and abilities (Box 4). These two sets of variables will contribute to the trainees' motivation to attend or learn the new skills (Box 5).

Once the training is completed, a set of multi-level evaluations need to be conducted. They include the trainees' reaction to the training program (Box 6); how much the trainees learned in training (Box 7); whether the trainees exhibited the new skills during training (Box 8) and back on the job (Box 9); as well as any differences in organizational effectiveness (e.g., better sales, higher productivity) as a result of the training (Box 10).

The model also postulates that one needs to be concerned about the trainee's ability and desire to transfer what was learned during training to the post-training environment (Box 11). Specifically, training effectiveness is influenced by whether the trainee has the ability, attitude, cognitive skills, and self-efficacy to properly implement the skills after the cessation of the training. Similarly, one must determine the organizational characteristics that may enhance or hinder training success (Box 12). Here, components such as the trainee's opportunity to practice and supervisory support will impact the trainee's ability to transfer the skills back to the job environment. This is important because it may influence the trainee's motivation to both transfer what was learned back to the job and maintain it (Box 13). Finally, to ensure that trainee motivation does not degrade over time, maintenance interventions (e.g., relapse prevention programs) must be employed (Box 14).

Perhaps the most important conclusion to be drawn from the model is that in order to understand training effectiveness research, several different classes of factors must be taken into consideration - many more than are exhibited in Figure 14-1. For example, trainee variables (e.g., expectations, attitudes) and organizational characteristics (e.g., the organization's climate and policies) are very much of interest to training researchers (both before and after the training) because they can affect the success of training. Also of interest is the transfer of the training back to the job, and the ways in which training is evaluated (e.g., trainee reactions, learning). We can now begin to examine to these variables, along with the manner in which they affect training effectiveness from a research perspective.

3.0 The Nature of Training Effectiveness Research

The previous discussion leads us to ask two critical research questions: (1) What factors facilitate or hinder training effectiveness? and (2) How can we determine whether training is or is not effective? To answer these questions, we must first ask ourselves some basic questions: What paradigm should we use? Where should we conduct the research? Who should we utilize as research participants? How do we capture performance and skill acquisition? What are our constraints? How should we analyze the data? The answers to these questions are not straight forward. In fact, they depend on, among other things, <u>what research question</u> is being asked. Once this is determined, it will help to dictate the appropriate paradigm, method, procedure, and subjects to use, as well as the generalizability of results.

As indicated in Figure 14-2, many variables facilitate or hinder the effectiveness of training regardless of the specific training objectives. For our purposes, we will only discuss the main influences: (1) individual characteristics, (2) organizational characteristics, (3) motivation - all of which can influence the effectiveness of the training before or after training actually takes place, and (4) the training program itself. To help clarify the discussion, we will refer to the box numbers in Figure 14-2 so as to illustrate where in the model our discussion has taken us. Moreover, we will provide examples pertaining to each variable of interest (or their subcomponents) to demonstrate how research is conducted in that particular area.

3.1 Individual Characteristics

Individual characteristics are qualities that the trainee brings into the training program. These qualities are especially important, because they can influence the effectiveness of the training before the training begins (see Box 4 in Figure 14-2), or after it ends (see Box 11). Some examples of relevant individual characteristics include cognitive ability (Tannenbaum, Mathieu, Salas, & Cannon-Bowers, 1991), physical ability (Hogan & Hogan, 1985), expectations (Martocchio, 1992; Hicks & Klimoski, 1987), meta-cognitive skills, attitudes (Noe & Schmitt, 1986), personality (Hogan, Arenson, & Salas, 1987), and self-efficacy (Gist, Schwoerer, & Rosen, 1989). For the sake of simplicity, however, we will focus primarily on those individual characteristics especially rich with current and emerging research: self-efficacy, expectations, and abilities. It is important to note, however, that our purpose is not to present a literature review on each characteristic. Rather, we hope to relay, with the assistance of a prominent experiment as an example, the proper tools with which to conduct this type of research.

3.1.1 Self-efficacy. Self-efficacy can be defined as *The belief in one's ability to perform a specific task* (Gist et al., 1989). Research suggests that individuals high in self-efficacy tend to perform better than individuals with low self-efficacy. For example, self-efficacy has been shown to positively influence performance on a flight simulator task (Travillian, Baker, & Cannon-Bowers, 1992), decisions to enroll in a computer class (Hill, Smith, & Mann, 1987), and sales performance among life insurance agents (Barling & Beattie, 1983), to name a few. Moreover, self-efficacy determines the level of effort and degree of persistence that an individual will expend on a task (Travillian et al., 1992).

The impact of self-efficacy in terms of the training has only become evident in the last few years. A predominant research question addressed in studies has been: "What variables, in particular, are influenced by trainees' self-efficacy?" Other questions which arise include: "How is self-efficacy measured?" and "What impact does the training have on subsequent self-efficacy?" Research in this regard has revealed significant relationships between self-efficacy, and trainee reactions to the training and training performance (Gist et al., 1989; Tannenbaum et al., 1991; Mathieu, Martineau, & Tannenbaum, 1993). That is, trainees who believe that they can do well in training have more positive reactions to the training and perform better.

3.1.2 Expectations. Individuals often enter training programs with differing expectations regarding the training. Some expectations may be in the form of the outcome that the training will have on the job (i.e., determining how the training will influence their performance back on the job). Other expectations may pertain more specifically to the training program itself; specifically, whether the trainees have a realistic preview of the training program (e.g., its length, content, structure, format, and so forth).

One theory that may help to explain the impact of expectations on training outcomes is Valence-Instrumentality-Expectancy (VIE) theory (Vroom, 1964). Briefly, this theory holds that people are motivated by their expectations; specifically, when they believe that their efforts will lead to appropriate performance (E); then performance outcomes will lead to desired rewards (I). Further, it suggests that more important expected rewards will be more motivating (V). In a training context, this theory predicts that if trainees believe that the training will benefit them, they will be more motivated to do well.

Research examining the effects of expectations on training effectiveness have found that they are significantly correlated with a number of different variables. For example, Martocchio (1992) found that pre-training expectations were positively correlated to trainee learning in a computer course. Alderfer, Alderfer, Bell, and Jones (1992) found that trainees who received a realistic preview of training also had significantly more favorable reactions to the program. Likewise, Hicks and Klimoski (1989) found that trainees who received a realistic preview of the training program had a significantly higher commitment to attend the training, and had higher levels of motivation to learn than those who did not.

3.1.3 Cognitive ability. Cognitive ability is another individual characteristic that has been a prominent feature in training research. Pertinent questions here include: "How does cognitive ability impact the effectiveness of training?" and "How is it best measured?" Many studies have addressed the effects of trainees' cognitive abilities in relation to their performance during training. Indeed, it has been shown in various studies that trainees high in cognitive ability perform better on all aspects of training.

This idea was only partially supported, however, in a study conducted by Tannenbaum et al. (1991). Results indicated that the trainees' cognitive abilities were positively correlated with performance scores, but negatively correlated with trainee reactions and motivation. That is, although trainees with high cognitive abilities scored well on training tests, they had lower levels of motivation toward the training (both before and after training), and more unfavorable training reactions. Baldwin, Magjuka, and Loher (1991), also studied cognitive ability and found that it was significantly related to performance on learning measures during a performance appraisal training program.

3.1.4 Example of an individual characteristic experiment. To facilitate the understanding of the tools utilized in conducting research in this area, we will provide an overview of a study that examined self-efficacy, expectations, and cognitive abilities. This study, conducted by Tannenbaum et al. (1991), was implemented to determine, among other things, what pre-training variables (e.g., self-efficacy, motivation) would influence specific posttraining variables (e.g., commitment).

Participants included 666 U.S. Navy recruits assessed throughout their 8-week recruit basic training program. Pre-training questionnaires (including self-efficacy and expectations about training) were completed immediately upon their arrival to training. Cognitive ability, measured by the recruits' scores on the Armed Forces Qualification Test (AFQT), was collected prior to training as part of the enlistment process. At the conclusion of the training, the trainees again completed a questionnaire which assessed self-efficacy, trainee reactions, and training perceptions.

Self-efficacy was measured via a Likert-type scale with items such as "I do well in activities where I have to remember lots of information" and "I feel in control when taking tests involving physical dexterity." Here, both pre- and post-training self-efficacy measures were significantly correlated with training motivation and trainee reactions (i.e., how much they liked the training). In contrast, they were shown to have a significantly negative relationship with cognitive ability and test performance.

As previously reported, recruits with higher cognitive ability (as measured by an aptitude test) were found to be less motivated both before and after training. Moreover, they were more likely to have higher test scores and stronger beliefs in their ability to do well, academically.

Recruit expectations about the training was termed "training fulfillment" (i.e., the extent to which training met or fulfilled the trainees' expectations or desires). Training fulfillment was assessed with 16 items such as "I expect that the material I learn will be presented to me in lecture format." Based on these measures, it was determined that training fulfillment was negatively correlated with pre-training motivation, but was positively correlated with post-training motivation, academic self-efficacy, and trainee reactions.

Overall, what can we learn from this example? First, it's important to have good training effectiveness criteria (e.g., the trainees' reactions, learning). We will discuss these issues in subsequent sections. Second, if changes in behavior can be examined over time, research can assess the evolutionary process of different variables (e.g., pre- and post-training motivation, pre- and post-training self-efficacy). Finally, you need to employ sound, reliable measures with which to gather data. Without them, your results may be inaccurate.

As evidenced by the Tannenbaum et al. (1991) example, typical independent variables include the trainee's self-efficacy, expectations about training, and cognitive ability. These are primarily assessed via theory-driven questionnaires or objective tests, depending on the variable being measured. Variables such as self-efficacy and expectations can also serve, however, as dependent variables in that some research examines the changes that take place due to a training manipulation. The design most popular for assessing individual characteristics is the "pre and post" design. With this, changes in the dependent variables can be assessed by comparing the measures taken before the training with the measures taken after the training. With regard to experimental setting, research pertaining to individual characteristics is conducted in a variety of situations. These include full-blown field studies in actual organizations, field studies that examine "real" tasks (e.g., diving performance, typing, bowling) but that do not necessarily take place in a traditional organization, and laboratory studies that employ realistic and contrived tasks.

In sum, individual characteristics impact a number of training effectiveness variables, and are therefore considered crucial. As evidenced by the studies previously discussed, trainee characteristics (e.g., expectations, self-efficacy) influence not only the trainees' motivation to attend the training, but also their reactions to the training once it has ended. Now we will turn our attention to another important area of training effectiveness, organizational characteristics.

3.2 Organizational Characteristics.

The organization in which the trainee must perform the newly acquired skills can be a critical influence on training effectiveness (see Box 3 in Figure 14-2). Organizational influences can include the procedure used to select trainees, organizational climate, situational constraints, and trainees' opportunity to practice.

3.2.1 Selection and notification. The manner in which trainees are selected and notified can influence the satisfaction, motivation, and the outcome of the training. For example, do you think that you would feel differently toward a task if you were given the choice of performing it rather than being forced? From a training perspective, would you have more motivation to attend and learn from a training program if you could volunteer as opposed to being mandated by either an organizational policy or your supervisor? This question has been an issue of interest in examining the impact of training selection on training effectiveness.

Research regarding trainee selection has indicated that yes, trainees do, in fact, have a higher motivation to learn if they are given the choice of attending (Baldwin et al., 1991; Hicks & Klimoski, 1987). Moreover, trainees have been found to score significantly higher on performance tests, and have more positive trainee reactions (Hicks & Klimoski, 1987). When training is mandatory, however, it must be made motivational by other means.

3.2.2 Situational constraints. Many of us have experienced the ordeal of not being thoroughly motivated to learn something due to a lack of the proper equipment. This could include improper lighting, or not having an appropriate textbook. As an example of a situational constraint, try to imagine taking piano lessons without a piano! Needless to say, you would probably feel quite constricted in how much you could learn. This illustrates only one facet of what the model labels situational constraints. Situational constraints are defined as: *Work characteristics that interfere with training effectiveness.* In training situations, too, trainees may question the relevance of the training content to their jobs, or may feel frustrated because of perceived barriers (e.g., lack of proper equipment) which may hinder the transfer of training content to the job.

In light of this, several studies have been conducted to determine how situational constraints (e.g., perceived obstacles, irrelevant content) impact training effectiveness, as well as to pinpoint which variables are most influenced by situational constraints.

One of the first studies to capture the magnitude of situational constraints was performed by Peters, O'Connor, and Rudolf (1980). They found that the quality and quantity of the work significantly lower when individuals perceived situational constraints, and subjects had significantly lower task satisfaction, and significantly higher frustration levels.

Studies that followed Peters et al. (1980) tended to utilize situational constraints as independent variables. For example, Mathieu et al. (1992) found that those trainees in a proof reading class who perceived themselves as having adequate equipment, ample supplies, sufficient authority to complete the tasks, and sufficient time were also more motivated, satisfied with training, and had higher proofreading scores than other trainees. Noe and Wilk (1993) also found that perceived situational constraints were negatively correlated with the trainees' motivation to learn in training programs. Further, they found that trainees who perceived situational constraints evaluated training programs more negatively, and had less motivation to enroll in upcoming training programs.

3.2.3 Organizational climate. The climate of an organization can play an integral role in the effectiveness of training. Organizational climate is widely defined as: *The shared perceptions of the organization's informal and formal policies, practices, and procedures* (Reichers & Schneider, 1990). The primary aspect of climate of interest here can be thought of as: *The perceived amount of support provided by the organization toward the training*. Just as individual differences can vary greatly from trainee to trainee, organizational climate can vary greatly from organization to organization. Some organizations are very supportive of both the training programs and the trainees, and encourage the transfer of the trained material to the work environment. Other organizations, however, may feel forced to provide training and, consequently, may put little effort toward supporting the training or the trainees. Training researchers have evidenced these differences and studied the impact of organizational climate on training effectiveness. Some of the questions challenging these research efforts include: "What specific organizational climate characteristics influence effectiveness?", "How can the organizational climate be captured and measured?", and "What is the difference between the training effectiveness level with respect to organizational climate?".

An early study examining the effects of organizational climate on training effectiveness was conducted by Hand, Richards, and Slocum (1973). They found that individuals perceiving the organization to be supportive, as having interactive decision making, supportive supervisors, and high performance goals (all measured with a Likert-type scale), also reported significantly more transfer of what was learned in training back to the job.

Ford, Quinones, Sego, and Sorra (1992) also examined organizational climate in the form of perceived supervisory and co-worker support provided to trainees after the completion of an Air Force technical training course with a 10-item Likert-type scale. They found that airmen who perceived themselves to be more likeable and competent by their supervisors and co-workers (thereby creating a positive climate for the trainees) obtained greater knowledge through training and were able to perform more difficult tasks back on the job. Likewise, Noe and Wilk (1993) used a 24-item Likert-type scale assessing respondents' perceptions regarding managerial and peer support and found that support was significantly correlated with trainees' motivation to learn and transfer the training content, their evaluation of the training, perceived personal benefits of the training, and career benefits. Finally, Tracey, Tannenbaum, and Kavanagh (1993) examined climate in the transfer environment (i.e., the extent to which the work environment facilitates or hinders the transfer of training). The results indicated that climate was significantly related to post-training behavior.

3.2.4 Opportunity to practice. The implications of having the opportunity to practice can also be found in our own experiences. One example may be learning to play a musical instrument. If the musician has the opportunity to practice frequently after learning how to play, he/she is much more likely to retain the skills than if practicing was discontinued after taking lessons. Obviously, this concept also holds true in the training context.

Oftentimes, training studies implicitly assume that individuals obtain ample opportunity to practice what was trained back on the job. Realistically, however, this situation varies greatly from organization to organization (Ford et al., 1992). Some people do, in fact, have ample opportunity to practice after the training is completed, while others do not.

One such study supporting this contention was conducted by Ford et al. (1992). Here, subjects were questioned four months after the completion of a technical training course as to whether or not they had performed each of the 34 tasks taught during training. On average, they found that only half of the 34 tasks trained had been performed on the job.

Additionally, Ford et al. (1992) tested the relationship between self-efficacy and supervisory support with trainees' opportunity to practice. They found that supervisory support and self-efficacy (both measured with questionnaires directed at the trainees and their immediate supervisors) were significantly correlated with the airmen's opportunity to practice the trained tasks.

3.2.5 Examples of an organizational characteristic study. To facilitate a better understanding of the influence of organizational characteristics, we will now examine two studies in detail. The first study, conducted by Baldwin et al. (1991), investigated the effects of trainee choice on pre-training attitudes and training outcome. Trainees were given a wide variety of training topics to choose from, including the program topic utilized for this study (i.e., performance appraisal training). Three conditions were then tested: (1) not giving the subjects a choice in attending the training, (2) initially giving subjects a choice, but not respecting that choice by mandating them to this training program, and (3) giving the subjects their choice (i.e., those trainees which chose this training program). Two hundred and seven students enrolled in the performance appraisal and feedback training program, derived from these three conditions, served as research participants. Results from the study indicated that trainees who originally received their choice of training program had a higher level of motivation to learn prior to training, than the other two groups. Moreover, trainees given a choice, which was not subsequently respected, were less motivated and scored lower on a performance appraisal test as compared to those trainees not given any choice.

Situational constraints and organizational climate were both examined in a study conducted by Noe and Wilk (1993). With the goal of determining the factors that influence employees' participation in training programs, Noe and Wilk queried approximately one thousand employees from engineering, banking, and HMO firms. Situational constraints were assessed with an 8-item, Likert-type questionnaire asking respondents for their perceptions regarding working conditions which inhibit training (e.g., "I don't have time in my job to try and strengthen my skill weaknesses"). Noe and Wilk found that perceived situational constraints were negatively correlated with the trainees' motivation to learn in training programs, evaluations of previous programs, perceived benefits from enrolling, and future plans to participate in other training programs.

Noe and Wilk (1993) also examined organizational climate in the form of supervisory and peer support and their relationship to training effectiveness. Support was assessed with a 24-item, Likert-type questionnaire including such items as "My manager is supportive of my efforts to acquire new knowledge and skills." As previously reported, the results indicated that the support provided by supervisors and peers was positively correlated with the trainees' motivation, their evaluations of the training, and perceived benefits of attending the training programs.

These studies merely provide a snapshot of the research being conducted to examine the influence of organizational characteristics. So what organizational characteristics do you need to concern yourself with? As previously discussed, independent variables such as organizational climate, trainee selection procedures, opportunities for practice, and situational constraints top the list of current research concerns and opportunities. While variables such as supervisory support can be measured with questionnaires (as can usually be done with individual characteristics), most organizational variables are more difficult to assess and control. For example, assessing the organizational climate oftentimes involves more than simply querying trainees as can be done with most individual characteristics. Trainees usually need to be observed on the job by objective raters to assess whether they are given the opportunity to practice or what their level of workload is back on the job.

As with individual characteristics, field studies are the setting of choice when studying the impact of organizational variables. Indeed, it would be difficult to study organizational characteristics in a laboratory environment, because they could not be easily created in a contrived situation. Moreover, it would be questionable to generalize the results of such a study to actual organizations. Sound studies of organizational characteristics also tend to be longitudinal in nature so that the impact of selected variables can be assessed before and after training.

In sum, characteristics at the organizational level impact several training effectiveness variables such as training motivation (both pre- and post-training), and performance back on the job. As evidenced by the previously discussed studies, organizational characteristics should be serious considerations when addressing training effectiveness. We will now examine another important facet of training effectiveness: Trainee motivation.

3.3 Motivation.

Research examining trainee motivation (see Boxes 5 and 13 in Figure 14-2) is critical to the understanding of training effectiveness. Why? To answer this, we can once again examine our own experiences. If you think about events in your past, you may remember how much more willing you were to learn various concepts or skills if you believed they were relevant to you. In contrast, if you were not interested in what was being taught, little effort was probably made on your part to learn the material. Herein lies one of the influences of training motivation.

Training motivation can be thought of as: *The direction, intensity, and persistence of attentional effort invested by the trainee toward training* (Tannenbaum et al., 1993). It can have an impact both prior to training and after training. Prior to training, motivation can affect the trainee's willingness to attend and to learn (see Box 5). After training, motivation affects the trainee's willingness to transfer the learning content back to the job and maintain it over time (see Box 13). In the past, research directed at gaining a better understanding of motivation has attempted to answer several predominant questions. For example, "Which variables influence training motivation?", "Which variables are influenced by training motivation?", "How is training motivation measured?", and "What are the theoretical underpinnings of training motivation?"

Several studies have shown that motivation influences a number of post-training variables. For example, Tannenbaum et al., (1991), found that trainees' motivation to do well correlated highly with their reactions to the training, and their confidence that they would be able to use what was learned (i.e., self-efficacy). Mathieu et al. (1992) also found motivation to be significantly correlated with trainee reactions. Moreover, Mathieu et al.

(1992), along with Mathieu et al., (1993) found that motivation was negatively correlated with situational constraints. Other variables such as choice of attending the training and realistic previews of what to expect have also been shown to influence pre-training motivation (Hicks and Klimoski, 1987).

In sum, many facets of training motivation can be studied. They include both motivation to attend and learn from the training program prior to its commencement, as well as motivation to transfer the skills after the training has ended. These studies typify the variables which influence various facets of training motivation (e.g., situational constraints), and which variables are influenced by training motivation (e.g., reactions to training). With regard to how training motivation is measured, most researchers, again, rely on questionnaires. The majority of these items, however, are theoretically-based. For example, Mathieu et al. (1992), Mathieu et al. (1993) and Tannenbaum et al. (1991) used the expectancy theory as their foundation. Some of the questions utilized included: "If I am successful in recruit training, it will better enable me to perform my job in the Navy" (Tannenbaum et al., 1991) and "Successful completion of this course will help me to produce high quality work" (Mathieu et al., 1992). These studies also reflect the benefit of using field studies and pre- and post-training measures in studying training motivation. Not only do they allow for more generalizability, but they also enhance the soundness of the results.

As is the case with much of the training research examining motivation, the studies mentioned above did not manipulate motivation per se. Instead, motivation was measured in response to the influence of other variables (e.g., self-efficacy). Future research should examine the influence of motivational manipulations on other variables and performance. Now we will turn our attention to the most well known area of training effectiveness - the training program itself.

3.4 Training Program.

The training program itself (see Box 2 in Figure 14-2) is another variable that can greatly influence training effectiveness. This is of interest most often when training effectiveness is studied. Therefore, countless studies investigating the effectiveness of various techniques for training various skills have been conducted. For example, training effectiveness might be hindered if the most optimal training technique is not utilized, if the content is not something of relevance to the job environment, or if the instructors are biased or not properly trained, themselves. These variables can impact effectiveness throughout the training program. While we cannot provide a comprehensive review of research conducted on training factors, we will instead focus on two of the more salient issues: training techniques and instructor training.

3.4.1 Training techniques. The training technique utilized can have a significant influence on training effectiveness. Thus, it is crucial that the most beneficial training technique or strategy be selected. Given the vast number of content areas which require training, along with the diverse and numerous training techniques available, this can be very challenging. For example, training techniques can range from sensitivity training and apprenticeship, to such technical methods as computer-aided instruction (CAI) and teleconferencing. For purposes of simplicity, our discussion is limited to techniques that have been frequently utilized in training research.

The critical question that drives most research is: "Which instructional strategies should be utilized to ensure the most effective method for training?" (i.e, What form should the training take?) You could argue that training contains four basic instructional strategies:

1. Presentation of information and concepts to be learned;
2. Demonstration of the skills to be learned;
3. Provision of opportunities to practice the skills;
4. Feedback given to the trainees on the skills demonstrated.

Almost all training techniques embed one or all of these strategies. Their use depends on the purpose (e.g., introduction to diversity training as opposed to flying skills) of the training.

Apart from instructional strategies, numerous techniques have been studied in training research. The most widely used training techniques are illustrated in Table 14-1, along with the components of each and examples of programs utilizing them. For example, the simulation technique consists of components such as role play, hands-on practice, feedback, and content-specific exercises. Examples of more specific simulation training programs include in-basket exercises, business games, and simulators.

Research examining these techniques has shown that behavioral modeling has worked with great success. In fact, a meta-analysis conducted on managerial training by Burke and Day (1986), supported the contention that behavioral modeling is a sound method for improving trainee learning. Moreover, when compared with other techniques, the results remain strong.

A study by Gist et al., (1989) compared behavioral modeling with computer-aided instruction (CAI) in a software training course offered to 108 university personnel. Participants in the behavioral modeling condition watched an instructor explain and demonstrate the steps that they should take with their computers. After each step was demonstrated, the trainees practiced. Feedback was then provided by the computers as to whether or not the step was executed correctly. In the CAI condition, the computer presented the necessary steps. Afterwards, trainees performed the steps and were then given feedback by the computers. Although CAI participants were told what to do, no modeling steps were included. Both training methods contained virtually identical content and took the same amount of time.

Table 14-1: Summary of the Most Common Training Techniques

Technique	Definition	Components	Examples	References
Behavior Role Modeling	Utilizes lecture, modeling, practice, and feedback to teach trainees appropriate behavior	Observation Demonstration Role Play Feedback	Self-Management Skills Training Behavioral Rehearsal Interpersonal Skill	Latham & Saari (1979) Gist, Schwoerer & Rosen (1989)
Simulation	Artificially duplicates the conditions that would be encountered in an actual situation or environment	Role Play Hands-On Practice Feedback Exercises	In-Basket Exercises Simulators Business Games	Wehrenberg (1986) Wolf & Guth (1975)
Lecture	Information presentation by an instructor to an audience with little or no interaction	Presentation of concepts, facts, etc. Presentation of requisite knowledge	CAI (Passive) Slide Presentation Video Presentation (Passive) Tutorials	Couch & Strother (1971) Gruenfeld (1966)
Conferenc e	Requires active participation by the trainee and is used to develop problem-solving and decision-making capabilities	Demonstration Limited Practice Exercises	Tele-Conference Video Presentation (Active) Distance Learning	Wexley, Sanders, & Yukl (1973) Butler (1967)
On-The-Job Training	Training conducted in the workplace by in-house training staff	Demonstration Simulation Hands-On Practice	Job Rotation Cross-Training Apprenticeship	Sullivan & Miklas (1985) Lefkowitz (1970)
Coaching	Discussions between super-visor and subordinate to lead to superior performance, commitment, etc.	Practice On-Line Feedback	Mentoring	Locke & Latham (1984) Silverman (1990)

Task performance was assessed with an objective performance test. This test was administered at the completion of the training and examined the trainees' ability to use the computer software. Participants in the behavioral modeling condition scored significantly higher on the performance test than did participants trained with CAI.

Similar results regarding the utility of behavioral modeling have been found in other studies. For example, Latham and Saari (1979) examined the success of behavioral modeling while training managers in interpersonal communication skills. When compared to a control group, the behavioral modeling group had positive reactions (found both immediately and 8 months after the cessation of the program), as well as significantly more learning (as measured by a performance test) and significantly improved interpersonal behavior. Corresponding results were also found in a study conducted by Smith and Salas (1991) examining assertiveness training. Here, subjects trained using behavioral modeling were more adept at using the assertiveness techniques than subjects trained with lecture or lecture with role play.

A growing trend in training research has been the use of simulation, especially in the military (Alluisi, 1991). While simulation is indeed helpful, it has often been assumed erroneously that simulation alone ensures that successful learning will result. While there is no doubt that simulations (e.g., role plays, simulators) are instrumental in much of the training, they cannot stand alone. Rather, what is needed to enhance skill acquisition and transfer of training are simulations coupled with some form of instructional support (e.g., feedback, performance monitoring).

One final thought on training techniques in general: As with simulations, it takes more than a good technique to ensure good transfer of training. Proper attention must be paid to the other variables (e.g., individual and organizational characteristics) that may equally influence the effectiveness of the training.

In summary, research into training techniques is typically concerned with the manner in which training is conducted. This type of research is conducted in a variety of settings, from lab studies that look at specific instructional strategies (e.g., practice or feedback) to field studies that assess entire training programs. The choice of setting is determined by the research questions being addressed. For example, it may not be necessary initially to conduct a full field study in order to determine the efficacy of a new type of cognitive feedback. Of course, once the effectiveness of this new technique is established, the next step would be to incorporate it into a larger training program and potentially investigate its effectiveness to the organization.

3.4.2 Training instructors. Training instructors, too, can impact the effectiveness of training. For example: "Do people perform better in training programs when they are expected to do so by the instructors?" Tannenbaum et al. (1993) asserted that instructor style does, in fact, influence trainee motivation and learning. "How can instructor style and instructor expectations be manipulated?", "How can instructor bias be reduced?" "What measures have been used to evaluate trainee differences resulting from instructor biases?" These are common questions to be addressed when examining research on instructors.

Eden and Shani (1982) considered these questions while observing how instructor expectations about trainees influenced trainee performance during a combat training course. Prior to training, instructors were erroneously told whether trainees had high, regular, or unknown command potential (potential was randomly assigned). Trainee learning of course content was assessed by a performance test, while trainee reactions were assessed via a Likert-type questionnaire (e.g., "I would recommend this course to my friends"). Results indicated that trainees whose instructors were led to expect more did, in fact, learn more. Additionally, they responded to the course with more favorable attitudes than those perceived as "moderate" or "unknown", and held their superiors in a more positive light.

There is a growing amount of research examining the influence of these training program issues (Tannenbaum et al., 1993). Indeed, the effectiveness of the training relies heavily on whether the most appropriate training technique was used, as well as whether the instructors were knowledgeable about the subject matter and skilled in instruction (Towne & Munro, 1991). The importance of the training program can be seen in the aforementioned studies. It is certainly an area which cannot be ignored when assessing training effectiveness. We now turn our discussion to what happens after the trainees have gone through the training program.

3.5 Transfer of Training.

Once the training program has concluded, researchers commonly focus on the issue of transfer of training. Transfer of training is an important component of training effectiveness research, because it allows researchers to determine whether or not the content of the training program successfully transferred back to the trainee's work environment. Transfer of training can be defined as: *The degree to which trainees effectively apply the knowledge, skills, and attitudes acquired through training to the job*. Therefore, for transfer of training to occur, the behavior learned in training must be generalized to the work environment and maintained over time on the job (Baldwin & Ford, 1988). Very little attention has been paid to transfer issues at the organizational level. As researchers have argued, however, transfer is of paramount importance to the effectiveness of training (Noe & Ford, 1992). Indeed, as reported by Wexley and Baldwin (1986) only 10 percent of the money invested into training actually results in behavior change back on the job. As such, transfer has become a major concern to training researchers.

So what factors facilitate/hinder the positive transfer of training? Researchers note that these factors include the variables that we have previously discussed: (1) individual characteristics, (2) organizational characteristics, (3) the training program, and (4) trainee motivation (Baldwin & Ford, 1988). For example, Hand et al. (1973) determined that trainees perceiving organizational support were more eager to transfer what was learned from the training. In sum, while little research has been conducted looking exclusively at training transfer in the past, studies are now beginning to emerge.

In order to study transfer of training, a field study is almost a necessity. This is due to the fact that the factors affecting transfer are typically organization-specific. That is, the impact of organizational factors on transfer behavior will vary depending on the particular configuration of those in a given organization. Moreover, an optimal design in this research is longitudinal. That is, some amount of time must pass between the training and the measurement of transfer so that the impact of the intervening variables can be assessed.

We will now turn our attention to the measurement issue which is also paramount to determining training effectiveness.

4.0 Measures Used to Assess Training Effectiveness

How do researchers judge whether or not training has worked? Specifically, what <u>criteria</u> are used to determine whether training was successful or unsuccessful? To date, Kirkpatrick's (1976) typology has remained the most prevalent framework used in research evaluating training (Tannenbaum & Yukl, 1992), although there is some progress in extending this framework (Kraiger et al., 1993). Kirkpatrick's (1976) typology consists of four levels of training effectiveness:

1. <u>Reaction</u> - how well the trainees liked the training program.
2. <u>Learning</u> - principles, facts, and skills which were understood by the trainee.
3. <u>Behavior</u> -whether trainees changed their behavior based on what was learned.
4. <u>Results</u> -whether changes in trainee behavior positively affected the organization.

According to Figure 14-2, all of these levels of measurement are important as a means to assess training effectiveness (see Boxes 6-10). However, the criterion most often used by organizations to evaluate the success of training has been trainee reactions. Reasons for this include the low expense and effort required. Kirkpatrick (1976) himself, however, pointed out that a trainee's positive reaction to a training program does not assure that proper learning has taken place. Nor does it assure that a behavioral change will occur back on the job (Goldstein, 1993). This can be evidenced in such studies as that conducted by Huczynski and Lewis (1980). In conducting a follow-up on participants from a management training program, they found that while the reaction to the program was enthusiastic, the level of attempted application of the trained skills was no higher than ten percent. Further support was attained by Alliger and Janak (1989) who found large differences between the criterion levels after conducting a literature review. Alliger and Janak did conclude, however, that most training studies do not focus exclusively on reactions.

Other criteria used in training research, beside reactions, are learning and behavior. Learning is usually measured by work samples or tests, while behavior is determined by observational questionnaires, performance ratings, or performance in a simulation. In contrast, organizational results are more difficult to obtain. Specifically, obtaining results such as cost savings, work output, and quality changes involve collecting data before and after (usually in terms of several months) the training. Moreover, efforts need to be made to isolate other variables which could have influenced an improvement in results.

4.1 Example of a Training Effectiveness Measures Study

One study which encompasses all of Kirkpatrick's (1976) levels of evaluation was conducted by Campion and Campion (1987). The purpose of their study was to evaluate an interviewee skills training program in a field setting using an industry sample. This was possible because the organization under examination was conducting a large number of interviews for transfer and promotional purposes. It is important to note the uniqueness of their opportunity to use a field study. In the past, interviewee skills training had been examined exclusively with college students in a laboratory environment.

Employees scheduled for interviews were notified about the interviewee training available, and were given the option to participate. Those responding were randomly assigned to a control group (n=140), whereby they were given reading material pertaining to interviewee skills, or assigned to the experimental group (n=158). The experimental group participated in a 4-hour training session in which learning objectives relating to maximizing interviewee skills were conveyed.

The measures used to evaluate the training included all four levels of Kirkpatrick's (1976) typology; this is also unique since studies utilizing all four levels of evaluation are rare (Alliger & Janak, 1989; Latham & Saari, 1979). Trainee reactions were measured with questions such as "To what extent did the (training) improve your knowledge in the interview taking process?" Learning was assessed with a three-question essay test administered both before and after training. Behavior measures were collected from the interviewers immediately after the interviews were conducted. Finally, results (the criterion measure so difficult to evaluate) were collected on the ratio of number of jobs interviewed for and received.

Results from the study indicated that training participants responded positively to the program and demonstrated substantial learning. No differences, were found however, between the trained group and untrained group with the behavior measures and results. More specifically, interviewee behaviors as assessed by the interviewer, along with the number of jobs received did not differ significantly between those who had the interview training and those who did not.

This provides a rare example of a study which assesses all four levels of Kirkpatrick's (1976) evaluation criteria. While many studies are able to evaluate training at the reaction, learning, and behavioral levels, organizational results are oftentimes more difficult to attain. Reasons for this include the time lag before changes in organizational results can surface, as well as difficulties which may be encountered in obtaining information at the organizational levels (e.g., quality improvement). While steps have been made to shape this typology for improved interpretability, the four criteria continue to thrive as the foundations for training evaluation.

4.2 Summary

Up to this point, we have discussed several concepts, variables, designs, measures, and theories, along with the training effectiveness variables with which they correspond. Indeed, training effectiveness is much more complex than that which is shown in Figure 14-1, as illustrated by the many variables to consider. Therefore, to summarize what we have discussed thus far, we have included Table 14-2. As you can see, many of the terms listed in each box will look familiar based on what you have read. Others will become more meaningful as we go through the next section, the Training Research Tool Box.

5.0 The Training Research Tool Box

The previous discussion provided a solid foundation for the elements and characteristics of training research. What follows will try to answer: If one wants to conduct training research, what tools are needed?

5.1 Theory

In shaping your training research, you need to start with theory, or a theoretical position. Indeed, as argued by Lewin, there is nothing more practical than a good theory (see Marrow, 1969). The importance of theory cannot be overstated. Without theory, training research is meaningless, trivial, and would prevent the accumulation of knowledge. One important feature of theory, of course, is that it contributes to the generation of testable hypotheses, which in turn, serve as the framework for determining which independent and dependent variables to incorporate, how these variables will be measured, and what research paradigm should be used.

Table 14-2. Illustrative Examples of Typical Training Effectiveness Research Variables, Methods, and Measures

Nature of Varible	Independent Variables	Dependent Variables	Measurement Technique	Theoretical Framework
Individual Characteristics	Self-efficacy Expectations Abilities	Reactions Learning Retention Task performance Task proficiency	Self-report Questionnaires Cognitive ability tests	Expectancy Information Processing Social Learning
Organizational Characteristics	Supervisor/Peer support Organizational climate Trainee choice Situational constraints	Job performance Task satisfaction Self-efficacy Attitudes Reactions	Self-report Questionnaires Objective ratings	
Motivation	Motivation to attend Motivation to learn Motivation to transfer what was learned	Reactions Motivation to learn Learning Behavioral change Self-efficacy	Self-report Questionnaires	Expectancy
Training Program	Instructor expectations Instructor style Training techniques	Task performance Reactions Learning Behavioral change	Self-report Questionnaires Interviews Performance results	Social Learning Mental Models
Transfer of Training		Task proficiency Retention over time Generalization of skills	Behavioral observation	

Theoretical foundations instrumental in training research are constantly getting richer. One such theory previously discussed is the expectancy theory. Expectancy theory was developed by Vroom (1964) and has been used as a foundation for much of the training motivation research (e.g., Mathieu et al., 1992; Tannenbaum et al., 1991). Another is the training effectiveness theory posed by Tannenbaum et al. (1993), which has been discussed throughout this chapter (i.e., research designed to examine the variables likely to influence the success or failure of training).

Another theoretical framework used in training research is the automatic/controlled processing theory (Schneider & Shiffrin, 1977). The first, automatic processing, is characterized by fast and effortless processing. The second, controlled processing, applies when there are no consistent rules or consistent sequences of information. Social learning theory (Bandura, 1986) is also a deeply embedded theory in the training research. Social learning theory, which stresses observation, modeling, and vicarious learning in modifying behavior, has been the foundation for the behavioral modeling technique (Goldstein, 1993). As a result, it has been used in the self-efficacy research. Further, Wexley and Latham (1991) predicted that the social learning theory will become increasingly useful as a theoretical framework for increasing training effectiveness in the years to come. Table 14-3 provides several theories which are prominent in training research. These theories can assist in determining training content, design, and effectiveness.

Table 14-3: Predominant Theories of Training

Theories	References
ACT Model	Anderson (1984)
Social Learning Theory	Bandura (1986)
Reinforcement Theory	Skinner (1954)
Mental Models Theory	Rouse & Morris (1986)
Meta-Cognition	Bereiter & Scardamalia (1985)
Information Processing Theory	Schneider & Shiffrin (1977)
Team Performance Model	Salas et al. (1992)
Gagne's Instructional Model	Gagne (1970)
Individual Differences	Ackerman (1987)
Transfer of Training Model	Baldwin & Ford (1988)
Training Climate	Rouillier & Goldstein (1991)
Self-Fulfilling Prophecy	Eden (1990)
Training Effectiveness Theory	Tannenbaum et al. (1993)
Expectancy Theory	Vroom (1964)

5.2 Measurement

The issue of measurement is of paramount concern to training researchers. It is used to determine what variables have influenced training effectiveness, as well as why. As previously discussed, training effectiveness is primarily evaluated with the typology developed by Kirkpatrick (1976). That is, assessing the trainees' reactions; measuring how well the trainees learned the skills; observing changes in behavior; and finally, measuring changes at the organizational level. Table 14-4 lists these evaluation criteria, along with the measurement techniques frequently associated with each.

Table 14-4. Measurement Criteria/Techniques

Criteria (Kirkpatrick, 1976)	**Typical Measurement Techniques**
Reactions	❍ Interviews ❍ Surveys
Learning	❍ Knowledge Tests ❍ Work Sample Tests ❍ Scaling Techniques
Behavior	❍ Performance Ratings ❍ Simulations ❍ Work Samples
Results	❍ Quality ❍ Quantity ❍ Safety ❍ Cost ❍ Absenteeism

Table 14-5. Representative Statistical Techniques Used In Training

Statistical Techniques	**References**
Posttest-Only Design Analysis	Arvey & Cole, 1989
Gain-Score Design Analysis	Arvey & Cole, 1989
Repeated Measures ANOVA	Arvey & Cole, 1989
Analysis of Covariance	Arvey & Cole, 1989
LISREL	Joreskog & Sorbom, 1989
Regression	Cohen & Cohen, 1983
Time Series	Mandell & Bretchneider, 1984

5.3 Statistics

Once you have developed and implemented a training program, the next step is to determine whether the behavioral change (if any) was statistically significant. The literature offers a number of options. Arvey and his colleagues have conducted extensive research on these issues (Arvey & Cole, 1989; Arvey, Cole, Hazucha, & Hartano, 1985). They offer a series of guidelines and recommendations on when to use these techniques, taken into consideration the power of the design (i.e., sample size requirement), the costs (Arvey, Maxwell, & Salas, 1992), or the reliability of the measures (see Arvey et al., 1985), as well as other indices. Table 14-5 provides some of the more common statistical techniques used.

5.4 Experimental Design

The choice of which design to use depends on a number of factors. The hypotheses to be tested, sample size required, whether one can randomize, the validity and reliability of the measures, the cost of conducting the evaluation, are just a few considerations. There are a number of rules of thumb that have been offered (see Cook, Campbell, & Peracchio, 1990; Goldstein, 1993, pp. 197-206; Arvey & Cole, 1989; Sackett & Mullen, 1993). Table 14-6 outlines the most common designs used in training.

Table 14-6. Common Experimental Designs Utilized in Training

Design	Description			
Case Study			- Training	- Measurement taken
Pretest-Posttest		-Measurement taken	- Training	- Measurement taken
Pretest-Posttest Control Group	Gr.1	-Measurement taken	- Training	- Measurement taken
	Gr.2	-Measurement taken	- No Training	
After-Only Control Group	Gr.1		- Training	- Measurement taken
	Gr.2			- Measurement taken
Time-Series		$^*M_1M_2M_3..M_{10}$	- Training	- $M_1M_2M_3..M_{10}$
Solomon 4-Group	Gr.1	-Measurement taken	- Training	- Measurement taken
	Gr.2	-Measurement taken	- No Training	- Measurement taken
	Gr 3		- Training	- Measurement taken
	Gr 4		- No Training	- Measurement taken

*M=Measurement

5.5 Odds & Ends Issues

The tool box would not be complete without several other pieces. For example, clear, concise communication is essential in many research areas; for training research, it is critical. That is, in order to test an idea, you must be able to "sell it". In order to sell the idea to professors, other researchers, managers, and/or journal reviewers, you must learn how to sell the research.

While this is a skill that develops with experience, awareness of this may help. Another important issue to consider are the trade-offs associated with conducting research (e.g., internal and external validity, construct validity) and choosing research strategies (e.g., lab or field). You should not ask first where the research should be conducted. The decision should be driven by the question: "What needs to be tested?" Other issues involve how to publish the results or how to present results to management. Table 14-7 provides some useful references to guide the research in sorting through these issues. Of course, acquiring the basic knowledge concerning theory, measurement, statistics, experimental design, and other relevant issues can oftentimes occur at the graduate school level (See Appendix 14-3).

Table 14-7. References for Odds and Ends Issues

Issue	Reference
Selling Ideas	Schumacher (1992)
Trade-offs Between Lab & Field	Cook et al. (1990)
Publishing the Results	Cummings & Frost (1985)
Construct Validity	Cook et al. (1990)
Research Strategies	Sackett & Larson (1990)
Presenting the Results to Organizations	Schumacher (1992)

6.0 Conclusion

As organizations invest more and more in various training programs, training effectiveness has become a more critical concern. Correspondingly, research examining training effectiveness has been on the rise, revealing its many facets and displaying the methods, steps, and techniques used for it's study. Studies have shown that training effectiveness is not simply a matter of how good the training program is. Rather, it can be influenced by characteristics of both the trainee and organization, as well as the trainee's motivation toward the training.

Based on these findings, we have offered a set of tools for those interested in investigating training effectiveness. Specifically, we have provided several theories, criteria, statistical techniques, and designs which are frequently utilized in training effectiveness research. Hopefully, these will be useful for students and researchers alike in their search for answers regarding training effectiveness.

7.0 Biography

Eduardo Salas is a Senior Research Psychologist with the Human Factors Division at Naval Air Warfare Center Training Systems Division (NAWCTSD), formally the Naval Training Systems Center. He received his Ph.D. in Industrial/Organizational Psychology from Old Dominion

University. He is now team leader for a variety of R & D projects dealing with team training and performance, team decision-making, training effectiveness, and stress and human performance.

Kerry A. Burgess is a Research Associate at the Human Factors Division of NAWCTSD. She received a bachelor's degree from the University of Central Florida, and is currently a master's candidate in Industrial/Organizational Psychology at the University of Central Florida. Her research interests include team leadership under stress, team training, and training effectiveness.

Janis A. Cannon-Bowers is a Research Psychologist at NAWCTSD. She received her M.A. and Ph.D. in Industrial/Organizational Psychology at the University of South Florida. She is currently involved in a variety of research efforts related to team training, the role of mental models in training, measures of team performance, and decision making under stress.

AUTHORS NOTES

The views expressed in this chapter are those of the authors and do not reflect the official position of the organization with which they are affiliated.

We wish to extend our appreciation to Pamela Hobson, Tara Cornelius, and Dorothy Wojciak for their assistance in gathering some of the information presented here. Also, we wish to extend our thanks to Clint Bowers and Scott Tannenbaum for their comments in earlier drafts.

REFERENCES

Ackerman, P.L. (1987). Individual differences in skill learning. An integration of psychometric and information processing perspectives. *Psychological Bulletin*, 102, 3-27.

Alderfer, C.P., Alderfer, C.J., Bell, E.L., & Jones, J. (1992). The race relations competence workshop: Theory and results. *Human Relations*, 45, 1259-1291.

Alliger, G.M., & Janak, E.A. (1989). Kirkpatrick's level of training criteria: Thirty years later. *Personnel Psychology*, 42, 331-341.

Alluisi, E.A. (1991). The development of technology for collective training: SIMNET, a case history. *Human Factors*, 33, 343-362.

Anderson, J.G. (1984). When leaders develop themselves. *Training and Development Journal*, 38, 18-22.

Arvey, R.D., & Cole, D.A. (1989). Evaluating change due to training. In I.L. Goldstein (Ed.), *Training and Development in Organizations* (pp. 89-118). San Francisco, CA: Jossey Bass.

Arvey, R.D., Cole, D.A., Hazucha, J.F., Hartanto, F.M. (1985). Statistical power of training evaluation designs. *Personnel Psychology*, 38, 493-507.

Arvey, R.D., Maxwell, S.E., & Salas, E. (1992). The relative power of training evaluation designs under different cost configurations. *Journal of Applied Psychology*, 77, 15-160.

Baldwin, T.T., & Ford, J.K. (1988). Transfer of training: A review and directions for future research. *Personnel Psychology*, 41, 63-105.

Baldwin, T.T., Magjuka, R.G., & Loher, B.T. (1991). The perils of participation: Effects of choice of training on trainee motivation and learning. *Personnel Psychology*, 44, 51-67.

Bandura, A. (1986). *Social Foundations of Thought and Action*. Englewood Cliffs, NJ: Prentice-Hall.

Barling, J., & Beattie, R. (1983). Self-efficacy beliefs and sales performance. *Journal of Organizational Behavior Management*, 5, 41-51.

Bereiter, C., & Scardamalia, M. (1985). Cognitive coping strategies and the problem of "inert" knowledge. In S. Chipman, J.W. Segal, & R. Glaser (Eds.), *Thinking and Learning Skills: Current Rsearch and Open Questions* (Vol. 2, pp. 65-80). Hillsdale, NJ: Erlbaum.

Burke, M.J., & Day, R.R. (1986). A cumulative study of the effectiveness of managerial training. *Journal of Applied Psychology*, 71, 232-245.

Butler, E.D. (1967). An experimental study of the case method in teaching the social foundations of education. *Dissertation Abstracts*, 27, 2912.

Campion, M.A., & Campion, J.E. (1987). Evaluation of an interviewee skills training program in a natural field experiment. *Personnel Psychology*, 40, 675-691.

Cannon-Bowers, J.A., Salas, E., Tannenbaum, S.I., & Mathieu, J.E. (in press). Toward theoretically-based principles of training effectiveness: A model and initial empirical investigation. *Military Psychology*.

Carnevale, A., Gainer, L., & Villet, J. (1990). *Training in America*. San Francisco: Jossey-Bass.

Cohen, J., & Cohen, P. (1983). *Applied Multiple Regression/Correlation Analysis for the Behavioral Sciences*. Hillsdale, NJ: Lawrence Erlbaum Associates, Inc.

Cook, T.D., & Campbell, D.T. (1979). *Quasi-Experimentation: Design and Analysis Issues for Field Settings*. Chicago: Rand McNally.

Cook, T.D., Campbell, D.T., & Peracchio, L. (1990). Quasi-experimentation. In M.D. Dunnette & L.M. Hough (Eds.). *Handbook of Industrial and Organizational Psychology* (pp. 491-576). Palo Alto, CA: Consulting Psychologists Press, Inc.

Couch, P.D., & Strother, G.B. (1971). A critical incident evaluation of supervisory training. *Training and Development Journal*, 25, 6-11.

Cummings, L.L., & Frost, P.J. (1985). *Publishing in the Organizational Sciences*. Homewood, IL: Richard D. Irwin, Inc.

Eden, D., & Shani, A.B. (1982). Pygmalion goes to boot camp: Expectancy, leadership, and trainee performance. *Journal of Applied Psychology*, 67, 194-199.

Eden, D. (1990). *Pygmalion in Management*. Lexington, MA: Lexington.

Ford, J.K., Quinones, M.A., Sego, D.J., & Sorra, J.S. (1992). Factors affecting the opportunity to perform trained tasks on the job. *Personnel Psychology*, 45, 511-527.

Gagne, R.M. (1970). *The Conditions for Learning*. New York: Holt, Rinehart, and Winston.

Gist, M.E., Schwoerer, C., & Rosen, B. (1989). Effects of alternative training methods on self-efficacy and performance in computer software training. *Journal of Applied Psychology*, 74, 884-891.

Goldstein, I.L. (1989). *Training and Development in Organizations*. San Francisco: Jossey-Bass Publishers.

Goldstein, I.L. (1993). *Training in Organizations* (3rd ed.). Belmont, CA: Waldsworth, Inc.

Gruenfeld, L.W. (1966). Management development effect on changes in values. *Training and Development Journal*, 20, 18-26.

Hand, H.H., Richards, M.D., & Slocum, J.W. (1973). Organizational climate and the effectiveness of a human relations training program. *Academy of Management Journal*, 16, 185-195.

Hicks, W.D., & Klimoski, R.J. (1987). Entry into training programs and its effects on training outcomes: A field experiment. *Academy of Management Journal*, 30, 542-552.

Hill, T., Smith, N.D., & Mann, M.F. (1987). Role of efficacy expectations in predicting the decision to use advanced technologies: The case of computers. *Journal of Applied Psychology*, 72, 307-313.

Hogan, J.C., Arenson, S., & Salas, E. (1987). *Individual Differences in Military Training Environments: Four Areas of Research* (NAVTRASYSCEN TR87-003). Orlando, FL: Naval Training Systems Center.

Hogan, J.C., & Hogan, R. (1985). *Psychological and Physical Performance Characteristics of Successful Explosive Ordinance Diver Technicians.* Tulsa, OK: University of Tulsa

Huczynski, A.A., & Lewis, J.W. (1980). An empirical study into the learning transfer process in management training. *Journal of Management Studies*, 17, 227-240.

Joreskog, K.G., & Sorbom, D. (1989). *LISREL VII User's Reference Guide.* Mooresville, IN: Scientific Software.

Kelley, H.H. (1972). Attribution in social interaction. In E.E. Jones, D.E. Kanhouse, H.H. Kelley, S. Valins, & B. Weiner (Eds.), *Attribution: Perceiving the Causes of Behavior*. Morristown, NJ: General Learning.

Kirkpatrick, D.L. (1976). Evaluation of training. In R.L. Craig (Ed.), *Training and Development Handbook*, (2nd ed.). New York: McGraw-Hill.

Kraiger, K., Ford, J.K., & Salas, E. (1993). Application of cognitive, skill-based, and affective theories of learning outcomes to new methods of training evaluation (Monograph). *Journal of Applied Psychology*, 78, 311-328.

Latham, G.P., & Saari, L.M. (1979). Applications of social learning theory to training supervisors through behavioral modeling. *Journal of Applied Psychology*, 64, 239-246.

Lefkowitz, J. (1970). Effect of training on the productivity and tenure of sewing machine operators. *Journal of Applied Psychology*, 54, 81-86.

Locke, E.A., & Latham, G.P. (1984). *A Theory of Goal Setting and Task Performance*. Englewood Cliffs, NJ: Prentice-Hall.

Mandell, M.B., & Bretchneider, S.I. (1984). Using exponential smoothing to specify intervention models for interrupted time series. *Evaluation Review*, 8, 663-691.

Marrow, A.J. (1969). *The Practical Theorist: The Life and Work of Kurt Lewin*. New York: Basic Books.

Martocchio, J.J. (1992). Microcomputer usage as an opportunity: The influence of context in employee training. *Personnel Psychology*, 45, 529-552.

Mathieu, J.E., Martineau, J., & Tannenbaum, S.I. (1993). Individual and situational influences on the development of self efficacy: Implications for training effectiveness. *Personnel Psychology*, 46, 125-147.

Mathieu, J.E., Tannenbaum, S.I., & Salas, E. (1992). The influence of individual and situational characteristics on measures of training effectiveness. *Academy of Management Journal*, 35, 828-847.

Noe, R.A., & Ford, J.K. (1992). Emerging issues and new directions for training research. *Research in Personnel and Human Resources Management*, 10, 345-384.

Noe, R.A., & Schmitt, N. (1986). The influence of trainee attitudes on training effectiveness: Test of a model. *Personnel Psychology*, 39, 497-523.

Noe, R.A., & Wilk, S.L. (1993). Investigation of the factors that influence employees' participation in development activities. *Journal of Applied Psychology*, 78, 291-302.

Peters, L.H., O'Connor, E.J., & Rudolf, C.J. (1980). The behavioral and affective consequences of performance - relevant situational variables. *Organizational Behavior and Human Performance*, 25, 79-96.

Pinder, C.C. (1984). *Work motivation: Theory, Issues, and Applications*. Glenview, IL: Scott, Foresman, and Company.

Reichers, A.E., & Schneider, B. (1990). Climate and culture: An evolution of constructs. In B. Schnieder (Ed.), *Organizational Climate and Culture* (pp. 5-39). San Francisco: Jossey-Bass.

Rouillier, J.Z., & Goldstein, I.L. (1991, April). *Determinants of the Climate for Transfer of Ttraining*. Paper presented at the 6th annual meeting of the Society of Industrial and Organizational Psychology, St. Louis, MO.

Rouse, W.B., & Morris, N.M. (1986). On looking into the black box: Prospects and limits in the search for mental models. *Psychological Bulletin*, 100, 349-363.

Sackett, P.R., & Larson, J.R. (1990). Research strategies and tactics in Industrial and Organizational Psychology. In M.D. Dunnette & L.M. Hough (Eds.), *Handbook of Industrial and Organizational Psychology* (2nd Ed., Vol. 1, pp.419-490). Palo Alto, CA: Consulting Psychologists Press, Inc.

Sackett, P.R., & Mullen, E.J. (1993). Beyond formal experimental design: Towards an expanded view of the training evaluation process. *Personnel Psychology*, 46, 613-627.

Salas, E., Dickinson, T.L., Converse, S.A., & Tannenbaum, S.I. (1992). Toward an understanding of team performance and training. In R.W. Swezey & E. Salas (Eds.), *Teams: Their Training and Performance*. Norwood, NJ: Ablex.

Schnieder, W., & Shiffrin, R.M. (1977). Controlled and automatic human information processing: I. Detection, search, attention. *Psychological Review*, 84, 1-66.

Schumacher, D. (1992). *Get funded! A Practical Guide for Scholars Seeking Research Support From Business*. Sage Publications: Newbury Park, CA.

Silverman, S.B. (1990). Increasing individual development through performance appraisal. In K.N. Wexley & J.R. Hinrichs (Eds.). *Developing Human Resources*. Washington, D.C.: Bureau of National Affairs.

Skinner, B.F. (1954). Science of learning and the art of teaching. *Harvard Educational Review*, 24, 86-97.

Smith, K.A., & Salas, E. (1991, March). *Training Assertiveness: The Importance of Active Participation*. Paper presented at the 37th Annual Meeting of the Southeastern Psychological Association, New Orleans, LA.

Sullivan, R.F., & Miklas, D.C. (1985). On-the-job training that works. *Training and Development Journal*, 39, 118-120.

Tannenbaum, S.I., Cannon-Bowers, J.A., Salas, E., & Mathieu, J.E. (1993). *Factors that Influence Training Effectiveness: A Conceptual Model and Longitudinal Analysis* (NTSC Technical Report Number 93-011). Orlando, FL: Naval Training Systems Center.

Tannenbaum, S.I., Mathieu, J.E., Salas, E., & Cannon-Bowers, J.A. (1991). Meeting trainees' expectation: The influence of training fulfillment on the development of commitment, self-efficacy, and motivation. *Journal of Applied Psychology*, 76, 759-769.

Tannenbaum, S.I., & Yukl, G. (1992). Training and development in work organizations. *Annual Review of Psychology*, 43, 399-411.

Towne, D.M., & Munro, A. (1991). Simulation-based instruction of technical skills. *Human Factors*, 33, 325-341.

Tracey, J.B., Tannenbaum, S.I., & Kavanagh, M.J. (1993, May). *Applying Trained Skills on the Job: The Importance of the Work Environment.* Paper presented at the 8th annual meeting of the Society of Industrial and Organizational Psychology, San Francisco, CA.

Travillian, K.K. Baker, C.V., & Cannon-Bowers, J.A. (1992,March). *Correlates of Self and Collective Efficacy with Team Functioning.* Paper presented at the 38th annual meeting of the Southeastern Psychological Association, Knoxville, TN.

Vroom, V.H. (1964). *Work and Motivation.* New York: Wiley.

Wehrenberg, S.B. (1986). Simulations: Capturing the experience of the real thing. *Personnel Journal*, 65, 101-103.

Wexley, K.N., & Baldwin, T.T. (1986). Posttraining strategies for facilitating positive transfer: An empirical exploration. *Academy of Management Journal*, 29, 503-520.

Wexley, K.N., & Latham, G.P. (1991). *Developing and Training Human Resources in Organizations* (2nd ed.). New York: Harper Collings Publishers Inc.

Wexley, K.N., Sanders, R.E., & Yukl, G.A. (1973). Training interviewers to eliminate contrast effects in employment interviews. *Journal of Applied Psychology*, 57, 233-236.

Wolf, J., & Guth, G.R. (1975). The case approach versus gaming in the teaching of business policy: An experimental evaluation. *Journal of Business*, 48, 349-364.

Appendix 14-1

The following is a list of selected societies which promote the science of training. For more information about each society, you can write to the address listed below each.

❍ **Society for Industrial and Organizational Psychology, Inc.**

Address: 617 East Golf Road, Suite 103
Arlington Heights, IL 60005

❍ **Human Factors and Ergonomics Society**

Address: P.O. Box 1369
Santa Monica, CA 90406-1369

❍ **Academy of Management**

Address: P.O. Box 209
Ada, OH 45810

❍ **American Society for Training and Development Inc.**

Address: 1640 King Street, Box 1443
Alexandria, VA 22313-2043

❍ **Society for Human Resource Management**

Address: 606 N. Washington St.
Alexandria, VA 22314

Appendix 14-2

The following selected journals frequently include training-relevant articles. For more information about subscriptions or publications, you can write to the address listed below each.

❍ *Academy of Management Journal*

Address: P.O. Box 209
Ada, OH 45810

❍ *Academy of Management Review*

Address: P.O. Box 209
Ada, OH 45810

❍ *Academy of Management Executive*

Address: P.O. Box 209
Ada, OH 45810

❍ *Human Factors*

Address: Human Factors and Ergonomics Society
Publications Division, Box 1369
Santa Monica, CA 90406-1369

❍ *Human Resources Development Quarterly*

Address: Jossey-Bass, Inc Publishers
350 Sansome Street
San Francisco, CA 94104

❍ *Human Resources Management Review*

Address: JAI Press
P.O. Box 1678
Greenich, CT 06836

❍ *Journal of Applied Psychology*

Address: American Psychological Association
750 First Street
Washington, DC 20002-4242

❍ *Journal of Vocational Behavior*

Address: Academic Press
6277 Sea Harbor Drive
Orlando, FL 32887-4900

❍ *Military Psychology*

Address: American Psychological Association
750 First Street
Washington, DC 20002-4242

❍ *Personnel Psychology*

Address: Managing Editor

Personnel Psychology, Inc.
745 Haskins Road, Suite A
Bowling Green, OH 43402

❍ *Training and Development*

Address: 1640 King Street, Box 1443
Alexandria, VA 22313-2043

❍ *Training Research Journal*

Address: Kurt Kraiger, Editor

Department of Psychology
University of Colorado at Denver
Denver, CO 80217

Appendix 14-3

To obtain information about graduate study in fields such as industrial/organizational psychology, organizational behavior, and personnel psychology, you can request a copy of *Graduate Training Programs in Industrial / Organizational Psychology and Related Fields* from:

The Society for Industrial and Organizational Psychology

617 East Golf Road, Suite 103

Arlington Heights, IL 60005

(708) 640-0068

If you are interested in obtaining more information about human factors, simulation, and/or engineering psychology, you can request a copy of the *Directory of Human Factors Graduate Programs* from:

The Human Factors and Ergonomics Society

P.O. Box 1369

Santa Monica, CA 90406-1369

(310) 394-1811

For more information about graduate studies in areas such as instructional systems design, instructional technology, educational psychology, and educational technology, you can request a copy of the *Graduate Curricula in Educational Communication* from:

Publications Department

1025 Vermont Ave., N.W.

Suite 820

Washington DC 20005

(202) 347-7834

INDEX

A

B

C

E

F

G

H

I

J

K

L

M

P

Q

R

U

X

Y